PRENTICE HALL

SCIENCE EXPLORER

Focus on Life Science

PRENTICE HALL
Needham, Massachusetts
Upper Saddle River, New Jersey
Glenview, Illinois

PRENTICE HALL SCIENCE EXPLORER

Focus on Life Science

Print Resources

Student Edition
Teacher's Edition
Unit Resource Books, including:
- Chapter Project Support
- Lesson Plans
- Section Summaries
- Review and Reinforce Worksheets
- Enrich Worksheets
- Skills Labs and Real-World Labs
- Complete Answer Keys

Chapter and Unit Tests
Performance Assessment
Interdisciplinary Explorations
Laboratory Manual, Student Edition
Laboratory Manual, Teacher's Edition
California Standards-Based Lesson Plans
California Standardized Test Preparation Book
Study Guides in English and Five Languages
Reading in the Content Area with Literature
   Connections
Guided Reading and Study Workbook
Inquiry Skills Activity Book
Student-Centered Science Activity Book
Prentice Hall Interdisciplinary Explorations series

Media and Technology

Interactive Student Tutorial CD-ROM
Assessment Resources with CD-ROM
   and Dial-A-Test®
Resource Pro® (Standards-Based
   Lesson Plans and Teaching
   Resources on CD-ROM)
Science Explorer Activity Videos
Internet Site at www.phschool.com
   (includes www.PlanetDiary.com)
Color Transparencies
Guided Reading English Audiotapes
Guided Reading Spanish Audiotapes
   and Spanish Section Summaries
Videotape Library
Spanish Videotape Library
Videodisc Library (English/Spanish)
Odyssey of Discovery (CD-ROMs for
   Life and Earth Science)
Interactive Earth CD-ROM

Materials Kits

Consumable Materials Kit
Nonconsumable Materials Kit
Materials List CD-ROM

Acknowledgments

Excerpt on page 132 from *James Herriot's Dog Stories.* Copyright © 1986 by James Herriot. Published by St. Martin's Press.

Excerpt on pages 504–505 from *Dragons and Dynasties: An Introduction to Chinese Mythology* by Yuan Ke, selected and translated by Kim Echlin and Nie Zhixiong, published by Penguin Books, 1993. First published in the People's Republic of China by Foreign Languages Press, Beijing, 1991. Copyright © Foreign Languages Press, 1991, 1992, 1993. Reprinted by permission of Penguin UK.

Excerpts on page 754 from *A Kind of Grace* by Jackie Joyner-Kersee. Copyright © 1997 by Jackie Joyner-Kersee. Reprinted by permission of Warner Books, Inc.

ISBN 0-13-044346-8
3 4 5 6 7 8 9 10   03 02 01 00

Cover: Bobcats *(Lynx rufus)* are found in many parts of California. They feed mainly on rabbits and rodents. These young bobcats are about 3 months old.

Program Authors

Michael J. Padilla, Ph.D.
Professor
Department of Science Education
University of Georgia
Athens, Georgia

Michael Padilla is a leader in middle school science education. He has served as an editor and elected officer for the National Science Teachers Association. He has been principal investigator of several National Science Foundation and Eisenhower grants and served as a writer of the National Science Education Standards.

As lead author of *Science Explorer*, Mike has inspired the team in developing a program that meets the needs of middle grades students, promotes science inquiry, and is aligned with the National Science Education Standards.

Ioannis Miaoulis, Ph.D.
Dean of Engineering
College of Engineering
Tufts University
Medford, Massachusetts

Martha Cyr, Ph.D.
Director, Engineering
   Educational Outreach
College of Engineering
Tufts University
Medford, Massachusetts

Science Explorer was created in collaboration with the College of Engineering at Tufts University. Tufts has an extensive engineering outreach program that uses engineering design and construction to excite and motivate students and teachers in science and technology education.

Faculty from Tufts University participated in the development of *Science Explorer* chapter projects, reviewed the student books for content accuracy, and helped coordinate field testing.

Book Authors

Elizabeth Coolidge-Stoltz, M.D.
Medical Writer
North Reading, Massachusetts

Donald Cronkite, Ph.D.
Professor of Biology
Hope College
Holland, Michigan

Joseph D. Exline, Ed.D.
Former Director of Science
Virginia Department of Education

Dawn Graff-Haight, Ph.D., CHES
Associate Professor, Health
   Education
Linfield College
McMinnville, Oregon

Jan Jenner, Ph.D.
Science Writer
Talladega, Alabama

Contributing Writers

Rose-Marie Botting
Science Teacher
Broward County School District
Fort Lauderdale, Florida

Douglas E. Bowman
Health/Physical Education
    Teacher
Welches Middle School
Welches, Oregon

Colleen Campos
Science Teacher
Laredo Middle School
Aurora, Colorado

Patricia M. Doran
Science Teacher
Rondout Valley Junior
    High School
Stone Ridge, New York

Fred Holtzclaw
Science Instructor
Oak Ridge High School
Oak Ridge, Tennessee

Theresa Holtzclaw
Former Science Instructor
Clinton, Tennessee

Jorie Hunken
Science Consultant
Woodstock, Connecticut

James Robert Kaczynski, Jr.
Science Teacher
Barrington Middle School
Barrington, Rhode Island

Susan Offner
Biology Teacher
Milton High School
Milton, Massachusetts

Warren Phillips
Science Teacher
Plymouth Community
    Intermediate School
Plymouth, Massachusetts

Evan P. Silberstein
Science Teacher
Spring Valley High School
Spring Valley, New York

Sharon Stroud
Science Teacher
Widefield High School
Colorado Springs, Colorado

Joseph Stukey, Ph.D.
Department of Biology
Hope College
Holland, Michigan

Thomas R. Wellnitz
Science Teacher
The Paideia School
Atlanta, Georgia

Reading Consultant

Bonnie B. Armbruster, Ph.D.
Department of Curriculum
    and Instruction
University of Illinois
Champaign, Illinois

Interdisciplinary Consultant

Heidi Hayes Jacobs, Ed.D.
Teacher's College
Columbia University
New York, New York

Safety Consultants

W. H. Breazeale, Ph.D.
Department of Chemistry
College of Charleston
Charleston, South Carolina

Ruth Hathaway, Ph.D.
Hathaway Consulting
Cape Girardeau, Missouri

California Reviewers

Stephanie Anderson
Sierra Vista Junior
   High School
Canyon Country, California

John W. Anson
Mesa Intermediate School
Palmdale, California

Dawn Smith Burgess, Ph.D.
Department of Geophysics
Stanford University
Stanford, California

Judy D'Albert
Harvard Day School
Corona Del Mar, California

Melody Law Ewey
Holmes Junior High School
Davis, California

Debra J. Goodding
Kraemer Middle School
Placentia, California

Jason Ho
Walter Reed Middle School
Los Angeles, California

Judy Jernstedt, Ph.D.
Department of Agronomy and
   Range Science
University of California, Davis
Davis, California

Dennis K. Lieu, Ph.D.
Department of Mechanical
   Engineering
University of California
Berkeley, California

Carol Ann Lionello
Kraemer Middle School
Placentia, California

Jaime A. Morales
Henry T. Gage Middle School
Huntington Park, California

Edward D. Walton, Ph.D.
Department of Chemistry
California State Polytechnic
   University
Pomona, California

Tufts University Program Reviewers

Behrouz Abedian, Ph.D.
Department of Mechanical
   Engineering

Wayne Chudyk, Ph.D.
Department of Civil and
   Environmental Engineering

Eliana De Bernardez-Clark, Ph.D.
Department of Chemical
   Engineering

Anne Marie Desmarais, Ph.D.
Department of Civil and
   Environmental Engineering

David L. Kaplan, Ph.D.
Department of Chemical
   Engineering

Paul Kelley, Ph.D.
Department of Electro-Optics

George S. Mumford, Ph.D.
Professor of Astronomy, Emeritus

Jan A. Pechenik, Ph.D.
Department of Biology

Livia Racz, Ph.D.
Department of Mechanical
   Engineering

Robert Rifkin, M.D.
School of Medicine

Jack Ridge, Ph.D.
Department of Geology

Chris Swan, Ph.D.
Department of Civil and
   Environmental Engineering

Peter Y. Wong, Ph.D.
Department of Mechanical
   Engineering

Content Reviewers

Jack W. Beal, Ph.D.
Department of Physics
Fairfield University
Fairfield, Connecticut

W. Russell Blake, Ph.D.
Planetarium Director
Plymouth Community
    Intermediate School
Plymouth, Massachusetts

Howard E. Buhse, Jr., Ph.D.
Department of Biological Sciences
University of Illinois
Chicago, Illinois

A. Campbell, Ph.D.
Assistant Professor
Davidson College
Davidson, North Carolina

Elizabeth A. De Stasio, Ph.D.
Associate Professor of Biology
Lawrence University
Appleton, Wisconsin

John M. Fowler, Ph.D.
Former Director of Special Projects
National Science Teacher's
    Association
Arlington, Virginia

Jonathan Gitlin, M.D.
School of Medicine
Washington University
St. Louis, Missouri

Dawn Graff-Haight, Ph.D., CHES
Department of Health, Human
    Performance, and Athletics
Linfield College
McMinnville, Oregon

Deborah L. Gumucio, Ph.D.
Associate Professor
Department of Anatomy and
    Cell Biology
University of Michigan
Ann Arbor, Michigan

William S. Harwood, Ph.D.
Dean of University Division and
    Associate Professor of Education
Indiana University
Bloomington, Indiana

Cyndy Henzel, Ph.D.
Department of Geography
    and Regional Development
University of Arizona
Tucson, Arizona

Greg Hutton
Science and Health
    Curriculum Coordinator
School Board of Sarasota County
Sarasota, Florida

Susan K. Jacobson, Ph.D.
Department of Wildlife Ecology
    and Conservation
University of Florida
Gainesville, Florida

John L. Kermond, Ph.D.
Office of Global Programs
National Oceanographic and
    Atmospheric Administration
Silver Spring, Maryland

David E. LaHart, Ph.D.
Institute of Science and
    Public Affairs
Florida State University
Tallahassee, Florida

Joe Leverich, Ph.D.
Department of Biology
St. Louis University
St. Louis, Missouri

Cynthia J. Moore, Ph.D.
Science Outreach Coordinator
Washington University
St. Louis, Missouri

Joseph M. Moran, Ph.D.
Department of Earth Science
University of Wisconsin–Green Bay
Green Bay, Wisconsin

Joseph Stukey, Ph.D.
Department of Biology
Hope College
Holland, Michigan

Seetha Subramanian
Lexington Community College
University of Kentucky
Lexington, Kentucky

Carl L. Thurman, Ph.D.
Department of Biology
University of Northern Iowa
Cedar Falls, Iowa

Robert S. Young, Ph.D.
Department of Geosciences and
    Natural Resource Management
Western Carolina University
Cullowhee, North Carolina

Edward J. Zalisko, Ph.D.
Department of Biology
Blackburn College
Carlinville, Illinois

Teacher Reviewers

Pamela Arline
Lake Taylor Middle School
Norfolk, Virginia

Lynn Beason
College Station Jr. High
    School
College Station, Texas

Richard Bothmer
Hollis School District
Hollis, New Hampshire

Jeffrey C. Callister
Newburgh Free Academy
Newburgh, New York

Betty Scott Dean
Guilford County Schools
McLeansville,
    North Carolina

Sarah C. Duff
Baltimore City Public
    Schools
Baltimore, Maryland

Sherry L. Fisher
Lake Zurich Middle
School North
Lake Zurich, Illinois

Melissa Gibbons
Fort Worth ISD
Fort Worth, Texas

Jack Grande
Weber Middle School
Port Washington,
    New York

Steve Hills
Riverside Middle School
Grand Rapids, Michigan

Patsy Partin
Cameron Middle School
Nashville, Tennessee

Deedra H. Robinson
Newport News Public
    Schools
Newport News, Virginia

Bonnie Scott
Clack Middle School
Abilene, Texas

Charles M. Sears
Belzer Middle School
Indianapolis, Indiana

Barbara M. Strange
Ferndale Middle School
High Point,
    North Carolina

Jackie Louise Ulfig
Ford Middle School
Allen, Texas

Kathy Usina
Belzer Middle School
Indianapolis, Indiana

Heidi M. von Oetinger
L'Anse Creuse Public
    School
Harrison Township,
    Michigan

Pam Watson
Hill Country Middle
    School
Austin, Texas

Activity Field Testers

Nicki Bibbo
Russell Street School
Littleton, Massachusetts

Connie Boone
Fletcher Middle School
Jacksonville Beach,
    Florida

Rose-Marie Botting
Broward County
    School District
Fort Lauderdale, Florida

Colleen Campos
Laredo Middle School
Aurora, Colorado

Elizabeth Chait
W. L. Chenery Middle
School
Belmont, Massachusetts

Holly Estes
Hale Middle School
Stow, Massachusetts

Laura Hapgood
Plymouth Community
    Intermediate School
Plymouth, Massachusetts

Sandra M. Harris
Winman Junior High
    School
Warwick, Rhode Island

Joanne Jackson
Winman Junior High
    School
Warwick, Rhode Island

Mary F. Lavin
Plymouth Community
    Intermediate School
Plymouth, Massachusetts

James MacNeil, Ph.D.
Concord Public Schools
Concord, Massachusetts

Lauren Magruder
St. Michael's Country
    Day School
Newport, Rhode Island

Jeanne Maurand
Glen Urquhart School
Beverly Farms,
    Massachusetts

Warren Phillips
Plymouth Community
    Intermediate School
Plymouth, Massachusetts

Carol Pirtle
Hale Middle School
Stow, Massachusetts

Kathleen M. Poe
Kirby-Smith Middle
    School
Jacksonville, Florida

Cynthia B. Pope
Ruffner Middle School
Norfolk, Virginia

Anne Scammell
Geneva Middle School
Geneva, New York

Karen Riley Sievers
Callanan Middle School
Des Moines, Iowa

David M. Smith
Howard A. Eyer Middle
    School
Macungie, Pennsylvania

Derek Strohschneider
Plymouth Community
    Intermediate School
Plymouth, Massachusetts

Sallie Teames
Rosemont Middle School
Fort Worth, Texas

Gene Vitale
Parkland Middle School
McHenry, Illinois

Zenovia Young
Meyer Levin Junior
    High School (IS 285)
Brooklyn, New York

State of California
Science Content Standards
Focus on Life Science

To Parents and Students:

The State of California has established guidelines, or standards, describing science knowledge and skills for which students in grades six through eight are responsible. State assessments of student achievement in science will be based on the content and skills described in these standards. The Focus on Life Science portion of the standards are listed below. The chapter and section references show where you can find specific support for each standard in this book.

To continue to develop proficiency in these content and skills standards, students may use the Chapter Assessments at the end of each chapter, the Interactive Student Tutorial CD-ROM, and the program's Web site at: **www.science-explorer.phschool.com**

1. All living organisms are composed of cells, from just one to many trillions, whose details usually are visible only through a microscope. As a basis for understanding this concept, students know:

   a. cells function similarly in all living organisms. *(Sections 1.1, 1.2, 1.4, 2.1, 2.2, 2.3, 3.3, 3.4, 7.1, 7.2, 7.4, 9.1, 9.3, 16.1, 19.1, 19.2, 19.3, 20.1, 20.3, 21.1, 21.2, 21.4, 21.5, 22.1, 22.2)*

   b. the characteristics that distinguish plant cells from animal cells, including chloroplasts and cell walls. *(Sections 1.2, 2.1, 9.1, 10.1, 11.1)*

   c. the nucleus is the repository for genetic information in plant and animal cells. *(Sections 1.2, 2.3, 3.3, 3.4, 10.1, 16.1)*

   d. mitochondria liberate energy for the work that cells do, and chloroplasts capture sunlight energy for photosynthesis. *(Sections 1.2, 2.1, 2.2, 9.1, 10.1, 11.1, 20.1)*

   e. cells divide to increase their numbers through a process of mitosis, which results in two daughter cells with identical sets of chromosomes. *(Sections 2.3, 2.4, 8.2, 21.4, 21.5, 23.3)*

   f. as multicellular organisms develop, their cells differentiate. *(Sections 7.1, 11.1, 11.2, 11.3, 11.4, 12.1, 13.2, 13.3, 17.1, 17.4, 23.3, 23.4)*

2. A typical cell of any organism contains genetic instructions that specify its traits. Those traits may be modified by environmental influences. As a basis for understanding this concept, students know:

   a. the differences between the life cycles and reproduction of sexual and asexual organisms. *(Sections 8.2, 9.1, 9.3, 10.1, 10.3, 10.4, 11.1, 11.2, 11.3, 11.4, 12.1, 12.3, 12.4, 13.2, 13.3, 13.5, 14.2, 14.3, 14.4, 15.1, 15.3, 15.4)*

   b. sexual reproduction produces offspring that inherit half their genes from each parent. *(Sections 3.1, 3.2, 3.3, 4.1, 4.2, 4.3, 23.2)*

   c. an inherited trait can be determined by one or more genes. *(Sections 3.1, 3.2, 3.3, 4.1, 4.2, 4.3)*

   d. plant and animal cells contain many thousands of different genes, and typically have two copies of every gene. The two copies (or alleles) of the gene may or may not be identical, and one may be dominant in determining the phenotype while the other is recessive. *(Sections 3.1, 3.2, 3.3, 4.1, 4.2, 4.3)*

   e. DNA is the genetic material of living organisms, and is located in the chromosomes of each cell. *(Sections 2.3, 3.4, 4.1, 4.2, 4.3, 23.2)*

3. Biological evolution accounts for the diversity of species developed through gradual processes over many generations. As a basis for understanding this concept, students know:

   a. both genetic variation and environmental factors are causes of evolution and diversity of organisms. *(Sections 5.1, 5.3, 7.3, 8.2, 9.1, 10.1, 10.3, 10.4, 11.1, 11.2, 11.3, 11.4, 12.1, 12.3, 12.4, 13.1, 13.2, 13.3, 13.5, 14.1, 14.2, 14.3, 14.4, 15.1, 15.3, 15.4)*

   b. the reasoning used by Darwin in making his conclusion that natural selection is the mechanism of evolution. *(Section 5.1)*

   c. how independent lines of evidence from geology, fossils, and comparative anatomy provide a basis for the theory of evolution. *(Sections 5.1, 5.2, 5.3, 6.1, 6.2, 6.3, 6.4, 6.5, 7.3, 14.1, 15.1, 15.3)*

   d. how to construct a simple branching diagram to classify living groups of organisms by shared derived characteristics, and expand the diagram to include fossil organisms. *(Sections 5.3, 7.3, 7.4, 12.1, 14.1)*

   e. extinction of a species occurs when the environment changes and the adaptive characteristics of a species are insufficient for its survival. *(Sections 5.2, 6.1, 6.5, 14.4)*

4. Evidence from rocks allows us to understand the evolution of life on Earth. As the basis for understanding this concept, students know:

   a. Earth processes today are similar to those that occurred in the past and slow geologic processes have large cumulative effects over long periods of time. *(Sections 5.2, 6.1, 6.2, 6.3, 6.5, 7.2)*

   b. the history of life on Earth has been disrupted by major catastrophic events, such as major volcanic eruptions or the impact of an asteroid. *(Section 6.5)*

   c. the rock cycle includes the formation of new sediment and rocks. Rocks are often found in layers with the oldest generally on the bottom. *(Sections 6.1, 6.2, 6.3, 14.5)*

   d. evidence from geologic layers and radioactive dating indicate the Earth is approximately 4.6 billion years old, and that life has existed for more than 3 billion years. *(Sections 6.3, 6.5, 7.2)*

   e. fossils provide evidence of how life and environmental conditions have changed. *(Sections 5.2, 6.1, 6.2, 6.5, 7.2, 13.1, 14.1, 14.5, 15.1, 15.3)*

   f. how movements of the Earth's continental and oceanic plates through time, with associated changes in climate and geographical connections, have affected the past and present distribution of organisms. *(Sections 5.1, 5.2, 6.5)*

   g. how to explain significant developments and extinctions of plant and animal life on the geologic time scale. *(Sections 6.4, 6.5, 14.1, 14.5, 15.1, 15.3)*

5. The anatomy and physiology of plants and animals illustrate the complementary nature of structure and function. As a basis for understanding this concept, students know:

   a. plants and animals have levels of organization for structure and function, including cells, tissues, organs, organ systems, and the whole organism. *(Sections 10.1, 10.3, 10.4, 11.1–11.4, 12.1–12.4, 13.1–13.5, 14.1–14.4, 16.1, 16.2, 17.1, 17.3, 17.4, 18.1–18.4, 19.1–19.4, 20.1–20.3, 21.1–21.5, 23.1–23.4)*

   b. organ systems function because of the contributions of individual organs, tissues, and cells. The failure of any part can affect the entire system. *(Sections 1.3, 1.4, 2.1, 2.2, 2.4, 4.2, 4.3, 8.1, 8.3, 9.2, 11.1–11.5, 12.1, 12.3, 12.4, 13.1–13.3, 13.5, 15.1–15.4, 16.1–16.3, 17.1, 17.3, 17.4, 18.1–18.4, 19.1–19.4, 20.1–20.3, 21.1–21.5, 22.1, 22.2, 22.4, 22.5, 23.1–23.4)*

   c. how bones and muscles work together to provide a structural framework for movement. *(Sections 14.1, 15.1, 15.2, 15.3, 17.1, 17.3, 20.1)*

   d. how the reproductive organs of the human female and male generate eggs and sperm, and how sexual activity may lead to fertilization and pregnancy. *(Sections 23.2, 23.3)*

   e. the function of the umbilicus and placenta during pregnancy. *(Sections 15.4, 23.3)*

   f. the structures and processes by which flowering plants generate pollen and ovules, seeds, and fruit. *(Sections 11.3, 11.4, 11.5)*

   g. how to relate the structures of the eye and ear to their functions. *(Sections 22.1, 22.3, 22.4)*

6. Physical principles underlie biological structures and functions. As a basis for understanding this concept, students know:

   a. visible light is a small band within a very broad electromagnetic spectrum. *(Sections 21.4, 21.5, 22.3, 22.4)*

   b. for an object to be seen, light emitted by or scattered from it must enter the eye. *(Sections 22.3, 22.4)*

   c. light travels in straight lines except when the medium it travels through changes. *(Sections 1.1, 22.3, 22.4)*

   d. how simple lenses are used in a magnifying glass, the eye, camera, telescope, and microscope. *(Sections 1.1, 22.3, 22.4)*

   e. white light is a mixture of many wavelengths (colors), and that retinal cells react differently with different wavelengths. *(Sections 10.2, 22.3, 22.4)*

   f. light interacts with matter by transmission (including refraction), absorption, or scattering (including reflection). *(Sections 1.1, 2.1, 10.2, 17.4, 21.4, 21.5, 22.3, 22.4)*

   g. the angle of reflection of a light beam is equal to the angle of incidence. *(Section 22.3)*

   h. how to compare joints in the body (wrist, shoulder, thigh) with structures used in machines and simple devices (hinge, ball-and-socket, and sliding joints). *(Sections 17.1, 17.2)*

   i. how levers confer mechanical advantage and how the application of this principle applies to the musculoskeletal system. *(Section 17.2)*

   j. contractions of the heart generate blood pressure, and heart valves prevent backflow of blood in the circulatory system. *(Sections 15.1, 15.3, 19.1, 19.2)*

7. Scientific progress is made by asking meaningful questions and conducting careful investigations. As a basis for understanding this concept, and to address the content in the other three strands, students should develop their own questions and perform investigations. Students will:

   a. select and use appropriate tools and technology (including calculators, computers, balances, spring scales, microscopes, and binoculars) to perform tests, collect data, and display data. *(Sections 1.2, 1.3, 2.1, 2.2, 2.3, 6.4, 7.1, 8.2, 11.3, 17.3, 18.1, 18.4, 21.4, Chapter Projects 2, 17)*

   b. utilize a variety of print and electronic resources (including the World Wide Web) to collect information as evidence as part of a research project. *(Chapter Projects 6, 8, 12, 16–23)*

   c. communicate the logical connection among hypothesis, science concepts, tests conducted, data collected, and conclusions drawn from the scientific evidence. *(Sections 1.2, 1.3, 2.2, 2.3, 3.1, 3.2, 4.2, 5.1–5.3, 6.1, 6.2, 6.5, 7.1, 7.3, 8.2, 9.2, 9.3, 10.1, 10.3, 11.4, 12.2, 12.4, 13.1, 13.3, 13.5, 14.2, 14.4, 15.1, 15.3, 17.4, 18.3, 19.2, 19.3, 21.2, 22.3, Chapter Projects 1, 2, 4, 8–13, 15, 22)*

   d. construct scale models, maps and appropriately labeled diagrams to communicate scientific knowledge (e.g., motion of Earth's plates and cell structure). *(Sections 1.2, 2.3, 2.4, 3.1, 3.2, 3.3, 4.1, 5.1, 5.3, 6.3, 6.4, 8.1, 8.3, 9.3, 12.1, 16.1, 18.3, 18.4, 19.3, 20.1, 21.2, Chapter Projects 3, 5, 6, 12, 14, 17, 19–21)*

   e. communicate the steps and results from an investigation in written reports and verbal presentations. *(Sections 3.1, 5.1, 5.2, 9.3, Chapter Projects 1–15, 18–23)*

Contents

Unit 1 Cell Biology and Genetics

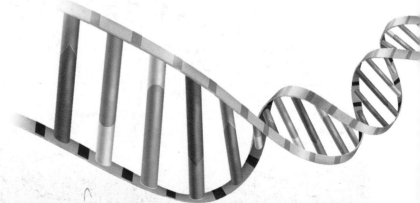

Unit 2 Evolution and Earth's History

Unit 3 Structure and Function in Living Things

Unit 4 Human Body Systems

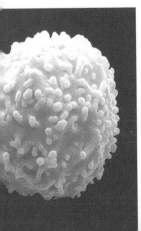

PRENTICE HALL SCIENCE EXPLORER

Reference Section

Giant redwood

Pileated woodpecker

Activities

Mountain lion

DISCOVER
Exploration and inquiry before reading

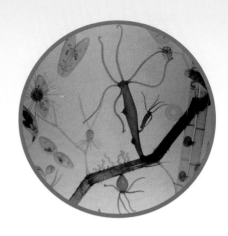

DISCOVER

continued

Lodgepole pine

xviii

Sharpen your *Skills*

Practice of specific science inquiry skills

 Melvin Calvin

TRY THIS

Reinforcement of key concepts

 Kingsnake

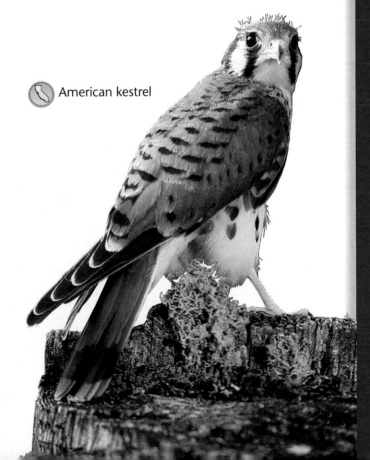

American kestrel

Interdisciplinary Activities

 Red tide in a California bay

PROTECTING DESERT WILDLIFE

Elroy Masters likes working outdoors. One day he hikes a mountain trail, looking for desert tortoises. The next morning he may be in a boat on the Colorado River, counting birds along the riverbank. Another day he may be in the Arizona hills, building a water container for thirsty bighorn sheep. Elroy is a biologist working for the federal government's Bureau of Land Management (BLM). His job is to protect wildlife habitat in the desert along the Colorado River between California and Arizona.

"People may come in wanting to run a pipeline across public land or needing to build a road," he explains. "Part of my job is to check out the biological effect of that action on different species of animals and plants. If people are going to build a road where there are a lot of tortoises, we might try to have them work from November to March. Since tortoises hibernate during those months, we reduce the chance of a tortoise getting run over."

Growing up in Arizona, Elroy lived in a farming community. "I was always outdoors. I was able to have animals that a lot of people don't have—chickens, pigeons, ducks, and a horse. I always loved animals. I always hoped for some type of career with them."

Elroy Masters studied biology at Phoenix College and Northern Arizona University. He started working for the Bureau of Land Management when he was still a college student. He now works as a Wildlife Management Biologist. In this photograph, Elroy is about to release a razorback sucker, an endangered species of fish, into the Colorado River.

Today, Elroy and his co-workers make surveys of desert animals. They count the animals in different areas and make maps of their habitats. They locate where the animals live, what they eat, and where they build their nests and raise their young. Elroy uses that information to protect the animals when natural events or human activities threaten them.

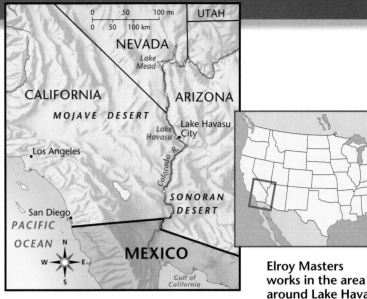

Elroy Masters works in the area around Lake Havasu, where the Colorado River forms the border of California and Arizona.

TALKING WITH ELROY MASTERS

Q *What wildlife do you protect?*

A One of the neatest animals we deal with is the desert bighorn sheep. In an average summer, it can get as hot as 120 degrees here. Sometimes the heat lasts for weeks. But with the number of people living around the river, the animals are no longer able to travel to water. So we go up into the mountains to construct catchments (containers)

to collect water and store it. That way the sheep can stay in the mountains without trying to cross freeways to get to water.

We fly in big storage tanks that hold about 10,000 gallons of water. We bury them in the ground or put them on a platform. We use paint to mask them into the color of the scenery. We sometimes build a dam or put out a metal sheet to catch drizzle rain.

A catchment can hold 10,000 gallons of water (right). It is buried in the ground. The drinking container provides water for desert bighorn sheep (below), mule deer, and other wildlife.

1

Q *What else are you doing to protect the bighorn sheep?*

A We're going to work with the Fish and Wildlife Department to capture and transplant bighorn sheep to a mountain range in my area. There are already sheep and some mountain lions here. But the sheep aren't doing as well as we expected. We want to bring in some bighorn sheep that are used to lions. We hope these lion-savvy sheep will teach the sheep in our area how to avoid lions. To catch the sheep, we'll use a helicopter. We'll shoot a net over the sheep and a couple of guys will jump out to secure the animals and then bring them to our herd.

The Colorado River valley is home to the Southwestern willow flycatcher and the desert tortoise.

Q *What other animals are you responsible for protecting?*

A I work a lot with desert tortoises. I'm responsible for two different populations, one on either side of the river. The tortoises live in the drier, hilly areas away from the river. Any time we go out into the field, we try to collect data. We keep track of where they've been and where they feed.

Q *How do you find the tortoises?*

A We have maps that indicate their habitat. Based on the habitat, we'll go out, walk around, and look under rocks and boulders to see if we can find a burrow. The tortoises are good diggers. They find a good boulder and go underground 10 or 12 feet. That's where they'll spend the winter.

Southwestern willow flycatcher

Desert tortoise

Q *Do you also work with birds?*

A Right now we're working with the Southwestern willow flycatcher. It's a small bird that depends on thick riparian (riverbank) vegetation to build nests and breed. The flycatcher is a migratory bird. Each spring, the birds fly to Arizona from Central America and Mexico. In the early summer months, we go out to find how many are breeding. We're trying to learn what's needed to prevent flycatchers from becoming extinct. We need to survey and protect the remaining stands of habitat. The flycatchers like to nest in thick stands of willow. But they will also build nests in another tree, salt cedar. The birds don't prefer it, but sometimes salt cedar is the only vegetation remaining, so they use it.

Q *What's threatening the riverbank plants?*

A The low water level in the river—due to human use—is a big threat. So is fire. During summer months, there are large numbers of recreational boats. Careless boaters can cause fires. Some fires get pretty big along the river and destroy a lot of the habitat where the birds nest and raise their young.

Q *Can you see the benefits of your work?*

A Yes, I see it especially in riverbank zones where areas are protected so that vegetation and trees can grow back. This year we did a new bird count in one area. Species that hadn't been seen in a while, like tanagers, showed up. Some of the migratory birds are already stopping in young cottonwood trees. That's the best gauge I've had—seeing birds returning to these new trees.

There are also quick results with the water catchments in the hills. We put the water in a year ago. They're aimed at bighorn sheep and mule deer. But now we've also got a lot of different birds—doves and quails— that come into the area.

Elroy Masters also works with populations of the California leaf-nosed bat. This bat has large ears and a leaf-shaped, turned-up nose. The bats are threatened by the loss of their habitat.

In Your Journal

Elroy Masters and his co-workers "survey" the wildlife in their area in order to learn how to protect them. Think of a wild animal that lives in a park or open area near you—squirrels, frogs, birds, even insects. Work out a step-by-step plan to draw a simple map marking the places where the animal is found.

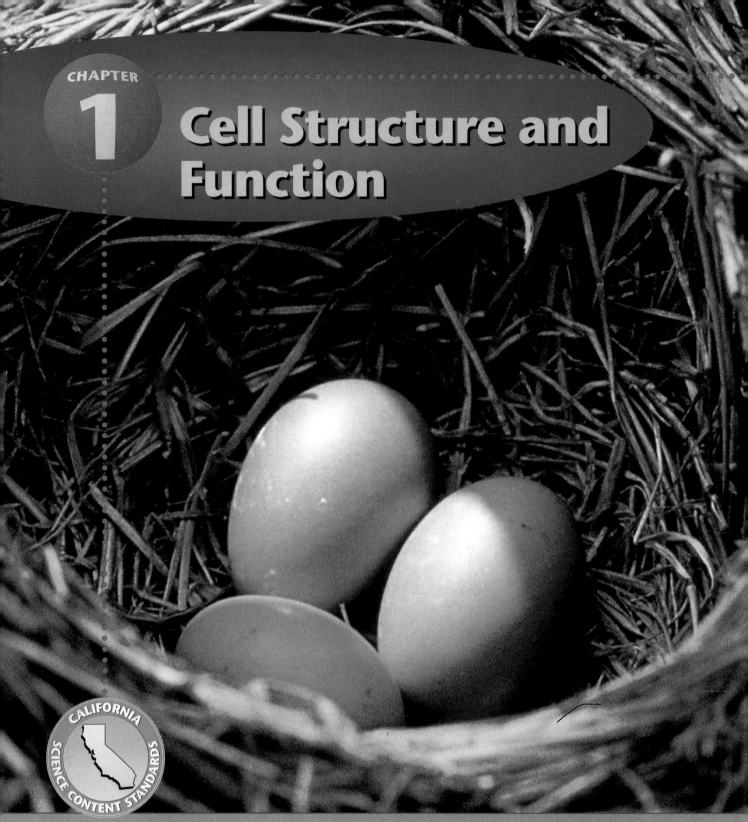

CHAPTER 1

Cell Structure and Function

CALIFORNIA SCIENCE CONTENT STANDARDS

The following California Science Content Standards are addressed in this chapter:

1. All living organisms are composed of cells, from just one to many trillions, whose details usually are visible only through a microscope.

   a. Cells function similarly in all living organisms.

   b. The characteristics that distinguish plant cells from animal cells, including chloroplasts and cell walls.

   c. The nucleus is the repository for genetic information in plant and animal cells.

   d. Mitochondria liberate energy for the work that cells do, and chloroplasts capture sunlight energy for photosynthesis.

5. The anatomy and physiology of plants and animals illustrate the complementary nature of structure and function.

   b. Organ systems function because of the contributions of individual organs, tissues, and cells. The failure of any part can affect the entire system.

6. Physical principles underlie biological structures and functions.

Egg-speriment With a Cell

Did you ever wonder how a baby chick can breathe when it's still inside the egg? The shell of the egg allows air through to reach the developing chick, while keeping out most other substances. Just as an egg needs to control which substances can enter, so too do all of the cells in your body.

In this chapter, you'll learn that all living things are made of cells—sometimes just one cell, sometimes trillions! You'll see the structures cells contain and how they work. You'll find out that important questions about life can be answered by understanding what happens in cells. You can start your discoveries right away by studying an everyday object that can serve as a model of a cell: an uncooked egg.

Your Goal To observe how various materials enter or leave a cell, using an egg as a model of the cell.

To complete this project, you will

◆ observe what happens when you soak an uncooked egg in vinegar, then in water, food coloring, salt water, and finally in a liquid of your choice

◆ measure the circumference of the egg every day, and graph your results

◆ explain the changes that your egg underwent

◆ follow the safety guidelines in Appendix A

The thin shells of these eggs control which substances reach the developing chick inside.

Get Started Predict what might happen when you put an uncooked egg in vinegar for two days. How might other liquids affect an egg? Find a place where you can leave your egg undisturbed. Then begin your egg-speriment!

Check Your Progress You will be working on this project as you study this chapter. To keep your project on track, look for Check Your Progress boxes at the following points.

Section 1 Review, page 12: Make measurements and record data.
Section 2 Review, page 21: Experiment with different liquids.
Section 4 Review, page 34: Graph your data and draw conclusions.

Wrap Up At the end of the chapter (page 37), you will display your egg and share your results.

c. Light travels in straight lines except when the medium it travels through changes.

d. How simple lenses are used in a magnifying glass, the eye, camera, telescope, and microscope.

f. Light interacts with matter by transmission (including refraction),

absorption, or scattering (including reflection).

7. Scientific progress is made by asking meaningful questions and conducting careful investigations.

a. Select and use appropriate tools and technology to perform tests, collect data, and display data.

c. Communicate the logical connection among hypothesis, science concepts, tests conducted, data collected, and conclusions drawn from the scientific evidence.

d. Construct scale models, maps and appropriately labeled diagrams to communicate scientific knowledge.

SECTION 1 Discovering Cells

Is Seeing Believing?

1. ✂ Cut a black-and-white photograph out of a page in a newspaper. With your eyes alone, closely examine the photo. Record your observations.

2. Examine the same photo with a hand lens. Record your observations.

3. Place the photo on the stage of a microscope. Use the clips to hold the photo in place. Shine a light down on the photo. Focus the microscope on part of the photo. (See Appendix B for instructions on using the microscope.) Record your observations.

Think It Over

Observing What did you see in the photo with the hand lens and the microscope that you could not see with your eyes alone?

GUIDE FOR READING

◆ How did the invention of the microscope contribute to scientists' understanding of living things?

◆ What is the cell theory?

◆ How does a lens magnify an object?

Reading Tip As you read, make a flowchart showing how the contributions of several scientists led to the development of the cell theory.

A majestic oak tree shades you on a sunny day at the park. A lumbering rhinoceros wanders over to look at you at the zoo. After a rain storm, mushrooms sprout in the damp woods. What do you think an oak tree, a rhinoceros, and a mushroom have in common? You might say that they are all living things. What makes these living things—and all other living things—alike? If you say they are made of cells, you are correct.

Cells are the basic units of structure and function in living things. Just as bricks are the building blocks of a house or school, cells are the building blocks of life. Since you are alive, you are made of cells, too. Look closely at the skin on your arm. No

Figure 1 This building is made up of individual bricks. Similarly, all living things are made up of individual cells.

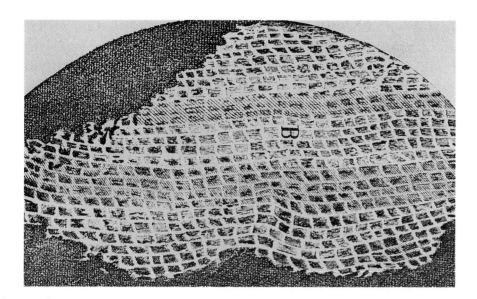

Figure 2 Robert Hooke made this drawing of dead cork cells that he saw through his microscope. Hooke called these structures *cells* because they reminded him of tiny rooms. *Comparing and Contrasting How are cells similar to the bricks in a building? How are they different?*

matter how hard you look with your eyes alone, you won't be able to see individual skin cells. The reason is that cells are very small. In fact, one square centimeter of your skin's surface contains over 100,000 cells.

First Sightings of Cells

Until the late 1500s there was no way to see cells. No one even knew that cells existed. Around 1590, the invention of the microscope enabled people to look at very small objects. **The invention of the microscope made it possible for people to discover and learn about cells.**

A **microscope** is an instrument that makes small objects look larger. Some microscopes do this by using lenses to focus light. The lenses used in light microscopes are similar to the clear curved pieces of glass used in eyeglasses. A simple microscope contains only one lens. A hand lens is an example of a simple microscope. A light microscope that has more than one lens is called a **compound microscope.**

Robert Hooke One of the first people to observe cells was the English scientist and inventor Robert Hooke. In 1663, Hooke observed the structure of a thin slice of cork using a compound microscope he had built himself. Cork, the bark of the cork oak tree, is made up of cells that are no longer alive. To Hooke, the cork looked like tiny rectangular rooms, which he called *cells.* Hooke described his observations this way: "These pores, or cells, were not very deep. . . ." You can see Hooke's drawings of cork cells in Figure 2. What most amazed Hooke was how many cells the cork contained. He calculated that in a cubic inch there were about twelve hundred million cells—a number he described as "most incredible."

Anton van Leeuwenhoek At about the same time that Robert Hooke made his discovery, Anton van Leeuwenhoek (LAY vun hook) also began to observe tiny objects with microscopes. Leeuwenhoek was a Dutch businessman and amateur scientist who made his own lenses. He then used the lenses to construct simple microscopes.

One of the things Leeuwenhoek looked at was water from a pond. He was surprised to see one-celled organisms, which he called *animalcules* (an uh MAL kyoolz), meaning "little animals."

SCIENCE & History

The Microscope—Improvements Over Time

The discovery of cells would not have been possible without the microscope. Microscopes have been improved in many ways over the last 400 years.

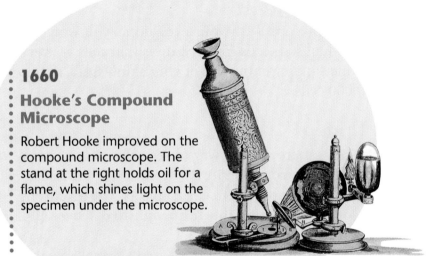

1660
Hooke's Compound Microscope

Robert Hooke improved on the compound microscope. The stand at the right holds oil for a flame, which shines light on the specimen under the microscope.

1600

1750

1590
First Compound Microscope

Hans Janssen and his son Zacharias, Dutch eyeglass makers, made one of the first compound microscopes. Their microscope was simply a tube with a lens at each end.

1683
Leeuwenhoek's Simple Microscope

Although Leeuwenhoek's simple microscope used only one tiny lens, it could magnify a specimen up to 266 times. Leeuwenhoek was the first person to see many one-celled organisms, including bacteria.

8

Leeuwenhoek looked at many other specimens, including scrapings from teeth. When Leeuwenhoek looked at the scrapings, he became the first person to see the tiny single-celled organisms that are now called bacteria. Leeuwenhoek's many discoveries caught the attention of other researchers. Many other people began to use microscopes to see what secrets they could uncover about cells.

☑ *Checkpoint* *How does a simple microscope differ from a compound microscope?*

In Your Journal

Choose one of the microscopes. Write an advertisement for it that might appear in a popular science magazine. Be creative. Emphasize the microscope's usefulness or describe the wonders that can be seen with it.

1933
Transmission Electron Microscope (TEM)

The German physicist Ernst Ruska created the first electron microscope. TEMs make images by sending electrons through a very thinly sliced specimen. They can only examine dead specimens, but are very useful for viewing internal cell structures. TEMs can magnify a specimen up to 500,000 times.

1981
Scanning Tunneling Microscope (STM)

A STM measures electrons that leak, or "tunnel," from the surface of a specimen. With a STM, scientists can see individual molecules on the outer layer of a cell. STMs can magnify a specimen up to 1,000,000 times.

1900   **2050**

1886
Modern Compound Light Microscope

German scientists Ernst Abbé and Carl Zeiss made a compound light microscope similar to this one. The horseshoe stand keeps the microscope steady. The mirror at the bottom focuses light up through the specimen. Modern compound light microscopes can magnify a specimen up to 1,000 times.

1965
Scanning Electron Microscope (SEM)

The first commercial SEM is produced. This microscope sends a beam of electrons over the surface of a specimen, rather than through it. The result is a detailed three-dimensional image of the specimen's surface. SEMs can magnify a specimen up to 150,000 times.

Plant cells

Animal cells

Figure 3 The cell theory states that all living things, including this giraffe and the leaf it is eating, are composed of cells.

The Cell Theory

Over the years, scientists have continued to use and improve the microscope. They have discovered that all kinds of living things were made up of cells. In 1838 a German scientist named Matthais Schleiden (SHLY dun) concluded that all plants are made of cells. He based this conclusion on his own research and on the research of others before him. The next year, another German scientist, Theodor Schwann, concluded that all animals are also made up of cells. Thus, stated Schwann, all living things are made up of cells.

Schleiden and Schwann had made an important discovery about living things. However, they didn't understand where cells came from. Until their time, most people thought that living things could come from nonliving matter. In 1855, a German doctor, Rudolf Virchow (FUR koh) proposed that new cells are formed only from existing cells. "All cells come from cells," wrote Virchow.

The observations and conclusions of Hooke, Leeuwenhoek, Schleiden, Schwann, Virchow, and others led to the development of the **cell theory**. The cell theory is a widely accepted explanation of the relationship between cells and living things. **The cell theory states:**

◆ **All living things are composed of cells.**

◆ **Cells are the basic unit of structure and function in living things.**

◆ **All cells are produced from other cells.**

The cell theory holds true for all living things, no matter how big or how small. Since cells are common to all living things, they can provide information about all life. Because all cells come from other cells, scientists can study cells to learn about growth, reproduction, and all other functions that living things perform.

☑ *Checkpoint* *What did Schleiden and Schwann conclude about cells?*

How a Light Microscope Works

INTEGRATING PHYSICS Microscopes use lenses to make small objects look larger. But simply enlarging a small object is not useful unless you can see the details clearly. For a microscope to be useful to a scientist, it must combine two important properties—magnification and resolution.

Magnification The first property, **magnification,** is the ability to make things look larger than they are. **The lens or lenses in a light microscope magnify an object by bending the light that passes through them.** If you examine a hand lens, you will see that the glass lens is curved, not flat. The center of the lens is thicker than the edges. A lens with this curved shape is called a **convex lens.** Look at Figure 4 to see how light is bent by a convex lens. The light passing through the sides of the lens bends inward. When this light hits the eye, the eye sees the object as larger than it really is.

Because a compound microscope uses more than one lens, it can magnify an object even more. Light passes through a specimen and then through two lenses. Figure 4 also shows the path that light takes through a compound microscope. The first lens near the specimen magnifies the object. Then a second lens near the eye further magnifies the enlarged image. The total magnification of the microscope is equal to the magnifications of the two lenses multiplied together. For example, if the first lens has a magnification of 10 and the second lens has a magnification of 40, then the total magnification of the microscope is 400.

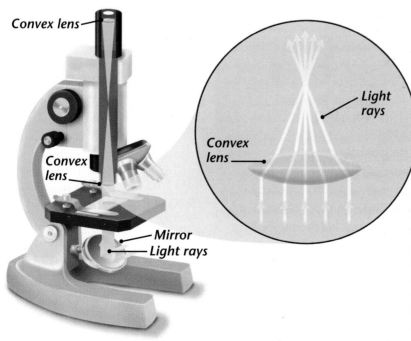

Figure 4 Microscopes use lenses to make objects look larger. A compound microscope has two convex lenses. Each convex lens bends light, making the image larger. *Calculating* If one lens has a magnification of 10 and the other lens has a magnification of 50, what would the total magnification be?

Resolution To create a useful image, a microscope must also help you see individual parts clearly. The ability to clearly distinguish the individual parts of an object is called **resolution.** Resolution is another term for the sharpness of an image.

For example, when you use your eyes to look at a photo printed in a newspaper, it looks like a complete picture from one side to the other. That picture, however, is really made up of a collection of small dots. To the unaided eye, two tiny dots close together appear as one. If you put the photo under a microscope, however, you can see the dots. You see the dots not only because they are magnified but also because the microscope improves resolution. Good resolution—being able to see fine detail—is not needed when you are reading the newspaper. But it is just what you need when you study cells.

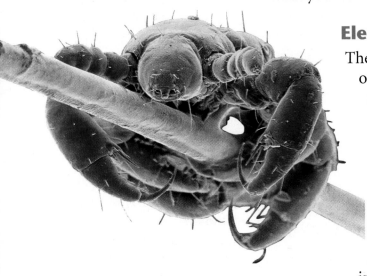

Figure 5 This head louse, shown clinging to a human hair, was photographed through a scanning electron microscope. It has been magnified to about 80 times its actual size.

Electron Microscopes

The microscopes used by Hooke, Leeuwenhoek, and other early researchers were all light microscopes. Since the 1930s, scientists have developed different types of electron microscopes. Electron microscopes use a beam of electrons instead of light to examine a specimen. Electrons are tiny particles that are smaller than atoms. Because they use tiny electrons to produce images, the resolution of electron microscopes is much better than the resolution of light microscopes. As the technology of microscopes keeps improving, scientists will continue to learn more about the structure and function of cells.

Section 1 Review

1. How did the invention of the microscope affect scientists' understanding of living things?
2. Explain the three main ideas of the cell theory.
3. How does a compound microscope use lenses to magnify an object?
4. Explain why both magnification and resolution are important when viewing a small object with a microscope.
5. **Thinking Critically** **Applying Concepts** Why do scientists learn more about cells each time the microscope is improved?

Check Your Progress **CHAPTER PROJECT**

By now you should have started your egg-speriment by soaking an uncooked egg in vinegar. Leave your egg in the vinegar for at least two days. Each day, rinse your egg in water and measure its circumference. Record all of your observations. (*Hint:* Handle the egg gently. If your egg breaks, don't give up or throw away your data. Simply start again with another egg and keep investigating.)

SECTION 2 Looking Inside Cells

DISCOVER

ACTIVITY

How Large Are Cells?

1. Look at the organism in the photo. The organism is an ameba, a large single-celled organism. This type of ameba is about 1 millimeter (mm) long.

2. Multiply your height in meters by 1,000 to get your height in millimeters. How many amebas would you have to stack end-to-end to equal your height?

3. Many of the cells in your body are about 0.01 mm long—one hundredth the size of an ameba. How many body cells would you have to stack end-to-end to equal your height?

Think It Over

Inferring Look at a metric ruler to see how small 1 mm is. Now imagine a distance one-hundredth as long, or 0.01 mm. Why can't you see your body's cells without the aid of a microscope?

Imagine you're in California standing next to a giant redwood tree. You have to bend your head way back to see the top of the tree. Some of these trees are over 110 meters tall and more than 10 meters in circumference! How do redwoods grow so large? How do they carry out all the functions necessary to stay alive?

To answer these questions, and to learn many other things about living things, you are about to take an imaginary journey. It will be quite an unusual trip. You will be traveling inside a living redwood tree, visiting its tiny cells. On your trip you will observe some of the structures found in plant cells. You will also learn about some of the differences between plant and animal cells.

GUIDE FOR READING

◆ What role do the cell membrane and nucleus play in the cell?

◆ What functions do other organelles in the cell perform?

◆ How do bacterial cells differ from plant and animal cells?

Reading Tip Before you read, preview *Exploring Plant and Animal Cells* on pages 16–17. Make a list of any unfamiliar terms. As you read, write a definition for each term.

◀ A giant redwood tree

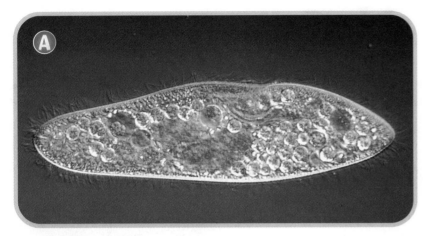

Figure 6 All cells have cell membranes, but not all cells have cell walls. **A.** The cell membrane of this single-celled paramecium controls what substances enter and leave the cell. **B.** The cell walls of these onion root cells have been stained green so you can see them clearly. Cell walls protect and support plant cells.

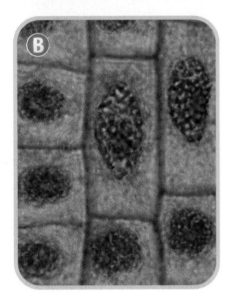

As you will discover on your journey, inside a cell are even smaller structures. These tiny cell structures, called **organelles,** carry out specific functions within the cell. Just as your stomach, lungs, and heart have different functions in your body, each organelle has a different function within the cell. You can see the organelles found in plant and animal cells in *Exploring Plant and Animal Cells* on pages 16 and 17. Now it's time to hop aboard your imaginary ship and prepare to enter a typical plant cell.

Cell Wall

Entering a plant's cell is a bit difficult. First you must pass through the cell wall. The **cell wall** is a rigid layer of nonliving material that surrounds the cells of plants and some other organisms. The cell wall is made of a tough, yet flexible, material called cellulose. If you think of a stalk of celery, you will have a good idea of what cellulose is. Celery contains a lot of cellulose.

The cells of plants and some other organisms have cell walls. In contrast, the cells of animals and some other organisms lack cell walls. A plant's cell wall helps to protect and support the cell. In woody plants, the cell walls are very rigid. This is why giant redwood trees can stand so tall. Each cell wall in the tree adds strength to the tree. Although the cell wall is stiff, many materials, including water and oxygen, can pass through the cell wall quite easily. So sail on through the cell wall and enter the cell.

☑ *Checkpoint* *What is the function of the cell wall?*

Cell Membrane

As you pass through the cell wall, the next structure you encounter is the **cell membrane.** All cells have cell membranes. In cells with cell walls, the cell membrane is located just inside the cell wall. In other cells, the cell membrane forms the outside boundary that separates the cell from its environment.

As your ship nears the edge of the cell membrane, you notice that there are tiny openings, or pores, in the cell membrane. You steer toward an opening. Suddenly, your ship narrowly misses being stuck by a chunk of waste material passing out of the cell. **You have discovered one of the cell membrane's main functions: the cell membrane controls what substances come into and out of a cell.**

Everything the cell needs—from food to oxygen—enters the cell through the cell membrane. Harmful waste products leave the cell through the cell membrane. For a cell to survive, the cell membrane must allow these materials to pass into and out of the cell. In a sense, the cell membrane is like a window screen. The screen keeps insects out of a room. But holes in the screen allow air to enter and leave the room.

Nucleus

As you sail inside the cell, a large, oval structure comes into view. This structure, called the **nucleus** (NOO klee us), acts as the "brain" of the cell. **You can think of the nucleus as the cell's control center, directing all of the cell's activities.**

Nuclear Membrane Notice in Figure 7 that the nucleus is surrounded by a nuclear membrane. Just as the cell membrane protects the cell, the nuclear membrane protects the nucleus. Materials pass in and out of the nucleus through small openings, or pores, in the nuclear membrane. So aim for that pore just ahead and carefully glide into the nucleus.

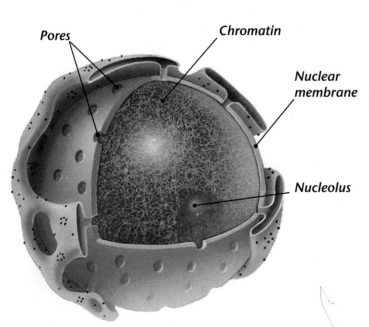

Pores

Chromatin

Nuclear membrane

Nucleolus

Figure 7 The nucleus is the cell's control center. The chromatin in the nucleus contains instructions for carrying out the cell's activities. *Interpreting Diagrams How do materials pass into and out of the nucleus?*

EXPLORING *Plant and Animal Cells*

On these pages, you can compare structures found in two kinds of cells: plant cells and animal cells. As you study these cells, remember that they are generalized cells. In living organisms, cells vary somewhat in shape and structure.

PLANT CELL

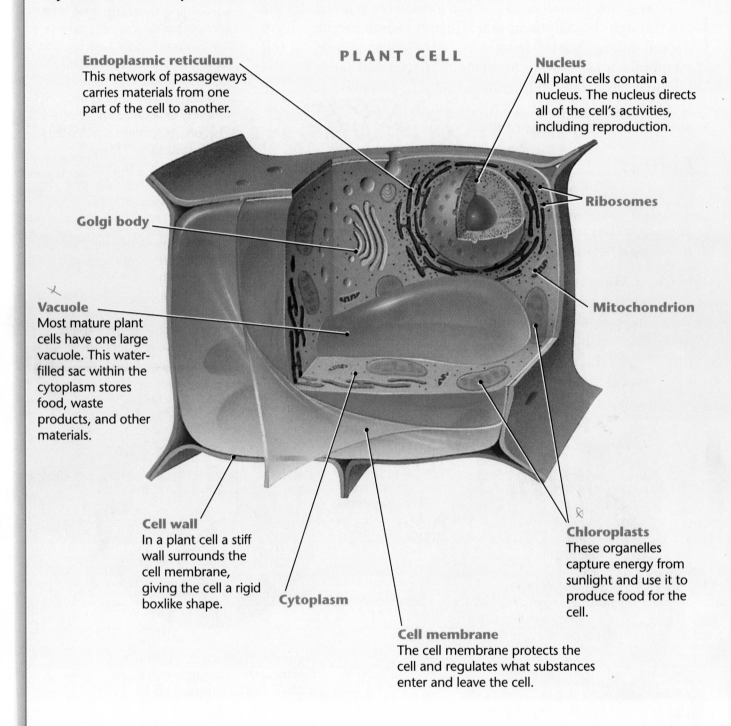

Endoplasmic reticulum
This network of passageways carries materials from one part of the cell to another.

Nucleus
All plant cells contain a nucleus. The nucleus directs all of the cell's activities, including reproduction.

Ribosomes

Golgi body

Mitochondrion

Vacuole
Most mature plant cells have one large vacuole. This water-filled sac within the cytoplasm stores food, waste products, and other materials.

Cell wall
In a plant cell a stiff wall surrounds the cell membrane, giving the cell a rigid boxlike shape.

Cytoplasm

Chloroplasts
These organelles capture energy from sunlight and use it to produce food for the cell.

Cell membrane
The cell membrane protects the cell and regulates what substances enter and leave the cell.

Vacuole
Some animal cells have vacuoles that store food, water, wastes, and other materials.

ANIMAL CELL

Ribosomes
These small structures function as factories to produce proteins. Ribosomes may be attached to the outer surfaces of the endoplasmic reticulum, or they may float free in the cytoplasm.

Golgi body
The Golgi bodies receive materials through the endoplasmic reticulum and send them to other parts of the cell.

Cytoplasm
The cytoplasm is the area between the cell membrane and the nucleus. It contains a gel-like fluid in which many different organelles are found.

Endoplasmic reticulum

Nucleus
Almost all animal cells contain a nucleus. The nucleus directs all of the cell's activities, including reproduction.

Mitochondria
Most of the cell's energy is produced within these rod-shaped organelles.

Cell membrane
Since an animal cell does not have a cell wall, the cell membrane forms a barrier between the cytoplasm and the environment outside the cell.

Lysosomes
These small organelles found in many animal cells contain chemicals that break down food particles and worn-out cell parts.

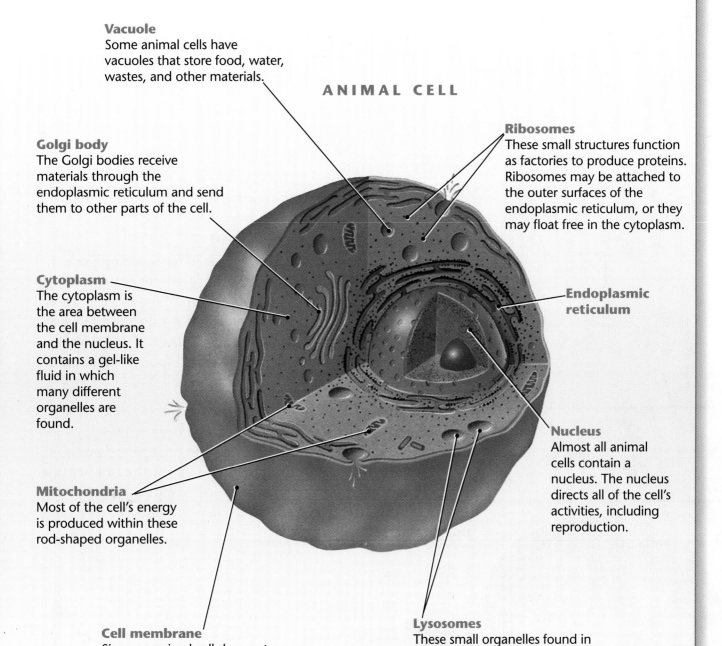

Chromatin You might wonder how the nucleus "knows" how to direct the cell. The answer lies in those thin strands floating directly ahead in the nucleus. These strands, called **chromatin,** contain the genetic material, the instructions that direct the functions of a cell. For example, the instructions in the chromatin ensure that leaf cells grow and divide to form more leaf cells. The genetic material is passed on to each new cell when an existing cell divides. You'll learn more about how cells divide in Chapter 2.

Nucleolus As you prepare to leave the nucleus, you spot a small object floating by. This structure, the nucleolus, is where ribosomes are made. Ribosomes are the organelles where proteins are produced.

☑ *Checkpoint* *Where in the nucleus is genetic material found?*

Organelles in the Cytoplasm

As you leave the nucleus, you find yourself in the **cytoplasm,** the region between the cell membrane and the nucleus. Your ship floats in a clear, thick, gel-like fluid. The fluid in the cytoplasm is constantly moving, so your ship does not need to propel itself. Many cell organelles are found in the cytoplasm. **The organelles function to produce energy, build and transport needed materials, and store and recycle wastes.**

Mitochondria As you pass into the cytoplasm, you see rod-shaped structures looming ahead. These organelles are called **mitochondria** (my tuh KAHN dree uh) (singular *mitochondrion*). Mitochondria are called the "powerhouses" of the cell because they produce most of the energy the cell needs to carry out its functions. Muscle cells and other very active cells have large numbers of mitochondria.

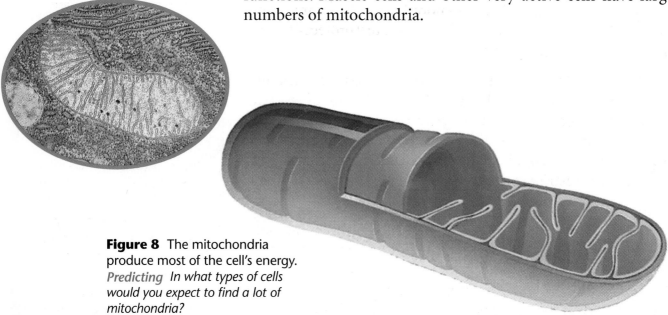

Figure 8 The mitochondria produce most of the cell's energy. *Predicting In what types of cells would you expect to find a lot of mitochondria?*

Figure 9 The endoplasmic reticulum is a passageway through which proteins and other materials move within the cell. The spots on the outside of the endoplasmic reticulum are ribosomes, structures that produce proteins.

Endoplasmic Reticulum As you sail farther into the cytoplasm, you find yourself in a maze of passageways called the **endoplasmic reticulum** (en duh PLAZ mik rih TIK yuh lum). These passageways carry proteins and other materials from one part of the cell to another. Now steer your ship into one of these passageways.

Ribosomes Attached to the outer surface of the endoplasmic reticulum are small grainlike bodies called **ribosomes.** Other ribosomes are found floating in the cytoplasm. Ribosomes function as factories to produce proteins. The ribosomes release some proteins through the wall of the endoplasmic reticulum. From the interior of the endoplasmic reticulum, the proteins will be transported to the Golgi bodies.

Golgi Bodies As you move through the endoplasmic reticulum, you see structures that look like a flattened collection of sacs and tubes. These structures, called **Golgi bodies,** can be thought of as the cell's mailroom. The Golgi bodies receive proteins and other newly formed materials from the endoplasmic reticulum, package them, and distribute them to other parts of the cell.

Chloroplasts Have you noticed the many large green structures floating in the cytoplasm? Only the cells of plants and some other organisms have these structures. These organelles, called **chloroplasts,** capture energy from sunlight and use it to produce food for the cell. It is the chloroplasts that give plants their green color. You will learn more about chloroplasts in Chapter 2.

Gelatin Cell

Make your own model of a cell.

1. Dissolve a packet of colorless gelatin in warm water. Pour the gelatin into a rectangular pan (for a plant cell) or a round pan (for an animal cell).

2. Choose different materials that resemble each of the cell structures found in the cell you are modeling. Insert these materials into the gelatin before it begins to solidify.

Making Models On a sheet of paper, develop a key that identifies each cell structure in your model. Describe the function of each structure.

Vacuoles Steer past the chloroplasts and head for that large, round, water-filled sac floating in the cytoplasm. This sac, called a **vacuole** (VAK yoo ohl), is the storage area of the cell. Most plant cells have one large vacuole. Some animal cells do not have vacuoles; others do.

Vacuoles store food and other materials needed by the cell. Vacuoles can also store waste products. Most of the water in plant cells is stored in vacuoles. When the vacuoles are full of water, they make the cell plump and firm. Without much water in the vacuoles, the plant wilts.

Lysosomes Your journey through the cell is almost over. Before you leave, take another look around you. If you carefully swing your ship around the vacuole, you may be lucky enough to see a lysosome. **Lysosomes** (LY suh sohmz) are small round structures that contain chemicals that break down large food particles into smaller ones. Lysosomes also break down old cell parts and release the substances so they can be used again. In this sense, you can think of the lysosomes as the cell's cleanup crew. Lysosomes are more common in animal cells than in plant cells.

Although lysosomes contain powerful chemicals, you need not worry about your ship's safety. The membrane around a lysosome keeps these harsh chemicals from escaping and breaking down the rest of the cell.

Bacterial Cells

The plant and animal cells that you just learned about are very different from the bacterial cell you see in Figure 10. First, bacterial cells are usually smaller than plant or animal cells. A human skin cell, for example, is about 10 times as large as an average bacterial cell.

There are several other ways in which bacterial cells are different from plant and animal cells. **While a bacterial cell does have a cell wall and a cell membrane, it does not contain a nucleus.** The bacterial cell's genetic material, which looks like a thick, tangled string, is found in the cytoplasm. Bacterial cells contain ribosomes, but none of the other organelles found in plant or animal cells.

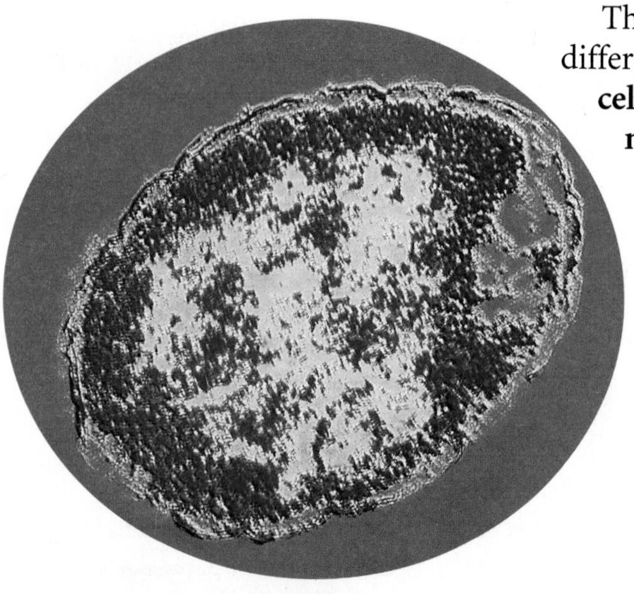

Figure 10 This single-celled organism is a type of bacteria. The cells of bacteria do not contain a nucleus or some other organelles. *Observing Where is the genetic material in a bacterial cell found?*

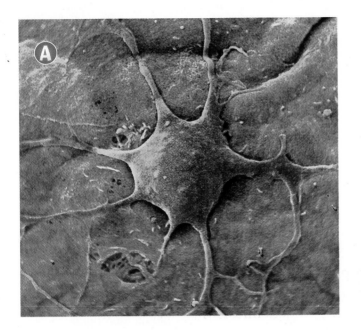

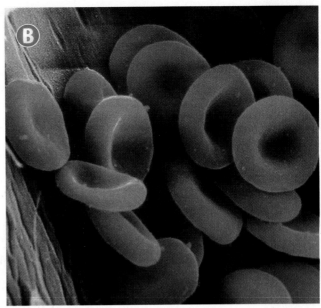

Specialized Cells

Unlike bacteria and other single-celled organisms, plants, animals (including yourself), and other organisms contain many cells. In a many-celled organism, the cells are often quite different from each other in size and structure. Think of the different parts of your body. You have skin, bones, muscles, blood, a brain, a liver, a stomach, and so on. Each of these body parts carries out a very different function. Yet all of these body parts are made up of cells. Figure 11 shows two examples of different kinds of cells in your body. The structure of each kind of cell is suited to the unique function it carries out within the organism.

Figure 11 Your body contains a variety of different types of cells. **A.** Nerve cells have long projections through which messages are sent throughout the body. **B.** Red blood cells are thin and flexible, which allows them to fit through tiny blood vessels.

Section 2 Review

1. What is the function of the cell membrane?
2. Why is the nucleus sometimes called the control center of the cell?
3. Name two plant cell parts that are not found in animal cells. What is the function of each part?
4. How do the cells of bacteria differ from those of other organisms?
5. **Thinking Critically Comparing and Contrasting** Compare the functions of the cell wall in a plant cell and the cell membrane in an animal cell. How are the functions of the two structures similar and different?

CHAPTER PROJECT
Check Your Progress
At this point, you should soak your egg for one or two days in water, then in water with food coloring, then in salt water, and finally in another liquid of your choice. Continue to rinse your egg and measure and record its circumference every day. Your egg should be going through some amazing changes in appearance.

A Magnified View of Life

In this lab, you will use your observation skills to compare plant and animal cells.

Problem

How are plant and animal cells alike and different?

Materials

plastic dropper
water
microscope slide
microscope
colored pencils
prepared slide of animal cells

Elodea leaf
forceps
coverslip

Procedure

1. Before you start this lab, read *Using the Microscope* (Appendix B) on pages 774–775. Be sure you know how to use a microscope correctly and safely.

Part 1 Observing Plant Cells

2. Use a plastic dropper to place a drop of water in the center of a slide. **CAUTION:** *Slides and coverslips are fragile. Handle them carefully. Do not touch broken glass.*

3. With forceps, remove a leaf from an *Elodea* plant. Place the leaf in the drop of water on the slide. Make sure that the leaf is flat. If it is folded, straighten it with the forceps.

4. Holding a coverslip by its edges, slowly lower it onto the drop of water and *Elodea* leaf. If any air bubbles form, tap the slide gently to get rid of them.

5. Use a microscope to examine the *Elodea* leaf under low power. Then, carefully switch to high power.

6. Observe the cells of the *Elodea* leaf. Draw and label what you see, including the colors of the cell parts. Record the magnification.

7. Discard the *Elodea* leaf as directed by your teacher. Carefully clean and dry your slide and coverslip. Wash your hands thoroughly.

Part 2 Observing Animals Cells

8. Obtain a prepared slide of animal cells. The cells on the slide have been stained with an artificial color.

9. Observe the animal cells with a microscope under both low and high power. Draw and label the cell parts that you see. Record the magnification.

Analyze and Conclude

1. How are plant and animal cells alike?
2. How are plant and animal cells different?
3. What natural color appeared in the plant cells? What structures give the plant cells this color?
4. **Think About It** Why is it important to record your observations while you are examining a specimen?

More to Explore

Observe other prepared slides of animal cells. Look for ways that animal cells differ from each other. Obtain your teacher's permission before carrying out these observations.

SECTION 3 Chemical Compounds in Cells

DISCOVER ·· ACTIVITY

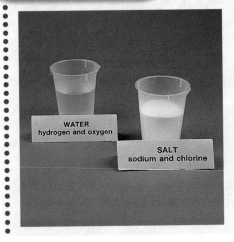

WATER
hydrogen and oxygen

SALT
sodium and chlorine

What Is a Compound?

1. Your teacher will provide you with containers filled with various substances. All of the substances are chemical compounds.

2. Examine each substance. Read the label on each container to learn what each substance is made of.

Think It Over

Forming Operational Definitions Write a definition of what you think a chemical compound is.

If cells are the basic building blocks of living things, then what substances are the basic building blocks of cells? In what ways are the basic building blocks of cells similar to those that make up other things around you? In this section you will explore how the substances that make up living cells differ from those that make up nonliving things.

Elements and Compounds

Think about the air around you. You probably know that air is a mixture of gases, including oxygen and nitrogen. Oxygen and nitrogen are examples of elements. An **element** is any substance that cannot be broken down into simpler substances. The smallest unit of an element is called an **atom.** An element is made up of only one kind of atom. The most common elements in living things, including you, are carbon, oxygen, hydrogen, and nitrogen.

When two or more elements combine chemically they form a **compound.** Water, for example, is a compound made up of the elements hydrogen and oxygen. The smallest unit of most compounds is called a **molecule.** Each water molecule is made up of two hydrogen atoms and one oxygen atom.

GUIDE FOR READING

◆ What are the four main kinds of organic molecules in living things?

◆ How is water important to the function of cells?

Reading Tip As you read, make a table of the main types of organic molecules and where in the cell each one is found.

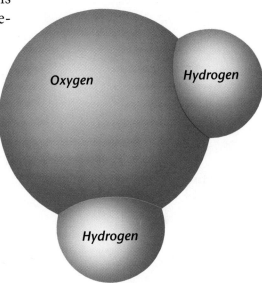

Oxygen

Hydrogen

Hydrogen

The structure of a water molecule ▶

Organic and Inorganic Compounds

Many of the compounds found in living things contain the element carbon, which is usually combined with other elements. Most compounds that contain carbon are called **organic compounds.**

The most important groups of organic compounds found in living things are carbohydrates, lipids, proteins, and nucleic acids. As you may know, many of these compounds are found in the foods you eat. This is not surprising, since the foods you eat come from living things.

Compounds that don't contain the element carbon are called **inorganic compounds.** One exception to this definition is carbon dioxide. Although carbon dioxide contains carbon, it is classified as an inorganic compound. Other inorganic compounds include water and sodium chloride, or table salt.

Carbohydrates

A **carbohydrate** is an energy-rich organic compound made of the elements carbon, hydrogen, and oxygen. Sugars and starches are examples of carbohydrates.

Sugars are produced during the food-making process that takes place in plants. Foods such as fruits and some vegetables are high in sugar content. Sugar molecules can combine, forming large molecules called starches. Plant cells store excess energy in molecules of starch. Many foods that come from plants contain starch. These foods include potatoes, noodles, rice, and bread. When you eat these foods, your body breaks down the starch into glucose, a sugar, which your cells can use to produce energy.

Carbohydrates are important components of some cell parts. The cellulose found in the cell walls of plants is a type of carbohydrate. Carbohydrates are also found in cell membranes.

Figure 12 These potatoes contain large amounts of starch, a type of carbohydrate. The blue grains you see in the closeup are starch granules in a potato. The grains have been colored blue to make them easier to see. *Classifying What types of carbohydrates combine to form starches?*

24

Figure 13 This bird's feathers are made up mainly of proteins. Proteins are important components of the cell membrane and many of the cell's organelles.

Proteins

What do a bird's feathers, a spider's web, and your fingernails have in common? All of these substances are made mainly of proteins. **Proteins** are large organic molecules made of carbon, hydrogen, oxygen, nitrogen, and, in some cases, sulfur. Foods that are high in protein include meat, eggs, fish, nuts, and beans.

Cells use proteins for many different things. For instance, proteins form parts of cell membranes. Proteins also make up many of the organelles within the cell. Certain cells in your body use proteins to build body parts such as hair.

Protein Structure Protein molecules are made up of smaller molecules called **amino acids.** Although there are only 20 common amino acids, cells can combine them in different ways to form thousands of different proteins. The kinds of amino acids and the order in which they link together determine the type of protein that forms. You can think of the 20 amino acids as being like the 26 letters of the alphabet. Those 26 letters can form thousands of words. The letters you use and their order determine the words you form. Even a change in one letter, for example, from *rice* to *mice*, creates a new word. Similarly, changes in the type or order of amino acids result in a different protein.

Enzymes An **enzyme** is a type of protein that speeds up a chemical reaction in a living thing. Without enzymes, many chemical reactions that are necessary for life would either take too long, or not occur at all. For example, enzymes in your saliva speed up the digestion of food by breaking down starches into sugars in your mouth.

☑ *Checkpoint* *What is the role of enzymes?*

What's That Taste?

Use this activity to **ACTIVITY** discover one role that enzymes play in your body.

1. Put an unsalted soda cracker in your mouth. Chew it up, but do not swallow. Note what the cracker tastes like.

2. Continue to chew the cracker for a few minutes, mixing it well with your saliva. Note how the taste of the cracker changes.

Inferring Soda crackers are made up mainly of starch, with little sugar. How can you account for the change in taste after you chewed the cracker for a few minutes?

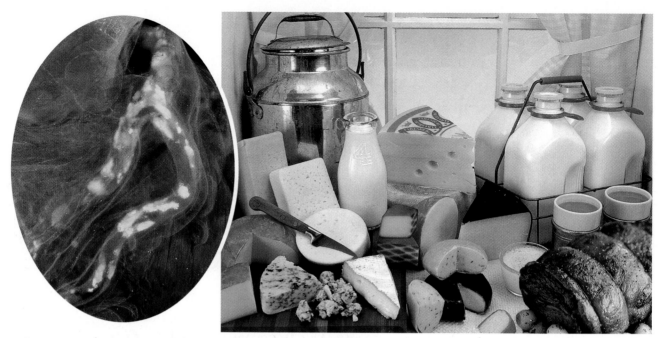

Figure 14 Cholesterol is a lipid found in foods that come from animals. Excess cholesterol in your diet can cause blood vessels to become blocked, as shown at the left.
Making Judgments Why is it a good idea to limit the amount of cholesterol you eat?

Lipids

Have you ever seen a cook trim the fat from a piece of meat before cooking it? The cook is trimming away a lipid. Fats, oils, and waxes are all **lipids.** Like carbohydrates, lipids are energy-rich organic compounds made of carbon, hydrogen, and oxygen.

Lipids contain even more energy than carbohydrates. Cells store energy in lipids for later use. For example, during winter a dormant bear lives on the energy stored as fat within its cells.

 INTEGRATING HEALTH One lipid that you may have heard about is cholesterol (kuh LES tuh rawl). Cholesterol is an important component of animal cell membranes. Your body requires a certain amount of this lipid. Your liver normally produces enough cholesterol to meet your body's needs. However, many of the foods you eat also contain cholesterol. Excess amounts of cholesterol can collect along the walls of blood vessels and block the flow of blood. For this reason, many nutritionists recommend that people limit their intake of foods that are high in cholesterol. Foods that come from animals, such as meat, cheese, and eggs, are high in cholesterol.

Nucleic Acids

Nucleic acids are very large organic molecules made of carbon, oxygen, hydrogen, nitrogen, and phosphorus. Nucleic acids contain the instructions that cells need to carry out all the functions of life.

There are two kinds of nucleic acids. Deoxyribonucleic acid (dee ahk see ry boh noo KLEE ik), or **DNA,** is the genetic material that carries information about an organism that is passed from parent to offspring. The information in DNA also directs all of the cell's functions. Most of the DNA in a cell is found in the chromatin in the nucleus. Ribonucleic acid (ry boh noo KLEE ik), or **RNA,** plays an important role in the production of proteins. RNA is found in the cytoplasm, as well as in the nucleus.

Water and Living Things

Did you know that water makes up about two thirds of your body? Water plays many vital roles in cells. For example, most chemical reactions that take place in cells can occur only when substances are dissolved in water. **Without water, most chemical reactions within cells could not take place.** Also, water molecules themselves take part in many chemical reactions in cells.

Water also helps cells keep their size and shape. In fact, a cell without water would be like a balloon without air. In addition, because water changes temperature slowly, it helps keep the temperature of cells from changing rapidly. In the next section, you'll learn about the role that water plays in carrying substances into and out of cells.

Figure 15 Water is essential for all living things to survive. The cells of these tulips need water to function.

Section 3 Review

1. Name the four main groups of organic molecules in living things. Describe the function of each type of molecule.
2. What roles does water play in cells?
3. How are elements related to compounds?
4. **Thinking Critically Predicting** Suppose a cell did not have a supply of amino acids and could not produce them. What effect might this have on the cell?

Science at Home

With family members, look at the "Nutrition Facts" labels on a variety of food products. Identify foods that contain large amounts of the following organic compounds: carbohydrates, proteins, and fats. Discuss with your family what elements each of these compounds are made of and what roles they play in cells and in your body.

What's in Your Lunch?

You might be surprised to learn that chemists help the food industry obey the law. Most foods must carry labels listing the types of compounds they contain. In this lab, you can find out how chemists obtain that kind of information.

Problem

Which foods contain starches and lipids?

Skills Focus

predicting, drawing conclusions

Materials

cornstarch, 1 gram	water
food samples	plastic cups
plastic stirrers	plastic dropper

plastic graduated cylinder
vegetable oil, 5 milliliters
iodine solution in dropper bottle
5-centimeter squares of brown paper

Procedure

Part 1 Identifying Tests for Starches and Lipids

1. Write a prediction describing one or more differences you expect to observe between starches and lipids. Then copy the data table into your notebook, adding at least five blank rows.

2. Obtain plastic cups containing samples of cornstarch (a starch) and vegetable oil (a lipid).

3. Take a pinch of cornstarch between your thumb and index finger. Feel the substance's texture, and record your observation. Wash your hands to remove the cornstarch.

4. Take a few drops of vegetable oil between your thumb and index finger. Feel the substance's texture, and record your observation. Wash your hands to remove the vegetable oil.

5. Pour 5 milliliters of water into a plastic cup, and add about half of the cornstarch. Use a plastic stirrer to blend the contents into a starch-water mixture.

6. Obtain a brown paper square and write "S" (for "starch") in the corner. Place 3 drops of the starch mixture on the square. Record your observations. Put the square aside to observe it again in about five minutes.

7. Obtain a fresh brown paper square and write "L" (for "lipid") in the corner. Place 3 drops of vegetable oil on the square. Record your observations. Put the square aside to observe again in about five minutes.

DATA TABLE

	Substance Tested	Texture	Brown Paper Test	Iodine Test	Type of Compound
1.	Cornstarch				Starch
2.	Vegetable oil				Lipid
3.					
4.					
5.					

8. Add 4 drops of iodine to the remaining starch mixture. Use a clean plastic stirrer to mix the contents well. Record your observations. **CAUTION:** *Handle iodine carefully; it can stain skin and clothing.*

9. Add 4 drops of iodine to the remaining vegetable oil. Use a clean plastic stirrer to mix the contents well. Record your observations.

Part 2 Testing Food Samples

10. Use what you learned in Part 1 to plan starch and lipid tests for food samples such as bread, butter, onion, cooked pasta, peanut butter, potato, potato chips, and rice. If a food is in the form of a single chunk, such as a potato cube, mash it or cut it into smaller pieces. (*Hint:* You can test a sample for lipids by rubbing the sample directly on brown paper.) Be sure to submit your plan for your teacher's approval.

11. List each food you are testing in the first column of the data table. Before beginning your tests, predict what the results will be, and write a reason for each prediction. In making your predictions, consider that some foods may contain both starches and lipids.

12. Carry out the tests as in Part 1 of this lab. Record your observations in the data table. **CAUTION:** *Do not put iodine or any of the food samples in your mouth.* Wash your hands after handling the food samples.

Analyze and Conclude

1. Based on your investigation, what test results indicate the presence of starch? The presence of lipids?

2. What does it mean if one food sample reacts both to the iodine, as cornstarch did, and to the brown paper test, as the vegetable oil did?

3. What does it mean if a food does not react to either the iodine test or the brown paper test?

4. What did you discover from the tests you carried out on specific food samples? Did the results for any of the foods surprise you?

5. **Apply** Why might people want to know what kinds of organic compounds a food contains?

Design an Experiment

Some foods, such as milk and milk products, are available in both regular and low-fat forms. Plan a procedure in which you could test whether various milk products are low in fat.

SECTION 4 The Cell in Its Environment

DISCOVER ·· ACTIVITY····

How Do Molecules Move?

1. With your classmates, stand so that you are evenly spaced throughout the classroom.

2. Your teacher will spray an air freshener into the room. When you first begin to smell the air freshener, raise your hand.

3. Note how long it takes for other students in the classroom to smell the scent.

Think It Over

Developing Hypotheses How was each student's distance from the teacher related to when he or she smelled the air freshener? Develop a hypothesis about why this pattern occurred.

GUIDE FOR READING

◆ By what three methods do materials move into and out of cells?

◆ What is the difference between passive transport and active transport?

Reading Tip Before you read, use the headings to make an outline about how materials move into and out of cells. As you read, make notes about each process.

▼ The *Mir* space station

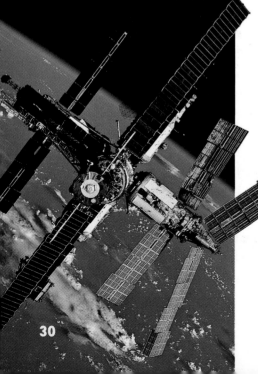

How is a cell like a space station? The walls of a space station protect the astronauts inside from the airless vacuum of space. Food, water, and other supplies must be brought to the space station by shuttles from Earth. In addition, the space station needs to be able to get rid of wastes. The doors of the space station allow the astronauts to bring materials in and move wastes out into the shuttle to be returned to Earth.

Like space stations, cells also have structures that protect them from the outside environment. As you learned, all cells are surrounded by a cell membrane that separates the cell from the outside environment. Just like the space station, the cell also has to take in needed materials and get rid of wastes. It is the cell membrane that controls what materials move into and out of the cell.

The Cell Membrane as Gatekeeper

The cell membrane is **selectively permeable,** which means that some substances can pass through it while others cannot. The term *permeable* comes from a Latin word that means "to pass through." You can think of the cell membrane as being like a gatekeeper at an ancient castle. It was the gatekeeper's job to decide when to open the gate to allow people to pass into and out of the castle. The gatekeeper made the castle wall "selectively permeable"—it was permeable to friendly folks but not to enemies.

A cell membrane is usually permeable to substances such as oxygen, water, and carbon dioxide. On the other hand, the cell membrane is usually not permeable to some large molecules and salts. **Substances that can move into and out of a cell do so by one of three methods: diffusion, osmosis, or active transport.**

30

Diffusion—Molecules in Motion

The main method by which small molecules move into and out of cells is diffusion. **Diffusion** (dih FYOO zhun) is the process by which molecules tend to move from an area of higher concentration to an area of lower concentration. The concentration of a substance is the amount of the substance in a given volume.

If you did the Discover activity, you observed diffusion in action. The area where the air freshener was sprayed had many molecules of freshener. The molecules gradually moved from this area of higher concentration to the other parts of the classroom, where there were few molecules of freshener, and thus a lower concentration.

What Causes Diffusion? Molecules are always moving. As they move, the molecules bump into one another. The more molecules there are in an area, the more collisions there will be. Collisions cause molecules to push away from one another. Over time, the molecules of a substance will continue to spread out. Eventually they will be spread evenly throughout the area.

Diffusion in Cells Have you ever used a microscope to observe one-celled organisms in pond water? These organisms obtain the oxygen they need to survive from the water around them. Luckily for them, there are many more molecules of oxygen in the water outside the cell than there are inside the cell. In other words, there is a higher concentration of oxygen molecules in the water than inside the cell. Remember that the cell membrane is permeable to oxygen molecules. The oxygen molecules diffuse from the area of higher concentration—the pond water—through the cell membrane to the area of lower concentration—the inside of the cell.

Figure 16 Molecules move by diffusion from an area of higher concentration to an area of lower concentration. **A.** There is a higher concentration of molecules outside the cell than inside. **B.** The molecules diffuse into the cell. Eventually, there is an equal concentration of molecules inside and outside the cell. *Predicting What would happen if the concentration of the molecules outside the cell was lower than the concentration inside?*

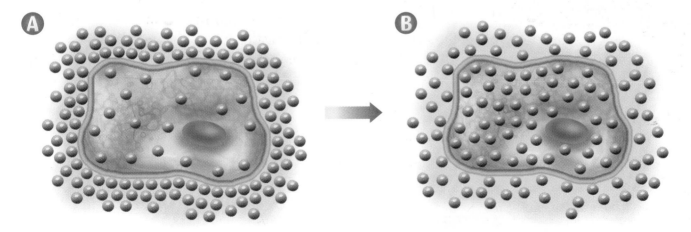

Osmosis—The Diffusion of Water Molecules

Like oxygen, water passes easily into and out of cells through the cell membrane. The diffusion of water molecules through a selectively permeable membrane is called **osmosis.** Osmosis is important to cells because cells cannot function properly without adequate water.

Remember that molecules tend to move from an area of higher concentration to an area of lower concentration. In osmosis, water molecules move by diffusion from an area where they are highly concentrated through the cell membrane to an area where they are less concentrated. This can have important consequences for the cell.

Look at Figure 17 to see the effect of osmosis on cells. In Figure 17 A, red blood cells are bathed in a solution in which the concentration of water is the same as it is inside the cells. This is the normal shape of a red blood cell.

Now look at Figure 17 B. The red blood cells are floating in water that contains a lot of salt. The concentration of water molecules outside the cells is lower than the concentration of water molecules inside the cells. This is because the salt takes up space in the salt water, so there are fewer water molecules. As a result, water moves out of the cells by osmosis, and the cells shrink.

Finally, consider Figure 17 C. The red blood cells are floating in water that contains a very small amount of salt. The water inside the cells contains more salt than the solution they are floating in. Thus, the concentration of water outside the cell is greater than it is inside the cell. The water moves into the cell, causing it to swell.

☑ *Checkpoint* **How is osmosis related to diffusion?**

Figure 17 Osmosis is the diffusion of water molecules through a selectively permeable membrane.

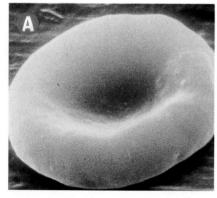

A. This is the normal shape of a red blood cell.

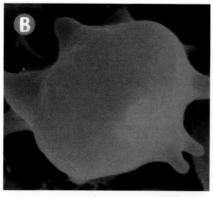

B. This cell has shrunk because water moved out of it by osmosis.

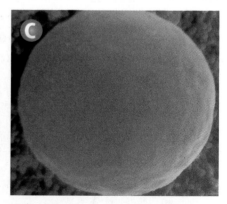

C. This cell is swollen with water that has moved into it by osmosis.

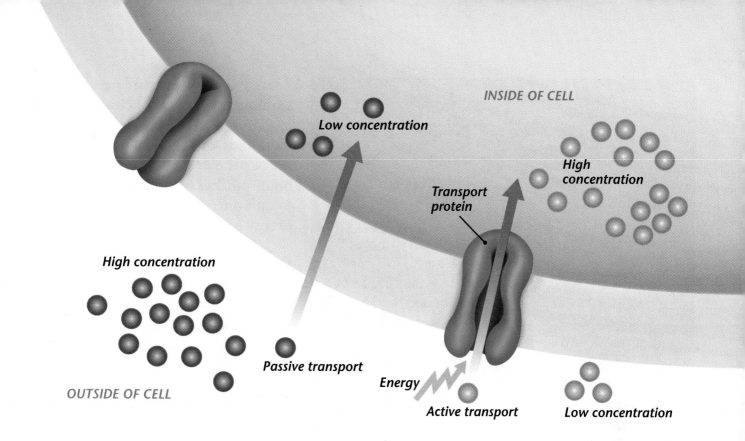

INSIDE OF CELL

Low concentration

High concentration

Transport protein

Passive transport

High concentration

OUTSIDE OF CELL

Energy

Active transport

Low concentration

Active Transport

If you have ever ridden a bicycle down a long hill, you know that it doesn't take any of your energy to go fast. But pedaling back up the hill does take energy. For a cell, moving materials through the cell membrane by diffusion and osmosis is like cycling downhill. These processes do not require the cell to use any energy. The movement of materials through a cell membrane without using energy is called **passive transport.**

What if a cell needs to take in a substance that is in higher concentration inside the cell than outside? The cell would have to move the molecules in the opposite direction than they naturally move by diffusion. Cells can do this, but they have to use energy—just as you would use energy to pedal back up the hill. **Active transport** is the movement of materials through a cell membrane using energy. **The main difference between passive transport and active transport is that active transport requires the cell to use energy while passive transport does not.**

Transport Proteins A cell has several ways of moving materials by active transport. In one method, transport proteins in the cell membrane "pick up" molecules outside the cell and carry them in, using energy in the process. Transport proteins also carry molecules out of cells in a similar way. Some substances that are carried into and out of cells in this way include calcium, potassium, and sodium.

Figure 18 Diffusion and osmosis are forms of passive transport. These processes do not require the cell to use any energy. Active transport, on the other hand, requires the use of energy. *Interpreting Diagrams How are passive and active transport related to the concentrations of the molecules inside and outside the cell?*

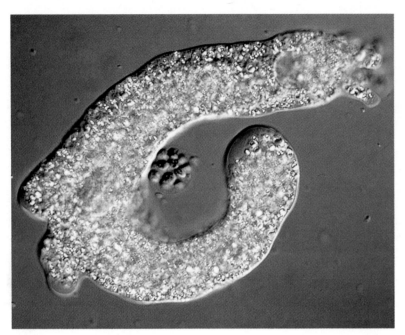

Figure 19 A cell can move some materials into the cell by engulfing them. This single-celled ameba is engulfing a smaller single-celled organism.

Transport by Engulfing You can see another method of active transport in Figure 19. First the cell membrane surrounds, or engulfs, a particle. Once the particle is engulfed, the cell membrane pinches off and forms a vacuole within the cell. The cell must use energy in this process.

Why Are Cells Small?

As you know, most cells are so small that you cannot see them without a microscope. Have you ever wondered why cells are so small? One reason is related to how materials move into and out of cells.

As a cell's size increases, more of its cytoplasm is located farther from the cell membrane. Once a molecule enters a cell, it is carried to its destination by a stream of moving cytoplasm, somewhat like the way currents of water in the ocean move a raft. But in a very large cell, the streams of cytoplasm must travel farther to bring materials to all parts of the cell. It would take much longer for a molecule to reach the center of a very large cell than it would in a small cell. Likewise, it would take a long time for wastes to be removed. If a cell grew too large, it could not function well enough to survive. When a cell reaches a certain size, it divides into two new cells. You will learn more about cell division in Chapter 2.

 Section 4 Review

1. Describe three methods by which substances can move into and out of cells.
2. How are passive transport and active transport similar? How do they differ?
3. Why is small size an advantage to a cell?
4. **Thinking Critically** **Predicting** A single-celled organism is transferred from a tank of fresh water into a tank of salt water. How will the cell change? Explain.

Check Your Progress **CHAPTER PROJECT**
Begin to think about why the egg changed as it did at each stage of the project. Consider how each of the different substances affected your egg. (*Hint:* Water plays a crucial role in the activities of a cell. How has water been involved in your investigation?) Organize your results into a report and make a graph of your egg's changing circumference. You may want to include diagrams to explain the processes that took place.

SECTION 1 Discovering Cells

Key Ideas

◆ The invention of the microscope made the discovery of the cell possible.

◆ The cell theory states that: all living things are made of cells; cells are the basic units of structure and function in organisms; all cells come from other cells.

◆ The lens or lenses in a light microscope magnify an object by bending the light that passes through.

Key Terms

cell	magnification
microscope	convex lens
compound microscope	resolution
cell theory	

 SECTION 2 Looking Inside Cells

Key Ideas

◆ The cell membrane protects the cell and controls what substances enter and leave it.

◆ The nucleus is the cell's control center. Chromatin in the nucleus contains genetic material that directs the cell's activities.

◆ Organelles in the cytoplasm include the mitochondria, endoplasmic reticulum, ribosomes, Golgi bodies, vacuoles, and lysosomes. Plant cells also contain chloroplasts.

◆ While a bacterial cell does have a cell membrane and a cell wall, it does not contain a nucleus.

Key Terms

organelle	cytoplasm	Golgi body
cell wall	mitochondrion	chloroplast
cell membrane	endoplasmic	vacuole
nucleus	reticulum	lysosome
chromatin	ribosome	

 SECTION 3 Chemical Compounds in Cells

INTEGRATING CHEMISTRY

Key Ideas

◆ When two or more elements combine chemically, they form a compound.

◆ The main groups of organic compounds found in living things are carbohydrates, lipids, proteins, and nucleic acids.

◆ Without water, most chemical reactions within cells could not take place.

Key Terms

element	protein
atom	amino acid
compound	enzyme
molecule	lipid
organic compound	nucleic acid
inorganic compound	DNA
carbohydrate	RNA

SECTION 4 The Cell in Its Environment

Key Ideas

◆ Substances can move into and out of a cell by diffusion, osmosis, or active transport.

◆ Diffusion is the process by which molecules move from an area of higher concentration to an area of lower concentration. Osmosis is the diffusion of water molecules through a selectively permeable membrane.

◆ The main difference between passive transport and active transport is that active transport requires the cell to use energy while passive transport does not.

◆ If a cell grew too large, it could not function well enough to survive.

Key Terms

selectively permeable	passive transport
diffusion	active transport
osmosis	

 ACTIVITY

USING THE INTERNET

www.science-explorer.phschool.com

CHAPTER 1 ASSESSMENT

California Test Prep: Reviewing Content

Multiple Choice
Choose the letter of the best answer.

1. The ability of microscopes to distinguish fine details is called
   a. resolution.
   b. bending.
   c. magnification.
   d. active transport.

2. In plant and animal cells, the control center of the cell is the
   a. chloroplast.
   b. ribosome.
   c. nucleus.
   d. Golgi body.

3. The storage compartment of a cell is the
   a. cell wall.
   b. lysosome.
   c. endoplasmic reticulum.
   d. vacuole.

4. Starch is an example of a
   a. nucleic acid.
   b. protein.
   c. lipid.
   d. carbohydrate.

5. The process by which water moves across a cell membrane is called
   a. osmosis.
   b. active transport.
   c. diffusion.
   d. resolution.

True or False
If the statement is true, write true. If it is false, change the underlined word or words to make the statement true.

6. Cells were discovered using <u>electron</u> microscopes.

7. <u>Vacuoles</u> are the "powerhouses" of the cell.

8. Bacterial cells differ from the cells of plants and animals in that they lack a <u>nucleus</u>.

9. Both DNA and RNA are <u>proteins</u>.

10. The <u>cell membrane</u> is selectively permeable.

Checking Concepts

11. What role did the microscope play in the development of the cell theory?

12. Describe the function of the cell wall in the cells that have these structures.

13. Explain the difference between organic and inorganic compounds.

14. How are enzymes important to living things?

15. What is diffusion? What role does diffusion play in the cell?

16. **Writing to Learn** Suppose you had been a reporter assigned to cover early scientists' discoveries about cells. Write a brief article for your daily newspaper that explains one scientist's discoveries. Be sure to explain both how the discoveries were made and why they are important.

Thinking Visually

17. **Concept Map** Copy the concept map about organic compounds onto a separate sheet of paper. Then complete the map and add a title. (For more about concept maps, see the Skills Handbook.)

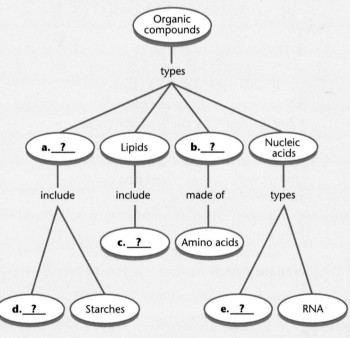

Test Prep: Skills

A scientist watered the plant in Figure A with salt water. After 30 minutes, the plant looked as you see it in Figure B. Use the drawings to answer Questions 18–20.

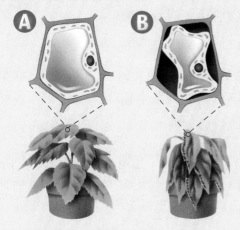

18. **Observing** How did the plant cells change after the plant was watered?
19. **Inferring** Describe a process that would lead to the changes in the plant cells.

20. **Predicting** Suppose the scientist were to water the plant in B with fresh water. Predict what would happen to the plant. Explain your prediction.

Thinking Critically

21. **Relating Cause and Effect** Suppose a microscope is invented that scientists could use to see molecules inside a cell's organelles. How could the microscope contribute to their understanding of the cell?
22. **Applying Concepts** Explain how the cell theory applies to a dog.
23. **Predicting** Could a cell survive without a cell membrane? Give reasons to support your answer.
24. **Making Generalizations** Why is the study of chemistry important to the understanding of living things?
25. **Comparing and Contrasting** How is active transport different from osmosis?

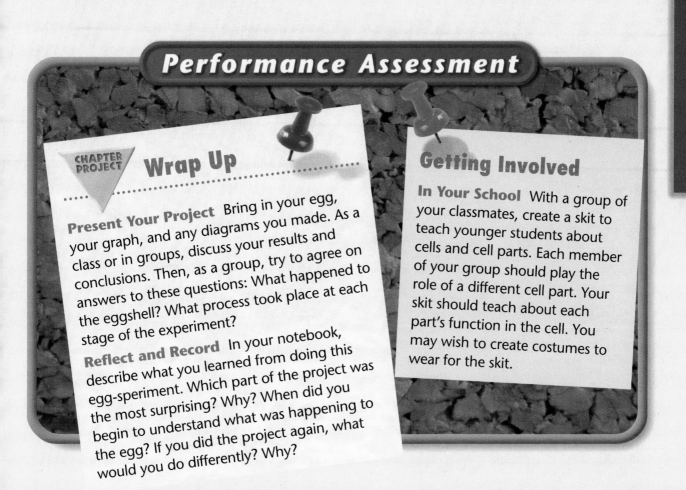

Performance Assessment

CHAPTER PROJECT — Wrap Up

Present Your Project Bring in your egg, your graph, and any diagrams you made. As a class or in groups, discuss your results and conclusions. Then, as a group, try to agree on answers to these questions: What happened to the eggshell? What process took place at each stage of the experiment?

Reflect and Record In your notebook, describe what you learned from doing this egg-speriment. Which part of the project was the most surprising? Why? When did you begin to understand what was happening to the egg? If you did the project again, what would you do differently? Why?

Getting Involved

In Your School With a group of your classmates, create a skit to teach younger students about cells and cell parts. Each member of your group should play the role of a different cell part. Your skit should teach about each part's function in the cell. You may wish to create costumes to wear for the skit.

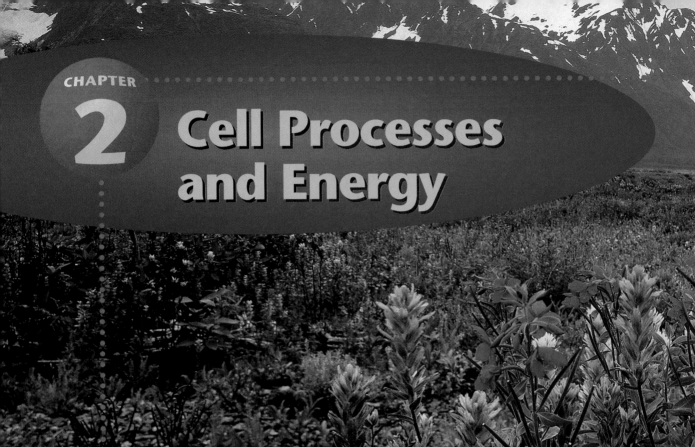

2 Cell Processes and Energy

CALIFORNIA
SCIENCE CONTENT STANDARDS

The following California Science Content Standards are addressed in this chapter:

1. All living organisms are composed of cells, from just one to many trillions, whose details usually are visible only through a microscope.

   a. Cells function similarly in all living organisms.

   b. The characteristics that distinguish plant cells from animal cells, including chloroplasts and cell walls.

   c. The nucleus is the repository for genetic information in plant and animal cells.

   d. Mitochondria liberate energy for the work that cells do, and chloroplasts capture sunlight energy for photosynthesis.

   e. Cells divide to increase their numbers through a process of mitosis, which results in two daughter cells with identical sets of chromosomes.

2. A typical cell of any organism contains genetic instructions that specify its traits. Those traits may be modified by environmental influences.

   e. DNA is the genetic material of living organisms, and is located in the chromosomes of each cell.

Shine On!

Every morning at sunrise, tiny living factories start a manufacturing process. These "factories" are cells that contain chloroplasts. The power they use is sunlight. The manufacturing process is called photosynthesis.

In this chapter, you'll learn what cells make during photosynthesis, and why nearly all organisms depend on this process. To begin your study, you'll investigate how light affects one familiar group of photosynthesizers—plants.

Your Goal To determine how different lighting conditions affect the health and growth of plants.

To complete the project you will
- write up a plan to grow plants under different lighting conditions
- care for your plants daily, and keep careful records of their health and growth for three weeks
- graph your data, and draw conclusions about the effect of light on plant growth
- follow the safety guidelines in Appendix A

Get Started Brainstorm with classmates to answer these questions: What different light conditions might you test? What plants will you use? How will you measure health and growth? How can you be sure your results are due to the light conditions? Write up your plan and submit it to your teacher.

Check Your Progress You'll be working on this project as you study this chapter. To keep your project on track, look for Check Your Progress boxes at the following points.

Section 1 Review: page 44: Place your plants in different light conditions.

Section 3 Review, page 58: Observe your plants daily.

Section 4 Review, page 63: Analyze and graph your results.

Wrap Up At the end of the chapter (page 67), you'll present your results to your classmates.

These paintbrush and dwarf fireweed plants in Glacier Bay National Park in Alaska depend on the sun for energy.

---

5. The anatomy and physiology of plants and animals illustrate the complementary nature of structure and function.

   b. Organ systems function because of the contributions of individual organs, tissues, and cells. The failure of any part can affect the entire system.

6. Physical principles underlie biological structures and functions.

f. Light interacts with matter by transmission (including refraction), absorption, or scattering (including reflection).

7. Scientific progress is made by asking meaningful questions and conducting careful investigations.

   a. Select and use appropriate tools and technology to perform tests, collect data, and display data.

c. Communicate the logical connection among hypothesis, science concepts, tests conducted, data collected, and conclusions drawn from the scientific evidence.

d. Construct scale models, maps and appropriately labeled diagrams to communicate scientific knowledge.

SECTION
① Photosynthesis

ACTIVITY

Where Does the Energy Come From?

1. Obtain a solar-powered calculator that does not use batteries. Place the calculator in direct light.

2. Cover the solar cells with your finger. Note how your action affects the number display.

3. Uncover the solar cells. What happens to the number display?

4. Now cover all but one of the solar cells. How does that affect the number display?

Think It Over

Inferring From your observations, what can you infer about the energy that powers the calculator?

GUIDE FOR READING

◆ **What happens during the process of photosynthesis?**

◆ **How does the sun supply living things with the energy they need?**

Reading Tip As you read, create a flowchart that shows the steps involved in the process of photosynthesis.

It's a beautiful summer afternoon—a perfect day for a picnic in the park. The aroma of chicken cooking on the grill fills the air. Your dog is busy chasing sticks under a nearby tree. Up above, bluejays swoop down from the tree's branches, hunting for food. "Let's go for a bike ride before lunch," suggests your cousin. "Great idea," you say, and you ride off down the path.

Dogs running, birds flying, people biking—all of these activities require energy. Where do you think this energy comes from? Believe it or not, all the energy used to perform such activities comes from the sun. In fact, the sun provides almost all the energy used by living things on Earth.

What Is Photosynthesis?

Every living thing needs energy. All cells need energy to carry out their functions, such as making proteins and transporting substances into and out of the cell. Your picnic lunch supplies your cells with the energy they need. But plants and other organisms, such as algae and some bacteria, obtain their energy in a different way. These organisms use the energy in sunlight to make their own food.

The process by which a cell captures the energy in sunlight and uses it to make food is called **photosynthesis** (foh toh SIN thuh sis). The term *photosynthesis* comes from the root words *photo*, which means "light," and *synthesis*, which means "putting together." Photosynthesis means using light to make food.

A Two-Stage Process

Photosynthesis is a very complicated process. **During photosynthesis, plants and some other organisms use energy from the sun to convert carbon dioxide and water into oxygen and sugars, including glucose.** You can think of photosynthesis as taking place in two stages: capturing the sun's energy and producing sugars. You're probably familiar with many two-stage processes. To make a cake, for example, the first stage is to combine the ingredients to make the batter. The second stage is to bake the batter in an oven. To get the desired result—the cake—both stages must occur in the correct order.

Capturing the Sun's Energy The first stage of photosynthesis involves capturing the energy in sunlight. In plants, this energy-capturing process occurs in the leaves and other green parts of the plant. Recall from Chapter 1 that chloroplasts are green organelles inside plant cells. In most plants, leaf cells contain more chloroplasts than do cells in other parts of the plant.

Figure 1 Photosynthesis occurs inside chloroplasts in the cells of plants and some other organisms. The chloroplasts are the green structures in the cell in the inset. *Applying Concepts Where in a plant are cells with many chloroplasts found?*

1. Cut a strip 5 cm by 20 cm out of a coffee filter.

2. Place a leaf on top of the paper strip, about 2 cm from the bottom.

3. Roll the edge of a dime over a section of the leaf, leaving a narrow band of color on the paper strip.

4. Pour rubbing alcohol into a plastic cup to a depth of 1 cm. Stand the paper strip in the cup so the color band is about 1 cm above the alcohol. Hook the other end of the strip over the top of the cup.

5. After 10 minutes, remove the paper strip and let it dry. Observe the strip.

6. Wash your hands.

What does the appearance of your paper strip reveal about the presence of pigments in the leaf?

The chloroplasts in plant cells give plants their green color. The green color comes from **pigments,** colored chemical compounds that absorb light. The main pigment found in the chloroplasts of plants is **chlorophyll.** Chloroplasts may also contain yellow and orange pigments, but they are usually masked by the green color of chlorophyll.

Chlorophyll and the other pigments function in a manner similar to that of the solar "cells" in a solar-powered calculator. Solar cells capture the energy in light and use it to power the calculator. Similarly, the pigments capture light energy and use it to power the second stage of photosynthesis.

Using Energy to Make Food In the second stage of photosynthesis, the cell uses the captured energy to produce sugars. The cell needs two raw materials for this stage: water (H_2O) and carbon dioxide (CO_2). In plants, the roots absorb water from the soil. The water then moves up through the plant's stem to the leaves. Carbon dioxide is one of the gases in the air. Carbon dioxide enters the plant through small openings on the undersides of the leaves called **stomata** (STOH muh tuh)(singular *stoma*). Once in the leaves, the water and carbon dioxide move into the chloroplasts.

Inside the chloroplasts, the water and carbon dioxide undergo a complex series of chemical reactions. The reactions are powered by the energy captured in the first stage. One of the products of the reactions is oxygen (O_2). The other products are sugars, including glucose ($C_6H_{12}O_6$). Recall from Chapter 1 that sugars are a type of carbohydrate. Cells can use the energy in the sugars to carry out important cell functions.

☑ *Checkpoint* *Why are plants green?*

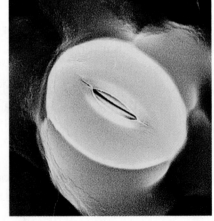

Figure 2 Stomata are small openings on the undersides of leaves. Stomata can open (left) or close (right) to control the movement of carbon dioxide and oxygen.

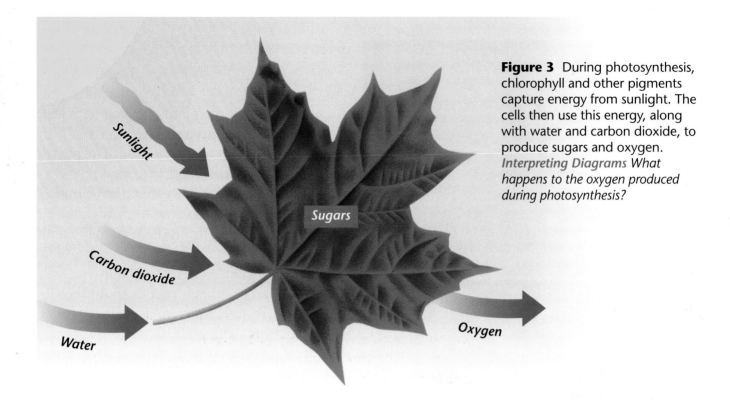

Figure 3 During photosynthesis, chlorophyll and other pigments capture energy from sunlight. The cells then use this energy, along with water and carbon dioxide, to produce sugars and oxygen. *Interpreting Diagrams What happens to the oxygen produced during photosynthesis?*

Sunlight

Sugars

Carbon dioxide

Water

Oxygen

The Photosynthesis Equation

The events of photosynthesis can be summed up by the following chemical equation:

$$6\,CO_2 \;+\; 6\,H_2O \;\xrightarrow{\text{light energy}}\; C_6H_{12}O_6 \;+\; 6\,O_2$$

carbon dioxide   water   glucose   oxygen

INTEGRATING CHEMISTRY Notice that the raw materials—six molecules of carbon dioxide and six molecules of water—are on the left side of the equation. The products—one molecule of glucose and six molecules of oxygen—are on the right side of the equation. An arrow, which is read as "yields," connects the raw materials to the products. Light energy, which is necessary for the chemical reaction to occur, is written above the arrow.

What happens to the products of photosynthesis? Plant cells use some of the sugar for food. The cells break down the sugar molecules to release the energy they contain. This energy can then be used to carry out the plant's functions. Some sugar molecules are converted into other compounds, such as cellulose. Other sugar molecules may be stored in the plant's cells for later use. When you eat food from plants, such as potatoes or carrots, you are eating the plant's stored food.

The other product of photosynthesis is oxygen. Most of the oxygen passes out of the plant through the stomata and into the air. All organisms that carry out photosynthesis release oxygen.

Photosynthesis and Life

INTEGRATING ENVIRONMENTAL SCIENCE If you were a caterpillar, you might be sitting on a plant chewing on a leaf. The plant is an **autotroph** (AW toh trohf), an organism that makes its own food. The plant's leaves contain sugars made during photosynthesis. Leaves also contain starches, cellulose, and other compounds made from sugars. The energy in these compounds originally came from the sun.

The caterpillar is a **heterotroph** (HET uh roh trohf), an organism that cannot make its own food. To live, grow, and perform other caterpillar functions, it needs the energy in the plant's sugars. By eating plants, the caterpillar gets its energy from the sun, although in an indirect way.

Watch out—there's a bird! The bird, a heterotroph, gets its energy by eating caterpillars. Since the energy in caterpillars indirectly comes from the sun, the bird too is living off the sun's energy. **Nearly all living things obtain energy either directly or indirectly from the energy of sunlight captured during photosynthesis.**

Photosynthesis is also essential for the air you breathe. Most living things need oxygen to survive. About 21% of Earth's atmosphere is oxygen—thanks to plants and other organisms that carry out photosynthesis. Almost all the oxygen in Earth's atmosphere was produced by living things through the process of photosynthesis.

Figure 4 Both the caterpillar and the western bluebird obtain their energy indirectly from the sun.

 Section 1 Review

1. What are the raw materials needed for photosynthesis? What are the products?
2. How do plants get energy? How do animals get energy?
3. What role does chlorophyll play in photosynthesis? Where is chlorophyll found?
4. **Thinking Critically Applying Concepts** List three ways that autotrophs were important to you today.

Check Your Progress
Make any necessary revisions to your experimental plan. Then create a data table in which to record your observations each day. Now it's time to place your plants in the different lighting conditions. (*Hint:* Be sure to keep all other conditions the same throughout the project. For example, give all your plants the same amount of water.)

CHAPTER PROJECT

SECTION 2 Respiration

DISCOVER · ACTIVITY · · ·

What Is a Product of Respiration?

1. Put on your goggles. Fill two test tubes half full of warm water. Add 5 milliliters of sugar to one of the test tubes. Put the tubes in a test tube rack.

2. Add 0.5 milliliter of dried yeast (a single-celled organism) to each tube. Stir the contents of each tube with a straw. Place a stopper snugly in the top of each tube.

3. Observe any changes that occur in the two test tubes over the next 10 to 15 minutes.

Think It Over
Observing What changes occurred in each test tube? How can you account for any differences that you observed?

Your friend stops along the trail ahead of you and calls out, "Let's eat!" He looks around for a flat rock to sit on. You're ready for lunch. You didn't have much breakfast this morning, and you've been hiking for the past hour. As you look around you, you see that the steepest part of the trail is still ahead of you. You'll need a lot of energy to make it to the top.

Everyone knows that food provides energy. But not everyone knows *how* food provides energy. The food you eat does not provide your body with energy immediately after you eat it. First, the food must pass through your digestive system. There, the food is broken down into small molecules. These small molecules can then pass out of the digestive system and into your bloodstream. Next, the molecules travel through the bloodstream to the cells of your body. Inside the cells, the energy in the molecules is released. In this section, you'll learn how your body's cells obtain energy from the food you eat.

GUIDE FOR READING

◆ What events occur during respiration?

◆ How are photosynthesis and respiration related?

◆ What is fermentation?

Reading Tip Before you read, write a definition of *respiration.* As you read, revise your definition based on what you have learned.

Figure 5 All organisms need energy to live. **A.** This leopard frog uses the energy stored in carbohydrates to leap great distances. **B.** Although these mushrooms don't move, they still need a continuous supply of energy to grow and reproduce. *Applying Concepts What is the name of the process by which cells obtain the energy they need?*

Storing and Releasing Energy

To understand how cells use energy, think about how people save money in a bank. You might, for example, put some money in a savings account. Then, when you want to buy something, you withdraw some of the money. Cells store and use energy in a similar way. During photosynthesis, plants capture the energy from sunlight and "save" it in the form of carbohydrates, including sugars and starches. When the cells need energy, they "withdraw" it by breaking down the carbohydrates. This process releases energy. Similarly, when you eat a meal, you add to your body's energy savings account. When your cells need energy, they make a withdrawal and break down the food to release energy.

Respiration

After you eat a meal, your body converts the carbohydrates in the food into glucose, a type of sugar. The process by which cells "withdraw" energy from glucose is called **respiration. During respiration, cells break down simple food molecules such as glucose and release the energy they contain.** Because living things need a continuous supply of energy, the cells of all living things carry out respiration continuously.

The term *respiration* might be confusing. You have probably used it to mean breathing, that is, moving air in and out of your lungs. Because of this confusion, the respiration process that takes place inside cells is sometimes called cellular respiration.

The double use of the term *respiration* does point out a connection that you should keep in mind. Breathing brings oxygen into your lungs, and oxygen is necessary for cellular respiration to occur in most cells. Some cells can obtain energy from glucose without using oxygen. But the most efficient means of obtaining energy from glucose requires the presence of oxygen.

The Respiration Equation Although respiration occurs in a series of complex steps, the overall process can be summarized in the following equation:

$$C_6H_{12}O_6 + 6\,O_2 \longrightarrow 6\,CO_2 + 6\,H_2O + energy$$
glucose   oxygen   carbon dioxide water

Notice that the raw materials for respiration are glucose and oxygen. Plants and other organisms that undergo photosynthesis make their own glucose. The glucose in the cells of animals and other organisms comes from the food they consume. The oxygen comes from the air or water surrounding the organism.

The Two Stages of Respiration Like photosynthesis, respiration is a two-stage process. The first stage takes place in the cytoplasm of the organism's cells. There, glucose molecules are broken down into smaller molecules. Oxygen is not involved in this stage of respiration. Only a small amount of the energy in glucose is released during this stage.

The second stage of respiration takes place in the mitochondria. There, the small molecules are broken down into even smaller molecules. These chemical reactions require oxygen, and a great deal of energy is released. This is why the mitochondria are sometimes called the "powerhouses" of the cell.

Figure 6 summarizes the process of respiration. If you trace the steps in the breakdown of glucose, you'll see that energy is released in both stages. Two other products of respiration are carbon dioxide and water. These products diffuse out of the cell. In animals, the carbon dioxide and some water leave the body when they breathe out. Thus, when you breathe in, you take in oxygen, a raw material for respiration. When you breathe out, you release carbon dioxide and water, products of respiration.

☑ *Checkpoint* *What are the raw materials for respiration?*

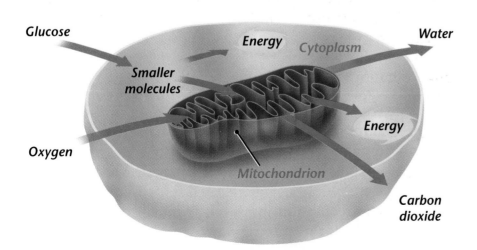

Figure 6 The first stage of respiration, which takes place in the cytoplasm, releases a small amount of energy. The second stage takes place in the mitochondria. A large amount of energy is released at this stage.

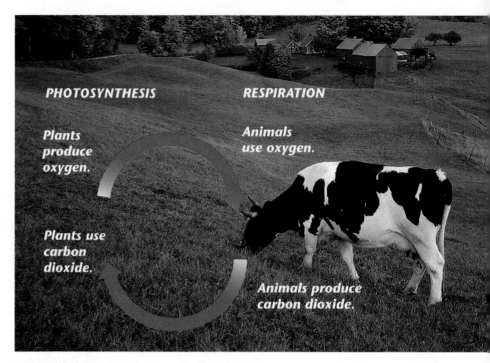

PHOTOSYNTHESIS

Plants produce oxygen.

Plants use carbon dioxide.

RESPIRATION

Animals use oxygen.

Animals produce carbon dioxide.

Figure 7 Photosynthesis and respiration can be thought of as opposite processes. *Interpreting Photographs How do these two processes keep the levels of oxygen and carbon dioxide in the atmosphere fairly constant?*

Comparing Photosynthesis and Respiration

Do you notice anything familiar about the equation for respiration? You are quite right if you said it is the opposite of the equation for photosynthesis. This is an important point to remember. During photosynthesis, carbon dioxide and water are used to produce sugars and oxygen. During respiration, glucose (a sugar) and oxygen are used to produce carbon dioxide and water. **Photosynthesis and respiration can be thought of as opposite processes.** Together, these two processes form a cycle that keeps the levels of oxygen and carbon dioxide fairly constant in the atmosphere. As you can see in Figure 7, living things use both gases over and over again.

Fermentation

Some cells are able to obtain energy from food without using oxygen. For example, some single-celled organisms live where there is no oxygen, such as deep in the ocean or in the mud of lakes or swamps. These organisms obtain their energy through **fermentation,** an energy-releasing process that does not require oxygen. **Fermentation provides energy for cells without using oxygen.** The amount of energy released from each sugar molecule during fermentation, however, is much lower than the amount released during respiration.

Alcoholic Fermentation One type of fermentation occurs in yeast and some other single-celled organisms. This process is sometimes called alcoholic fermentation because alcohol is one of the products made when these organisms break down sugars. The other products are carbon dioxide and a small amount of energy.

The products of alcoholic fermentation are important to bakers and brewers. The carbon dioxide produced by yeast causes dough to rise, and it creates the air pockets you see in bread. Carbon dioxide is also the source of bubbles in alcoholic drinks such as beer and sparkling wine.

Lactic-Acid Fermentation Another type of ![INTEGRATING HEALTH] fermentation takes place at times in your body, and you've probably felt its effects. Think of a time when you've run as fast as you could for as long as you could. Your leg muscles were pushing hard against the pavement, and you were breathing quickly. Eventually, however, your legs became tired and you couldn't run any more.

No matter how hard you breathed, your muscle cells used up the oxygen faster than it could be replaced. Because your cells lacked oxygen, fermentation occurred. One product of this type of fermentation is an acid known as lactic acid. When lactic acid builds up, you feel a painful sensation in your muscles. Your muscles feel weak and sore.

Figure 8 When an athlete's muscles run out of oxygen, lactic-acid fermentation occurs. The athlete's muscles feel tired and sore.

Section 2 Review

1. Why is respiration important for a cell?
2. Explain the relationship between photosynthesis and respiration.
3. Which raw material is *not* needed for fermentation to occur?
4. How do plants and animals maintain the level of oxygen in the atmosphere?
5. **Thinking Critically** **Applying Concepts** Do plant cells need to carry out respiration? Explain.

Science at Home

With an adult family member, follow a recipe in a cookbook to make a loaf of bread using yeast. Explain to your family what causes the dough to rise. After you bake the bread, observe a slice and look for evidence that fermentation occurred.

Gases in Balance

Problem

How are photosynthesis and respiration related?

Skills Focus

controlling variables, interpreting data

Materials

marking pens straws
2 *Elodea* plants light source
plastic graduated cylinder, 100-mL
bromthymol blue solution
3 flasks with stoppers, 250-mL

Procedure 🧍🫁🧪🫧

1. Bromthymol blue can be used to test for carbon dioxide. To see how this dye works, pour 100 mL of bromthymol blue solution into a flask. Record its color. **CAUTION:** *Bromthymol blue can stain skin and clothing. Avoid spilling or splashing it on yourself.*

2. Provide a supply of carbon dioxide by gently blowing into the solution through a straw until the dye changes color. Record the new color. **CAUTION:** *Do not inhale any of the solution through the straw.*

3. Copy the data table into your notebook. Add 100 mL of bromthymol blue to the other flasks. Then blow through clean straws into each solution until the color changes.

4. Now you will test to see what gas is used by a plant in the presence of light. Obtain two *Elodea* plants of about the same size.

5. Place one plant into the first flask. Label the flask "L" for light. Place the other plant in the second flask. Label the flask "D" for darkness. Label the third flask "C" for control. Put stoppers in all three flasks.

DATA TABLE

Flask	Color of Solution	
	Day 1	Day 2
L (light)		
D (dark)		
C (control)		

6. Record the colors of the three solutions under Day 1 in your data table.

7. Place the flasks labeled L and C in a lighted location as directed by your teacher. Place the flask labeled D in a dark location as directed by your teacher. Wash your hands thoroughly when you have finished.

8. On Day 2, examine the flasks and record the colors of the solutions in your data table.

Analyze and Conclude

1. Explain why the color of each solution did or did not change from Day 1 to Day 2.
2. Why was it important to include the flask labeled C as part of this experiment?
3. Predict what would happen if you blew into the flask labeled L after you completed Step 8. Explain your prediction.
4. **Apply** How does this lab show that photosynthesis and respiration are opposite processes? Why are both processes necessary to maintain an environment suitable for living things?

More to Explore

Suppose you were to put an *Elodea* plant and a small fish in a stoppered flask. Predict what would happen to the levels of oxygen and carbon dioxide in the flask. Explain your prediction.

SECTION 3 Cell Division

DISCOVER •••••••••••••••••••••••••••••••••••••• ACTIVITY

What Are the Cells Doing?

1. 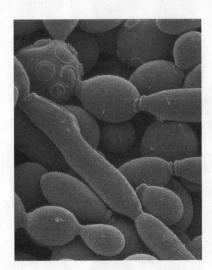 Use a plastic dropper to transfer some yeast cells from a yeast culture to a microscope slide. Your teacher has prepared the slide by drying methylene blue stain onto it. Add a cover-slip and place the slide under a microscope.

2. Examine the cells on the slide. Use low power first, then high power. Look for what appears to be two cells attached to each other. One cell may be larger than the other. Draw what you see.

Think It Over

Developing Hypotheses What process do you think the "double cells" are undergoing? Develop a hypothesis that might explain what you see.

In the early autumn, many local fairs run pumpkin contests. Proud growers enter their largest pumpkins, hoping to win a prize. If you've never seen these prize-winning pumpkins, you would be amazed. Some have masses close to 400 kilograms and can be as big as a doghouse. What's even more amazing is that these giant pumpkins began as small flowers on pumpkin plants. How did the pumpkins grow so big?

A pumpkin grows in size by increasing both the size and the number of its cells. A single cell divides, forming two cells. Then two cells divide, forming four, and so on. This process of cell division does not occur only in pumpkins, though. In fact, many cells in your body are undergoing cell division as you read this page.

GUIDE FOR READING

◆ What events take place during the three stages of the cell cycle?

◆ What is the role of DNA replication?

Reading Tip Before you read, use the headings to outline the process of cell division. As you read, fill in information under each heading.

Figure 9 The cells that make up this young monkey are the same size as those that make up its mother. However, the adult has many more cells in its body.

The Cell Cycle

Think about the cells you learned about in Chapter 1. Each cell contains many different structures, including a cell membrane, a nucleus, mitochondria, and ribosomes. To divide into two equal parts, the cell would need to either duplicate the structures or divide them equally between the two new cells. Both cells would then contain everything they need in order to survive and carry out their life functions.

The regular sequence of growth and division that cells undergo is known as the **cell cycle.** You can see details of the cell cycle in *Exploring the Cell Cycle* on pages 54 and 55. Notice that the cell cycle is divided into three main stages. As you read about each stage, follow the events that occur as one "parent" cell divides to form two identical "daughter" cells.

Stage 1: Interphase

The first stage of the cell cycle is called **interphase.** Interphase is the period before cell division occurs. Even though it is not dividing, the cell is quite active during this stage. **During interphase, the cell grows to its mature size, makes a copy of its DNA, and prepares to divide into two cells.**

Growth During the first part of interphase, the cell doubles in size and produces all the structures needed to carry out its functions. For example, the cell enlarges its endoplasmic reticulum, makes new ribosomes, and produces enzymes. Both mitochondria and chloroplasts make copies of themselves during the growth stage. The cell matures to its full size and structure.

DNA Replication After a cell has grown to its mature size, the next part of interphase begins. The cell makes a copy of the DNA in its nucleus in a process called **replication.** Recall that DNA is a nucleic acid found in the chromatin in a cell's nucleus. DNA holds all the information that the cell needs to carry out its functions. The replication of a cell's DNA is very important, since each daughter cell must have a complete set of DNA to survive. At the end of DNA replication, the cell contains two identical sets of DNA. One set will be distributed to each daughter cell. You will learn the details of DNA replication later in this section.

Preparation for Division Once the cell's DNA has replicated, preparation for cell division begins. The cell produces structures that it will use to divide during the rest of the cell cycle. At the end of interphase, the cell is ready to divide.

Stage 2: Mitosis

Once interphase is complete, the second stage of the cell cycle begins. **Mitosis** (my TOH sis) is the stage during which the cell's nucleus divides into two new nuclei. **During mitosis, one copy of the DNA is distributed into each of the two daughter cells.**

Scientists divide mitosis into four parts, or phases: prophase, metaphase, anaphase, and telophase. During prophase, the threadlike chromatin in the cell's nucleus begins to condense and coil, like fishing line wrapping around a ball. Under a light microscope, the condensed chromatin looks like tiny rods, as you can see in Figure 10. Since the cell's DNA has replicated, each rod has doubled. Each is an exact copy of the other. Scientists call each doubled rod of condensed chromatin a **chromosome.** Each identical rod, or strand, of the chromosome is called a **chromatid.** The two strands are held together by a structure called a centromere.

As the cell progresses through metaphase, anaphase, and telophase, the chromatids separate from each other and move to opposite ends of the cell. Then two nuclei form around the chromatids at the two ends of the cell. You can follow this process in *Exploring the Cell Cycle*.

☑ *Checkpoint* *During which stage of mitosis does the chromatin condense and form rodlike structures?*

Modeling Mitosis

Refer to *Exploring the Cell Cycle* as you carry out this activity.

ACTIVITY

1. Construct a model of a cell that has three chromosomes. Use a piece of construction paper to represent the cell. Use different colored pipe cleaners to represent the chromosomes. Make sure that the chromosomes look like double rods.

2. Position the chromosomes in the cell where they would be during prophase.

3. Repeat Step 2 for metaphase, anaphase, and telophase.

Making Models How did the model help you understand the events of mitosis?

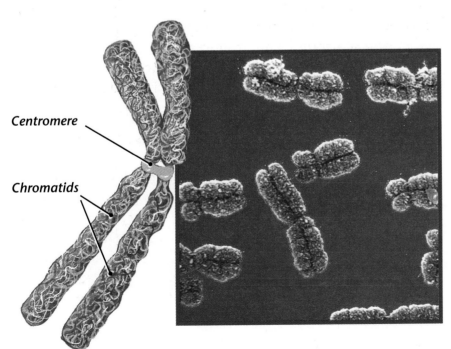

Centromere

Chromatids

Figure 10 During mitosis, the chromatin condenses to form rodlike chromosomes. Each chromosome consists of two identical strands, or chromatids. *Interpreting Diagrams What is the name of the structure that holds the chromatids together?*

EXPLORING *the Cell Cycle*

Cells undergo an orderly sequence of events as they grow and divide. The sequence shown here is a typical cell cycle in an animal cell. Plant cells have somewhat different cell cycles.

① INTERPHASE
The cell grows to its mature size, makes a copy of its DNA, and prepares to divide into two cells.

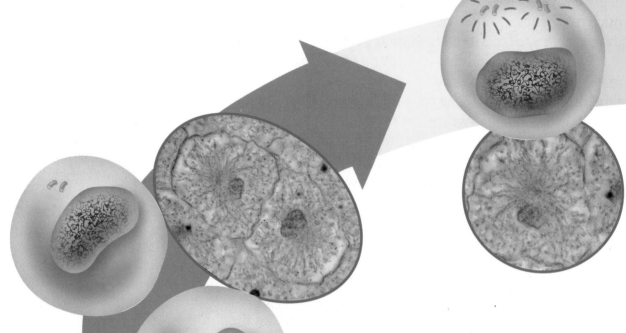

③ CYTOKINESIS
The cell membrane pinches in around the middle of the cell. Eventually, the cell pinches in two. Each daughter cell ends up with the same number of identical chromosomes and about half the organelles and cytoplasm.

②ⓓ MITOSIS: Telophase
The chromosomes begin to stretch out and lose their rodlike appearance. This occurs in the two regions at the ends of the cell. A new nuclear membrane forms around each region of chromosomes.

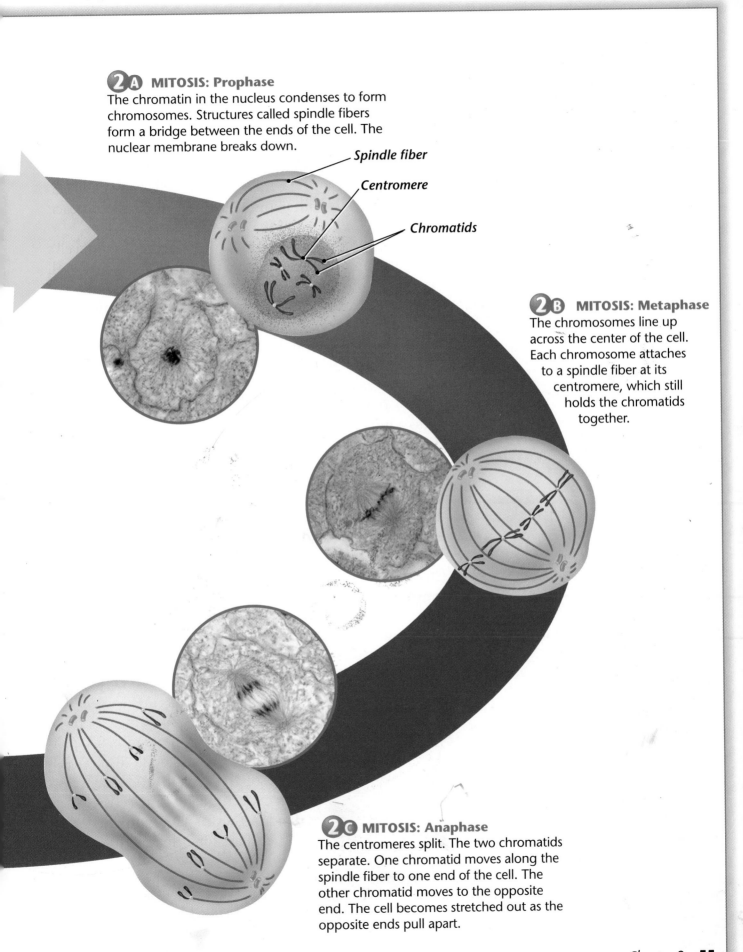

2A MITOSIS: Prophase
The chromatin in the nucleus condenses to form chromosomes. Structures called spindle fibers form a bridge between the ends of the cell. The nuclear membrane breaks down.

Spindle fiber

Centromere

Chromatids

2B MITOSIS: Metaphase
The chromosomes line up across the center of the cell. Each chromosome attaches to a spindle fiber at its centromere, which still holds the chromatids together.

2C MITOSIS: Anaphase
The centromeres split. The two chromatids separate. One chromatid moves along the spindle fiber to one end of the cell. The other chromatid moves to the opposite end. The cell becomes stretched out as the opposite ends pull apart.

Interpreting Data

ACTIVITY

Use the circle graph shown in Figure 11 to answer the following questions.

1. How long is the cell cycle shown in the graph?
2. Which stage of the cell cycle would you expect more of the cells to be in at any given time—interphase, mitosis, or cytokinesis? Explain.

Stage 3: Cytokinesis

After mitosis, the final stage of the cell cycle, called **cytokinesis** (sy toh kih NEE sis), completes the process of cell division. **During cytokinesis, the cytoplasm divides, distributing the organelles into each of the two new cells.** Cytokinesis usually starts at about the same time as telophase.

During cytokinesis in animal cells, the cell membrane squeezes together around the middle of the cell. The cytoplasm pinches into two cells with about half of the organelles in each daughter cell.

Cytokinesis is somewhat different in plant cells. A plant cell's rigid cell wall cannot squeeze together in the same way that a cell membrane can. Instead, a structure called a cell plate forms across the middle of the cell. The cell plate gradually develops into new cell membranes between the two daughter cells. New cell walls then form around the cell membranes.

There are many variations of the basic pattern of cytokinesis. For example, yeast cells divide, though not equally. A small daughter cell, or bud, pinches off of the parent cell. The bud then grows into a full-sized yeast cell.

Cytokinesis marks the end of the cell cycle. Two new cells have formed. Each daughter cell has the same number of chromosomes as the original parent cell. At the end of cytokinesis, each cell enters interphase, and the cycle begins again.

☑ *Checkpoint* *When in the cell cycle does cytokinesis begin?*

Length of the Cell Cycle

How long does it take for a cell to go through one cell cycle? The answer depends on the type of cell. In a young sea urchin, for example, one cell cycle takes about 2 hours. In contrast, a human liver cell completes one cell cycle in about 22 hours, as shown in Figure 11. The length of each stage in the cell cycle also varies greatly from cell to cell. Some cells, such as human brain cells, never divide—they remain in the first part of interphase for as long as they live.

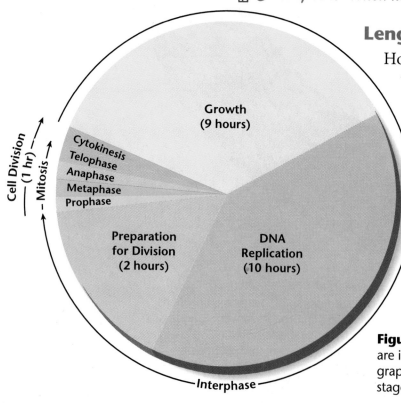

Figure 11 The main stages of the cell cycle are interphase, mitosis, and cytokinesis. This graph shows the average length of each stage in a human liver cell.

DNA Replication

A cell makes a copy of its DNA before mitosis occurs. **DNA replication ensures that each daughter cell will have all of the genetic information it needs to carry out its activities.**

Only in the last 50 years have scientists understood the importance of DNA. By the early 1950s, the work of several scientists showed that DNA carries all of the cell's instructions. They also learned that DNA is passed from a parent cell to its daughter cells. In 1953, two scientists, James Watson and Francis Crick, figured out the structure of DNA. This discovery revealed important information about how DNA copies itself.

The Structure of DNA Notice in Figure 12 that a DNA molecule looks like a twisted ladder, or spiral staircase. Because of its shape, a DNA molecule is often called a "double helix." A helix is a shape that twists like the threads of a screw.

The two sides of the DNA ladder are made up of molecules of a sugar called deoxyribose, alternating with molecules known as phosphates. Each rung of the DNA ladder is made up of a pair of molecules called nitrogen bases. Nitrogen bases are molecules that combine the element nitrogen with other elements. There are four kinds of nitrogen bases: adenine (AD uh neen), thymine (THY meen), guanine (GWAH neen), and cytosine (SY tuh seen). The capital letters A, T, G, and C are used to represent the four bases.

Look closely at Figure 12. Notice that the bases on one side of the ladder match up in a specific way with the bases on the other side. Adenine (A) only pairs with thymine (T), while guanine (G) only pairs with cytosine (C). This pairing pattern is the key to understanding how DNA replication occurs.

Figure 12 A DNA molecule is shaped like a twisted ladder. The sides are made up of sugar and phosphate molecules. The rungs are formed by pairs of nitrogen bases. *Classifying Which base always pairs with adenine?*

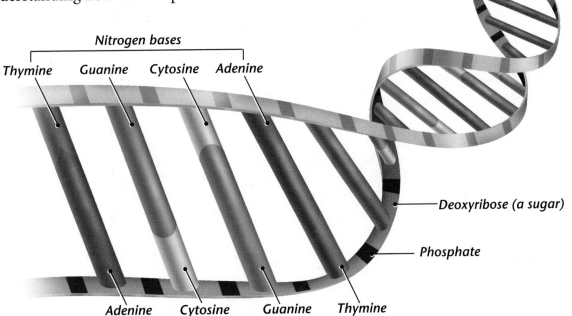

Nitrogen bases

Thymine Guanine Cytosine Adenine

Deoxyribose (a sugar)

Phosphate

Adenine Cytosine Guanine Thymine

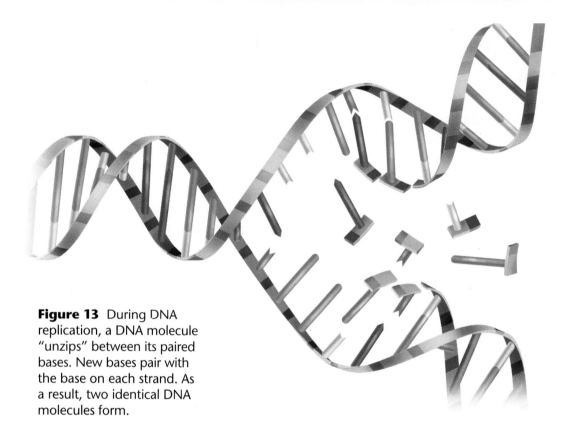

Figure 13 During DNA replication, a DNA molecule "unzips" between its paired bases. New bases pair with the base on each strand. As a result, two identical DNA molecules form.

The Replication Process DNA replication begins when the two sides of the DNA molecule unwind and separate, like a zipper unzipping. As you can see in Figure 13, the molecule separates between the paired nitrogen bases on each rung. Next, nitrogen bases that are floating in the nucleus pair up with the bases on each half of the DNA molecule. Remember that the pairing of bases follows definite rules: A always pairs with T, while G always pairs with C. Once the new bases are attached, two new DNA molecules are formed. The order of the bases in each new DNA molecule will exactly match the order in the original DNA molecule.

Section 3 Review

1. What are the three main stages of the cell cycle? Briefly describe the events that occur at each stage.
2. Why must the DNA in a cell replicate before the cell divides?
3. How does cytokinesis differ in plant and animal cells?
4. **Thinking Critically** **Predicting** Suppose that during anaphase, the centromeres did not split and the chromatids did not separate. Predict the results.

Check Your Progress

CHAPTER PROJECT

At this point, you should be observing the health of your plants, and measuring their growth. Make drawings to show the appearance of the plants at different stages of the project. (*Hint:* In addition to overall height, you may wish to note the number and length of stems, and the number, size, color, and firmness of the leaves.)

Multiplying by Dividing

Problem

How long do the stages of the cell cycle take?

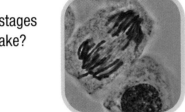

Materials

microscope
colored pencils
calculator (optional)
prepared slides of onion root tip cells
　undergoing cell division

Procedure 🧪

1. Place the slide on the stage of a microscope. Use low power to locate a cell in interphase. Then switch to high power, and make a labeled drawing of the cell. **CAUTION:** *Slides and coverslips break easily. Do not allow the objective to touch the slide. If the slide breaks, notify your teacher. Do not touch broken glass.*

2. Repeat Step 1 to find cells in prophase, metaphase, anaphase, and telophase. Then copy the data table into your notebook.

3. Return to low power. Find an area of the slide with many cells undergoing cell division. Switch to the magnification that lets you see about 50 cells at once (for example, 100 ×).

4. Examine the cells row by row, and count the cells that are in interphase. Record that number in the data table under *First Sample.*

5. Examine the cells row-by-row four more times to count the cells in prophase, metaphase, anaphase, and telophase. Record the results.

6. Move to a new area on the slide. Repeat Steps 3–5 and record your counts in the column labeled *Second Sample.*

7. Fill in the column labeled *Total Number* by adding the numbers across each row in your data table.

8. Add the totals for the five stages to find the total number of cells counted.

Analyze and Conclude

1. Which stage of the cell cycle did you observe most often?

2. The cell cycle for onion root tips takes about 720 minutes (12 hours). Use your data and the formula below to find the number of minutes each stage takes.

$$\text{Time for each stage} = \frac{\text{Number of cells at each stage}}{\text{Total number of cells counted}} \times 720 \text{ min}$$

3. **Think About It** Use the data to compare the amount of time spent in mitosis with the total time for the whole cell cycle.

More to Explore

Examine prepared slides of animal cells undergoing cell division. Use drawings and descriptions to compare plant and animal mitosis.

DATA TABLE

Stage of Cell Cycle	First Sample	Second Sample	Total Number
Interphase			
Mitosis: Prophase			
Metaphase			
Anaphase			
Telophase			
Total number of cells counted			

SECTION 4 Cancer

DISCOVER •• ACTIVITY

What Happens When There Are Too Many Cells?

1. Use tape to mark off a one meter-by-one meter square on the floor. The square represents an area inside the human body. Have two students stand in the square to represent cells.

2. Suppose each cell divides every 30 seconds, and then one cell dies. With a group of students, model this situation. After 30 seconds, two new students should enter the square and one student should leave the square.

3. Model another round of cell division by having three new students enter the square while one student leaves. Continue this process until no more students can fit in the square.

Think It Over

Predicting Use this activity to predict what would happen if some cells in a person's body divided faster than they should.

GUIDE FOR READING

◆ How is cancer related to the cell cycle?

◆ What are some ways that cancer can be treated?

Reading Tip As you read, make a list of the main causes of cancer and how to prevent them.

Imagine that you are planting a flower garden near your home. After careful planning, you plant snapdragons, geraniums, and petunias exactly where you think they will look best. You also plant a ground ivy that you think will look nice between the flowers. You water your garden and wait for it to grow.

Much to your dismay, after a few months you notice that the ground ivy has taken over the garden. Where there should be flowers, there is nothing but a tangle of vines. Only a few flowers have survived. The ivy has used up more than its share of garden space and soil nutrients. A neighbor remarks, "That vine is so out of control, it's like a cancer."

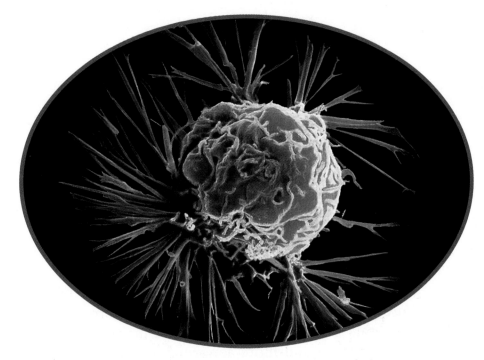

Figure 14 A cancer tumor begins as a single abnormal cell, like this breast cancer cell. A mutation occurs in the cell's DNA and disrupts the normal cell cycle. *Relating Cause and Effect How does the cell behave as a result of the mutation?*

What Is Cancer?

Your neighbor compared the ground ivy to a cancer because it grew uncontrollably and destroyed the other plants. **Cancer** is a disease in which cells grow and divide uncontrollably, damaging the parts of the body around them.

Cancer is actually not just one disease. In fact, there are more than 100 types of cancer. Cancer can occur in almost any part of the body. Cancers are often named by the place in the body where they begin. In the United States today, lung cancer is the leading cause of cancer deaths among both men and women.

How Cancer Begins Scientists think that cancer begins when something damages a portion of the DNA in a chromosome. The damage causes a change in the DNA called a **mutation.** Remember that DNA contains all the instructions necessary for life. Damage to the DNA can cause cells to function abnormally.

Normally, the cells in one part of the body live in harmony with the cells around them. Cells that go through the cell cycle divide in a controlled way. Other cells don't divide at all. **Cancer begins when mutations disrupt the normal cell cycle, causing cells to divide in an uncontrolled way.** The cells stop behaving as they normally do. Without the normal controls on the cell cycle, the cells grow too large and divide too often.

How Cancer Spreads At first, one cell develops in an abnormal way. As the cell divides, more and more abnormal cells like it grow near it. In time, these cells form a tumor. A **tumor** is a mass of abnormal cells that develops when cancerous cells divide and grow uncontrollably.

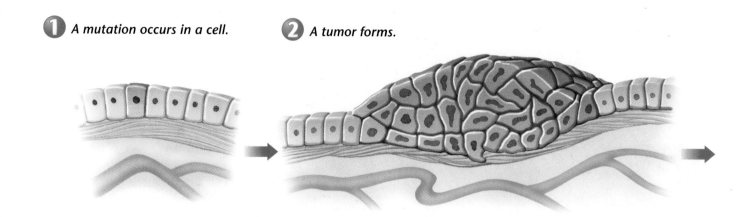

1 *A mutation occurs in a cell.*   **2** *A tumor forms.*

Figure 15 A tumor is a mass of cells that divide uncontrollably. It may take years for a tumor to grow large enough to be noticed. *Interpreting Diagrams How can cancer spread from one part of the body to another?*

Figure 15 shows the process by which a tumor forms. Tumors often take years to grow to a noticeable size. During that time, the cells become more and more abnormal as they continue to divide. Some of the cancerous cells may break off the tumor and enter the bloodstream. In this way, the cancer can spread to other areas of the body.

✓ *Checkpoint* *What is the first step that leads to the development of a tumor?*

Treating Cancer

If a person is stricken with cancer, there are a variety of treatments that may be effective in fighting the disease. **Doctors usually treat cancer in one or more of three ways: surgery, radiation, or drugs that destroy the cancer cells.**

When a cancer is detected before it has spread to other parts of the body, surgery is usually the best treatment. If doctors can completely remove the cancerous tumor, a person may be cured of the disease. If, however, the cancer has spread or if the tumor cannot be removed, doctors may use radiation, beams of high-energy waves. Fast-growing cancer cells are more likely than normal cells to be destroyed by radiation.

Chemotherapy, or the use of drugs to kill cancer cells, is another form of treatment. Chemotherapy is effective because the drugs spread throughout the body, killing cancer cells or slowing their growth.

Unfortunately, none of these cancer treatments is perfect. Most have unpleasant, or even dangerous, side effects. Scientists continue to look for new ways to treat cancer. If, for example, scientists can discover how the cell cycle is controlled, they may find ways to stop cancer cells from going through the cell cycle.

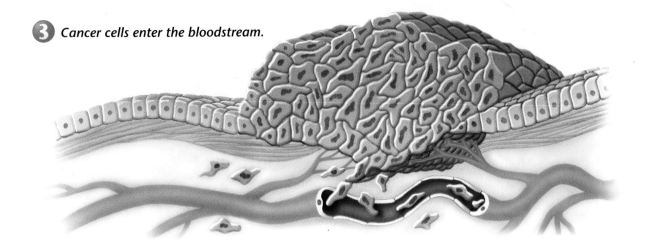

3 *Cancer cells enter the bloodstream.*

They might be able to "turn off" cancer before it causes too much damage to the body. Another possible treatment for cancer is to use drugs that block the flow of blood to tumors. Without a blood supply, tumors might not be able to continue growing.

Cancer Prevention

Scientists estimate that almost two thirds of all cancer deaths are caused either by tobacco use or unhealthful diets. Smoking is the main cause of lung cancer. When people repeatedly expose their bodies to the chemicals in tobacco, their cells will likely become damaged. Cancer may result.

It might surprise you to learn that unhealthful diets may lead to almost as many cancer deaths as does tobacco. A diet high in fat is especially harmful. Regularly eating high-fat foods, such as fatty meats and fried foods, can put a person at risk for cancer. A diet that includes a lot of fruits, vegetables, and grain products can help lower a person's risk of some types of cancer.

Section 4 Review

1. Explain the relationship between cancer and the cell cycle.
2. Describe three ways that cancer can be treated.
3. What two health habits can help prevent cancer?
4. **Thinking Critically Relating Cause and Effect** How could smoking tobacco cause cancer to develop inside the lungs?

Check Your Progress
It is now time to make your final observations of your plants. Then examine all of the data that you have collected. Which data can you present in graphs? Which of your diagrams show the major differences between your two plants? Write a brief summary that describes your experimental plan and your results.

CHAPTER PROJECT

Who Owns Your Cells?

John Moore was seriously ill. He had leukemia—cancer of the blood cells—and his spleen was in danger of bursting. Doctors removed his spleen, but Moore's condition was still serious. Surprisingly, however, Moore made a remarkable recovery. The doctors wondered whether Moore's body produced disease-fighting cells that fought off the cancer.

Without telling Moore why, his doctors gathered more of his cells. They discovered that Moore's cells were a natural "factory" of lifesaving chemicals. After years of investigation, the doctors sold the cells for several million dollars to a company that wanted to use the cells to manufacture medicines. When Moore found out, he sued the doctors, claiming that he owned his cells. Who do you think was right?

The Issues

Do Patients Have a Right to Their Cells?
Once a person's cells are outside his or her body, the person usually can no longer control what is done with them. For example, people who donate blood cannot tell blood banks what to do with their blood. On the other hand, people are able to decide whether or not to donate their organs when they die. Similarly, many people think they should be able to decide whether their cells can be used in medical research.

Do Doctors Have the Right to Use People's Cells? If people could control what was done with their cells, some doctors think it would be harder to find new cures for diseases. Scientists need to be free to experiment and to learn from their research. But who should make money from life-saving research? The doctors argued that the profits from Moore's cells

belonged to them. Moore had signed a consent form that gave the doctors permission to operate and remove his cells. It was the doctors' hard work and knowledge that turned the cells into something valuable.

Other people argue that there is not enough protection for patients. When Moore agreed to have the operation, he wasn't thinking about what would happen to his cells. His only concern was his need for the life-saving operation.

What Decision Was Reached? In Moore's case, the California Supreme Court ruled that the doctors owned the cells once they were out of Moore's body. However, the Court also said that Moore's doctors should have specifically asked for permission to use his cells. Moore was awarded a small amount of money, barely enough to pay his legal fees.

You Decide

1. Identify the Problem
In your own words, describe the controversy raised in John Moore's lawsuit against his doctors.

2. Analyze the Options
List some of the options the California Supreme Court might have considered in their decision. Be sure to include solutions in which neither Moore nor his doctors would get everything they want.

3. Find a Solution
Suppose you were one of the judges in Moore's court case. Choose a solution that you think is fair to both Moore and his doctors, and is best for society. Give reasons to support your decision.

SECTION 1 Photosynthesis

Key Ideas

◆ During photosynthesis, plants and some other organisms use energy from the sun to convert carbon dioxide and water into oxygen and sugars, including glucose.

◆ In the first stage of photosynthesis, chlorophyll and other plant pigments capture energy from sunlight. In the second stage, the cell uses the energy to produce sugars from carbon dioxide and water.

◆ Nearly all living things obtain the energy they need either directly or indirectly from the sun.

Key Terms

photosynthesis   chlorophyll   autotroph
pigment   stomata   heterotroph

SECTION 2 Respiration

Key Ideas

◆ Respiration is a process in which cells break down simple food substances, such as glucose, and release the energy they contain.

◆ During respiration, glucose and oxygen are converted into carbon dioxide and water.

◆ Photosynthesis and respiration can be thought of as opposite processes. These two processes form a cycle that keeps the levels of oxygen and carbon dioxide fairly constant in the atmosphere.

◆ Fermentation provides energy for cells without using oxygen.

Key Terms

respiration   fermentation

SECTION 3 Cell Division

Key Ideas

◆ Cells go through a regular cycle of growth and division called the cell cycle.

◆ During interphase, the cell grows to its mature size, makes a copy of its DNA, and prepares to divide into two cells. During mitosis, one copy of the DNA is distributed into each of the two daughter cells. During cytokinesis, the cell's cytoplasm divides, distributing the organelles into each of the two new cells.

◆ DNA replication ensures that each daughter cell will have all of the genetic information it needs to carry out its activities.

Key Terms

cell cycle   chromosome
interphase   chromatid
replication   cytokinesis
mitosis

SECTION 4 Cancer

INTEGRATING HEALTH

Key Ideas

◆ Cancer begins when the normal cell cycle is disrupted by mutations, causing cells to divide in an uncontrolled way.

◆ A tumor grows as the cells continue to divide. Cancerous cells may break off the tumor, enter the bloodstream, and spread to other areas of the body.

◆ Cancer is usually treated with surgery, radiation, or chemotherapy.

Key Terms

cancer   tumor
mutation   chemotherapy

USING THE INTERNET

www.science-explorer.phschool.com

CHAPTER 2 ASSESSMENT

California Test Prep: Reviewing Content

Multiple Choice

Choose the letter of the best answer.

1. The organelle in which photosynthesis takes place is the
   a. mitochondrion.
   b. chloroplast.
   c. chlorophyll.
   d. nucleus.
2. What process is responsible for producing most of Earth's oxygen?
   a. photosynthesis   b. replication
   c. mutation   d. respiration
3. The process in which a cell makes an exact copy of its DNA is called
   a. fermentation.   b. respiration.
   c. replication.   d. reproduction.
4. Chromatids are held together by a
   a. spindle.
   b. chloroplast.
   c. centromere.
   d. cell membrane.
5. A mass of cancer cells is called a
   a. tumor.
   b. chromosome.
   c. mutation.
   d. mitochondrion.

True or False

If the statement is true, write true. If it is false, change the underlined word or words to make the statement true.

6. An organism that makes its own food is an <u>autotroph</u>.
7. The process of respiration takes place mainly in the <u>mitochondria</u>.
8. An energy-releasing process that does not require oxygen is <u>replication</u>.
9. The stage of the cell cycle when DNA replication occurs is <u>telophase</u>.
10. Uncontrolled cell division is a characteristic of <u>cancer</u>.

Checking Concepts

11. Briefly explain what happens to energy from the sun during photosynthesis.
12. Explain how heterotrophs depend on the sun for energy.
13. Why do organisms need to carry out the process of respiration?
14. Describe what happens during interphase.
15. How do the events of the cell cycle ensure that the daughter cells will be identical to the parent cell?
16. Describe how cancer usually begins to develop in the body.
17. **Writing to Learn** Write a paragraph describing the journey of an oxygen molecule as it moves between a plant and another organism.

Thinking Visually

18. **Cycle Diagram** Copy the cycle diagram about the cell cycle onto a separate sheet of paper. Then complete it and add a title. (For more on cycle diagrams, see the Skills Handbook.)

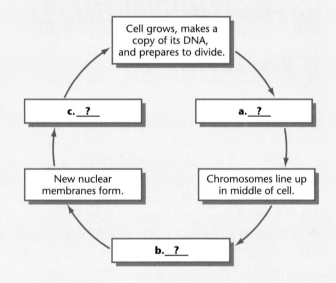

Cell grows, makes a copy of its DNA, and prepares to divide.

c. _?_

a. _?_

Chromosomes line up in middle of cell.

New nuclear membranes form.

b. _?_

Test Prep: Skills

Use the table below to answer Questions 19–21.

**Percentages of Nitrogen Bases
In the DNA of Various Organisms**

Nitrogen Base	Human	Wheat	E. coli bacterium
Adenine	30%	27%	24%
Guanine	20%	23%	26%
Thymine	30%	27%	24%
Cytosine	20%	23%	26%

19. **Graphing** For each organism, draw a bar graph to show the percentages of each nitrogen base in its DNA.

20. **Interpreting Data** What is the relationship between the amounts of adenine and thymine in the DNA of each organism? Between the amounts of guanine and cytosine?

21. **Inferring** Based on your answer to Question 20, what can you infer about the structure of DNA in these three organisms?

Thinking Critically

22. **Predicting** Suppose a volcano spewed so much ash into the air that it blocked most of the sunlight that usually strikes Earth. How might this affect the ability of animals to obtain the energy they need to live?

23. **Applying Concepts** Explain the relationship between the processes of breathing and respiration.

24. **Comparing and Contrasting** Compare and contrast photosynthesis and respiration in terms of raw materials, products, and where each occurs.

25. **Inferring** Suppose one strand of a DNA molecule contained the following bases: A C G T C T G. What would the bases on the other strand be?

26. **Making Generalizations** Suppose you want to reduce your risks for getting cancer. Outline three steps you could take to lower your risk.

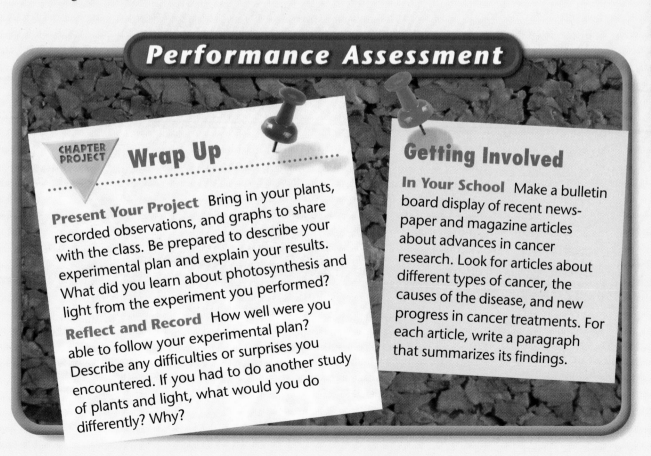

Performance Assessment

Wrap Up

CHAPTER PROJECT

Present Your Project Bring in your plants, recorded observations, and graphs to share with the class. Be prepared to describe your experimental plan and explain your results. What did you learn about photosynthesis and light from the experiment you performed?

Reflect and Record How well were you able to follow your experimental plan? Describe any difficulties or surprises you encountered. If you had to do another study of plants and light, what would you do differently? Why?

Getting Involved

In Your School Make a bulletin board display of recent newspaper and magazine articles about advances in cancer research. Look for articles about different types of cancer, the causes of the disease, and new progress in cancer treatments. For each article, write a paragraph that summarizes its findings.

Genetics: The Science of Heredity

CALIFORNIA
SCIENCE CONTENT STANDARDS

The following California Science Content Standards are addressed in this chapter:

1. All living organisms are composed of cells, from just one to many trillions, whose details usually are visible only through a microscope.

   a. Cells function similarly in all living organisms.

   c. The nucleus is the repository for genetic information in plant and animal cells.

2. A typical cell of any organism contains genetic instructions that specify its traits. Those traits may be modified by environmental influences.

   b. Sexual reproduction produces offspring that inherit half their genes from each parent.

   c. An inherited trait can be determined by one or more genes.

   d. Plant and animal cells contain many thousands of different genes, and typically have two copies of every gene. The two copies (or alleles) of the gene may or may not be identical, and one may be dominant in determining the phenotype while the other is recessive.

All In The Family

Did you ever wonder why some offspring resemble their parents while others do not? In this chapter, you'll learn how offspring come to have traits similar to those of their parents. In this project, you'll create a family of "paper pets" to explore how traits pass from parents to offspring.

Your Goal To create a "paper pet" that will be crossed with a pet belonging to a classmate, and to determine what traits the offspring will have.

To complete this project successfully, you must
◆ create your own unique paper pet with five different traits
◆ cross your pet with another pet to produce six offspring
◆ determine what traits the offspring will have, and explain how they came to have those traits

Get Started Cut out your pet from either blue or yellow construction paper. Choose other traits for your pet from this list: female or male; square eyes or round eyes; oval nose or triangular nose; pointed teeth or square teeth. Then create your pet using materials of your choice.

Check Your Progress You'll be working on this project as you study this chapter. To keep your project on track, look for Check Your Progress boxes at the following points.

Section 1 Review, page 75: Identify your pet's genotype.
Section 3 Review, page 90: Determine what traits your pet's offspring have.
Section 4 Review, page 96: Make a display of your pet's family.

Wrap Up At the end of the chapter (page 99), you and your partner will display your pet's family and analyze the inheritance patterns.

e. DNA is the genetic material of living organisms, and is located in the chromosomes of each cell.
7. Scientific progress is made by asking meaningful questions and conducting careful investigations.
c. Communicate the logical connection among hypothesis, science concepts, tests conducted, data collected, and conclusions drawn from the scientific evidence.
d. Construct scale models, maps and appropriately labeled diagrams to communicate scientific knowledge.
e. Communicate the steps and results from an investigation in written reports and verbal presentations.

These boxer puppies and their mother resemble each other in many ways. However, there are also noticeable differences between one dog and the next.

What Does the Father Look Like?

1. Observe the colors of each kitten in the photo. Record each kitten's coat colors and patterns. Include as many details as you can.

2. Observe the mother cat in the photo. Record her coat color and pattern.

Think It Over

Inferring Based on your observations, describe what you think the kittens' father might look like. Identify the evidence on which you based your inference.

GUIDE FOR READING

◆ What factors control the inheritance of traits in organisms?

Reading Tip Before you read, preview the section and make a list of the boldfaced terms. As you read, write a definition for each term in your own words.

Gregor Mendel in the monastery garden ▼

The year was 1851. Gregor Mendel, a young priest from a monastery in Central Europe, entered the University of Vienna to study mathematics and science. Two years later, Mendel returned to the monastery and began teaching at a nearby high school.

Mendel also cared for the monastery's garden, where he grew hundreds of pea plants. He became curious about why some of the plants had different physical characteristics, or **traits.** Some pea plants grew tall while others were short. Some plants produced green seeds, while others had yellow seeds.

Mendel observed that the pea plants' traits were often similar to those of their parents. Sometimes, however, the pea plants had different traits than their parents. The passing of traits from parents to offspring is called **heredity.** For more than ten years, Mendel experimented with thousands of pea plants to understand the process of heredity. Mendel's work formed the foundation of **genetics,** the scientific study of heredity.

Mendel's Peas

Mendel made a wise decision when he chose to study peas rather than other plants in the monastery garden. Pea plants are easy to study because they have many traits that exist in only two forms. For example, pea plant stems are either tall or short, but not medium height. Also, garden peas produce a large number of offspring in one generation. Thus, it is easy to collect large amounts of data to analyze.

Petal

Pistil

Stamens

Figure 1 shows a flowering pea plant. Notice that the flower's petals surround the pistil and the stamens. The pistil produces female sex cells, or eggs, while the stamens produce pollen, which contains the male sex cells.

In nature, pea plants are usually self-pollinating. This means that pollen from one flower lands on the pistil of the same flower. Mendel developed a method by which he could cross-pollinate, or "cross," pea plants. To cross two plants, he removed pollen from a flower on one plant and brushed it onto a flower on a second plant. To prevent the pea plants from self-pollinating, he carefully removed the stamens from the flowers on the second plant.

Mendel's Experiments

Suppose you had a garden full of pea plants, and you wanted to study the inheritance of traits. What would you do? Mendel decided to cross plants with opposite forms of a trait, for example, tall plants and short plants. He started his experiments with purebred plants. A **purebred** plant is one that always produces offspring with the same form of a trait as the parent. For example, purebred short pea plants always produce short offspring. Purebred tall pea plants always produce tall offspring. To produce purebred plants, Mendel allowed peas with one particular trait to self-pollinate for many generations. By using purebred plants, Mendel knew that the offspring's trait would always be identical to that of the parents.

In his first experiment, Mendel crossed purebred tall plants with purebred short plants. He called these parent plants the parental generation, or P generation. He called the offspring from this cross the first filial (FIL ee ul) generation, or the F_1 generation. The word *filial* means "son" in Latin.

Gregor Mendel presented a detailed description of his observations in a scientific paper in 1866. In the excerpt that follows, notice how clearly he describes his observations of the two different seed shapes in peas.

"These are either round or roundish, the depressions, if any, occur on the surface, being always only shallow; or they are irregularly angular and deeply wrinkled."

In Your Journal

Choose an everyday object, such as a piece of fruit or a pen. Make a list of the object's features. Then write a short paragraph describing the object. Use clear, precise language in your description.

You can see the results of Mendel's first cross in Figure 2. To Mendel's surprise, all of the offspring in the F_1 generation were tall. Despite the fact that one of the parent plants was short, none of the offspring were short. The shortness trait had disappeared!

Mendel let the plants in the F_1 generation grow and allowed them to self-pollinate. The results of this experiment also surprised Mendel. The plants in the F_2 (second filial) generation were a mix of tall and short plants. This occurred even though none of the F_1 parent plants were short. The shortness trait had reappeared. Mendel counted the number of tall and short plants in the F_2 generation. He found that about three fourths of the plants were tall, while one fourth of the plants were short.

☑ *Checkpoint* *What is a purebred plant?*

Other Traits

In addition to stem height, Mendel studied six other traits in garden peas: seed shape, seed color, seed coat color, pod shape, pod color, and flower position. Compare the two forms of each trait in Figure 3. Mendel crossed plants with these traits in the same manner as he did for stem height. The results in each experiment were similar to those that he observed with stem height. Only one form of the trait appeared in the F_1 generation. However, in the F_2 generation the "lost" form of the trait always reappeared in about one fourth of the plants.

Figure 2 When Mendel crossed purebred tall and short pea plants, all the offspring in the F_1 generation were tall. In the F_2 generation, three fourths of the plants were tall, while one fourth were short.

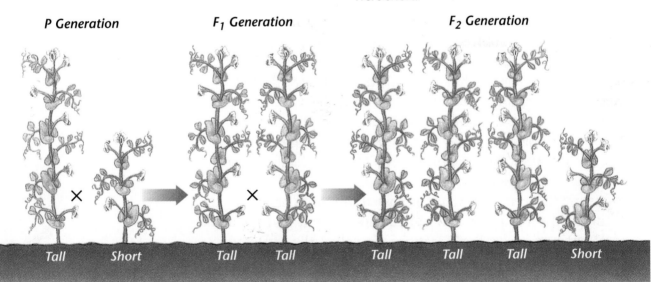

P Generation		F₁ Generation		F₂ Generation			
Tall	Short	Tall	Tall	Tall	Tall	Tall	Short

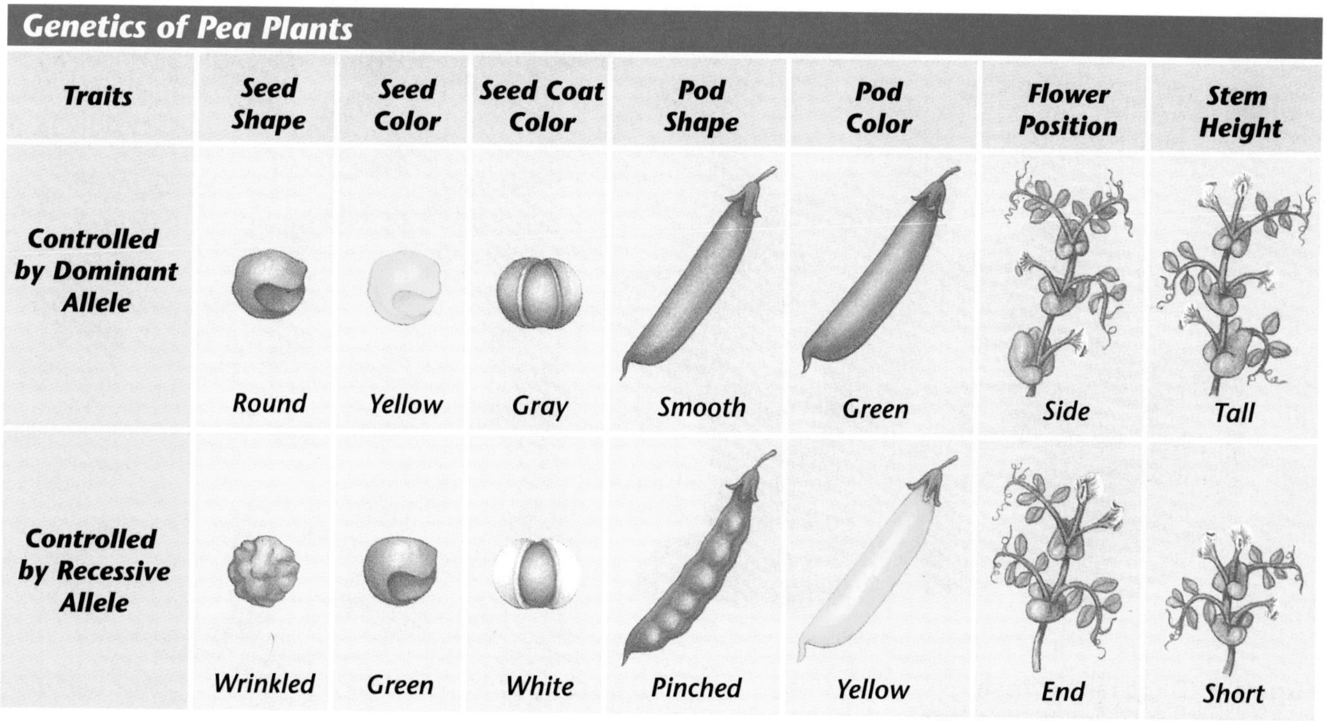

Genetics of Pea Plants

Traits	Seed Shape	Seed Color	Seed Coat Color	Pod Shape	Pod Color	Flower Position	Stem Height
Controlled by Dominant Allele	Round	Yellow	Gray	Smooth	Green	Side	Tall
Controlled by Recessive Allele	Wrinkled	Green	White	Pinched	Yellow	End	Short

Figure 3 Mendel studied seven different traits in pea plants. Each trait has two different forms. *Interpreting Diagrams Is yellow seed color controlled by a dominant allele or a recessive allele? What type of allele controls pinched pod shape?*

Dominant and Recessive Alleles

From his results, Mendel reasoned that individual factors must control the inheritance of traits in peas. The factors that control each trait exist in pairs. The female parent contributes one factor, while the male parent contributes the other factor.

Mendel went on to reason that one factor in a pair can mask, or hide, the other factor. The tallness factor, for example, masked the shortness factor in the F_1 generation.

Today, scientists call the factors that control traits **genes.** They call the different forms of a gene **alleles** (uh LEELZ). The gene that controls stem height in peas, for example, has one allele for tall stems and one allele for short stems. Each pea plant inherits a combination of two alleles from its parents—either two alleles for tall stems, two alleles for short stems, or one of each.

Individual alleles control the inheritance of traits. Some alleles are dominant, while other alleles are recessive. A **dominant allele** is one whose trait always shows up in the organism when the allele is present. A **recessive allele,** on the other hand, is masked, or covered up, whenever the dominant allele is present. A trait controlled by a recessive allele will only show up if the organism does not have the dominant allele.

In pea plants, the allele for tall stems is dominant over the allele for short stems. Pea plants with one allele for tall stems and one allele for short stems will be tall. The allele for tall stems masks the allele for short stems. Only pea plants that inherit two recessive alleles for short stems will be short.

Figure 4 These rabbits have some traits controlled by dominant alleles and other traits controlled by recessive alleles. For example, the allele for black fur is dominant over the allele for white fur. *Inferring What combination of alleles must the white rabbit have?*

Understanding Mendel's Crosses

You can understand Mendel's results by tracing the inheritance of alleles in his experiments. The purebred plants in the P generation had two identical alleles for stem height. The purebred tall plants had two alleles for tall stems. The purebred short plants had two alleles for short stems. In the F_1 generation, all of the plants received one allele for tall stems from the tall parent. They received one allele for short stems from the short parent. The F_1 plants are called **hybrids** (HY bridz) because they have two different alleles for the trait. All the F_1 plants are tall because the dominant allele for tall stems masks the recessive allele for short stems.

When Mendel crossed the hybrid plants in the F_1 generation, some of the plants inherited two dominant alleles for tall stems. These plants were tall. Other plants inherited one dominant allele for tall stems and one recessive allele for short stems. These plants were also tall. Other plants inherited two recessive alleles for short stems. These plants were short.

☑ *Checkpoint If a pea plant has a tall stem, what possible combinations of alleles could it have?*

Using Symbols in Genetics

Geneticists today use a standard shorthand method to write about alleles in genetic crosses. Instead of using words such as "tall stems" to represent alleles, they simply use letters. A dominant allele is represented by a capital letter. For example, the allele for tall stems is represented by *T*. A recessive allele is represented by the lowercase version of the letter. So, the allele for short stems would be represented by *t*. When a plant inherits two dominant alleles for tall stems, its alleles are written as *TT*. When a plant inherits two recessive alleles for short stems, its alleles are written as *tt*. When a plant inherits one allele for tall stems and one allele for short stems, its alleles are written as *Tt*.

Mendel's Contribution

In 1866, Mendel presented his results to a scientific society that met regularly near the monastery. In his paper, Mendel described the principles of heredity he had discovered. Unfortunately, other scientists did not understand the importance of Mendel's work. Some scientists thought that Mendel had oversimplified the process of inheritance. Others never read his paper, or even heard about his work. At that time, scientists in different parts of the world were isolated from each other. Mendel was especially isolated because he wasn't at a university. Remember, there were no telephones, and no computers to send electronic mail.

Mendel's work was forgotten for 34 years. In 1900, three different scientists rediscovered Mendel's work. They had made many of the same observations as Mendel had. The scientists quickly recognized the importance of Mendel's work. Many of the genetic principles that Mendel discovered still stand to this day. Because of his work, Mendel is often called the Father of Genetics.

Figure 5 The dominant allele for yellow skin color in summer squash is represented by the letter *Y*. The recessive allele for green skin color is represented by the letter *y*.

Section 1 Review

1. Explain how the inheritance of traits is controlled in organisms. Use the terms *genes* and *alleles* in your explanation.
2. What is a dominant allele? What is a recessive allele? Give an example of each.
3. The allele for round seeds is represented by *R*. Suppose that a pea plant inherited two recessive alleles for wrinkled seeds. How would you write the symbols for its alleles?
4. **Thinking Critically Applying Concepts** Can a short pea plant ever be a hybrid? Why or why not?

Check Your Progress

CHAPTER PROJECT

By now you should have constructed your paper pet. On the back, write what alleles your pet has for each trait. Use XX for a female, and XY for a male. The dominant alleles for the other four traits are: *B* (blue skin), *R* (round eyes), *T* (triangular nose), and *P* (pointed teeth). (*Hint:* If your pet has a trait controlled by a dominant allele, you can choose which of the possible combinations of alleles your pet has.)

Take a Class Survey

In this lab, you'll explore how greatly traits can vary in a group of people—your classmates.

Problem

Are traits controlled by dominant alleles more common than traits controlled by recessive alleles?

Materials

mirror (optional)   PTC paper

Procedure

Part 1 Dominant and Recessive Alleles

1. Write a hypothesis reflecting your ideas about the problem question. Then copy the data table.

2. For traits A, B, C, D, and E, work with a partner to determine which trait you have. Circle that trait in your data table.

3. For trait F, wash and dry your hands. Taste the PTC paper your teacher gives you. Circle either "can taste PTC" or "cannot taste PTC" in your data table. **CAUTION:** *Never taste any substance in the lab unless directed to by your teacher.*

4. Count the number of students who have each trait. Record that number in your data table. Also record the total number of students.

DATA TABLE

Total Number _____

	Trait 1	Number	Trait 2	Number
A	Free ear lobes		Attached ear lobes	
B	Hair on fingers		No hair on fingers	
C	Widow's peak		No widow's peak	
D	Curly hair		Straight hair	
E	Cleft chin		Smooth chin	
F	Can taste PTC*		Cannot taste PTC*	

*PTC stands for phenylthiocarbamide.

Free ear lobe

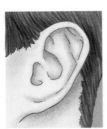

Attached ear lobe

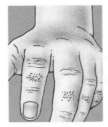

Hair on fingers

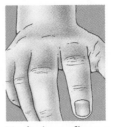

No hair on fingers

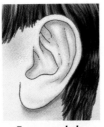

Widow's peak

No widow's peak

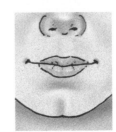

Cleft chin

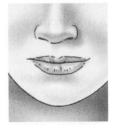

No cleft chin

Part 2 Are Your Traits Unique?

5. Look at the circle of traits below. All the traits in your data table appear in the circle. Place the eraser end of your pencil on the trait in the small central circle that applies to you—either free ear lobes or attached ear lobes.

6. Look at the two traits touching the space your eraser is on. Move your eraser onto the next description that applies to you. Continue using your eraser to trace your traits until you reach a number on the outside rim of the circle. Share that number with your classmates.

Analyze and Conclude

1. The traits listed under Trait 1 in the data table are controlled by dominant alleles. The traits listed under Trait 2 are controlled by recessive alleles. Which traits controlled by dominant alleles were shown by a majority of students? Which traits controlled by recessive alleles were shown by a majority of students?

2. How many students ended up on the same number on the circle of traits? How many students were the only ones to have their number? What do the results suggest about each person's combination of traits?

3. **Think About It** Do your data support the hypothesis you proposed in Step 1? Explain your answer with examples.

Design an Experiment

Do people who are related to each other show more genetic similarity than unrelated people? Write a hypothesis. Then design an experiment to test your hypothesis.

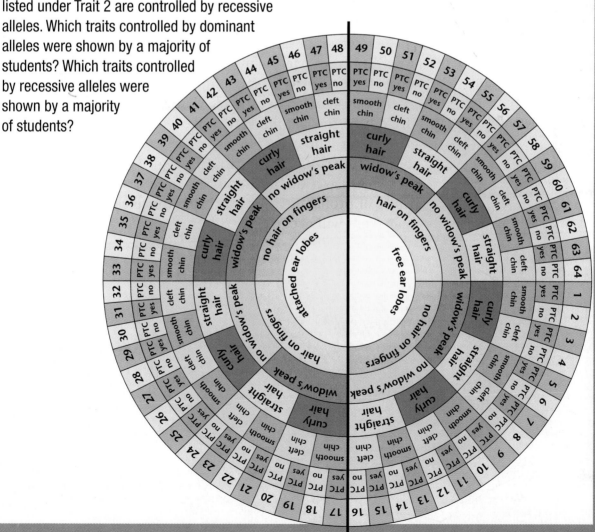

SECTION 2 Probability and Genetics

What's the Chance?

1. Suppose you were to toss a coin 20 times. Predict how many times the coin would land "heads up" and how many times it would land "tails up."

2. Now test your prediction by tossing a coin 20 times. Record the number of times the coin lands heads up and the number of times it lands tails up.

3. Combine the data from the entire class. Record the total number of tosses, the number of heads, and the number of tails.

Think It Over

Predicting How did your results in Step 2 compare to your prediction? How can you account for any differences between your results and the class results?

GUIDE FOR READING

◆ How do the principles of probability help explain Mendel's results?

◆ How do geneticists use Punnett squares?

Reading Tip Before you read, rewrite the headings in the section as questions that begin with *how, what,* or *why.* As you read, look for answers to these questions.

The city of Portland, Oregon, was founded in the mid-1800s. Two men, Asa L. Lovejoy and Francis W. Pettygrove, owned the land on which the new city was built. Lovejoy, who was from Massachusetts, wanted to name the new town Boston. Pettygrove, however, thought the town should be named after his hometown, Portland, Maine. To settle the dispute, they decided to toss a coin. Pettygrove won, and the new town was named Portland.

What was the chance that Pettygrove would win the coin toss? To answer this question, you need to understand the principles of probability. **Probability** is the likelihood that a particular event will occur.

Principles of Probability

If you did the Discover activity, you used the principles of probability to predict the results of a particular event. Each time you toss a coin, there are two possible ways that the coin can land—heads up or tails up. Each of these two events is equally likely to occur. In mathematical terms, you can say that the probability that a tossed coin will land heads up is 1 in 2. There is also a 1 in 2 probability that the coin will land tails up. A 1 in 2 probability can also be expressed as the fraction $\frac{1}{2}$ or as a percent—50 percent.

If you tossed a coin 20 times, you might expect it to land heads up 10 times and tails up 10 times. However, you might not actually get these results. You might get 11 heads and 9 tails, or 8 heads and 12 tails. Remember that the laws of probability predict what is likely to occur, not necessarily what will occur. However, the more tosses you make, the closer your actual results will be to the results predicted by probability.

When you toss a coin more than once, the results of one toss do not affect the results of the next toss. Each event occurs independently. For example, suppose you toss a coin five times and it lands heads up each time. What is the probability that it will land heads up on the next toss? Because the coin landed heads up on the previous five tosses, you might think that it would be likely to land heads up on the next toss. However, this is not the case. The probability of the coin landing heads up on the next toss is still 1 in 2, or 50 percent. The results of the first five tosses do not affect the results of the sixth toss.

☑ *Checkpoint* *Why is there a 1 in 2 probability that a tossed coin will land heads up?*

Math TOOLBOX

Calculating Percent

One way you can express a probability is as a percent. A percent (%) is a number compared to 100. For example, 50% means 50 out of 100.

Suppose that 3 out of 5 tossed coins landed heads up. Here's how you can calculate what percent of the coins landed heads up.

1. Write the comparison as a fraction.

$$3 \text{ out of } 5 = \frac{3}{5}$$

2. Multiply the fraction by 100% to express it as a percent.

$$\frac{3}{5} \times \frac{100\%}{1} = 60\%$$

60% of the coins landed heads up.

Now, suppose 3 out of 12 coins landed tails up. How can you express this as a percent?

Figure 6 According to the laws of probability, there is a 50 percent probability that the coin will land heads up. *Calculating* *What is the probability that the coin will land tails up?*

Mendel and Probability

How is probability related to genetics? To answer this question, think back to Mendel's experiments with peas. Remember that Mendel carefully counted the offspring from every cross that he carried out. When Mendel crossed two plants that were hybrid for stem height (Tt), three fourths of the F_1 plants had tall stems. One fourth of the plants had short stems.

Each time Mendel repeated the cross, he obtained similar results. Mendel realized that the mathematical principles of probability applied to his work. He could say that the probability of such a cross producing a tall plant was 3 in 4. The probability of producing a short plant was 1 in 4. **Mendel was the first scientist to recognize that the principles of probability can be used to predict the results of genetic crosses.**

Punnett Squares

A tool that can help you understand how the laws of probability apply to genetics is called a Punnett square. A **Punnett square** is a chart that shows all the possible combinations of alleles that can result from a genetic cross. **Geneticists use Punnett squares to show all the possible outcomes of a genetic cross and to determine the probability of a particular outcome.**

The Punnett square in Figure 7 shows a cross between two hybrid tall pea plants (Tt). Each parent can pass either of its alleles, T or t, to its offspring. The possible alleles that one parent can pass on are written across the top of the Punnett square. The possible alleles that the other parent can pass on are written down the left side of the Punnett square. The boxes in the Punnett square represent the possible combinations of alleles that the offspring can inherit. The boxes are filled in like a multiplication problem, with one allele contributed by each parent.

Using a Punnett Square You can use a Punnett square to calculate the probability that offspring with a certain combination of alleles will result. The allele that each parent will pass on is based on chance, just like the toss of a coin. Thus, there are four possible combinations of alleles that can result. The

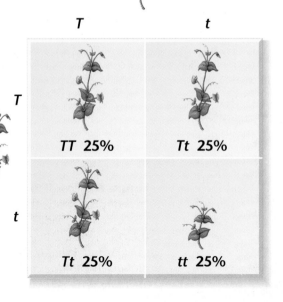

Figure 7 This Punnett square shows a cross between two hybrid tall pea plants. *Interpreting Charts Which allele combinations will result in tall offspring?*

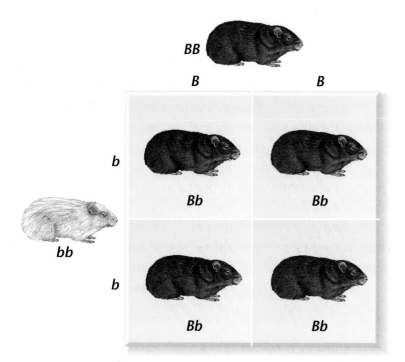

BB

B   B

b   Bb   Bb

b   Bb   Bb

bb

Figure 8 This Punnett square shows a cross between a black guinea pig (*BB*) and a white guinea pig (*bb*). *Calculating What is the probability that an offspring will have white fur?*

probability that an offspring will be *TT* is 1 in 4, or 25 percent. The probability that an offspring will be *tt* is also 1 in 4, or 25 percent. Notice, however, that the *Tt* allele combination appears in two boxes in the Punnett square. This is because there are two possible ways in which this combination can occur. The probability, then, that an offspring will be *Tt* is 2 in 4, or 50 percent.

Recall that when Mendel performed this cross, he discovered that about three fourths of the plants (75%) had tall stems. The remaining one fourth of the plants (25%) had short stems. Now you can understand why that was true. Plants with the *TT* allele combination would be tall. So too would those plants with the *Tt* allele combination. Remember that the dominant allele masks the recessive allele. Only those plants with the *tt* allele combination would be short.

Predicting Probabilities You can also use a Punnett square to predict probabilities. For example, Figure 8 shows a cross between a purebred black guinea pig and a purebred white guinea pig. The allele for black fur is dominant over the allele for white fur. Notice that only one allele combination is possible in the offspring—*Bb*. All of the offspring will inherit the dominant allele for black fur. Because of this, all of the offspring will have black fur. You can predict that there is a 100% probability that the offspring will have black fur.

☑ *Checkpoint* *If two guinea pigs with the alleles Bb are crossed, what is the probability that an offspring will have white fur?*

Coin Crosses

Here's how you can use coins to model Mendel's cross between two *Tt* pea plants.

ACTIVITY

1. Place a small piece of masking tape on each side of two coins.
2. Write a *T* (for tall) on one side of each coin and a *t* (for short) on the other.
3. Toss both coins together 20 times. Record the letter combinations that you obtain from each toss.

Interpreting Data How many of the offspring would be tall plants? (*Hint:* What different letter combinations would result in a tall plant?) How many would be short? Convert your results to percents. Then compare your results to Mendel's.

Phenotypes and Genotypes	
Phenotype	**Genotype**
Tall	*TT*
Tall	*Tt*
Short	*tt*

Figure 9 The phenotype of an organism is its physical appearance. Its genotype is its genetic makeup.

Phenotypes and Genotypes

Two useful terms that geneticists use to describe organisms are phenotype and genotype. An organism's **phenotype** (FEE noh typ) is its physical appearance, or its visible traits. For example, pea plants can have one of two different phenotypes for stem height—short or tall.

An organism's **genotype** (JEN uh typ) is its genetic makeup, or allele combinations. To understand the difference between phenotype and genotype, look at the table in Figure 9. Although all of the tall plants have the same phenotype (they are all tall), they can have two different genotypes—*TT* or *Tt*. If you were to look at the tall plants, you would not be able to tell the difference between those with the *TT* genotype and those with the *Tt* genotype. The short pea plants, on the other hand, would all have the same phenotype—short stems—as well as the same genotype—*tt*.

Geneticists use two additional terms to describe an organism's genotype. An organism that has two identical alleles for a trait is said to be **homozygous** (hoh moh ZY gus) for that trait. A tall pea plant that has the alleles *TT* and a short pea plant with the alleles *tt* are both homozygous. An organism that has two different alleles for a trait is said to be **heterozygous** (het ur oh ZY gus) for that trait. A tall pea plant with the alleles *Tt* is heterozygous. Mendel used the term *hybrid* to describe heterozygous pea plants.

☑ *Checkpoint* *If a pea plant's genotype is* Tt, *what is its phenotype?*

Codominance

For all of the traits that Mendel studied, one allele was dominant while the other was recessive. This is not always the case. For some alleles, an inheritance pattern called codominance exists. In **codominance,** the alleles are neither dominant nor recessive. As a result, neither allele is masked in the offspring.

Look at the Punnett square in Figure 11. Mendel's principle of dominant and recessive alleles does not explain why the heterozygous chickens have both black and white feathers. The alleles for feather color are

Figure 10 In Erminette chickens, the alleles for black feathers and white feathers are codominant.

$F^B F^B$

F^B F^B

F^W

$F^W F^W$

F^W

$F^B F^W$ $F^B F^W$

$F^B F^W$ $F^B F^W$

Figure 11 The offspring from the cross in this Punnett square will have both black and white feathers. *Classifying Will the offspring be heterozygous or homozygous? Explain your answer.*

codominant—neither dominant nor recessive. As you can see, neither allele is masked in the heterozygous chickens. Notice also that the codominant alleles are written as capital letters with superscripts—F^B for black feathers and F^W for white feathers. As the Punnett square shows, heterozygous chickens have the $F^B F^W$ allele combination.

Another example of codominance can be found in cattle. Red hair and white hair are codominant. Heterozygous cattle have coats with both white hairs and red hairs. From a distance, heterozygous cattle look pinkish brown, a color called roan.

Section 2 Review

1. What is meant by the term *probability*? How is probability related to genetics?
2. How are Punnett squares useful to geneticists?
3. What is the difference between a phenotype and a genotype? Give an example of each.
4. A white cow is crossed with a red bull. The calf is neither white nor red, but roan. Explain how this happens.
5. **Thinking Critically Problem Solving** In pea plants, the allele for round seeds (*R*) is dominant over the allele for wrinkled seeds (*r*). Construct a Punnett square that shows a cross between a heterozygous plant with round seeds (*Rr*) and a homozygous plant with wrinkled seeds (*rr*). What is the probability that an offspring will have wrinkled seeds?

Science at Home

Have a family member think of a number between 1 and 5. Then try to guess the number. Discuss the probability of guessing the correct number. Then repeat the guessing activity four more times. How did your success rate compare to the probability of guessing correctly? How can you account for any difference between your success rate and the results predicted by probability?

MAKE THE RIGHT CALL!

Y ou know that making predictions is an important part of science. An accurate prediction can be a sign that you understand the event you are studying. In this lab, you will make predictions as you model the events involved in genetic crosses.

Problem

How can you predict the possible results of genetic crosses?

Materials

2 small paper bags
marking pen
3 blue marbles
3 white marbles

Procedure

1. Label one bag "Bag 1, Female Parent." Label the other bag "Bag 2, Male Parent." Then read over Part 1, Part 2, and Part 3 of this lab. Write a prediction about the kinds of offspring you expect from each cross.

Part 1 Crossing Two Homozygous Parents

2. Copy the data table and label it *Data Table Number 1.* Then place two blue marbles in Bag 1. This pair of marbles represents the female parent's alleles. Use the letter *B* to represent the dominant allele for blue color.

3. Place two white marbles in Bag 2. Use the letter *b* to represent the recessive allele for white color.

4. For Trial 1, remove one marble from Bag 1 without looking in the bag. Record the result in your data table. Return the marble to the bag. Again, without looking in the bag, remove one marble from Bag 2. Record the result in your data table. Return the marble to the bag.

5. In the column labeled *Offspring's Alleles,* write *BB* if you removed two blue marbles, *bb* if you removed two white marbles, or *Bb* if you removed one blue marble and one white marble.

6. Repeat Steps 4 and 5 nine more times.

DATA TABLE

Number _____

Trial	Allele From Bag 1 (Female Parent)	Allele From Bag 2 (Male Parent)	Offspring's Alleles
1			
2			
3			
4			
5			
6			

Part 2 Crossing a Homozygous Parent With a Heterozygous Parent

7. Place two blue marbles in Bag 1. Place one white marble and one blue marble in Bag 2. Copy the data table again, and label it *Data Table Number 2.*
8. Repeat Steps 4 and 5 ten times.

Part 3 Crossing Two Heterozygous Parents

9. Place one blue marble and one white marble in Bag 1. Place one blue marble and one white marble in Bag 2. Copy the data table again and label it *Data Table Number 3.*
10. Repeat Steps 4 and 5 ten times.

Analyze and Conclude

1. Make a Punnett square for each of the crosses you modeled in Part 1, Part 2, and Part 3.
2. According to your results in Part 1, how many different kinds of offspring are possible when the homozygous parents (*BB* and *bb*) are crossed? Do the results you obtained using the marble model agree with the results shown by a Punnett square?

3. According to your results in Part 2, what percent of offspring are likely to be homozygous when a homozygous parent (*BB*) and a heterozygous parent (*Bb*) are crossed? What percent of offspring are likely to be heterozygous? Does the model agree with the results shown by a Punnett square?
4. According to your results in Part 3, what different kinds of offspring are possible when two heterozygous parents (*Bb* × *Bb*) are crossed? What percent of each type of offspring are likely to be produced? Does the model agree with the results of a Punnett square?
5. For Part 3, if you did 100 trials instead of 10 trials, would your results be closer to the results shown in a Punnett square? Explain.
6. **Think About It** How does the marble model compare with a Punnett square? How are the two methods alike? How are they different?

More to Explore

In peas, the allele for yellow seeds (*Y*) is dominant over the allele for green seeds (*y*). What possible crosses do you think could produce a heterozygous plant with yellow seeds (*Yy*)? Use the marble model and Punnett squares to test your predictions.

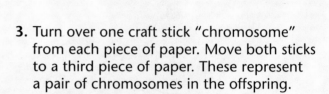

SECTION
3 The Cell and Inheritance

Which Chromosome Is Which?

Mendel did not know that chromosomes play a role in genetics. Today we know that genes are located on chromosomes.

1. Label two craft sticks with the letter *A*. The craft sticks represent a pair of chromosomes in the female parent. Turn the sticks face down on a piece of paper.

2. Label two more craft sticks with the letter *a*. These represent a pair of chromosomes in the male parent. Turn the sticks face down on another piece of paper.

3. Turn over one craft stick "chromosome" from each piece of paper. Move both sticks to a third piece of paper. These represent a pair of chromosomes in the offspring. Note the allele combination that the offspring received.

Think It Over
Inferring Use this model to explain how chromosomes are involved in the inheritance of alleles.

GUIDE FOR READING

◆ What role do chromosomes play in inheritance?

◆ What events occur during meiosis?

Reading Tip Before you read, preview *Exploring Meiosis* on page 89. Predict what role chromosomes play in the inheritance of traits.

Sperm cells ▼

When Mendel's results were rediscovered in 1900, scientists around the world became excited about Mendel's principles of inheritance. They were eager to identify the structures inside of cells that carried Mendel's hereditary factors, or genes.

In 1903, Walter Sutton, an American geneticist, added an important piece of information to scientists' understanding of genetics. Sutton was studying the cells of grasshoppers. He was trying to understand how sex cells—sperm and egg—form. During his studies, Sutton examined sex cells in many different stages of formation. He became particularly interested in the movement of chromosomes during the formation of sex cells. Sutton hypothesized that chromosomes were the key to understanding how offspring come to have traits similar to those of their parents.

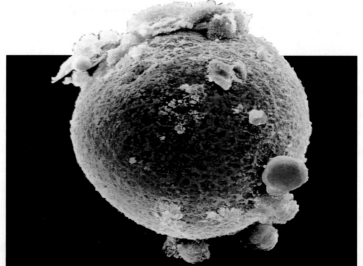

◄ Egg cell

Figure 12 Grasshoppers have 24 chromosomes in each of their body cells. *Applying Concepts How many chromosomes did Sutton observe in the sperm cells and egg cells of grasshoppers?*

Chromosomes and Inheritance

Sutton knew that structures inside cells must be responsible for the inheritance of genes. He needed evidence to support his hypothesis that chromosomes were those structures. Sutton compared the number of chromosomes in a grasshopper's sex cells with the number of chromosomes in the other cells in the grasshopper's body. As you can see in Figure 12, the body cells of grasshoppers have 24 chromosomes. To his surprise, Sutton found that the grasshopper's sex cells have only 12 chromosomes. In other words, a grasshopper's sex cells have exactly half the number of chromosomes found in its body cells.

Sutton knew that he had discovered something important. He observed what happened when a sperm cell (with 12 chromosomes) and an egg cell (with 12 chromosomes) joined. The fertilized egg that formed had 24 chromosomes—the original number. As a result, the grasshopper offspring had exactly the same number of chromosomes in its cells as did each of its parents. The 24 chromosomes existed in 12 pairs. One chromosome in each pair came from the male parent, while the other chromosome came from the female parent.

Sutton concluded that the chromosomes carried Mendel's hereditary factors, or genes, from one generation to the next. In other words, genes are located on chromosomes. Sutton's idea came to be known as the chromosome theory of inheritance. **According to the chromosome theory of inheritance, genes are carried from parents to their offspring on chromosomes.**

✓ *Checkpoint How does the number of chromosomes in a grasshopper's sex cells compare to the number in its body cells?*

Meiosis

How do sex cells end up with half the number of chromosomes as body cells? To answer this question, you need to understand the events that occur during meiosis. **Meiosis** (my OH sis) is the process by which the number of chromosomes is reduced by half to form sex cells—sperm and eggs.

You can trace the events of meiosis in *Exploring Meiosis.* In this example, each parent cell has four chromosomes arranged in two pairs. **During meiosis, the chromosome pairs separate and are distributed to two different cells. The resulting sex cells have only half as many chromosomes as the other cells in the organism.** In *Exploring Meiosis,* notice that the sex cells end up with only two chromosomes each—half the number found in the parent cell. Only one chromosome from each chromosome pair ends up in each sex cell.

When sex cells combine to produce offspring, each sex cell will contribute half the normal number of chromosomes. Thus, the offspring gets the normal number of chromosomes—half from each parent.

☑ *Checkpoint* *What types of cells form by meiosis?*

Meiosis and Punnett Squares

The Punnett squares that you learned about earlier in this chapter are actually a shorthand way to show the events that occur at meiosis. When the chromosome pairs separate into two different sex cells, so do the alleles carried on each chromosome. One allele from each pair goes to each sex cell. In Figure 13, you can see how the Punnett square accounts for the separation of alleles during meiosis.

As shown across the top of the Punnett square, half of the sperm cells from the male parent will receive the chromosome with the *T* allele. The other half of the sperm cells will receive the chromosome with the *t* allele. In this example, the same is true for the egg cells from the female parent, as shown down the left side of the Punnett square. Depending on which sperm cell combines with which egg cell, one of the allele combinations shown in the boxes will result.

Figure 13 This Punnett square shows how alleles separate when sex cells form during meiosis. It also shows the possible allele combinations that can result after fertilization occurs. *Interpreting Charts What is the probability that a sperm cell will contain a* T *allele?*

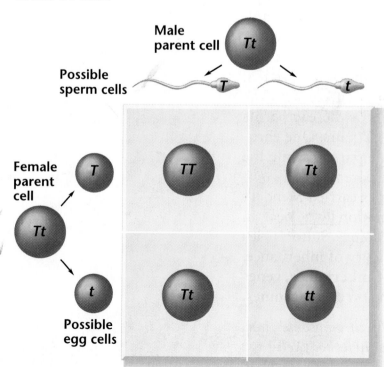

Male parent cell *Tt*

Possible sperm cells *T* *t*

Female parent cell *Tt*

Possible egg cells *T* *t*

TT Tt Tt tt

EXPLORING Meiosis

During meiosis, a cell undergoes two divisions to produce sex cells that have half the number of chromosomes.

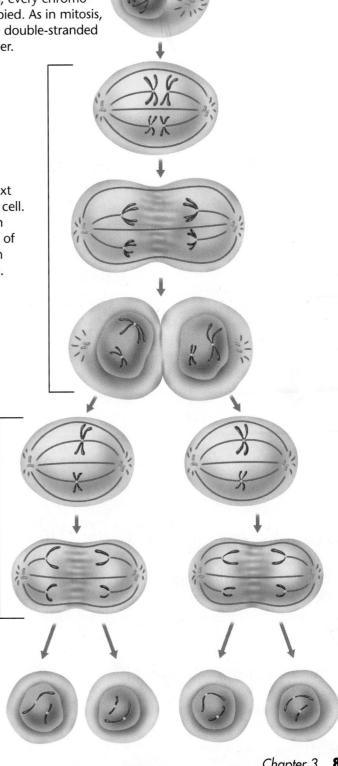

1 Beginning of Meiosis
Before meiosis begins, every chromosome in the cell is copied. As in mitosis, centromeres hold the double-stranded chromosomes together.

2 Meiosis I
The chromosome pairs line up next to each other in the center of the cell. The pairs then separate from each other and move to opposite ends of the cell. Two cells form, each with half the number of chromosomes. Each chromosome is still double-stranded.

3 Meiosis II
The double-stranded chromosomes move to the center of the cell. The centromeres split and the two strands of each chromosome separate. The two strands move to opposite ends of the cell.

4 End of Meiosis
Four sex cells have been produced. Each cell has only half the number of chromosomes that the parent cell had at the beginning of meiosis. Each cell has only one chromosome from each original pair.

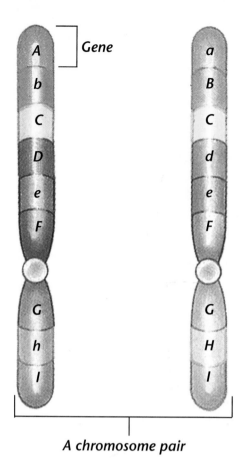

A chromosome pair

Figure 14 Genes are located on chromosomes. The chromosomes in a pair may have different alleles for some genes and the same alleles for others. *Classifying For which genes is this organism homozygous? For which genes is it heterozygous?*

Chromosomes

Since Sutton's time, scientists have studied the chromosomes of many different organisms. The body cells of humans, for example, contain 23 pairs, or 46 chromosomes. The body cells of dogs have 78 chromosomes, while the body cells of silkworms have 56 chromosomes. As you can see, larger organisms don't always have more chromosomes.

Chromosomes are made up of many genes joined together like beads on a string. Sutton reasoned that chromosomes must contain a large number of genes because organisms have so many traits. Although you have only 23 pairs of chromosomes, your body cells contain more than 60,000 genes. Each of the genes controls a particular trait.

Look at the pair of chromosomes in Figure 14. One chromosome in the pair came from the female parent. The other chromosome came from the male parent. Notice that each chromosome in the pair has the same genes. The genes are lined up in the same order from one end of the chromosome to the other. However, the alleles for some of the genes might be different. For example, the organism has the *A* allele on one chromosome and the *a* allele on the other. As you can see, this organism is heterozygous for some traits and homozygous for others.

Section 3 Review

1. Explain the role that chromosomes play in inheritance.
2. Briefly describe what happens to chromosomes during meiosis.
3. On what structures in a cell are genes located?
4. How is a Punnett square a model for what happens during meiosis?
5. **Thinking Critically** **Inferring** The body cells of hamsters have 44 chromosomes. How many chromosomes would the sex cells of a hamster have?

Check Your Progress CHAPTER PROJECT

At this point, you should find a classmate with a paper pet of the opposite sex. Suppose the two pets were crossed and produced six offspring. For each trait, use coin tosses to determine which allele the offspring will inherit from each parent. Construct a paper pet for each offspring, showing the traits that each one has inherited. Write the genotype for each trait on their backs.

SECTION 4 The DNA Connection

DISCOVER · ACTIVITY · · ·

A •–	N –•
B –•••	O –––
C –•–•	P •––•
D –••	Q ––•–
E •	R •–•
F ••–•	S •••
G ––•	T –
H ••••	U ••–
I ••	V •••–
J •–––	W •––
K –•–	X –••–
L •–••	Y –•––
M ––	Z ––••

Can You Crack the Code?

1. Use the Morse code in the chart to decode the question in the message below. The letters are separated by slash marks.

W H E R E A R

•––/••••/•/•–•/•/•–/•–•/•/––•/•/–•/
•/•••/•–••/–––/–•–•/•–/–/•/–••/

2. Write your answer to the question in Morse code.

3. Exchange your coded answer with a partner. Then decode your partner's answer.

Think It Over
Forming Operational Definitions Based on your results from this activity, write a definition of the word *code*. Then compare your definition to one in a dictionary.

A white buffalo calf was born on Childs Place Farm near Hanover, Michigan, in 1998. White buffaloes are extremely rare, occurring only once in every 10 million births. Why was this calf born with such an uncommon phenotype? To answer this question, you need to know how the genes on a chromosome control an organism's traits.

The Genetic Code

Today scientists know that the main function of genes is to control the production of proteins in the organism's cells. Proteins help to determine the size, shape, and many other traits of an organism.

GUIDE FOR READING
◆ What is meant by the term "genetic code"?
◆ How does a cell produce proteins?
◆ How do mutations affect an organism?

Reading Tip As you read, create a flowchart that shows how a cell produces proteins.

Figure 15 The white color of this buffalo calf is very unusual. Both of the calf's parents had brown coats.

Recall from Chapter 2 that chromosomes are composed mostly of DNA. In Figure 16, you can see the relationship between chromosomes and DNA. Notice that a DNA molecule is made up of four different nitrogen bases—adenine (A), thymine (T), guanine (G), and cytosine (C). These bases form the rungs of the DNA "ladder." A single gene on a chromosome may contain anywhere from several hundred to a million or more of these bases. The bases are arranged in a specific order—for example, ATGACGTAC.

The order of the nitrogen bases along a gene forms a genetic code that specifies what type of protein will be produced. In the genetic code, a group of three bases codes for the attachment of a specific amino acid. Amino acids are the building blocks of proteins. The order of the bases determines the order in which amino acids are put together to form a protein. You can think of the bases as three-letter code words. The code words tell the cell which amino acid to add to the growing protein chain.

☑ *Checkpoint* *What is the main function of genes?*

How Cells Make Proteins

The production of proteins is called protein synthesis. **During protein synthesis, the cell uses information from a gene on a chromosome to produce a specific protein.** Protein synthesis takes place on the ribosomes in the cytoplasm of the cell. As you know, the cytoplasm is outside the nucleus. The chromosomes, however, are found inside the nucleus. How, then, does the information needed to produce proteins get out of the nucleus and into the cytoplasm?

Figure 16 A chromosome contains thousands of genes along its length. The sequence of bases along a gene forms a code that tells the cell what protein to produce. *Interpreting Diagrams* *Where in the cell are the chromosomes located?*

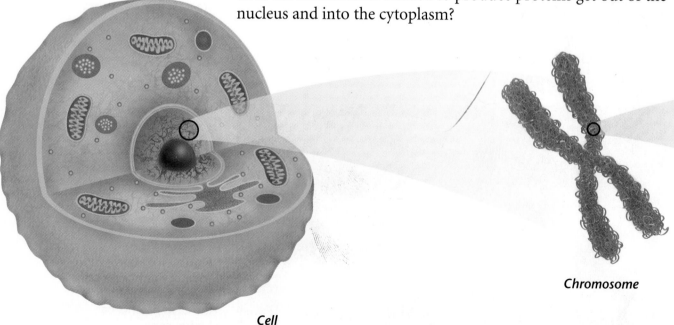

Chromosome

Cell

The Role of RNA Before protein synthesis can take place, a "messenger" must first carry the genetic code from the DNA inside the nucleus into the cytoplasm. This genetic messenger is called ribonucleic acid, or RNA.

Although RNA is similar to DNA, the two molecules differ in some important ways. Unlike DNA, which looks like a twisted ladder, an RNA molecule looks like only one side, or strand, of the ladder. RNA also contains a different sugar molecule from the sugar found in DNA. Another difference between DNA and RNA is in their nitrogen bases. Like DNA, RNA contains adenine, guanine, and cytosine. However, instead of thymine, RNA contains uracil (YOOR uh sil).

There are several types of RNA involved in protein synthesis. **Messenger RNA** copies the coded message from the DNA in the nucleus, and carries the message into the cytoplasm. Another type of RNA, called **transfer RNA,** carries amino acids and adds them to the growing protein.

Translating the Code The process of protein synthesis is shown in *Exploring Protein Synthesis* on the next page. The first step is for a DNA molecule to "unzip" between its base pairs. Then one of the strands of DNA directs the production of a strand of messenger RNA. To form the RNA strand, RNA bases pair up with the DNA bases. Instead of thymine, however, uracil pairs with adenine. The messenger RNA then leaves the nucleus and attaches to a ribosome in the cytoplasm. There, molecules of transfer RNA pick up the amino acids specified by each three-letter code word. Each transfer RNA molecule puts the amino acid it is carrying in the correct order along the growing protein chain.

☑ *Checkpoint* *What is the function of transfer RNA?*

 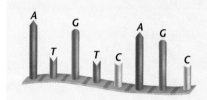
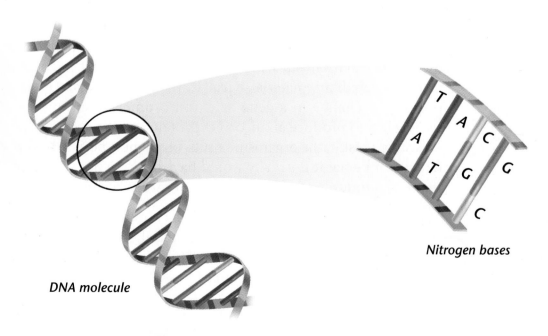

DNA molecule

Nitrogen bases

EXPLORING Protein Synthesis

To make proteins, messenger RNA copies information from DNA in the nucleus. Transfer RNA then uses this information to produce proteins in the ribosomes.

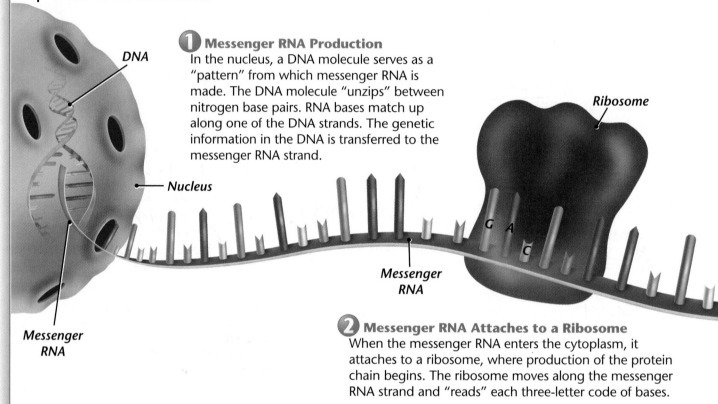

1 Messenger RNA Production
In the nucleus, a DNA molecule serves as a "pattern" from which messenger RNA is made. The DNA molecule "unzips" between nitrogen base pairs. RNA bases match up along one of the DNA strands. The genetic information in the DNA is transferred to the messenger RNA strand.

DNA

Ribosome

Nucleus

Messenger RNA

Messenger RNA

G A C

2 Messenger RNA Attaches to a Ribosome
When the messenger RNA enters the cytoplasm, it attaches to a ribosome, where production of the protein chain begins. The ribosome moves along the messenger RNA strand and "reads" each three-letter code of bases.

Mutations

Suppose that a mistake occurred in one gene of a chromosome. Instead of the base A, for example, the DNA molecule might have the base G. Such a mistake is one type of mutation that can occur in a cell's hereditary material. Recall from Chapter 2 that a mutation is any change in a gene or chromosome. Mutations can cause a cell to produce an incorrect protein during protein synthesis. As a result, the organism's traits, or phenotype, will be different from what it normally would have been. In fact, the term *mutation* comes from a Latin word that means "change."

Types of Mutations Some mutations are the result of small changes in an organism's hereditary material, such as the substitution of a single base for another. This type of mutation can occur during the DNA replication process. The white coat on the

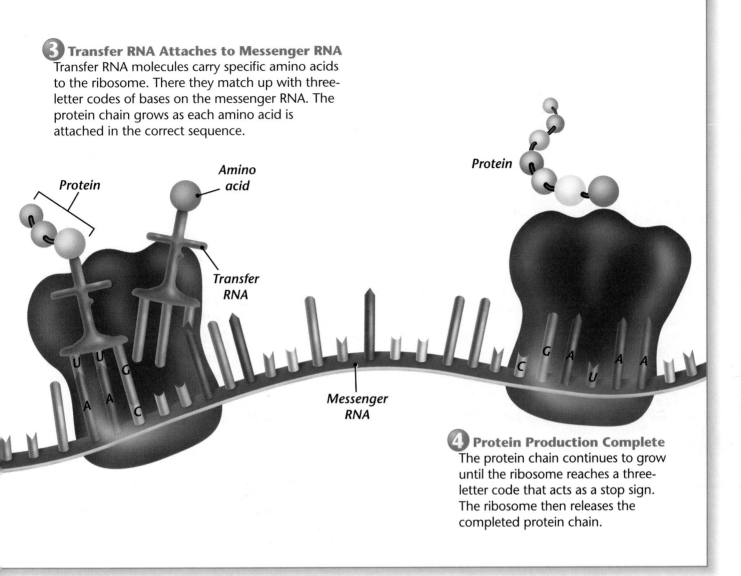

③ Transfer RNA Attaches to Messenger RNA
Transfer RNA molecules carry specific amino acids to the ribosome. There they match up with three-letter codes of bases on the messenger RNA. The protein chain grows as each amino acid is attached in the correct sequence.

Protein

Amino acid

Transfer RNA

Protein

Messenger RNA

④ Protein Production Complete
The protein chain continues to grow until the ribosome reaches a three-letter code that acts as a stop sign. The ribosome then releases the completed protein chain.

buffalo calf you read about at the start of this section might have resulted from this type of mutation. Other mutations may occur when chromosomes don't separate correctly during meiosis. When this type of mutation occurs, a cell can end up with too many or too few chromosomes. The cell could also end up with extra segments of chromosomes.

If a mutation occurs in a body cell, such as a skin cell, the mutation will affect only the cell that carries it. If, however, a mutation occurs in a sex cell, the mutation can be passed on to an offspring and affect the offspring's phenotype.

The Effects of Mutations Because mutations can introduce changes in an organism, they can be a source of genetic variety. **Some of the changes brought about by mutations are harmful to an organism. Other mutations, however, are helpful, and still others are neither harmful nor helpful.** A mutation is

Figure 17 Mutations can affect an organism's traits, or phenotype. The unusually large strawberries on the left are the result of a mutation. The cells of these strawberries have extra sets of chromosomes.

harmful to an organism if it reduces the organism's chance for survival and reproduction.

Whether a mutation is harmful or not depends partly on the organism's environment. The mutation that led to the production of a white buffalo calf would probably be harmful to an organism in the wild. Its white color would make it more visible, and thus easier for predators to find. However, a white buffalo calf raised on a farm has the same chance for survival as a brown buffalo. On the farm, the mutation is neutral—it neither helps nor harms the buffalo.

INTEGRATING HEALTH Some diseases in humans are caused by harmful mutations. For example, some forms of cancer are caused by mutations in an organism's body cells. Overexposure to the ultraviolet radiation in sunlight, for example, may lead to mutations that could cause skin cancer. In Chapter 4, you will learn more about other diseases that result from harmful mutations.

Helpful mutations, on the other hand, improve an organism's chances for survival and reproduction. For example, a gene mutation in potatoes led to the production of a new variety of potato called the Katahdin potato. This potato is resistant to some diseases that attack other varieties of potatoes. As a bonus for humans, it also looks and tastes better than other types of potatoes.

Section 4 Review

1. How do the nitrogen bases along a gene serve as a genetic code?
2. Briefly describe the process by which a cell produces proteins.
3. What possible effects can a mutation have on an organism?
4. Where in a cell does protein synthesis take place?
5. **Thinking Critically Relating Cause and Effect** Why are mutations that occur in an organism's body cells not passed on to its offspring?

Check Your Progress CHAPTER PROJECT

With your partner, plan a display of your pet's family. Label the parents the P generation. Label the offspring the F_1 generation. Construct a Punnett square for each trait to help explain the inheritance pattern in your pet's family. *(Hint: Attach your pets to the display in a way that lets viewers turn the pets over to read their genotypes.)*

SECTION 1 — Mendel's Work

Key Ideas

◆ Gregor Mendel's work was the foundation for understanding why offspring have traits similar to those of their parents.

◆ Traits are controlled by alleles of genes. Organisms inherit one allele from each parent.

◆ Some alleles are dominant over others. A dominant allele is one whose trait always shows up in the organism when the allele is present. A recessive allele is masked whenever the dominant allele is present.

Key Terms

trait	allele
heredity	dominant allele
genetics	recessive allele
purebred	hybrid
gene	

SECTION 2 — Probability and Genetics

INTEGRATING MATHEMATICS

Key Ideas

◆ Probability is the likelihood that a particular event will happen.

◆ Mendel was the first scientist to interpret his data using the principles of probability.

◆ Geneticists use Punnett squares to show all the possible outcomes of a genetic cross. Punnett squares allow a person to determine the probability of a particular outcome.

◆ An organism's phenotype is its physical appearance. An organism's genotype is its genetic makeup.

Key Terms

probability
Punnett square
phenotype
genotype
homozygous
heterozygous
codominance

SECTION 3 — The Cell and Inheritance

Key Ideas

◆ According to the chromosome theory of inheritance, genes are carried from parents to their offspring on chromosomes.

◆ During meiosis, chromosome pairs separate to form sex cells. The sex cells have half the number of chromosomes as the body cells. Only one chromosome from each chromosome pair ends up in each sex cell.

Key Term
meiosis

SECTION 4 — The DNA Connection

Key Ideas

◆ The nitrogen bases along a gene form a code that specifies the order in which amino acids will be put together to produce a protein.

◆ During protein synthesis, messenger RNA copies the coded message from the DNA in the nucleus and carries the message into the cytoplasm. Transfer RNA adds amino acids to the growing protein.

◆ A mutation is a change in a gene or chromosome. Some mutations are harmful, some are helpful, and some are neutral.

Key Terms

messenger RNA   transfer RNA

USING THE INTERNET

ACTIVITY

www.science-explorer.phschool.com

California Test Prep: Reviewing Content

Multiple Choice

Choose the letter of the best answer.

1. The different forms of a gene are called
   a. alleles.
   b. chromosomes.
   c. phenotypes.
   d. genotypes.

2. In a coin toss, the probability of the coin landing heads up is
   a. 100 percent.
   b. 75 percent.
   c. 50 percent.
   d. 25 percent.

3. An organism with two identical alleles for a trait is
   a. heterozygous.
   b. homozygous.
   c. recessive.
   d. dominant.

4. If the body cells of an organism have 10 chromosomes, then its sex cells would have
   a. 5 chromosomes.
   b. 10 chromosomes.
   c. 15 chromosomes.
   d. 20 chromosomes.

5. During protein synthesis, messenger RNA
   a. "reads" each three-letter code of bases.
   b. releases the completed protein chain.
   c. copies information from DNA in the nucleus.
   d. carries amino acids to the ribosome.

True or False

If the statement is true, write true. If it is false, change the underlined word or words to make the statement true.

6. The scientific study of heredity is called <u>genetics</u>.

7. An organism's physical appearance is its <u>genotype</u>.

8. In <u>codominance</u>, neither of the alleles is dominant or recessive.

9. <u>Heredity</u> is the process by which sex cells form.

10. Proteins are made in the <u>nucleus</u> of the cell.

Checking Concepts

11. Describe what happened when Mendel crossed purebred tall pea plants with purebred short pea plants.

12. You toss a coin five times and it lands heads up each time. What is the probability that it will land heads up on the sixth toss? Explain your answer.

13. In guinea pigs, the allele for black fur (*B*) is dominant over the allele for white fur (*b*). In a cross between a heterozygous black guinea pig (*Bb*) and a homozygous white guinea pig (*bb*), what is the probability that an offspring will have white fur? Use a Punnett square to answer the question.

14. In your own words, describe the sequence of steps in the process of meiosis.

15. Describe the role of transfer RNA in protein synthesis.

16. **Writing to Learn** Imagine that you are a student in the 1860s visiting Gregor Mendel in his garden. Write a letter to a friend describing Mendel's experiments with pea plants.

Thinking Visually

17. **Compare/Contrast Table** Copy the table comparing DNA and messenger RNA onto a separate sheet of paper. Then complete the table. (For more about compare/contrast tables, see the Skills Handbook.)

Characteristic	DNA	Messenger RNA
Nitrogen bases	a. __?__, b. __?__ c. __?__, d. __?__	Adenine, uracil, guanine, cytosine
Structure	Twisted ladder	e. __?__
Function	Forms a genetic code that specifies what type of protein will be produced	f. __?__

Test Prep: Skills

In peas, the allele for green pods (G) is dominant over the allele for yellow pods (g). The table shows the phenotypes of the offspring produced from a cross of two plants with green pods. Use the data to answer Questions 18–20.

Phenotype	Number of Offspring
Green pods	9
Yellow pods	3

18. **Calculating** Calculate what percent of the offspring have green pods. Calculate what percent have yellow pods.
19. **Inferring** What is the genotype of the offspring with yellow pods? What are the possible genotypes of the offspring with green pods?
20. **Drawing Conclusions** What are the genotypes of the parents? How do you know?

Thinking Critically

21. **Applying Concepts** In rabbits, the allele for a spotted coat is dominant over the allele for a solid-colored coat. A spotted rabbit was crossed with a solid-colored rabbit. The offspring all had spotted coats. What were the genotypes of the parents? Explain.
22. **Problem Solving** Suppose you are growing purebred green-skinned watermelons. One day you find a mutant striped watermelon. You cross the striped watermelon with a purebred green watermelon. Fifty percent of the offspring are striped, while fifty percent are solid green. Is the allele for the striped trait dominant or recessive? Explain your answer.
23. **Predicting** A new mutation in mice causes the coat to be twice as thick as normal. In what environment would this mutation be helpful? In what environment would it be harmful?

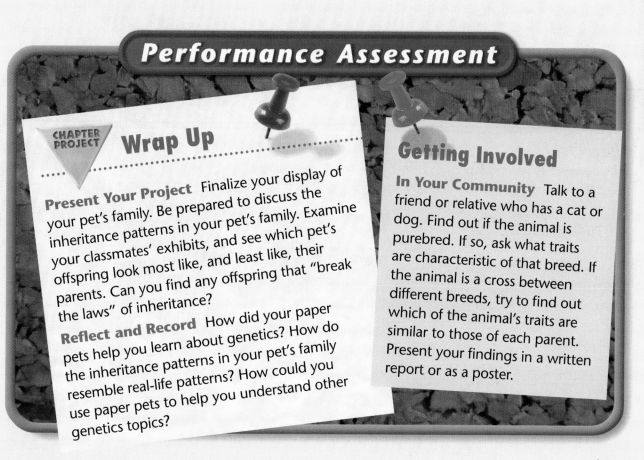

Performance Assessment

CHAPTER PROJECT Wrap Up

Present Your Project Finalize your display of your pet's family. Be prepared to discuss the inheritance patterns in your pet's family. Examine your classmates' exhibits, and see which pet's offspring look most like, and least like, their parents. Can you find any offspring that "break the laws" of inheritance?

Reflect and Record How did your paper pets help you learn about genetics? How do the inheritance patterns in your pet's family resemble real-life patterns? How could you use paper pets to help you understand other genetics topics?

Getting Involved

In Your Community Talk to a friend or relative who has a cat or dog. Find out if the animal is purebred. If so, ask what traits are characteristic of that breed. If the animal is a cross between different breeds, try to find out which of the animal's traits are similar to those of each parent. Present your findings in a written report or as a poster.

The following California Science Content Standards are addressed in this chapter:

2. A typical cell of any organism contains genetic instructions that specify its traits. Those traits may be modified by environmental influences.

   b. Sexual reproduction produces offspring that inherit half their genes from each parent.

c. An inherited trait can be determined by one or more genes.

d. Plant and animal cells contain many thousands of different genes, and typically have two copies of every gene. The two copies (or alleles) of the gene may or may not be identical, and one

may be dominant in determining the phenotype while the other is recessive.

e. DNA is the genetic material of living organisms, and is located in the chromosomes of each cell.

5. The anatomy and physiology of plants and animals illustrate the complementary nature of structure and function.

A Family Portrait

The children in this family have some traits like their mother's and some traits like their father's.

A pedigree, or family tree, is a branched drawing that shows many generations of a family. In some cases, a pedigree may show centuries of a family's history.

In genetics, pedigrees are used to show how traits are passed from one generation to the next. In this project, you will create a genetic pedigree for an imaginary family. Although the family will be imaginary, your pedigree must show how real human traits are passed from parents to children.

Your Goal To create a pedigree for an imaginary family that shows the transfer of genetic traits from one generation to the next.

To complete the project you will
- ◆ choose two different genetic traits, and identify all the possible genotypes and phenotypes
- ◆ create pedigrees that trace each trait through three generations of your imaginary family
- ◆ prepare a family "photo" album to show what each family member looks like

Get Started With a partner, review the human traits described on page 76 in Chapter 3. List what you already know about human inheritance. For example, which human traits are controlled by dominant alleles? Which are controlled by recessive alleles? Then preview Section 1 of this chapter, and list the traits you'll be studying. Choose two traits that you would like to focus on in your project.

Check Your Progress You'll be working on this project as you study this chapter. To keep your project on track, look for Check Your Progress boxes at the following points.

Section 1 Review, page 108: Create a pedigree for the first trait you chose.

Section 2 Review, page 113: Create the second pedigree, and begin your family album.

Wrap Up At the end of the chapter (page 127), you will present your family's pedigrees and "photo" album to the class.

---

b. Organ systems function because of the contributions of individual organs, tissues, and cells. The failure of any part can affect the entire system.

7. Scientific progress is made by asking meaningful questions and conducting careful investigations.

c. Communicate the logical connection among hypothesis, science concepts, tests conducted, data collected, and conclusions drawn from the scientific evidence.

d. Construct scale models, maps and appropriately labeled diagrams to communicate scientific knowledge.

e. Communicate the steps and results from an investigation in written reports and verbal presentations.

Human Inheritance

How Tall Is Tall?

1. Choose a partner. Measure each other's height to the nearest 5 centimeters. Record your measurements on the chalkboard.

2. Create a bar graph showing the number of students at each height. Plot the heights on the horizontal axis and the number of students on the vertical axis.

Think It Over

Inferring If Gregor Mendel had graphed the heights of his pea plants, the graph would have had two bars—one for tall stems and one for short stems. Do you think height in humans is controlled by a single gene, as it is in peas? Explain your answer.

Have you ever heard someone say "He's the spitting image of his dad" or "She has her mother's eyes"? Children often resemble their parents. The reason for this is that alleles for eye color, hair color, and thousands of other traits are passed from parents to their children. People inherit some alleles from their mother and some from their father. This is why most people look a little like their mother and a little like their father.

Traits Controlled by Single Genes

In Chapter 3, you learned that many traits in peas and other organisms are controlled by a single gene with two alleles. Often one allele is dominant, while the other is recessive. Many human traits are also controlled by a single gene with one dominant allele and one recessive allele. As with tall and short pea plants, these human traits have two distinctly different phenotypes, or physical appearances.

For example, a widow's peak is a hairline that comes to a point in the middle of the forehead. The allele for a widow's peak is dominant over the allele for a straight hairline. The Punnett square in Figure 1 illustrates a cross between two parents who are heterozygous for a widow's peak. Trace the possible combinations of alleles that a child may inherit. Notice that each child has a 3 in 4, or 75 percent, probability of having a widow's peak. There is only a 1 in 4, or 25 percent, probability that a child will have a straight hairline. Recall from Chapter 3 that when Mendel crossed peas that were heterozygous for a trait, he obtained similar percentages in the offspring.

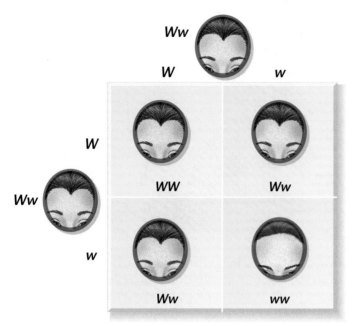

Figure 1 This Punnett square shows a cross between two parents with widow's peaks. *Interpreting Diagrams What are the possible genotypes of the offspring? What percent of the offspring will have each genotype?*

Do you have dimples when you smile? If so, then you have the dominant allele for this trait. Like having a widow's peak, having smile dimples is controlled by a single gene. People who have two recessive alleles do not have smile dimples.

Multiple Alleles

Some human traits are controlled by a single gene that has more than two alleles. Such a gene is said to have **multiple alleles**—three or more forms of a gene that code for a single trait. You can think of multiple alleles as being like flavors of pudding. Pudding usually comes in more flavors than just chocolate and vanilla!

Even though a gene may have multiple alleles, a person can carry only two of those alleles. This is because chromosomes exist in pairs. Each chromosome in a pair carries only one allele for each gene.

One human trait that is controlled by a gene with multiple alleles is blood type. There are four main blood types—A, B, AB, and O. Three alleles control the inheritance of blood types. The allele for blood type A and the allele for blood type B are codominant. The codominant alleles are written as capital letters with superscripts—I^A for blood type A and I^B for blood type B. The allele for blood type O—written i—is recessive. Recall that when two codominant alleles are inherited, neither allele is masked. A person who inherits an I^A allele from one parent and an I^B allele from the other parent will have type AB blood. Figure 2 shows the allele combinations that result in each blood type. Notice that only people who inherit two i alleles have type O blood.

☑ *Checkpoint* *If a gene has multiple alleles, why can a person only have two of the alleles for the gene?*

Blood Types	
Blood Type	**Combination of Alleles**
A	$I^A I^A$ or $I^A i$
B	$I^B I^B$ or $I^B i$
AB	$I^A I^B$
O	ii

Figure 2 Blood type is determined by a single gene with three alleles. This chart shows which combinations of alleles result in each blood type.

Figure 3 Skin color in humans is determined by three or more genes. Different combinations of alleles at each of the genes result in a wide range of possible skin colors.

Traits Controlled by Many Genes

If you did the Discover activity, you observed that height in humans has more than two distinct phenotypes. In fact, there is an enormous variety of phenotypes for height. What causes this wide range of phenotypes? **Some human traits show a large number of phenotypes because the traits are controlled by many genes. The genes act together as a group to produce a single trait.** At least four genes control height in humans, so there are many possible combinations of genes and alleles.

Like height, skin color is determined by many genes. Human skin color ranges from almost white to nearly black, with many shades in between. Skin color is controlled by at least three genes. Each gene, in turn, has at least two possible alleles. Various combinations of alleles at each of the genes determine the amount of pigment that a person's skin cells produce. Thus, a wide variety of skin colors is possible.

The Effect of Environment

The effects of genes are often altered by the environment—the organism's surroundings. For example, people's diets can affect their height. A diet lacking in protein, minerals, and vitamins can prevent a person from growing to his or her potential maximum height. Since the late 1800s, the average height of adults in the United States has increased by almost 10 centimeters. During that time, American diets have become more healthful. Other environmental factors, such as medical care and living conditions, have also improved since the late 1800s.

☑ *Checkpoint* *How can environmental factors affect a person's height?*

The Eyes Have It

One inherited trait is eye dominance—the tendency to use one eye more than the other. Here's how you can test yourself for this trait.

1. Hold your hand out in front of you at arm's length. Point your finger at an object across the room.
2. Close your right eye. With only your left eye open, observe how far your finger appears to move.
3. Repeat Step 2 with the right eye open. With which eye did your finger seem to remain closer to the object? That eye is dominant.

Designing Experiments Is eye dominance related to hand dominance—whether a person is right-handed or left-handed? Design an experiment to find out. Obtain your teacher's permission before carrying out your experiment.

Male or Female?

"Congratulations, Mr. and Mrs. Gonzales. It's a baby girl!" What factors determine whether a baby is a boy or a girl? As with other traits, the sex of a baby is determined by genes on chromosomes. Among the 23 pairs of chromosomes in each body cell is a single pair of chromosomes called the sex chromosomes. The sex chromosomes determine whether a person is male or female.

The sex chromosomes are the only pair of chromosomes that do not always match. If you are female, your two sex chromosomes match. The two chromosomes are called X chromosomes. If you are male, your sex chromosomes do not match. One of your sex chromosomes is an X chromosome. The other chromosome is a Y chromosome. The Y chromosome is much smaller than the X chromosome.

What happens to the sex chromosomes when egg and sperm cells form? As you know, each egg and sperm cell has only one chromosome from each pair. Since both of a female's sex chromosomes are X chromosomes, all eggs carry one X chromosome. Males, however, have two different sex chromosomes. This means that half of a male's sperm cells carry an X chromosome, while half carry a Y chromosome.

When a sperm cell with an X chromosome fertilizes an egg, the egg has two X chromosomes. The fertilized egg will develop into a girl. When a sperm with a Y chromosome fertilizes an egg, the egg has one X chromosome and one Y chromosome. The fertilized egg will develop into a boy. Thus it is the sperm that determines the sex of the child, as you can see in Figure 4.

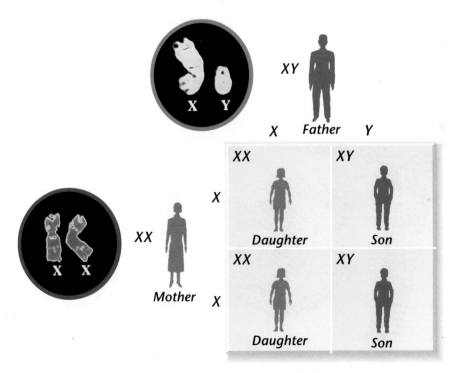

Figure 4 As this Punnett square shows, there is a 50 percent probability that a child will be a girl and a 50 percent probability that a child will be a boy. *Interpreting Diagrams What sex will the child be if a sperm with a Y chromosome fertilizes an egg?*

You can model how the sex of an offspring is determined.

ACTIVITY

1. Label one paper bag "female." Label another paper bag "male."

2. Place two red marbles in the bag labeled "female." The red marbles represent X chromosomes.

3. Place one red marble and one white marble in the bag labeled "male." The white marble represents a Y chromosome.

4. Without looking, pick one marble from each bag. Two red marbles represent a female offspring. One red marble and one white marble represent a male offspring. Record the sex of the "offspring."

5. Put the marbles back in the correct bags. Repeat Step 4 nine more times.

Making Models How many males were produced? How many females? How close were your results to the expected probabilities for male and female offspring?

Sex-Linked Genes

Some human traits occur more often in one sex than the other. The genes for these traits are often carried on the sex chromosomes. Genes on the X and Y chromosomes are often called **sex-linked genes** because their alleles are passed from parent to child on a sex chromosome. Traits controlled by sex-linked genes are called sex-linked traits.

Like other genes, sex-linked genes can have dominant and recessive alleles. Recall that females have two X chromosomes, whereas males have one X chromosome and one Y chromosome. In females, a dominant allele on one X chromosome will mask a recessive allele on the other X chromosome. The situation is not the same in males, however. In males, there is no matching allele on the Y chromosome to mask, or hide, the allele on the X chromosome. As a result, any allele on the X chromosome—even a recessive allele—will produce the trait in a male who inherits it. **Because males have only one X chromosome, males are more likely than females to have a sex-linked trait that is controlled by a recessive allele.**

One example of a sex-linked trait that is controlled by a recessive allele is red-green colorblindness. A person with red-green colorblindness cannot distinguish between red and green. A common test for red-green colorblindness is shown in Figure 5.

Many more males than females have red-green colorblindness. You can understand why this is the case by examining the Punnett square in Figure 6. Both parents in this example have normal color vision. Notice, however, that the mother is a carrier of colorblindness. A **carrier** is a person who has one recessive allele for a trait and one dominant allele. Although a carrier does not have the trait, the carrier can pass the recessive allele on to his or her offspring.

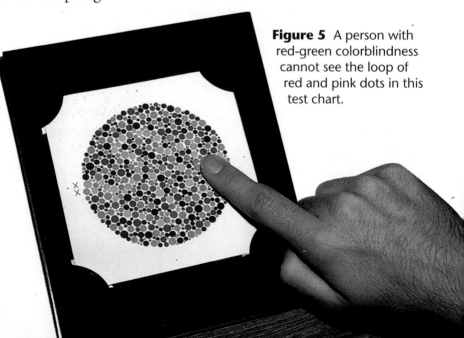

Figure 5 A person with red-green colorblindness cannot see the loop of red and pink dots in this test chart.

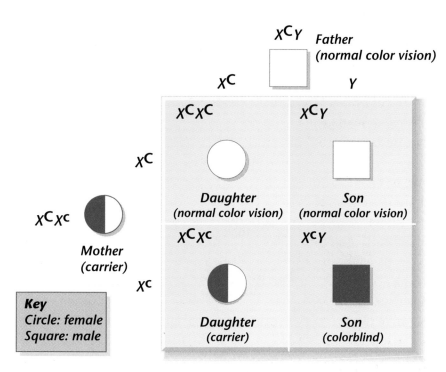

Figure 6 Red-green color-blindness is a sex-linked trait. A girl who receives only one recessive allele (written X^c) for red-green colorblindness will not have the trait. However, a boy who receives one recessive allele will be colorblind. *Applying Concepts What allele combination would a daughter need to inherit to be colorblind?*

As you can see in Figure 6, there is a 25 percent probability that this couple will have a colorblind child. Notice that none of the couple's daughters will be colorblind. On the other hand, the sons have a 50 percent probability of being colorblind. For a female to be colorblind, she must inherit two recessive alleles for colorblindness, one from each parent. A male needs to inherit only one recessive allele. This is because there is no gene for color vision on the Y chromosome. Thus, there is no allele that could mask the recessive allele on the X chromosome.

Pedigrees

Imagine that you are a geneticist interested in studying inheritance patterns in humans. What would you do? You can't set up crosses with people as Mendel did with peas. Instead, you would need to trace the inheritance of traits through many generations in a number of families.

One important tool that geneticists use to trace the inheritance of traits in humans is a pedigree. A **pedigree** is a chart or "family tree" that tracks which members of a family have a particular trait. The trait recorded in a pedigree can be an ordinary trait such as widow's peak, or it could be a sex-linked trait such as colorblindness. In *Exploring a Pedigree* on page 108, you can trace the inheritance of colorblindness through three generations of a family.

☑ *Checkpoint* How is a pedigree like a "family tree"?

EXPLORING a Pedigree

This pedigree traces the occurrence of colorblindness in three generations of a family. Colorblindness is a sex-linked trait that is controlled by a recessive allele. Notice that specific symbols are used in pedigrees to communicate genetic information.

A circle represents a female.

A square represents a male.

A horizontal line connecting a male and female represents a marriage.

A vertical line and a bracket connect the parents to their children.

A half-shaded circle or square indicates that a person is a carrier of the trait.

A completely shaded circle or square indicates that a person has the trait.

A circle or square that is not shaded indicates that a person neither has the trait nor is a carrier of the trait.

 ## Section 1 Review

1. Why do human traits such as height and skin color have many different phenotypes?
2. Explain why red-green colorblindness is more common in males than in females.
3. What is a pedigree? How are pedigrees used?
4. **Thinking Critically Predicting** Could two people with widow's peaks have a child with a straight hairline? Could two people with straight hairlines have a child with a widow's peak? Explain.

Check Your Progress CHAPTER PROJECT

By now, you should be creating your pedigree for the first trait you chose. Start with one couple, and show two generations of offspring. The couple should have five children. It is up to you to decide how many children each of those children has. Use Punnett squares to make sure that your imaginary family's inheritance pattern follows the laws of genetics.

② Human Genetic Disorders

DISCOVER •••••••••••••••••••••••••••••••••••• ACTIVITY

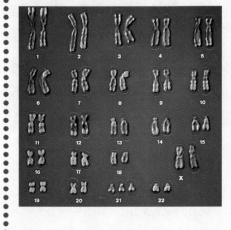

How Many Chromosomes?

The photo at the left shows the chromosomes from a cell of a person with Down syndrome, a genetic disorder. The chromosomes have been sorted into pairs.

1. Count the number of chromosomes in the photo.

2. How does the number of chromosomes compare to the usual number of chromosomes in human cells?

Think It Over

Inferring How do you think a cell could have ended up with this number of chromosomes? (*Hint:* Think about the events that occur during meiosis.)

The air inside the stadium was hot and still. The crowd cheered loudly as eight runners approached the starting blocks. The runners shook out their arms and legs to loosen up their muscles and calm their jitters. When the starter raised the gun, all eyes focused on the runners. At the crack of the starter's gun, the runners leaped into motion and sprinted down the track.

Seconds later, the race was over. The runners, bursting with pride, hugged each other and their coaches. It didn't matter where each of the runners placed. All that mattered was that they had finished the race and done their best. These athletes were running in the Special Olympics, a competition for people with disabilities.

Many of the athletes who compete in the Special Olympics have disabilities that result from genetic disorders. A **genetic disorder** is an abnormal condition that a person inherits through genes or chromosomes. **Genetic disorders are caused by mutations, or changes in a person's DNA.** In some cases, a mutation occurs when sex cells form during meiosis. In other cases, a mutation that is already present in a parent's cells is passed on to the offspring. In this section, you will learn about some common genetic disorders.

GUIDE FOR READING

◆ What causes genetic disorders?

◆ How are genetic disorders diagnosed?

Reading Tip As you read, make a list of different types of genetic disorders. Write a sentence about each disorder.

A runner at the Special Olympics ▶

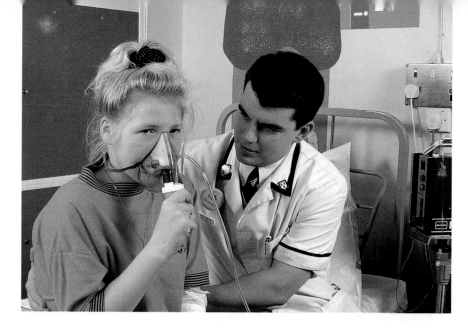

Figure 7 Cystic fibrosis is a genetic disorder that causes thick mucus to build up in a person's lungs and intestines. This patient is inhaling a fine mist that will help loosen the mucus in her lungs.

Cystic Fibrosis

Cystic fibrosis is a genetic disorder in which the body produces abnormally thick mucus in the lungs and intestines. The thick mucus fills the lungs, making it hard for the affected person to breathe. Bacteria that grow in the mucus can cause infections and, eventually, lung damage. In the intestines, the mucus makes it difficult for digestion to occur.

The mutation that leads to cystic fibrosis is carried on a recessive allele. The cystic fibrosis allele is most common among people whose ancestors are from Northern Europe. Every day in this country, four babies are born with cystic fibrosis.

Currently there is no cure for cystic fibrosis. Medical treatments include drugs to prevent infections and physical therapy to break up mucus in the lungs. Recent advances in scientists' understanding of the disease may lead to better treatments and longer lifespans for people with cystic fibrosis.

☑ *Checkpoint* What are some symptoms of cystic fibrosis?

Sickle-Cell Disease

Sickle-cell disease is a genetic disorder that affects the blood. The mutation that causes the disorder affects the production of an important protein called hemoglobin. Hemoglobin is the protein in red blood cells that carries oxygen. People with sickle-cell disease produce an abnormal form of hemoglobin. When oxygen concentrations are low, their red blood cells have an unusual sickle shape, as you can see in Figure 8.

Sickle-shaped red blood cells cannot carry as much oxygen as normal-shaped cells. Because of their shape, the cells become stuck in narrow blood vessels, blocking them. People with sickle-cell disease suffer from lack of oxygen in the blood and experience pain and weakness.

Figure 8 Normally, red blood cells are shaped like round disks (top). In a person with sickle-cell disease, red blood cells can become sickle-shaped (bottom). *Relating Cause and Effect What combination of alleles leads to sickle-cell disease?*

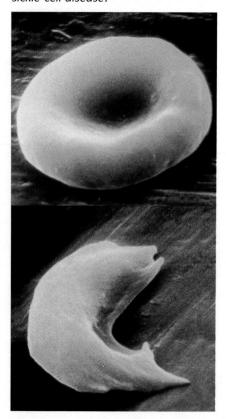

The allele for the sickle-cell trait is most common in people of African ancestry. About 9 percent of African Americans carry the sickle-cell allele. The allele for the sickle-cell trait is codominant with the normal allele. A person with two sickle-cell alleles will have the disease. A person with one sickle-cell allele will produce both normal hemoglobin and abnormal hemoglobin. This person usually will not have symptoms of the disease.

Currently, there is no cure for sickle-cell disease. People with sickle-cell disease are given drugs to relieve their painful symptoms and to prevent blockages in blood vessels. As with cystic fibrosis, scientists are hopeful that new, successful treatments will soon be found.

Hemophilia

Hemophilia is a genetic disorder in which a person's blood clots very slowly or not at all. People with the disorder do not produce one of the proteins needed for normal blood clotting. A person with hemophilia can bleed to death from a minor cut or scrape. The danger of internal bleeding from small bumps and bruises is also very high.

Hemophilia is an example of a disorder that is caused by a recessive allele on the X chromosome. Because hemophilia is a sex-linked disorder, it occurs more frequently in males than in females. **INTEGRATING HEALTH** People with hemophilia must get regular doses of the missing clotting protein. In general, people with hemophilia can lead normal lives. However, they are advised to avoid contact sports and other activities that could cause internal injuries.

Figure 9 Empress Alexandra of Russia (center row, left) passed the allele for hemophilia to her son Alexis (front).

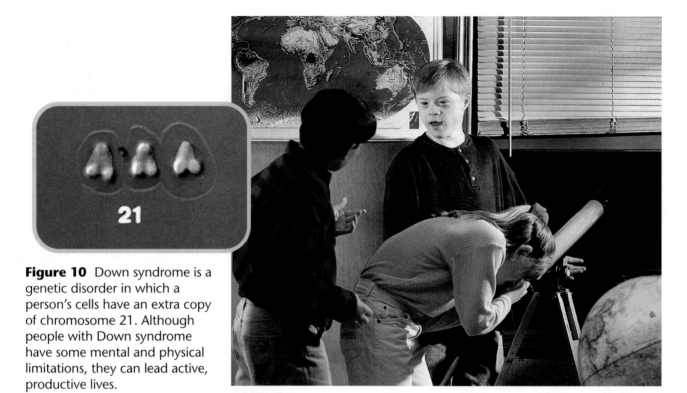

Figure 10 Down syndrome is a genetic disorder in which a person's cells have an extra copy of chromosome 21. Although people with Down syndrome have some mental and physical limitations, they can lead active, productive lives.

Down Syndrome

Some genetic disorders are the result of too many or too few chromosomes. In one such disorder, called Down syndrome, a person's cells have an extra copy of chromosome 21. The extra chromosome is the result of an error during meiosis. Recall that in meiosis, cells divide and chromosomes separate to produce sex cells with half the normal chromosome number. Down syndrome most often occurs when chromosomes fail to separate properly during meiosis.

People with Down syndrome have a distinctive physical appearance, and have some degree of mental retardation. Heart defects are also common, but can be treated. Despite their limitations, many people with Down syndrome lead full, active lives.

Diagnosing Genetic Disorders

INTEGRATING TECHNOLOGY Years ago, doctors had only Punnett squares and pedigrees to help them predict whether a child might have a genetic disorder. **Today doctors use tools such as amniocentesis and karyotypes to help detect genetic disorders.**

Before a baby is born, doctors can use a procedure called **amniocentesis** (am nee oh sen TEE sis) to determine whether the baby will have some genetic disorders. During amniocentesis, a doctor uses a very long needle to remove a small amount of the fluid that surrounds the developing baby. The fluid contains cells from the baby.

The doctor then examines the chromosomes from the cells. To do this, the doctor creates a karyotype. A **karyotype** (KA ree uh typ) is a picture of all the chromosomes in a cell. The chromosomes in a karyotype are arranged in pairs. A karyotype can reveal whether a developing baby has the correct number of chromosomes in its cells and whether it is a boy or a girl. If you did the Discover activity, you saw a karyotype from a girl with Down syndrome.

Genetic Counseling

A couple that has a family history or concern about a genetic disorder may turn to a genetic counselor for advice. Genetic counselors help couples understand their chances of having a child with a particular genetic disorder. Genetic counselors use tools such as karyotypes, pedigree charts, and Punnett squares to help them in their work.

Suppose, for example, that a husband and wife both have a history of cystic fibrosis in their families. If they are considering having children, they might seek the advice of a genetic counselor. The genetic counselor might order a test to determine whether they are carriers of the allele for cystic fibrosis. The genetic counselor would then apply the same principles of probability that you learned about in Chapter 3 to calculate the couple's chances of having a child with cystic fibrosis.

Figure 11 Couples may meet with a genetic counselor and their doctor in order to understand their chances of having a child with a genetic disorder.

Section 2 Review

1. Explain how genetic disorders occur in humans. Give two examples of genetic disorders.
2. Describe two tools that doctors use to detect genetic disorders.
3. How do the cells of people with Down syndrome differ from those of others? How might this difference arise?
4. **Thinking Critically Problem Solving** A couple with a family history of hemophilia is about to have a baby girl. What information about the parents would you want to know? How would this information help you determine whether the baby will have hemophilia?

Check Your Progress

CHAPTER PROJECT

At this point, you should begin to trace the inheritance of another trait through the same family members that are in your first pedigree. Also, start making your family "photo" album. Will you use drawings or some other method to show what the family members look like? (*Hint:* Photo albums show phenotypes. Remember that more than one genotype can have the same phenotype.)

Family Puzzles

Imagine that you are a genetic counselor. Two couples come to you for advice. Their family histories are summarized in the boxes labeled *Case Study 1* and *Case Study 2.* They want to understand the probability that their children might inherit certain genetic disorders. In this lab, you will find answers to their questions.

Problem

How can you investigate inheritance patterns in families?

Materials

12 index cards
scissors
marker

Procedure

Part 1 Investigating Case Study 1

1. Read over Case Study 1. In your notebook, draw a pedigree that shows all the family members. Use circles to represent the females, and squares to represent the males. Shade in the circles or squares representing the individuals who have cystic fibrosis.

Case Study 1: Joshua and Bella

◆ Joshua and Bella have a son named Ian. Ian has been diagnosed with cystic fibrosis.
◆ Joshua and Bella are both healthy.
◆ Bella's parents are both healthy.
◆ Joshua's parents are both healthy.
◆ Joshua's sister, Sara, has cystic fibrosis.

2. You know that cystic fibrosis is controlled by a recessive allele. To help you figure out Joshua and Bella's family pattern, create a set of cards to represent the alleles. Cut each of six index cards into four smaller cards. On 12 of the small cards, write *N* to represent the dominant normal allele. On the other 12 small cards, write *n* for the recessive allele.
3. Begin by using the cards to represent Ian's alleles. Since he has cystic fibrosis, what alleles must he have? Write in this genotype next to the pedigree symbol for Ian.
4. Joshua's sister, Sara, also has cystic fibrosis. What alleles does she have? Write in this genotype next to the pedigree symbol that represents Sara.

Case Study 2: Li and Mai

- ◆ The father, Li, has a skin condition. The mother, Mai, has normal skin.
- ◆ Li and Mai's first child, a girl named Gemma, has the same skin condition as Li.
- ◆ Mai's sister has a similar skin condition, but Mai's parents do not.

- ◆ Li has one brother whose skin is normal, and one sister who has the skin condition.
- ◆ Li's mother has the skin condition. His father does not.
- ◆ Li's family lives in a heavily wooded area. His family has always thought the skin condition was a type of allergy.

5. Now use the cards to figure out what genotypes Joshua and Bella must have. Write their genotypes next to their symbols in the pedigree.

6. Work with the cards to figure out the genotypes of all other family members. Fill in each person's genotype next to his or her symbol in the pedigree. If more than one genotype is possible, write in both genotypes.

Part 2 Investigating Case Study 2

7. Read over Case Study 2.

8. You suspect that Gemma and Li's skin condition is caused by an inherited recessive allele. Begin to investigate this possibility by drawing a family pedigree in your notebook. Use shading to indicate which individuals have the skin condition.

9. Fill in the genotype *ss* beside each individual who has the skin condition. Then use cards as you did in Case Study 1 to figure out each family member's genotype. If more than one genotype is possible, fill in both genotypes.

Analyze and Conclude

1. In Case Study 1, what were the genotypes of Joshua's parents? What were the genotypes of Bella's parents?

2. In Case Study 1, Joshua also has a brother. What is the probability that he has cystic fibrosis? Explain.

3. Can you conclude that the skin condition in Case Study 2 is most likely an inherited trait controlled by a recessive allele? Explain.

4. What is the probability that Mai and Li's next child will have the skin condition? Explain.

5. **Apply** Why do genetic counselors need information about many generations of a family in order to draw conclusions about a hereditary condition?

More to Explore

Review the two pedigrees that you just studied. What data suggests that the traits are not sex-linked? Explain.

SECTION 3 Advances in Genetics

DISCOVER ·· **ACTIVITY**

What Do Fingerprints Reveal?

1. Label a sheet of paper with your name. Then roll one of your fingers from side to side on an ink pad. Make a fingerprint by carefully rolling your inked finger from side to side on the paper.

2. Divide into groups. Each group should choose one member to use the same finger to make a second fingerprint on a sheet of paper. Leave the paper unlabeled.

3. Exchange your group's fingerprints with those from another group. Compare each labeled fingerprint with the fingerprint on the unlabeled paper. Decide whose fingerprint it is.

4. Wash your hands after completing this activity.

Think It Over

Observing Why are fingerprints a useful tool for identifying people?

GUIDE FOR READING

◆ What are three ways in which an organism's traits can be altered?

◆ What is the goal of the Human Genome Project?

Reading Tip As you read, make a concept map of the methods used to produce organisms with desirable traits. Include at least one example of each technique.

Dolly ▼

In the summer of 1996, a lamb named Dolly was born in Scotland. Dolly was an ordinary lamb in every way except one. The fertilized cell that developed into Dolly was produced in a laboratory by geneticists using experimental techniques. You will learn more about the techniques used by the geneticists later in the section.

Although the techniques used to create Dolly are new, the idea of producing organisms with specific traits is not. For thousands of years, people have tried to produce plants and animals with desirable traits. **Three methods that people have used to develop organisms with desirable traits are selective breeding, cloning, and genetic engineering.**

Selective Breeding

More than 5,000 years ago, people living in what is now central Mexico discovered that a type of wild grass could be used as food. They saved the seeds from those plants that produced the best food, and planted them to grow new plants. By repeating this process over many generations of plants, they developed an early variety of the food crop we now call corn. The process of selecting a few organisms with desired traits to serve as parents of the next generation is called **selective breeding.**

People have used selective breeding with many different plants and animals. Breeding programs usually focus on increasing the value of the plant or animal to people. For

Figure 12 For thousands of years, people have used selective breeding to produce plants and animals with desirable traits. *Making Generalizations What are some traits for which corn may be bred?*

example, dairy cows are bred to produce larger quantities of milk. Many varieties of fruits and vegetables are bred to resist diseases and insect pests.

Inbreeding One useful selective breeding technique is called inbreeding. **Inbreeding** involves crossing two individuals that have identical or similar sets of alleles. The organisms that result from inbreeding have alleles that are very similar to those of their parents. Mendel used inbreeding to produce purebred pea plants to use in his experiments.

One goal of inbreeding is to produce breeds of animals with specific traits. For example, by only crossing horses with exceptional speed, breeders can produce purebred horses that can run very fast. Purebred dogs, such as Labrador retrievers and German shepherds, were produced by inbreeding.

Unfortunately, because inbred organisms are genetically similar, inbreeding reduces an offspring's chances of inheriting new allele combinations. Inbreeding also increases the probability that organisms may inherit alleles that lead to genetic disorders. For example, inherited hip problems are common in many breeds of dogs.

Hybridization Another selective breeding technique is called hybridization. In **hybridization** (hy brid ih ZAY shun), breeders cross two genetically different individuals. The hybrid organism that results is bred to have the best traits from both parents. For example, a farmer might cross corn that produces many kernels with corn that is resistant to disease. The result might be a hybrid corn plant with both of the desired traits. Today, most crops grown on farms and in gardens were produced by hybridization.

Figure 13 Plants can be easily cloned by making a cutting. Once the cutting has grown roots, it can be planted and will grow into a new plant. *Applying Concepts Why is the new plant considered to be a clone of the original plant?*

Cloning

One problem with selective breeding is that the breeder cannot control whether the desired allele will be passed from the parent to its offspring. This is because the transmission of alleles is determined by probability, as you learned in Chapter 3. For some organisms, another technique, called cloning, can be used to produce offspring with desired traits. A **clone** is an organism that is genetically identical to the organism from which it was produced. This means that a clone has exactly the same genes as the organism from which it was produced. Cloning can be done in plants and animals, as well as other organisms.

Cloning Plants One way to produce a clone of a plant is through a cutting. A cutting is a small part of a plant, such as a leaf or a stem, that is cut from the plant. The cutting can grow into an entire new plant. The new plant is genetically identical to the plant from which the cutting was taken.

Cloning Animals Producing a clone of an animal is much more difficult than producing a clone of a plant. It isn't possible to use a cutting from a cow to produce a new cow. However, scientists have been experimenting with various techniques to produce clones of animals. Remember Dolly, the lamb described at the beginning of this section? Dolly was the first clone of an adult mammal ever produced.

To create Dolly, researchers first removed an egg cell from one sheep. The cell's nucleus was replaced with the nucleus from a cell of a six-year-old sheep. The egg was then implanted into the uterus of a third sheep. Five months later, Dolly was born. Dolly is genetically identical to the six-year-old sheep that supplied the cell nucleus. Dolly is a clone of that sheep.

Checkpoint **How can a clone of a plant be produced?**

Genetic Engineering

In the past few decades, geneticists have developed another powerful technique for producing organisms with desired traits. In this process, called **genetic engineering,** genes from one organism are transferred into the DNA of another organism. Genetic engineering is sometimes called "gene splicing" because a DNA molecule is cut open and a gene from another organism is spliced into it. Researchers use genetic engineering to produce medicines, to improve food crops, and to try to cure human genetic disorders.

EXPLORING Genetic Engineering

Scientists use genetic engineering to create bacterial cells that produce important human proteins, such as insulin.

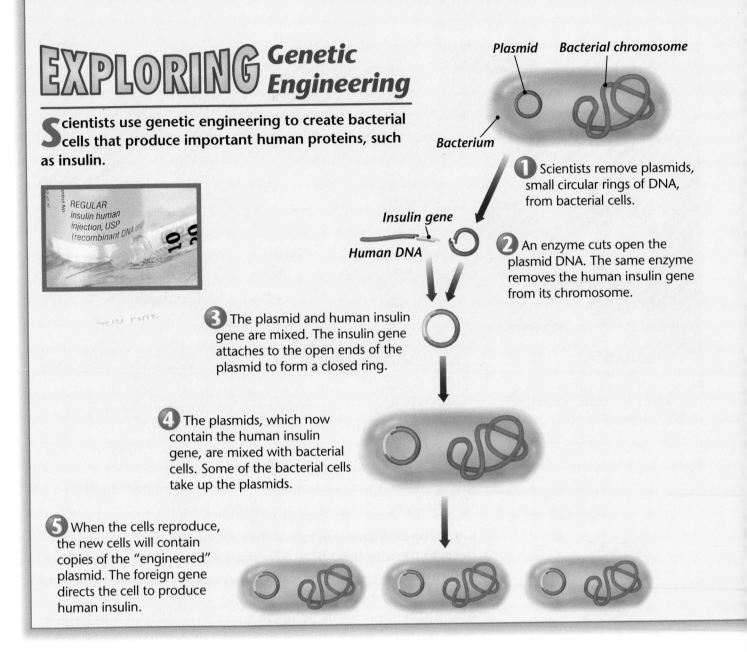

REGULAR
insulin human
injection, USP
(recombinant DNA o...)

Plasmid   **Bacterial chromosome**

Bacterium

1 Scientists remove plasmids, small circular rings of DNA, from bacterial cells.

Insulin gene

Human DNA

2 An enzyme cuts open the plasmid DNA. The same enzyme removes the human insulin gene from its chromosome.

3 The plasmid and human insulin gene are mixed. The insulin gene attaches to the open ends of the plasmid to form a closed ring.

4 The plasmids, which now contain the human insulin gene, are mixed with bacterial cells. Some of the bacterial cells take up the plasmids.

5 When the cells reproduce, the new cells will contain copies of the "engineered" plasmid. The foreign gene directs the cell to produce human insulin.

Genetic Engineering in Bacteria Researchers had their first successes with genetic engineering when they inserted DNA from other organisms into bacteria. Recall that the single DNA molecule of bacterial cells is found in the cytoplasm. Some bacterial cells also contain small circular pieces of DNA called plasmids.

In *Exploring Genetic Engineering,* you can see how scientists insert a human gene into the plasmid of a bacterium. Once the DNA is spliced into the plasmid, the bacterial cell and all its offspring will contain this human gene. As a result, the bacteria produce the protein that the human gene codes for, in this case insulin. Because bacteria reproduce quickly, large amounts of insulin can be produced in a short time. The insulin can be collected and used to treat people with diabetes, a disorder in which the body does not produce enough of this protein.

Figure 14 Scientists created this new variety of tomatoes using genetic engineering. The tomatoes taste better and keep longer than other varieties. *Making Judgments What other traits would be desirable in tomatoes?*

Today, many human proteins are produced in genetically engineered bacteria. For example, human growth hormone is a protein that controls the growth process in children. Children whose bodies do not produce enough human growth hormone can be given injections of the hormone. Today, an unlimited supply of the hormone exists, thanks to genetically engineered bacteria.

Genetic Engineering in Other Organisms Genetic engineering has also been used to insert genes into the cells of other organisms. Scientists have inserted genes from bacteria into the cells of tomatoes, wheat, rice, and other important crops. Some of the genes enable the plants to survive in colder temperatures or in poor soil conditions, and to resist insect pests.

Genetic engineering techniques can also be used to insert genes into animals, which then produce important medicines for humans. For example, scientists can insert human genes into the cells of cows. The cows then produce the human protein for which the gene codes. Scientists have used this technique to produce the blood clotting protein needed by people with hemophilia. The protein is produced in the cows' milk, and can easily be extracted and used to treat people with the disorder.

Gene Therapy Researchers are also using genetic engineering to try to correct some genetic disorders. This process, called **gene therapy,** involves inserting working copies of a gene directly into the cells of a person with a genetic disorder. For example, people with cystic fibrosis do not produce a protein that is needed for proper lung function. Both copies of the gene that codes for the protein are defective in these people.

Scientists can insert working copies of the gene into harmless viruses. The "engineered" viruses can then be sprayed into the lungs of patients with cystic fibrosis. Researchers hope that the working copies of the gene in the viruses will function in the patient to produce the protein. Gene therapy is still an experimental method for treating genetic disorders. Researchers are working hard to improve this promising technique.

DNA Fingerprinting

In courtrooms across the country, a genetic technique called DNA fingerprinting is being used to help solve crimes. If you did the Discover activity, you know that fingerprints can help to identify people. No two people have the same fingerprints. Detectives routinely use fingerprints found at a crime scene to help identify the person who committed the crime. In a similar way, DNA from samples of hair, skin, and blood can also be used to identify a person. No two people, except for identical twins, have the same DNA.

In DNA fingerprinting, enzymes are used to cut the DNA in the sample found at a crime scene into fragments. An electrical current then separates the fragments by size to form a pattern of bands, like the ones you see in Figure 15. Each person's pattern of DNA bands is unique. The DNA pattern can then be compared to the pattern produced by DNA taken from people suspected of committing the crime.

☑ *Checkpoint* *In what way is DNA like fingerprints?*

Figure 15 This scientist is explaining how DNA fingerprinting can be used to help solve crimes. DNA from blood or other substances collected at a crime scene can be compared to DNA from a suspect's blood.

Figure 16 The Human Genome Project is an attempt to identify the sequence of every DNA base pair in the human genome.

The Human Genome Project

Imagine trying to crack a code that is 3 billion characters long. Then imagine working with people all over the world to accomplish this task. That's exactly what scientists working on the Human Genome Project are doing. A **genome** is all the DNA in one cell of an organism. Researchers estimate that the 23 pairs of chromosomes that make up the human genome contain about 60,000 to 80,000 genes—or about 3 billion DNA base pairs.

The main goal of the Human Genome Project is to identify the DNA sequence of every gene in the human genome. When the Human Genome Project is completed, an encyclopedia of genetic information about humans will be available. Scientists will know the DNA sequence of every human gene, and thus the amino acid sequence of every protein.

With the information from the Human Genome Project, researchers may gain a better understanding of how humans develop from a fertilized egg to an adult. They may also learn what makes the body work, and what causes things to go wrong. New understandings may lead to new treatments and prevention strategies for many genetic disorders and for diseases such as cancer.

Section 3 Review

1. Name three techniques that people have used to produce organisms with desired traits.
2. Why do scientists want to identify the DNA sequence of every human gene?
3. What is genetic engineering? Describe three possible benefits of this technique.
4. Explain how a DNA fingerprint is produced. What information can a DNA fingerprint reveal?
5. **Thinking Critically Making Judgments** Do you think there should be any limitations on genetic engineering? Give reasons to support your position.

Science at Home

With a parent or other adult family member, go to a grocery store. Look at the different varieties of potatoes, apples, and other fruits and vegetables. Discuss how these varieties were created by selective breeding. Then chose one type of fruit or vegetable and make a list of different varieties. If possible, find out what traits each variety was bred for.

Who Should Have Access to Genetic Test Results?

Scientists working on the Human Genome Project have identified many alleles that put people at risk for certain diseases, such as breast cancer and Alzheimer's disease. Through techniques known as genetic testing, people can have their DNA analyzed to find out whether they have any of these alleles. If they do, they may be able to take steps to prevent the illness or to seek early treatment.

Some health insurance companies and employers want access to this type of genetic information. However, many people believe that genetic testing results should be kept private.

The Issues

Why Do Insurance Companies Want Genetic Information? Health insurance companies set their rates based on a person's risk of health problems. To determine a person's insurance rate, insurance companies often require that a person have a physical examination. If the examination reveals a condition such as high blood pressure, the company may charge that person more for an insurance policy. This is because he or she would be more likely to need expensive medical care.

Insurance companies view genetic testing as an additional way to gather information about a person's health status. Insurers argue that if they were unable to gather this information, they would need to raise rates for everyone. This would be unfair to people who are in good health.

Why Do Employers Want Genetic Information? Federal laws forbid employers with 15 or more workers from choosing job applicants based on their health status. These laws do not apply to smaller companies, however. Employers may not want to hire employees with health problems because they often miss more work time than other employees. In addition, employers who hire people with health problems may be charged higher health insurance rates. Many small companies cannot afford to pay these higher rates.

Should Genetic Information Be Kept Private? Some people think that the government should prohibit all access to genetic information. Today, some people fear that they will be discriminated against as a result of genetic test results. Because of this fear, some people avoid genetic testing—even though testing might allow them to seek early treatment for a disorder. These people want tighter control of genetic information. They want to be sure that insurers and employers will not have access to genetic test results.

You Decide

1. Identify the Problem

In your own words, explain the problem of deciding who should have access to genetic test results.

2. Analyze the Options

Examine the pros and cons of keeping genetic test results private. List reasons to maintain privacy. List reasons why test results should be shared.

3. Find a Solution

Create a list of rules to control access to genetic information. Who should have access, and under what circumstances? Explain your reasoning.

Guilty or Innocent?

In this lab, you will investigate how DNA fingerprinting can be used to provide evidence related to a crime.

Problem

How can DNA be used to identify individuals?

Skills Focus

observing, making models, drawing conclusions

Materials

4–6 bar codes

Procedure

1. Look at the photograph of DNA band patterns shown at right. Each person's DNA produces a unique pattern of these bands.
2. Now look at the Universal Product Code, also called a bar code, shown below the DNA bands. A bar code can be used as a model of a DNA band pattern. Compare the bar code with the DNA bands to see what they have in common. Record your observations.
3. Suppose that a burglary has taken place, and you're the detective leading the investigation. Your teacher will give you a bar code that represents DNA from blood found at the crime scene. You arrange to have DNA samples taken from several suspects. Write a sentence describing what you will look for as you try to match each suspect's DNA to the DNA sample from the crime scene.
4. You will now be given bar codes representing DNA samples taken from the suspects. Compare those bar codes with the bar code that represents DNA from the crime scene.

5. Use your comparisons to determine whether any of the suspects was present at the crime scene.

Analyze and Conclude

1. Based on your findings, were any of the suspects present at the crime scene? Support your conclusion with specific evidence.
2. Why do people's DNA patterns differ so greatly?
3. How would your conclusions be affected if you learned that the suspect whose DNA matched the evidence had an identical twin?
4. **Apply** In everyday life, do you think that DNA evidence is enough to determine that a suspect committed the crime? Explain.

More to Explore

Do you think the DNA fingerprints of a parent and a child would show any similarities? Draw what you think they would look like. Then explain your thinking.

SECTION 1 — Human Inheritance

Key Ideas

◆ Some human traits are controlled by a single gene that has multiple alleles—three or more forms.

◆ Some human traits show a wide range of phenotypes because these traits are controlled by many genes. The genes act together as a group to produce a single trait.

◆ Traits are often influenced by the organism's environment.

◆ Males have one X chromosome and one Y chromosome. Females have two X chromosomes. Males are more likely than females to have a sex-linked trait controlled by a recessive allele.

◆ Geneticists use pedigrees to trace the inheritance pattern of a particular trait through a number of generations of a family.

Key Terms

multiple alleles   carrier
sex-linked gene   pedigree

SECTION 2 — Human Genetic Disorders

Key Ideas

◆ Genetic disorders are abnormal conditions that are caused by mutations, or DNA changes, in genes or chromosomes.

◆ Common genetic disorders include cystic fibrosis, sickle-cell disease, hemophilia, and Down syndrome.

◆ Amniocentesis and karyotypes are tools used to diagnose genetic disorders.

◆ Genetic counselors help couples understand their chances of having a child with a genetic disorder.

Key Terms

genetic disorder   karyotype
amniocentesis

SECTION 3 — Advances in Genetics

INTEGRATING TECHNOLOGY

Key Ideas

◆ Selective breeding is the process of selecting a few organisms with desired traits to serve as parents of the next generation.

◆ Cloning is a technique used to produce genetically identical organisms.

◆ Genetic engineering can be used to produce medicines and to improve food crops. Researchers are also using genetic engineering to try to cure human genetic disorders.

◆ DNA fingerprinting can be used to help determine whether material found at a crime scene came from a particular suspect.

◆ The goal of the Human Genome Project is to identify the DNA sequence of every gene in the human genome.

Key Terms

selective breeding
inbreeding
hybridization
clone
genetic engineering
gene therapy
genome

USING THE INTERNET

www.science-explorer.phschool.com

ACTIVITY

CHAPTER 4 ASSESSMENT

California Test Prep: Reviewing Content

Multiple Choice

Choose the letter of the best answer.

1. A human trait that is controlled by multiple alleles is
   a. dimples.
   b. blood type.
   c. height.
   d. skin color.

2. A genetic disorder caused by a sex-linked gene is
   a. cystic fibrosis.
   b. sickle-cell disease.
   c. hemophilia.
   d. Down syndrome.

3. Sickle-cell disease is characterized by
   a. abnormally shaped red blood cells.
   b. abnormally thick body fluids.
   c. abnormal blood clotting.
   d. an extra copy of chromosome 21.

4. Inserting a human gene into a bacterial plasmid is an example of
   a. inbreeding.
   b. selective breeding.
   c. DNA fingerprinting.
   d. genetic engineering.

5. DNA fingerprinting is a way to
   a. clone organisms.
   b. breed organisms with desirable traits.
   c. identify people.
   d. map and sequence human genes.

True or False

If the statement is true, write true. If it is false, change the underlined word or words to make the statement true.

6. A <u>widow's peak</u> is a human trait that is controlled by a single gene.

7. A person who inherits two X chromosomes will be <u>male</u>.

8. A <u>karyotype</u> is a chart that shows the relationships between the generations of a family.

9. <u>Hybridization</u> is the crossing of two genetically similar organisms.

10. A <u>clone</u> is an organism that is genetically identical to another organism.

Checking Concepts

11. Explain how both genes and the environment determine how tall a person will be.

12. Explain why traits controlled by recessive alleles on the X chromosome are more common in males than in females.

13. What is sickle-cell disease? How is this disorder inherited?

14. How can amniocentesis be used to detect a disorder such as Down syndrome?

15. Explain how a horse breeder might use selective breeding to produce horses that have golden coats.

16. Describe how gene therapy might be used in the future to treat a person with hemophilia.

17. **Writing to Learn** As the webmaster for a national genetics foundation, you must create a Web site to inform the public about genetic disorders. Choose one human genetic disorder discussed in this chapter. Write a description of the disorder that you will use for the Web site.

Thinking Visually

18. **Concept Map** Copy the concept map about human traits onto a separate sheet of paper. Then complete it and add a title. (For more on concept maps, see the Skills Handbook.)

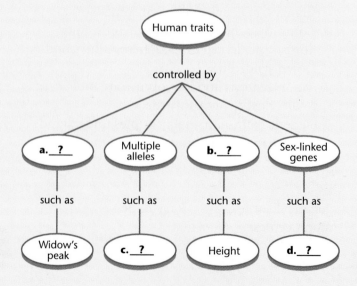

126

Test Prep: Skills

A genetic counselor has gathered the information listed below. Use the information to answer Questions 19–21.

- Bob and Helen have three children.
- Bob and Helen have one son who has albinism, an inherited condition in which the skin does not have brown pigments.
- Bob and Helen have two daughters who do not have albinism.
- Neither Bob nor Helen has albinism.
- Albinism is neither sex-linked nor codominant.

19. **Interpreting Data** Use the information to construct a pedigree. If you don't know whether someone is a carrier, leave their symbol empty. If you decide later that a person is a carrier, change your pedigree.

20. **Drawing Conclusions** Is albinism controlled by a dominant allele or by a recessive allele? Explain your answer.

21. **Predicting** Suppose Bob and Helen were to have another child. What is the probability that the child will have albinism? Explain.

Thinking Critically

22. **Inferring** How could ancient people selectively breed corn if they didn't know about genes and inheritance?

23. **Calculating** If a mother is a carrier of hemophilia, what is the probability that her son will have the trait? Explain your answer.

24. **Comparing and Contrasting** How are selective breeding and genetic engineering different? How are they similar?

25. **Applying Concepts** Why can a person be a carrier of a trait caused by a recessive allele but not of a trait caused by a dominant allele?

26. **Problem Solving** A woman with normal color vision has a colorblind daughter. What are the genotypes and phenotypes of both parents?

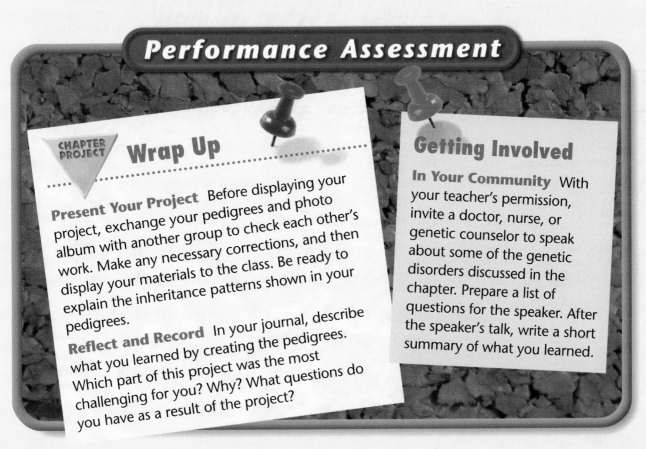

Performance Assessment

CHAPTER PROJECT Wrap Up

Present Your Project Before displaying your project, exchange your pedigrees and photo album with another group to check each other's work. Make any necessary corrections, and then display your materials to the class. Be ready to explain the inheritance patterns shown in your pedigrees.

Reflect and Record In your journal, describe what you learned by creating the pedigrees. Which part of this project was the most challenging for you? Why? What questions do you have as a result of the project?

Getting Involved

In Your Community With your teacher's permission, invite a doctor, nurse, or genetic counselor to speak about some of the genetic disorders discussed in the chapter. Prepare a list of questions for the speaker. After the speaker's talk, write a short summary of what you learned.

DOGS

LOYAL COMPANIONS

WHAT'S YOUR IMAGE OF A DOG?

+ A small, floppy-eared spaniel?

+ A large, powerful Great Dane?

+ A protective German shepherd guide dog?

+ A shaggy sheepdog?

+ A tiny, lively Chihuahua?

+ A friendly, lovable mutt?

The gray wolf is the ancestor of most modern breeds of dogs.

More than 3,000 years ago, an artist in ancient Egypt drew three dogs chasing a hyena. ▼

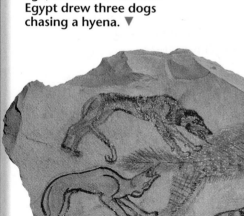

Most dogs are descendants of the gray wolf, which was originally found throughout Europe, Asia, and North America. Dogs were the first animals to be domesticated, or tamed. As far back as 9,000 years ago, farmers who raised sheep, cattle, and goats tamed dogs to herd and guard the livestock.

After taming dogs, people began to breed them for traits that people valued. Early herding dogs helped shepherds. Speedy hunting dogs learned to chase deer and other game. Strong, sturdy working dogs pulled sleds and even rescued people. Small, quick terriers hunted animals, such as rats. "Toy" dogs were companions to people of wealth and leisure. More recently, sporting dogs were trained to flush out and retrieve birds. Still others were bred to be guard dogs. But perhaps the real reason people bred dogs was for their loyalty and companionship.

From Wolf to Purebred

About ten thousand years ago, some wolves may have been attracted to human settlements. They may have found it easier to feed on food scraps than to hunt for themselves. Gradually the wolves came to depend on people for food. The wolves, in turn, kept the campsites clean and safe. They ate the garbage and barked to warn of approaching strangers. These wolves were the ancestors of the dogs you know today.

Over time dogs became more and more a part of human society. People began to breed dogs for the traits needed for tasks such as herding sheep and hunting. Large, aggressive dogs, for example, were bred to be herding dogs, while fast dogs with a keen sense of smell were bred to be hunting dogs. Today there are hundreds of breeds. They range from the tiny Chihuahua to the massive Saint Bernard, one of which can weigh as much as fifty Chihuahuas.

Today, people breed dogs mostly for their appearance and personality. Physical features such as long ears or a narrow snout are valued in particular breeds of dogs. To create "pure" breeds of dogs, breeders use a method known as inbreeding. Inbreeding involves mating dogs that are genetically very similar. Inbreeding is the surest way to produce dogs with a uniform physical appearance.

One undesirable result of inbreeding is an increase in genetic disorders. Experts estimate that 25 percent of all purebred dogs have a genetic disorder. Dalmatians, for example, often inherit deafness. German shepherds may develop severe hip problems. Mixed-breed dogs, in contrast, are less likely to inherit genetic disorders.

In Labrador retrievers, the allele for dark-colored fur is dominant over the allele for yellow fur.

Science Activity

Most traits that dogs are bred for are controlled by more than one gene. A few traits, however, show simpler inheritance patterns. For example, in Labrador retrievers, a single gene with one dominant and one recessive allele determines whether the dog's fur will be dark or yellow. The allele for dark fur (D) is dominant over the allele for yellow fur (d).

◆ Construct a Punnett square for a cross between 2 Labrador retrievers that are both heterozygous for dark fur (Dd).

◆ Suppose there were 8 puppies in the litter. Predict how many would have dark fur and how many would have yellow fur.

◆ Construct a second Punnett square for a cross between a Labrador retriever with yellow fur (dd) and one with dark fur (Dd). In a litter with 6 puppies, predict how many would have dark fur and how many would have yellow fur.

Golden Retriever
Great Britain, A.D. 1870s
Lord Tweedsmouth developed this breed to help hunters retrieve waterfowl and other small animals.

Border Collie
Great Britain, after A.D. 1100
This breed was developed in the counties near the border of England and Scotland for herding sheep. The Border collie's ancestors were cross-breeds of local sheepdogs and dogs brought to Scotland by the Vikings.

Dachshund
Germany, A.D. 1700s
These dogs were bred to catch badgers or rats. Their short legs and long body can fit into a badger's burrow. In fact, in German the word *Dachshund* means "badger dog."

Basset Hound
France, A.D. 1600s
Second only to the bloodhound at following a scent, the basset hound has short legs and a compact body that help it run through underbrush.

Greyhound
Egypt, 3500 B.C.
These speedy, slender hounds were bred for chasing prey. Today, greyhounds are famous as racers.

Dogs and People

Over thousands of years, people have developed many different breeds of dogs. Each of the dogs shown on the map was bred for a purpose—hunting, herding, guarding, pulling sleds—as well as companionship. Every breed has its own story.

Siberian Husky
Siberia, 1000 B.C.
The Chukchi people of northeastern Siberia used these strong working dogs to pull sleds long distances across the snow.

Pekingese
China, A.D. 700s
These lapdogs were bred as pets in ancient China. One Chinese name for a Pekingese means "lion dog," which refers to the dog's long, golden mane.

Chow Chow
China, 150 B.C.
Chow chows, the working dogs of ancient China, worked as hunters, herders, and guard dogs.

Akita
Japan, A.D. 1600s
This breed was developed in the cold mountains of northern Japan as a guard dog and hunting dog. The Akita is able to hunt in deep snow and is also a powerful swimmer.

Lhasa Apso
Tibet, A.D. 1100
This breed has a long, thick coat to protect it from the cold air of the high Tibetan plateau. In spite of its small size, the Lhasa apso guarded homes and temples.

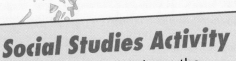

Social Studies Activity

Draw a time line that shows the approximate date of origin of different breeds of domestic dogs from 7000 B.C. to the present. Use the information on the map to fill out your time line. Include information about where each breed was developed.

Picking a Puppy

People look for different traits in the dogs they choose. Here is how one expert selected his dog based on good breeding and personality.

James Herriot, a veterinarian in England, had owned several dogs during his lifetime. But he had always wanted a Border terrier. These small, sturdy dogs are descendants of working terrier breeds that lived on the border of England and Scotland. For centuries they were used to hunt foxes, rats, and other small animals. In this story, Herriot and his wife Helen follow up on an advertisement for Border terrier puppies.

Language Arts Activity

James Herriot describes this scene using dialog and first-person narrative. The narrative describes Herriot's feelings about a memorable event—finally finding the dog he had wanted for so long. Write a first-person narrative describing a memorable event in your life. You might choose a childhood memory or a personal achievement at school. What emotions did you feel? How did you make your decision? If possible, use dialog in your writing.

Border terrier ▶

She [Helen, his wife] turned to me and spoke agitatedly, "I've got Mrs. Mason on the line now. There's only one pup left out of the litter and there are people coming from as far as eighty miles away to see it. We'll have to hurry. What a long time you've been out there!"

We bolted our lunch and Helen, Rosie, granddaughter Emma and I drove out to Bedale. Mrs. Mason led us into the kitchen and pointed to a tiny brindle creature twisting and writhing under the table.

"That's him," she said.

I reached down and lifted the puppy as he curled his little body round, apparently trying to touch his tail with his nose. But that tail wagged furiously and the pink tongue was busy at my hand. I knew he was ours before my quick examination for hernia and overshot jaw.

The deal was quickly struck and we went outside to inspect the puppy's relations. His mother and grandmother were out there. They lived in little barrels which served as kennels and both of them darted out and stood up at our legs, tails lashing, mouths panting in delight. I felt vastly reassured. With happy, healthy ancestors like those I knew we had every chance of a first rate dog.

As we drove home with the puppy in Emma's arms, the warm thought came to me. The wheel had indeed turned. After nearly fifty years I had my Border terrier.

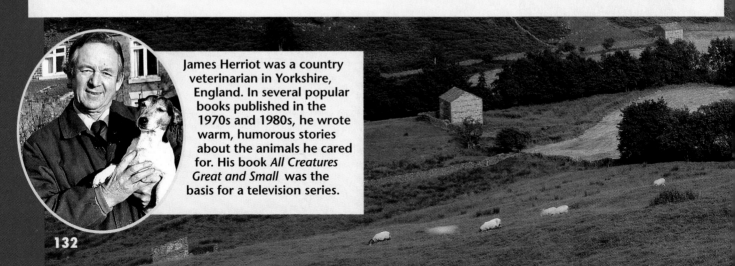

James Herriot was a country veterinarian in Yorkshire, England. In several popular books published in the 1970s and 1980s, he wrote warm, humorous stories about the animals he cared for. His book *All Creatures Great and Small* was the basis for a television series.

Breed	1970	1980	1990	1997
Poodle	265,879	92,250	71,757	54,773
Labrador Retriever	25,667	52,398	99,776	158,366
Cocker Spaniel	21,811	76,113	105,642	41,439

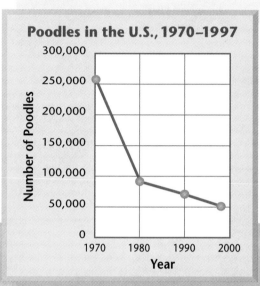

Poodles in the U.S., 1970–1997

Math Activity

The popularity of different breeds of dogs changes over time. For example, the line graph shows how the number of poodles registered with the American Kennel Club changed between 1970 and 1997. Use the table to create your own line graph for Labrador retrievers and cocker spaniels.

Which breed was more popular in 1980, Labrador retrievers or cocker spaniels? How has the number of Labrador retrievers changed from 1970 to 1997? How has the number of cocker spaniels changed over the same time?

Tie It Together

Best of Breed Show

In many places proud dog owners of all ages bring their animals to compete in dog shows. Organize your own dog show. With a partner, choose one specific breed of dog. Pick a breed shown on the map on pages 130–131, or use library resources to research another breed.

◆ Find out what the breed looks like, the time and place where it originated, and what traits it was first bred for.

◆ List your breed's characteristics, height, weight, and coloring.

◆ Research the breed's personality and behavior.

◆ Find out your breed's strengths. Learn what weakness may develop as a result of inbreeding.

◆ Make a poster for your breed. Include a drawing or photo and the information that you researched.

◆ With your class, organize the dog displays into categories of breeds, such as hunting dogs, herding dogs, and toy dogs.

CHAPTER 5 Evolution

Royal penguins on Macquarie Island climb a streambed to their nesting area high above the Pacific Ocean.

CALIFORNIA SCIENCE CONTENT STANDARDS

The following California Science Content Standards are addressed in this chapter:

3. Biological evolution accounts for the diversity of species developed through gradual processes over many generations.

  a. Both genetic variation and environmental factors are causes of evolution and diversity of organisms.

  b. The reasoning used by Darwin in making his conclusion that natural selection is the mechanism of evolution.

  c. How independent lines of evidence from geology, fossils, and comparative anatomy provide a basis for the theory of evolution.

  d. How to construct a simple branching diagram to classify living groups of organisms by shared derived characteristics, and expand the diagram to include fossil organisms.

  e. Extinction of a species occurs when the environment changes and the adaptive characteristics of a species are insufficient for its survival.

4. Evidence from rocks allows us to understand the evolution of life on Earth.

  a. Earth processes today are similar to those that occurred in the past and slow

PROJECT 5

Island Inhabitants

Royal penguins are found only on Macquarie Island, a small island between Australia and Antarctica in the Pacific Ocean. Many other islands also have unique species. Island species often differ from similar species on the mainland of nearby continents. These differences include size, body structure, behavior, and the foods the animals eat. In this chapter, you will learn how species evolve adaptations to different environments and why unusual species are found on islands.

In your chapter project, you will research a group of related species that live on an island, a group of islands, or in Australia.

Your Goal To make a documentary about a group of unusual island species and how they are adapted to their particular environment.

To complete the project you will
◆ describe the location and group of species you chose
◆ explain how each species is adapted to its environment
◆ construct a branching tree to show how the species in the group are related to each other

Get Started Preview Section 1 to learn how species evolve and why unusual species are often found on islands. Brainstorm with a group of other students which location you would like to learn about. Then pick a group of related species on that island to study further. Your teacher may suggest some islands and species to investigate. What research resources will your group need? Start planning how you want to present your documentary. You might consider overhead transparencies, posters, or a multimedia presentation.

Check Your Progress You will be working on this project as you study this chapter. To keep your project on track, look for Check Your Progress boxes at the following points.
Section 1 Review, page 146: Select the location and group of species you will study, and begin collecting information.
Section 3 Review, page 155: Organize your materials and prepare your documentary.

Wrap Up At the end of the chapter (page 159), practice your presentation and then present your documentary to your class.

---

geologic processes have large cumulative effects over long periods of time.

e. Fossils provide evidence of how life and environmental conditions have changed.

f. How movements of the Earth's continental and oceanic plates through time, with associated changes in climate and geographical connections, have affected the past and present distribution of organisms.

7. **Scientific progress is made by asking meaningful questions and conducting careful investigations.**

c. Communicate the logical connection among hypothesis, science concepts, tests conducted, data collected, and conclusions drawn from the scientific evidence.

d. Construct scale models, maps and appropriately labeled diagrams to communicate scientific knowledge.

e. Communicate the steps and results from an investigation in written reports and verbal presentations.

DISCOVER

How Do Living Things Vary?

1. Use a ruler to measure the length and width of 10 sunflower seeds. Record each measurement.

2. Now use a hand lens to carefully examine each seed. Record each seed's shape, color, and number of stripes.

Think It Over

Classifying In what ways are the seeds in your sample different from one another? In what ways are they similar? How could you group the seeds based on their similarities and differences?

GUIDE FOR READING

◆ How did Darwin explain the differences between species on the Galapagos Islands and on mainland South America?

◆ How does natural selection lead to evolution?

◆ How do new species form?

Reading Tip As you read, make a list of main ideas and supporting details about evolution.

In December 1831, the British naval ship HMS *Beagle* set sail from England on a five-year-long trip around the world. On board was a 22-year-old named Charles Darwin. Darwin eventually became the ship's naturalist—a person who studies the natural world. His job was to learn as much as he could about the living things he saw on the voyage.

During the voyage, Darwin observed plants and animals he had never seen before. He wondered why they were so different from those in England. Darwin's observations led him to develop one of the most important scientific theories of all time: the theory of evolution by natural selection.

◀ *Charles Darwin as a young man*

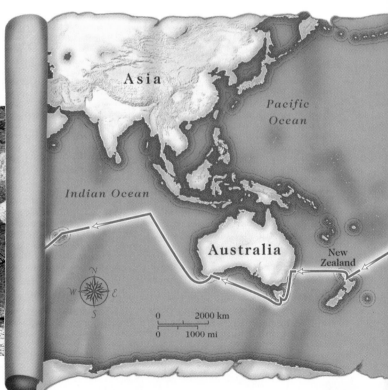

Darwin's Observations

One of the *Beagle's* first stops was the coast of South America. In Brazil, Darwin saw insects that looked like flowers, and ants that marched across the forest floor like huge armies. In Argentina, he saw armadillos—burrowing animals covered with small, bony plates. He also saw sloths, animals that moved very slowly and spent much of their time hanging upside down in trees.

Darwin was amazed by the tremendous diversity, or variety, of living things he saw. Today scientists know that living things are even more diverse than Darwin could ever have imagined. Scientists have identified more than 2.5 million species of organisms on Earth. A **species** is a group of similar organisms that can mate with each other and produce fertile offspring.

Darwin saw something else in Argentina that puzzled him: the bones of animals that had died long ago. From the bones, Darwin inferred that the animals had looked like the sloths he had seen. However, the bones were much larger than those of the living sloths. He wondered why only smaller sloths were alive today. What had happened to the giant creatures from the past?

In 1835, the *Beagle* reached the Galapagos Islands, a group of small islands in the Pacific Ocean off the west coast of South America. It was on the Galapagos Islands that Darwin observed some of the greatest diversity of life forms. The giant tortoises, or land turtles, he saw were so tall that they could look him in the eye. There were also seals covered with fur, and lizards that ate nothing but tough, prickly cactus plants.

Figure 1 Charles Darwin sailed on HMS *Beagle* from England to South America and then to the Galapagos Islands. He saw many unusual organisms on the Galapagos Islands, such as those shown below.

Galapagos hawk ▼

▲ *Giant tortoise*

▲ *Sally light-foot crab*

◄ *Blue-footed booby*

Similarities and Differences

Darwin was surprised that many of the plants and animals on the Galapagos Islands were similar to organisms on mainland South America. For example, many of the birds on the islands, including hawks, mockingbirds, and finches, resembled those on the mainland. Many of the plants were also similar to plants Darwin had collected on the mainland.

However, there were also important differences between the organisms on the islands and those on the mainland. Large sea birds called cormorants, for example, lived in both places. The cormorants on the mainland were able to fly, while those on the Galapagos Islands were unable to fly. The iguanas on the Galapagos Islands had large claws that allowed them to keep their grip on slippery rocks, where they fed on seaweed. The iguanas on the mainland had smaller claws. Smaller claws allowed the mainland iguanas to climb trees, where they ate leaves.

From his observations, Darwin inferred that a small number of different plant and animal species had come to the Galapagos Islands from the mainland. They might have been blown out to sea during a storm or set adrift on a fallen log. Once the plants and animals reached the islands, they reproduced. Eventually, their offspring became different from their mainland relatives.

Darwin also noticed many differences among similar organisms as he traveled from one Galapagos island to the next. For example, the tortoises on one island had dome-shaped shells. Those on another island had saddle-shaped shells. The governor of one of the islands told Darwin that he could tell which island a tortoise came from just by looking at its shell.

☑ *Checkpoint* *How did Darwin think plants and animals had originally come to the Galapagos Islands?*

Figure 2 Darwin observed many differences between organisms in South America and similar organisms on the Galapagos Islands. For example, green iguanas (left) live in South America. Marine iguanas (right) live on the Galapagos Islands. *Comparing and Contrasting How are the two species similar? How are they different?*

Figure 3 Darwin made these drawings of four species of Galapagos finches. The beak of each finch is adapted to the type of food it eats.

Adaptations

Like the tortoises, the finches on the Galapagos Islands were noticeably different from one island to another. The most obvious differences were the varied sizes and shapes of the birds' beaks. As Darwin studied the different finches, he noticed that each species was well suited to the life it led. Finches that ate insects had sharp, needlelike beaks. Finches that ate seeds had strong, wide beaks. Beak shape is an example of an **adaptation,** a trait that helps an organism survive and reproduce.

Evolution

After he returned home to England, Darwin continued to think about what he had seen during his voyage on the *Beagle.* Darwin spent the next 20 years consulting with many other scientists, gathering more information, and thinking through his ideas. He especially wanted to understand how the variety of organisms with different adaptations arose on the Galapagos Islands.

Darwin reasoned that plants or animals that arrived on one of the Galapagos Islands faced conditions that were different from those on the mainland. **Perhaps, Darwin thought, the species gradually changed over many generations and became better adapted to the new conditions.** The gradual change in a species over time is called **evolution.**

Darwin's ideas are often referred to as the theory of evolution. A **scientific theory** is a well-tested concept that explains a wide range of observations.

It was clear to Darwin that evolution had occurred on the Galapagos Islands. He did not know, however, how this process had occurred. Darwin had to draw on other examples of changes in living things to help him understand how evolution occurs.

Darwin knew that people used selective breeding to produce organisms with desired traits. For example, English farmers used selective breeding to produce sheep with fine wool. Darwin himself had bred pigeons with large, fan-shaped tails. By repeatedly allowing only those pigeons with many tail feathers to mate, Darwin produced pigeons with two or three times the usual number of tail feathers. Darwin thought that a process similar to selective breeding must happen in nature. But he wondered why certain traits were selected for, and how.

☑ *Checkpoint* *What observations led Darwin to propose his theory of evolution?*

Natural Selection

In 1858, Darwin and another British biologist, Alfred Russel Wallace, proposed an explanation for how evolution occurs. The next year, Darwin described this mechanism in a book entitled *The Origin of Species.* In his book, Darwin explained that evolution occurs by means of natural selection. **Natural selection** is the process by which individuals that are better adapted to their environment are more likely to survive and reproduce than other members of the same species. Darwin identified a number of factors that affect the process of natural selection: overproduction, competition, and variations.

Overproduction Most species produce far more offspring than can possibly survive. In many species, so many offspring are produced that there are not enough resources—food, water, and living space—for all of them. For example, each year a female sea turtle may lay more than 100 eggs. If all the young turtles survived, the sea would soon be full of turtles. Darwin knew that this doesn't happen. Why not?

Figure 4 Most newly hatched loggerhead sea turtles will not survive to adulthood.
Making Generalizations
What factors limit the number of young that survive?

Figure 5 The walruses lying on this rocky beach in Alaska must compete for resources. All organisms compete for limited resources such as food.

Competition Since food and other resources are limited, the offspring must compete with each other to survive. Competition does not usually involve direct physical fights between members of a species. Instead, competition is usually indirect. For example, some turtles may fail to find enough to eat. Others may not be able to escape from predators. Only a few turtles will survive long enough to reproduce.

Variations As you learned in your study of genetics, members of a species differ from one another in many of their traits. Any difference between individuals of the same species is called a **variation.** For example, some newly hatched turtles are able to swim faster than other turtles.

Selection Some variations make certain individuals better adapted to their environment. Those individuals are more likely to survive and reproduce. When those individuals reproduce, their offspring may inherit the allele for the helpful trait. The offspring, in turn, will be more likely to survive and reproduce, and thus pass on the allele to their offspring. After many generations, more members of the species will have the helpful trait. In effect, the environment has "selected" organisms with helpful traits to be the parents of the next generation—hence the term "natural selection." **Over a long period of time, natural selection can lead to evolution. Helpful variations gradually accumulate in a species, while unfavorable ones disappear.**

For example, suppose a new fast-swimming predator moves into the turtles' habitat. Turtles that are able to swim faster would be more likely to escape from the new predator. The faster turtles would thus be more likely to survive and reproduce. Over time, more and more turtles in the species would have the "fast-swimmer" trait.

Sharpen your Skills

Inferring   **ACTIVITY**

Scatter 15 black buttons and 15 white buttons on a sheet of white paper. Have a partner time you to see how many buttons you can pick up in 10 seconds. Pick up the buttons one at a time.

Did you collect more buttons of one color than the other? Why? How can a variation such as color affect the process of natural selection?

Nature at Work

In this lab, you will investigate how natural selection can lead to changes in a species over time. You'll explore how both genetic and environmental factors play a part in natural selection.

Problem

How do species change over time?

Materials

scissors
marking pen
construction paper, 2 colors

Procedure

1. Work on this lab with two other students. One student should choose construction paper of one color and make the team's 50 "mouse" cards, as described in Table 1. The second student should choose a different color construction paper and make the team's 25 "event" cards, as described in Table 2. The third student should copy the data table and record all the data.

Part 1 A White Sand Environment

2. Mix up the mouse cards.
3. Begin by using the cards to model what might happen to a group of mice in an environment of white sand dunes. Choose two mouse cards. Allele pairs *WW* and *Ww* produce a white mouse. Allele pair *ww* produces a brown mouse. Record the color of the mouse with a tally mark in the data table.

4. Choose an event card. An "S" card means the mouse survives. A "D" or a "P" card means the mouse dies. A "C" card means the mouse dies if its color contrasts with the white sand dunes. (Only brown mice will die when a "C" card is drawn.) Record each death with a tally mark in the data table.
5. If the mouse lives, put the two mouse cards in a "live mice" pile. If the mouse dies, put the cards in a "dead mice" pile. Put the event card at the bottom of its pack.
6. Repeat Steps 3 through 5 with the remaining mouse cards to study the first generation of mice. Record your results.
7. Leave the dead mice cards untouched. Mix up the cards from the live mice pile. Mix up the events cards.
8. Repeat Steps 3 through 7 for the second generation. Then repeat Steps 3 through 6 for the third generation.

Table 1: "Mouse" Cards

Number	Label	Meaning
25	*W*	Dominant allele for white fur
25	*w*	Recessive allele for brown fur

Table 2: "Event" Cards

Number	Label	Meaning
5	S	Mouse survives.
1	D	Disease kills mouse.
1	P	Predator kills mice of all colors.
18	C	Predator kills mice that contrast with the environment.

DATA TABLE

Type of Environment: _____

| Generation | White Mice | Brown Mice | Deaths | |
			White Mice	Brown Mice
1				
2				
3				

Part 2 A Forest Floor Environment

9. How would the data differ if the mice in this model lived on a dark brown forest floor? Record your prediction in your notebook.

10. Make a new copy of the data table. Then use the cards to test your prediction. Remember that a "C" card now means that any mouse with white fur will die.

Analyze and Conclude

1. In Part 1, how many white mice were there in each generation? How many brown mice? In each generation, which color mouse had the higher death rate? (*Hint:* To calculate the death rate for white mice, divide the number of white mice that died by the total number of white mice, then multiply by 100%.)

2. If the events in Part 1 occurred in nature, how would the group of mice change over time?

3. How did the results in Part 2 differ from those in Part 1?

4. What are some ways in which this investigation models natural selection? What are some ways in which natural selection differs from this model?

5. **Think About It** How would it affect your model if you increased the number of "C" cards? If you decreased the number?

Design an Experiment

Choose a different species with a trait that interests you. Make a set of cards similar to these cards to investigate how natural selection might bring about the evolution of that species.

The case of the English peppered moth is an example of how human actions can affect natural selection. In the late 1700s, most English peppered moths were light gray in color. The light-colored moths had an advantage over black peppered moths because birds could not see them against the light-gray trees. Natural selection favored the light-colored moths over the black moths.

The Industrial Revolution began in England in the late 1700s. People built factories to make cloth and other goods. Over time, smoke from the factories blackened the trunks of the trees. Now the light-colored moths were easier to see than the black ones. As a result, birds caught more light-colored moths. Natural selection favored the black moths. By about 1850, almost all the peppered moths were black.

In Your Journal

Since the 1950s, strict pollution laws have reduced the amount of smoke released into the air in England. Predict how this has affected the trees and the moths.

The Role of Genes in Evolution

Without variations, all the members of a species would have the same traits. Evolution by natural selection would not occur because all individuals would have an equal chance of surviving and reproducing. But where do variations come from? How are they passed on from parents to offspring? Darwin could not answer these questions.

Darwin did not know anything about genes or mutations. It is not surprising that he could not explain what caused variations or how they were passed on. As scientists later learned, variations can result from mutations in genes or from the shuffling of alleles during meiosis. Only genes are passed from parents to their offspring. Because of this, only traits that are inherited, or controlled by genes, can be acted upon by natural selection.

Evolution in Action

Since Darwin published his book, scientists have observed many examples of evolution in action. In a 1977 study of the finches on Daphne Major, one of the Galapagos Islands, scientists observed that beak size could change very quickly by natural selection. That year, little rain fell on the island—only 25 millimeters instead of the usual 130 millimeters or so. Because of the lack of rain, many plants died. Fewer of the seeds that the finches usually ate were available. Instead, the birds had to eat large seeds that were enclosed in tough, thorny seed pods.

Finches with larger and stronger beaks were better able to open the tough pods than were finches with smaller, weaker beaks. Many of the finches with smaller beaks did not survive the drought. The next year, more finches on the island had larger and stronger beaks. Evolution by natural selection had occurred in just one year.

Figure 6 The Industrial Revolution affected natural selection in peppered moths in England. As pollution blackened the tree trunks, black moths became more likely to survive and reproduce.

How Do New Species Form?

Darwin's theory of evolution by natural selection explains how variations can lead to changes in a species. But how does an entirely new species evolve? Since Darwin's time, scientists have come to understand that geographic isolation is one of the main ways that new species form. Isolation, or complete separation, occurs when some members of a species become cut off from the rest of the species.

Sometimes a group is separated from the rest of its species by a river, volcano, or mountain range. Even an ocean wave can separate a few individuals from the rest of their species by sweeping them out to sea and later washing them ashore on an island. This may have happened on the Galapagos Islands. Once a group becomes isolated, members of the isolated group can no longer mate with members of the rest of the species.

A new species can form when a group of individuals remains separated from the rest of its species long enough to evolve different traits. The longer the group remains isolated from the rest of the species, the more likely it is to evolve into a new species. For example, the Abert squirrel and the Kaibab squirrel live in forests in the Southwest. About 10,000 years ago both types of squirrels were members of the same species. About that time, however, a small group of squirrels became isolated in a forest on the north side of the Grand Canyon in Arizona. Over time, this group evolved into the Kaibab squirrel, which has a distinctive black belly. Scientists are not sure whether the Kaibab squirrel has become different enough from the Abert squirrel to be considered a separate species.

☑ *Checkpoint* How did geographic isolation affect the Kaibab squirrel?

Figure 7 About 10,000 years ago, a group of squirrels became isolated from the rest of the species. As a result, the Kaibab squirrel (left) has evolved to become different from the Abert squirrel (right). *Interpreting Maps* What geographic feature separates the range of the Kaibab squirrel from that of the Abert squirrel?

Continental Drift

Geographic isolation has also occurred on a world-wide scale. For example, hundreds of millions of years ago all of Earth's landmasses were connected as one landmass. It formed a supercontinent called Pangaea. Organisms could migrate from one part of the supercontinent to another. Over millions of years, Pangaea gradually split apart in a process called continental drift. As the continents separated, species became isolated from one another and began to evolve independently.

Perhaps the most striking example of how continental drift affected the evolution of species is on the continent of Australia. The organisms living in Australia have been isolated from all other organisms on Earth for millions of years. Because of this, unique organisms have evolved in Australia. For example, most mammals in Australia belong to the group known as marsupials. Unlike other mammals, a marsupial gives birth to very small young that continue to develop in a pouch on the mother's body. Figure 8 shows two of the many marsupial species that exist in Australia. In contrast, few species of marsupials exist on other continents.

Figure 8 As a result of continental drift, many species of marsupials evolved in Australia. Australian marsupials include the numbat (top) and the spotted cuscus (bottom).

Section 1 Review

1. What is evolution? What did Darwin observe on the Galapagos Islands that he thought was the result of evolution?
2. Explain why variations are needed for natural selection to occur.
3. Describe how geographic isolation can result in the formation of a new species.
4. **Thinking Critically Applying Concepts** Some insects look just like sticks. How could this be an advantage to the insects? How could this trait have evolved through natural selection?

Check Your Progress

CHAPTER PROJECT

Start by selecting the location and group of species you will study. For example, you could study the honeycreepers of Hawaii or the lemurs of Madagascar. Look for answers to the following questions: How did the group first get to the island? How did the different species within the group evolve? What is the island's environment like, and what part of the island environment does each species inhabit? What adaptations helped each species survive in its environment? Begin your research and take notes on the information you collect.

SECTION 2 The Fossil Record

What Can You Learn From Fossils?

1. Look at the fossil in the photograph. Describe the fossil's characteristics in as much detail as you can.

2. From your description in Step 1, try to figure out how the organism lived. How did it move? Where did it live?

Think It Over

Inferring What type of present-day organism do you think is related to the fossil? Why?

A burglary has been committed. You and another detective arrive at the crime scene to piece together what happened. You begin searching for clues. First you notice a broken first-floor window, then footprints in the mud. As you gather these and other clues, you slowly piece together a picture of what happened and who the burglar might be.

What Is a Fossil?

To understand events that occurred long ago, scientists act like detectives. Some of the most important clues to Earth's past are fossils. A **fossil** is the preserved remains or traces of an organism that lived in the past. A fossil can be formed from a bone, tooth, shell, or other part of an organism. Other fossils can be traces of the organism, such as footprints or worm burrows left in mud that later turned to stone. When plants form fossils, the leaves, stems, and seeds are most often preserved.

Very few fossils are of complete organisms. Often when an animal dies, the soft parts of its body decay or are eaten before a fossil can form. Usually only the hard parts of the animal, such as the bones or shells, remain to form a fossil.

The formation of any fossil is a rare event. The conditions must be just right for a fossil to form. **Most fossils form when organisms that die become buried in sediments.** Sediments are particles of soil and rock. Fossils form as layers of sediments build up and cover dead organisms then harden to become rock. You will learn more about how fossils form in the next chapter.

GUIDE FOR READING

◆ How do most fossils form?

◆ What does the fossil record reveal about extinction and evolution?

Reading Tip Before you read, preview *Exploring the Evolution of Elephants* on page 149. Make a list of questions you have about extinction and evolution.

A fossilized shark tooth ▼

What Do Fossils Reveal?

Like pieces in a jigsaw puzzle, fossils help scientists piece together Earth's past. The millions of fossils that scientists have collected are called the **fossil record.** But the fossil record is incomplete. The remains of most organisms never become fossils. As a result, there are gaps in the fossil record. Despite these gaps, the fossil record contains much information about past life on Earth.

Almost all of the species preserved as fossils are now extinct. A species is **extinct** if no members of that species are still alive. A species can become extinct when the environment changes and the adaptations of the species are not sufficient for its survival. **Most of what scientists know about extinct species is based on the fossil record.** Scientists use fossils of bones and teeth to build models of extinct animals. Fossil footprints provide clues about how fast an animal could move and how tall it was.

The fossil record also provides clues about how and when new groups of organisms evolved. The first animals appeared in the seas about 540 million years ago. These animals included worms, sponges, and other invertebrates—animals without backbones. About 500 million years ago, fishes evolved. These early fishes were the first vertebrates—animals with backbones. The first land plants, which were similar to mosses, evolved around 410 million years ago. Look at *Exploring the Evolution of Elephants* to see how evolution and extinction have changed one group of animals.

☑ *Checkpoint* *What is the fossil record?*

How Fast Does Evolution Occur?

Because the fossil record is incomplete, many questions remain about the evolution of species. For example, scientists cannot always tell from the fossil record how quickly a particular species evolved. Some scientists think evolution occurs very gradually, while others think it occurs in occasional rapid bursts. The two theories are known as gradualism and punctuated equilibria.

Gradualism The theory that evolution occurs slowly but steadily is called **gradualism.** According to this theory, tiny changes gradually add up to major changes over very long periods of time. This is how Darwin thought evolution occurred. Many biologists since his day have also assumed that evolution occurs this way.

If the theory of gradualism is correct, intermediate forms for all species should have existed. There should be fossils showing only minor differences as an organism slowly evolved from one time period to the next. Instead, scientists usually have found fossils showing no differences from one another for long periods of time.

Preservation in Ice

A fossil formed **ACTIVITY** by freezing can preserve the soft parts of an organism. Remains of the extinct woolly mammoth have been found preserved in ice in the Arctic regions of North America, Europe, and Asia.

1. Place fresh fruit, such as apple slices, strawberries, and blueberries, in an open plastic container.
2. Completely cover the fruit with water. Put the container in a freezer.
3. Place the same type and amount of fresh fruit in another open container. Leave it somewhere where no one will disturb it.
4. After three days, observe the fruit in both containers.

Inferring Use your observations to explain why fossils preserved in ice are more likely to include soft, fleshy body parts.

EXPLORING the Evolution of Elephants

Here are some members of the elephant family. Modern elephants, mammoths, and mastodons all evolved from a common ancestor that lived about 34 million years ago.

Asian Elephant present day
Asian elephants live in India and Southeast Asia. They can be trained to move objects with their trunks and to carry heavy loads on their backs.

African Elephant present day
About 4 meters high at the shoulder, the African elephant is larger than the Asian elephant. African elephants are fierce and difficult to tame.

Woolly Mammoth 2 million years ago
The woolly mammoth lived during the last Ice Age. Hunting by humans may have led to their extinction about 10,000 years ago.

Mastodon 25–30 million years ago
Mastodons developed long, flexible trunks and long tusks. Later mastodons looked similar to mammoths, but were smaller and stockier. Mastodons became extinct about 10,000 years ago.

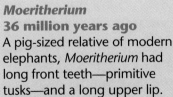

Gomphotherium 23 million years ago
Gomphotherium stood over 2 meters at the shoulder. It had a small trunk, two tusks on the upper jaw, and two tusks on the lower jaw.

Moeritherium 36 million years ago
A pig-sized relative of modern elephants, *Moeritherium* had long front teeth—primitive tusks—and a long upper lip.

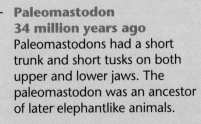

Paleomastodon 34 million years ago
Paleomastodons had a short trunk and short tusks on both upper and lower jaws. The paleomastodon was an ancestor of later elephantlike animals.

Figure 9 According to the theory of gradualism, new species of horses evolved slowly and continuously. Intermediate forms were common. According to punctuated equilibria, new species evolved rapidly during short periods of time. Intermediate forms were rare.

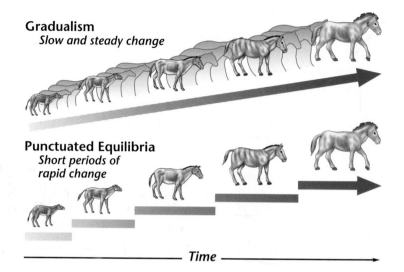

Gradualism
Slow and steady change

Punctuated Equilibria
Short periods of rapid change

Time

Then, suddenly, fossils appear that are distinctly different. One explanation for the lack of intermediate forms may be that the fossil record is incomplete. Scientists may eventually find more fossils to fill the gaps. Find the intermediate forms in the diagram of gradualism in Figure 9.

Punctuated Equilibria Rather than assuming the fossil record is incomplete, two scientists, Stephen Jay Gould and Niles Eldridge, have developed a theory that explains the lack of intermediate forms. According to their theory, called **punctuated equilibria,** evolution occurs during short periods of rapid change separated by long periods of little or no change.

According to this theory, most new species form when small populations become isolated. Small, isolated populations can evolve quickly and adapt to a different environment. They may even evolve into new species in just a few hundred years. With evolution occurring rapidly in small populations, there is not much chance of intermediate forms being preserved as fossils.

Today most scientists think that evolution can occur gradually at some times and fairly rapidly at others. Both forms of evolution seem to have occurred during Earth's history.

Section 2 Review

1. Describe the process by which most fossils form.
2. What is the fossil record? What does the fossil record reveal about extinct species?
3. **Thinking Critically** *Comparing and Contrasting* How are the theories of gradualism and punctuated equilibria similar? How are they different?

Science at Home

With an adult family member, spread some mud in a shallow, flat-bottomed pan. Smooth the surface of the mud. Use your fingertips to make "footprints" across the mud. Let the mud dry and harden, so that the footprints become permanent. Explain to your family how this is similar to the way some fossils form.

3 Other Evidence for Evolution

How Can You Classify Species?

1. Collect six to eight different pens. Each pen will represent a different species of similar organisms.

2. Choose a trait that varies among your pen species, such as size or ink color. Using this trait, try to divide the pen species into two groups.

3. Now choose another trait. Divide each group into two smaller groups.

Think It Over

Classifying Which of the pen species share the most characteristics? What might the similarities suggest about how the pen species evolved?

D o you know anyone who has had their appendix out? The appendix is a tiny organ attached to the large intestine. You might think that having a part of the body removed might cause a problem. After all, you need your heart, lungs, stomach and other body parts to live. However, this is not the case with the appendix. In humans, the appendix does not seem to have much function. In some other species of mammals, though, the appendix is much larger and plays an important role in digestion. To scientists, this is a clue that the ancestors of modern-day humans had a larger appendix that was important for digestion.

The appendix is just one example of how modern-day organisms can provide clues about evolution. By comparing organisms, scientists can infer how closely related the organisms are in an evolutionary sense. **Scientists compare body structures, development before birth, and DNA sequences to determine the evolutionary relationships among organisms.**

Similarities in Body Structure

Scientists long ago began to compare the body structures of living species to look for clues about evolution. In fact, this is how Darwin came to understand that evolution had occurred on the Galapagos Islands. An organism's body structure is its basic body plan, such as how its bones are arranged. Fishes, amphibians, reptiles, birds, and mammals, for example, all have a similar body

Drawing Conclusions

ACTIVITY

Look at the drawing below of the bones in a crocodile's leg. Compare this drawing to Figure 10. Do you think that crocodiles share a common ancestor with birds, dolphins, and dogs? Support your answer with evidence.

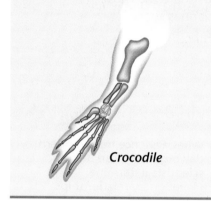

Crocodile

structure—an internal skeleton with a backbone. This is why scientists classify all five groups of animals together as vertebrates. Presumably, these groups all inherited these similarities in structure from an early vertebrate ancestor that they shared.

Look closely at the structure of the bones in the bird's wing, dolphin's flipper, and dog's leg shown in Figure 10. Notice that the bones in the forelimbs of these three animals are arranged in a similar way. These similarities provide evidence that these three organisms all evolved from a common ancestor. Similar structures that related species have inherited from a common ancestor are called **homologous structures** (hoh MAHL uh gus).

Sometimes scientists find fossil evidence that supports the evidence provided by homologous structures. For example, scientists have recently found fossils of ancient whale-like creatures. The fossils show that the ancestors of today's whales had legs and walked on land. This evidence supports other evidence that whales and humans share a common ancestor.

☑ *Checkpoint* *What information do homologous structures reveal?*

Similarities in Early Development

Scientists can also make inferences about evolutionary relationships by comparing the early development of different organisms. Suppose you were asked to compare an adult turtle, a chicken, and a rat. You would probably say they look quite different from each other. However, during early development, these three organisms go through similar stages, as you can see

Figure 10 A bird's wing, dolphin's flipper, and dog's leg are all adapted to performing different tasks. However, the structure of the bones in each forelimb is very similar. In the diagrams, color shows which bones are homologous. These homologous structures provide evidence that these animals evolved from a common ancestor.
Observing What similarities in structure do the three forelimbs share?

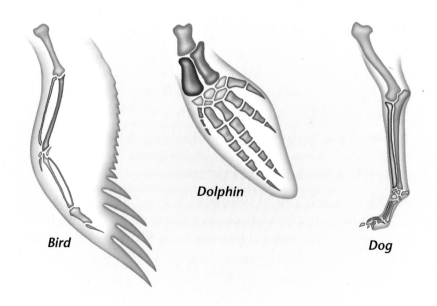

Bird

Dolphin

Dog

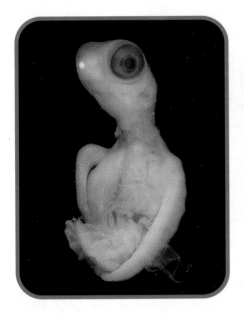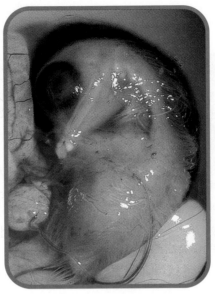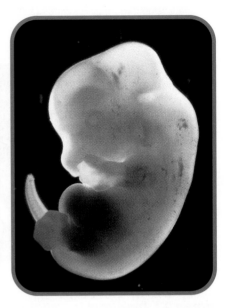

Figure 11 Turtles (left), chickens (center), and rats (right) look similar during the earliest stages of development. These similarities provide evidence that these three animals evolved from a common ancestor.

in Figure 11. For example, during the early stages of development all three organisms have a tail and tiny gill slits in their throats. These similarities suggest that these three vertebrate species are related and share a common ancestor.

When scientists study early development more closely, they notice that the turtle appears more similar to the chicken than it does to the rat. This evidence supports the conclusion that turtles are more closely related to chickens than they are to rats.

Similarities in DNA

Why do related species have similar body structures and development patterns? Scientists infer that the species inherited many of the same genes from a common ancestor. Recently, scientists have begun to compare the genes of different species to determine how closely related the species are.

Recall that genes are made of DNA. By comparing the sequence of nitrogen bases in the DNA of different species, scientists can infer how closely related the species are. The more similar the sequences, the more closely related the species are.

Recall also that the DNA bases along a gene specify what type of protein will be produced. Thus, scientists can compare the order of amino acids in a protein to see how closely related two species are.

Sometimes DNA evidence does not confirm earlier conclusions about relationships between species. For example, aside from its long nose, the tiny elephant shrew looks very similar to rodents such as mice. Because of this, biologists used to think that the elephant shrew was closely related to rodents. But when scientists compared DNA from elephant shrews to that of both

Figure 12 Because of its appearance, the tiny elephant shrew was thought to be closely related to mice and other rodents. Surprisingly, DNA comparisons showed that the elephant shrew is actually more closely related to elephants.

rodents and elephants, they got a surprise. The elephant shrew's DNA was more similar to the elephant's DNA than it was to the rodent's DNA. Scientists now think that elephant shrews are more closely related to elephants than to rodents.

INTEGRATING TECHNOLOGY Recently, scientists have developed techniques that allow them to extract, or remove, DNA from fossils. Using these techniques, scientists have now extracted DNA from fossils of bones, teeth, and plants, and from insects trapped in amber. The DNA from fossils has provided scientists with new evidence about evolution.

Combining the Evidence

Scientists have combined evidence from fossils, body structures, early development, and DNA and protein sequences to determine the evolutionary relationships among species. In most cases, DNA and protein sequences have confirmed conclusions based on earlier evidence. For example, recent DNA comparisons show that dogs are more similar to wolves than they are to coyotes. Scientists had already reached this conclusion based on similarities in the structure and development of these three species.

Another example of how scientists combined evidence from different sources is shown in the branching tree in Figure 13. A **branching tree** is a diagram that shows how scientists think different groups of organisms are related. Based on similar body structures, lesser pandas were thought to be closely related to giant pandas. The two panda species also resemble both bears and raccoons. Until recently, scientists were not sure how these four groups were related. DNA analysis and other methods have shown that giant pandas and lesser pandas are not closely related. Instead, giant pandas are more closely related to bears, while lesser pandas are more closely related to raccoons.

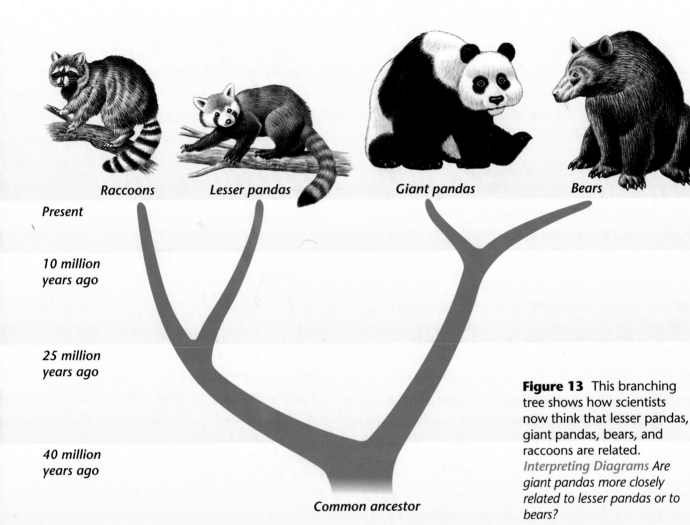

Raccoons   Lesser pandas   Giant pandas   Bears

Present

10 million
years ago

25 million
years ago

40 million
years ago

Common ancestor

Figure 13 This branching tree shows how scientists now think that lesser pandas, giant pandas, bears, and raccoons are related. *Interpreting Diagrams* Are giant pandas more closely related to lesser pandas or to bears?

Section 3 Review

1. Name three types of evidence from modern-day organisms that scientists use to determine evolutionary relationships.
2. What are homologous structures?
3. What information did scientists learn by comparing the early developmental stages of turtles, chickens, and rats?
4. If two species are closely related, what would you expect a comparison of their DNA base sequences to reveal?
5. **Thinking Critically Making Judgments** Most scientists today consider similarities in DNA to be the best indicator of how closely two species are related. Why do you think this is the case?

Check Your Progress

CHAPTER PROJECT

By now you should have collected information about your species and how each one is adapted to its environment. Construct a branching tree to show how the different species in the group are related to each other. Plan your documentary and decide what materials you will need. Make sure any overhead transparencies, posters, or a multimedia presentation will be easy for your audience to understand. Check the length of your presentation.

TELLTALE MOLECULES

In this lab, you will compare the structure of one protein in a variety of animals. You'll use the data to draw conclusions about how closely related those animals are.

Problem

What information can protein structure reveal about evolutionary relationships among organisms?

Procedure

1. Examine the table below. It shows the sequence of amino acids in one region of a protein, cytochrome c, for six different animals. Each letter represents a different amino acid.
2. Predict which of the five other animals is most closely related to the horse. Which animal do you think is most distantly related?
3. Compare the amino acid sequence of the horse to that of the donkey. How many amino acids differ between the two species? Record that number in your notebook.
4. Compare the amino acid sequences of each of the other animals to that of the horse. Record the number of differences in your notebook.

Analyze and Conclude

1. Which animal's amino acid sequence was most similar to that of the horse? What similarities and difference(s) did you observe?
2. How did the amino acid sequences of each of the other animals compare with that of the horse?
3. Based on this data, which species is the most closely related to the horse? Which is the most distantly related?
4. For the entire cytochrome c protein, the horse's amino acid sequence differs from the other animals as follows: donkey, 1 difference; rabbit, 6; snake, 22; turtle, 11; and whale, 5. How do the relationships indicated by the entire protein compare with those for the region you examined?
5. **Think About It** Explain why data about amino acid sequences can provide information about evolutionary relationships among organisms.

More to Explore

Use the amino acid data to construct a branching tree that includes horses, donkeys, and snakes. The tree should show one way that the three species could have evolved from a common ancestor.

Section of Cytochrome c Protein in Animals														
Amino Acid Position														
Animal	39	40	41	42	43	44	45	46	47	48	49	50	51	52	53
Horse	A	B	C	D	E	F	G	H	I	J	K	L	M	N	O
Donkey	A	B	C	D	E	F	G	H	Z	J	K	L	M	N	O
Rabbit	A	B	C	D	E	Y	G	H	Z	J	K	L	M	N	O
Snake	A	B	C	D	E	Y	G	H	Z	J	K	W	M	N	O
Turtle	A	B	C	D	E	V	G	H	Z	J	K	U	M	N	O
Whale	A	B	C	D	E	Y	G	H	Z	J	K	L	M	N	O

SECTION 1 — Darwin's Voyage

Key Ideas

◆ Darwin thought that species gradually changed over many generations as they became better adapted to new conditions. This process is called evolution.

◆ Darwin's observations led him to propose that evolution occurs through natural selection. Natural selection occurs due to overproduction, competition, and variations.

◆ As scientists after Darwin learned, only traits that are inherited, or controlled by genes, can change over time as a result of natural selection.

◆ If a group of individuals remains separated from the rest of its species long enough to evolve different traits, a new species can form.

Key Terms

species
adaptation
evolution

scientific theory
natural selection
variation

SECTION 2 — The Fossil Record

INTEGRATING EARTH SCIENCE

Key Ideas

◆ Most fossils form when organisms die and sediments bury them. The sediments harden, preserving parts of the organisms.

◆ Most of what scientists know about extinct species is based on the fossil record. The fossil record also provides clues about how and when new groups of organisms evolved.

◆ Scientists have developed two theories about the rate of evolution: the theory of gradualism and the theory of punctuated equilibria.

Key Terms

fossil
fossil record
extinct
gradualism
punctuated equilibria

SECTION 3 — Other Evidence for Evolution

Key Ideas

◆ By comparing modern-day organisms, scientists can infer how closely related they are in an evolutionary sense.

◆ Homologous structures can provide evidence of how species are related and of how they evolved from a common ancestor.

◆ Similarities in early developmental stages are evidence that species are related and shared a common ancestor.

◆ Scientists can compare DNA and protein sequences to determine more precisely how species are related.

◆ A branching tree is a diagram that shows how scientists think different groups of organisms are related.

Key Terms

homologous structure
branching tree

ACTIVITY

USING THE INTERNET

www.science-explorer.phschool.com

C H A P T E R 5 A S S E S S M E N T

California Test Prep: Reviewing Content

Multiple Choice

Choose the letter of the best answer.

1. Changes in a species over long periods of time are called
   a. multiple alleles.
   b. evolution.
   c. homologous structures.
   d. developmental stages.

2. A trait that helps an organism survive and reproduce is called a(n)
   a. variation.   b. adaptation.
   c. species.   d. selection.

3. After continental drift split apart Pangaea, new species evolved through
   a. meiosis.   b. selective breeding.
   c. mutation.   d. geographic isolation.

4. The preserved remains or traces of an organism that lived in the past are called
   a. species.   b. fossils.
   c. sediments.   d. homologous structures.

5. Which of these is *not* used as evidence for evolution?
   a. DNA sequences
   b. stages of development
   c. body size
   d. body structures

True or False

If the statement is true, write true. If it is false, change the underlined word or words to make the statement true.

6. Darwin's idea about how evolution occurs is called <u>extinction</u>.

7. Most members of a species show differences, or <u>variations</u>.

8. As a result of <u>adaptation</u>, there are too many offspring of a species in relation to the amount of resources for all of them.

9. Fossils most often form from the <u>soft</u> parts of an organism.

10. <u>Homologous structures</u> are similar structures in related organisms.

Checking Concepts

11. What role does the overproduction of offspring play in the process of natural selection?

12. Use an example to explain how natural selection can lead to evolution.

13. Briefly describe what scientists have learned from the fossil record about past life on Earth.

14. According to the theory of punctuated equilibria, why does the fossil record include very few intermediate forms?

15. Explain why similarities in the early development of different species suggest that the species are related.

16. **Writing to Learn** You are a young reporter for a local newspaper near the home of Charles Darwin. You have been asked to interview Darwin about his theory of evolution. Write three questions that you would ask Darwin. Then choose one question and answer it as Darwin would have.

Thinking Visually

17. **Flowchart** Copy the flowchart about natural selection onto a separate sheet of paper. Complete the flowchart by writing a sentence describing each factor that leads to natural selection. Then add a title. (For more on flowcharts, see the Skills Handbook.)

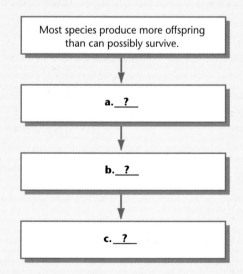

Most species produce more offspring than can possibly survive.

↓

a. ?

↓

b. ?

↓

c. ?

Test Prep: Skills

Biologists used fossil evidence and similarity of structure to construct the branching tree of plant evolution below. Use the information to answer Questions 18–20.

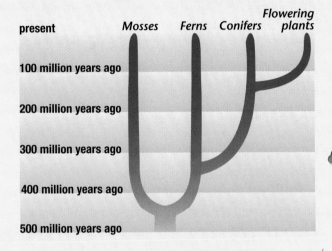

present
Mosses Ferns Conifers Flowering plants

100 million years ago

200 million years ago

300 million years ago

400 million years ago

500 million years ago

18. Interpreting Diagrams About how long ago did mosses evolve? About how long ago did flowering plants evolve?

19. Inferring According to the branching tree, which are more closely related to conifers: flowering plants or mosses?

20. Predicting Which group of plants would have DNA that was most similar to the DNA of flowering plants? Which group's DNA would be least similar?

Thinking Critically

21. Applying Concepts Why did Darwin's visit to the Galapagos have such an important influence on the development of the theory of evolution by natural selection?

22. Relating Cause and Effect What is the role of geographic isolation in the formation of new species?

23. Inferring The fossil record shows that an organism evolved through many small changes over time. Which theory best describes the organism's evolution: gradualism or punctuated equilibria? Explain.

24. Applying Concepts A seal's flipper and a human arm have very different functions. What evidence might help to show that both structures evolved from the forelimb of a common ancestor?

25. Predicting Predict how an extreme change in climate might affect natural selection in a species.

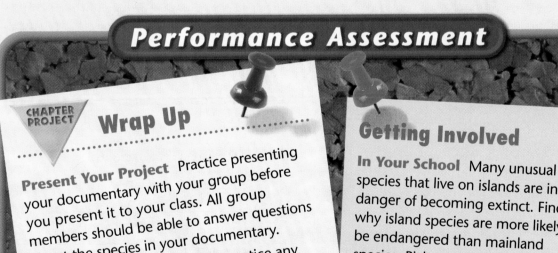

Performance Assessment

Wrap Up

CHAPTER PROJECT

Present Your Project Practice presenting your documentary with your group before you present it to your class. All group members should be able to answer questions about the species in your documentary.

Reflect and Record Did you notice any pattern in the adaptations you found in your group of species? How were the adaptations of the species the other groups studied similar to those of the species you studied? In your journal, make notes about how you could have improved your presentation.

Getting Involved

In Your School Many unusual species that live on islands are in danger of becoming extinct. Find out why island species are more likely to be endangered than mainland species. Pick an endangered island species and learn more about it. Make a poster describing the species you chose, why it is endangered, and what can be done to protect it. With your teacher's permission, display your poster in your school for other students to read.

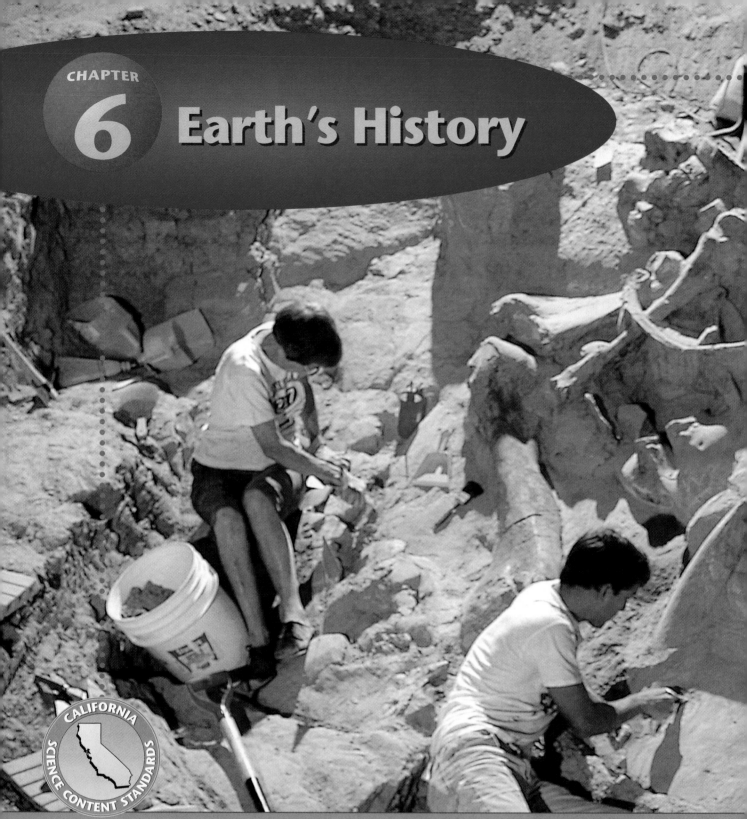

CALIFORNIA
SCIENCE CONTENT STANDARDS

The following California Science Content Standards are addressed in this chapter:

3. Biological evolution accounts for the diversity of species developed through gradual processes over many generations.

   e. Extinction of a species occurs when the environment changes and the adaptive characteristics of a species are insufficient for its survival.

4. Evidence from rocks allows us to understand the evolution of life on Earth.

a. Earth processes today are similar to those that occurred in the past and slow geologic processes have large cumulative effects over long periods of time.

b. The history of life on Earth has been disrupted by major catastrophic events, such as major volcanic eruptions or the impact of an asteroid.

c. The rock cycle includes the formation of new sediment and rocks. Rocks are often found in layers with the oldest generally on the bottom.

d. Evidence from geologic layers and radioactive dating indicate the Earth is approximately 4.6 billion years old, and that life has existed for more than 3 billion years.

A Journey Back in Time

With great care, scientists remove soil covering the bones of a mammoth. At this site, they have unearthed fossils of more than 30 other animals. These animals lived on the Great Plains during the last Ice Age. From such fossils, scientists can develop a picture of life in the distant past.

This chapter will take you back on a journey through geologic time. You will learn how fossils reveal the history of life on Earth. To guide you on your journey, you and your classmates will make a time line showing the many periods of geologic time.

Your Goal To become an expert on one geologic time period and assist in constructing a time line.

To complete this project, you must
◆ research a geologic time period of your choice
◆ create a travel brochure that shows what life was like in this time period
◆ illustrate your time period for the time line

Get Started Begin by previewing *Exploring Life's History* on pages 188–191. Select a time period you would like to investigate. Check with your teacher to be sure that all the time periods will be covered by members of your class.

Check Your Progress You will be working on this project as you study this chapter. To keep your project on track, look for Check Your Progress boxes at the following points.
Section 2 Review, page 173: Collect information on the animals, plants, and environment of your time period.
Section 4 Review, page 181: Write a travel brochure about the animals, plants, and environment of your selected time period.
Section 5 Review, page 196: Create illustrations that depict your time period and complete your travel brochure.

Wrap Up At the end of the chapter (page 199), place your illustrations on the time line. Use the travel brochure to present your geologic time period to your classmates.

At a site in South Dakota, scientists uncover mammoth bones that are 26,000 years old. Mammoths were relatives of modern elephants.

---

e. Fossils provide evidence of how life and environmental conditions have changed.

f. How movements of the Earth's continental and oceanic plates through time, with associated changes in climate and geographical connections, have affected the past and present distribution of organisms.

g. How to explain significant developments and extinctions of plant and animal life on the geologic time scale.

7. Scientific progress is made by asking meaningful questions and conducting careful investigations.

b. Utilize a variety of print and electronic resources (including the World Wide Web) to collect information as evidence as part of a research project.

c. Communicate the logical connection among hypothesis, science concepts, tests conducted, data collected, and conclusions drawn from the scientific evidence.

DISCOVER

What's in a Rock?

1. Use a hand lens to carefully observe the rock sample provided by your teacher.

2. Make a drawing of any shapes you see in the rock. Include as many details as you can. Beneath your drawing, write a short description of what you see.

Think It Over

Inferring What do you think the rock contains? How do you think the shapes you observed in the rock got there?

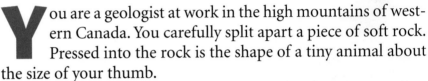

GUIDE FOR READING

◆ What is the rock cycle?

◆ What are the different kinds of fossils?

Reading Tip As you read, use the headings to make an outline showing what fossils are, how they form, and why they are important.

You are a geologist at work in the high mountains of western Canada. You carefully split apart a piece of soft rock. Pressed into the rock is the shape of a tiny animal about the size of your thumb.

The rock is from a layer of rocks called the Burgess shale. The creatures in the Burgess shale are tiny, soft-bodied animals without backbones. Some look like present-day crabs or worms. These animals lived on the bottom of a shallow sea more than 500 million years ago. Scientists hypothesize that a mudslide suddenly buried the animals. Over millions of years, as the mud slowly turned to shale, the remains of the animals also became solid rock.

Earth's Rocks and the Rock Cycle

The Burgess shale is one of many different types of rock that make up Earth's crust. **Rocks** are made of mixtures of minerals and other materials.

The three major groups of rocks are igneous, sedimentary, and metamorphic. **Igneous rock** forms when molten material cools and hardens below or on Earth's surface. **Sedimentary rock** forms when particles of other rocks or the remains of plants and animals are pressed and cemented together. Sedimentary rock forms in layers below the surface. **Metamorphic rock** is formed when an existing rock is changed by heat, pressure, or chemical reactions. Most metamorphic rock forms deep underground.

Forces inside Earth and at the surface produce a rock cycle that builds, destroys, and changes the rocks in the crust. The **rock cycle** is a series of processes on and beneath Earth's surface that slowly change rocks from one kind to another.

Figure 1 Paleontologists chip out the fossil-bearing rock of the Burgess shale.

Figure 2 shows that the rock cycle can follow many different pathways. Here is one possible pathway: the igneous rock granite formed beneath the surface millions of years ago. Then, the forces of mountain building slowly pushed the granite upward, forming a mountain. Slowly, water and weather wore away the granite through the process of erosion. These granite particles became sand, carried by streams to the ocean.

Over millions of years, layers of sandy sediment piled up on the ocean floor. Slowly, the sediments were pressed together and cemented to form sandstone, a sedimentary rock.

Over time, more and more sediment piled up on the sandstone. As the sandstone became deeply buried, pressure on the rock increased. The rock became hot. Heat and pressure changed the rock's texture from gritty to smooth. After millions of years, the sandstone changed into the metamorphic rock quartzite.

Metamorphic rock does not end the rock cycle. Sometimes, forces inside Earth push all three types of rock many kilometers beneath the surface. There the heat of Earth's interior melts the rock. This molten material can form new igneous rock.

☑ *Checkpoint* **What are the three types of rocks?**

Figure 2 Igneous, sedimentary, and metamorphic rocks change continuously through the rock cycle. *Interpreting Diagrams What steps in the rock cycle could change a sedimentary rock into an igneous rock?*

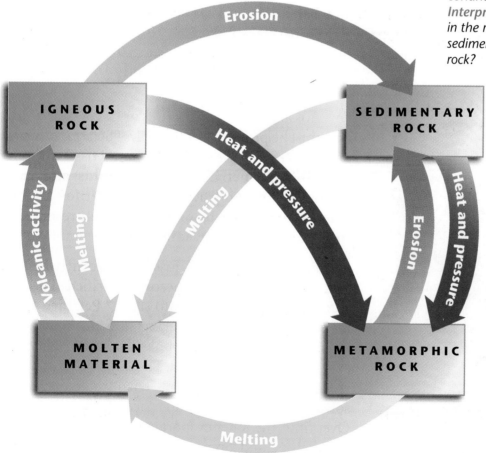

Figure 3 A fossil may form when sediment quickly covers an animal's body.
Predicting What would the fossil be like if part of the fish had been eaten by another animal in Step A?

A. An animal dies and sinks into shallow water.

B. Sediment covers the animal.

C. The sediment becomes rock, preserving parts of the animal.

D. Mountain building, weathering, and erosion eventually expose the fossil at the surface.

Evidence of Ancient Life

Fossils are usually found in sedimentary rock. Most fossils form from animals or plants that once lived in or near quiet water, such as swamps, lakes, or shallow seas, where sediments build up. In Figure 3 you can see how a fossil might form.

As you learned in the last chapter, fossils provide evidence of how life has changed over time. But fossils also help scientists infer how Earth's surface has changed. Fossils are clues to what past environments were like. Scientists who study fossils are called **paleontologists** (pay lee un TAHL uh jists).

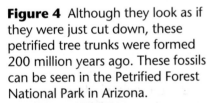

Figure 4 Although they look as if they were just cut down, these petrified tree trunks were formed 200 million years ago. These fossils can be seen in the Petrified Forest National Park in Arizona.

Kinds of Fossils

For a fossil to form, the remains or traces of an organism must be protected from decay. Then one of several processes may cause a fossil to form. **Fossils found in rock include petrified fossils, molds and casts, carbon films, and trace fossils. Other fossils form when the remains of organisms are preserved in substances such as tar, amber, or ice.**

Petrified Fossils A fossil may form when the remains of an organism become petrified. The term *petrified* means "turning into stone." **Petrified fossils** are fossils in which minerals replace all or part of an organism. The fossil tree trunks shown in Figure 4 are examples of petrified wood. These fossils formed after sediment covered the wood. Then water rich in dissolved minerals seeped into spaces in the plant's cells. Over time, the water evaporated, leaving the hardened minerals behind. Some of the original wood remains, but the minerals have hardened and preserved it.

Petrified fossils may also form by replacement. In replacement, the minerals in water make a copy of the organism. For example, water containing dissolved minerals may slowly dissolve a clamshell buried in sediment. At the same time, the minerals in the water harden to form rock. The result is a copy of the clamshell made of rock.

Molds and Casts The most common fossils are molds and casts. Both copy the shape of ancient organisms. A **mold** is a hollow area in sediment in the shape of an organism or part of an organism. A mold forms when the hard part of the organism, such as a shell, is buried in sediment.

Later, water carrying dissolved minerals and sediment may seep into the empty space of a mold. If the water deposits the minerals and sediment there, the result is a cast. A **cast** is a copy of the shape of an organism. Figure 5 shows a mold (top) that became filled with minerals to form a cast (bottom). As you can see, a cast is the opposite of its mold. Also notice how the mold and cast have preserved details of the animal's structure.

Sweet Fossils

1. Wrap a piece of clay around one sugar cube so that half of it is covered with clay.
2. Wrap clay entirely around a second sugar cube and seal it tightly.
3. Drop both cubes into a bowl of water, along with an uncovered sugar cube.
4. Stir until the uncovered sugar cube dissolves completely.
5. Remove the other cubes from the water and examine the remains.

Observing Describe the appearance of the two sugar cubes. Did the clay preserve the sugar cubes? How does this activity model the way fossils form?

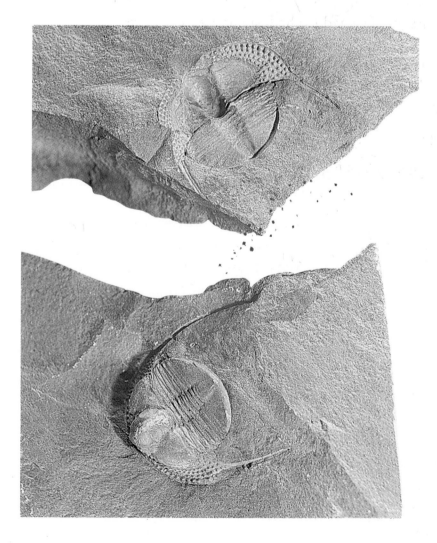

Figure 5 The fossil mold (top) clearly shows the shape of the animal called *Cryptolithus.* So does the fossil cast (bottom). *Cryptolithus* lived in the oceans about 450 million years ago.

Figure 6 This carbon film fossil of insects is between 5 million and 23 million years old.

Carbon Films Another type of fossil is a **carbon film,** an

extremely thin coating of carbon on rock. How does a carbon film form? Remember that all living things contain carbon. When sediment buries an organism, some of the materials that make up the organism can become gases. These gases escape from the sediment, leaving carbon behind. Eventually, only a thin film of carbon remains. This process can preserve the delicate parts of plant leaves and insects.

Trace Fossils Most types of fossils preserve the shapes of ancient animals and plants. In contrast, **trace fossils** provide evidence of the activities of ancient organisms. A fossilized footprint is one example of a trace fossil. A dinosaur made the fossil footprints shown in Figure 7. The mud or sand that the animal stepped into eventually was buried by layers of sediment. Slowly the sediment became solid rock, preserving the footprints for millions of years.

Fossil footprints provide clues about an animal's size and behavior. How fast could the animal move? Did it walk on two or four legs? Did it live by itself or with others of its kind? A paleontologist sometimes can infer the answers to such questions by looking at fossil footprints.

Other examples of trace fossils include the trails that animals followed or the burrows that they lived in. A trail or burrow can give clues about the size and shape of the organism, where it lived, and how it obtained food.

Figure 7 These dinosaur footprints are in the Painted Desert in Arizona.
Inferring What can you infer about this dinosaur from its footprints?

Figure 8 Complete skeletons of animals that lived thousands of years ago have been found in the Rancho La Brea tar pits. The photo shows a model of an elephant-like animal. Scientists created the model based on information learned from the fossils.

Preserved Remains Some processes preserve the remains of organisms with little or no change. For example, some remains are preserved when organisms become trapped in tar. Tar is sticky oil that seeps from Earth's surface. Many fossils preserved in tar have been found at the Rancho La Brea tar pits in Los Angeles, California. Thousands of years ago, animals came to drink the water that covered these pits. Somehow, they became stuck in the tar and then died. The tar soaked into their bones, preserving the bones from decay.

Ancient organisms also have been preserved in amber. Amber is the hardened resin, or sap, of evergreen trees. First, an insect is trapped on sticky resin. After the insect dies, more resin covers it, sealing it from air and protecting its body from decay.

Freezing is another way in which remains can be preserved. The frozen remains of woolly mammoths, relatives of elephants, have been found in very cold regions of Siberia and Alaska. Freezing has preserved even the mammoths' hair and skin.

☑ *Checkpoint* *What are three ways in which the remains of an organism can be preserved?*

Figure 9 A fossil preserved in amber provides a window into the history of past life on Earth. Body parts, including the hairlike bristles on an insect's legs, its antennae, and its delicate wings, are often perfectly preserved.

Figure 10 These are fossils of brachiopods and crinoids that lived more than 435 million years ago. Similar organisms still live in the oceans today. From these fossils, scientists know that the environment where they were found was once a shallow sea.

Fossils and Past Environments

Paleontologists use fossils to build up a picture of Earth's environments in the past. The fossils found in an area tell whether the area was a shallow bay, an ocean bottom, or a fresh-water swamp.

Fossils also provide evidence of Earth's climate in the past. For example, coal has been found in Antarctica. But coal only forms from the remains of plants that grow in warm, swampy regions. As you probably know, thick layers of ice and snow now cover Antarctica. The presence of coal shows that the climate of Antarctica was once much warmer than it is today.

Scientists can use fossils to learn about changes in Earth's surface. For example, corals are organisms that thrive in warm, shallow seas. Yet fossil corals are often found in many areas of the midwestern United States. From this fact, scientists infer that shallow seas once covered those areas.

Section 1 Review

1. What process gradually changes rock from one form to another?
2. What are the five types of fossils that can be found in rock?
3. Describe one way in which the remains of an organism can be preserved.
4. **Thinking Critically** **Inferring** Fossil seashells have been found in rock beds on land. What can you infer about how the area has changed?

Science at Home

A fossil is something old that has been preserved. Why is it that some old things are preserved, while others are destroyed? With your parents' permission, look around your house for the oldest object you can find. Interview family members to determine how old the object is, why it has been preserved, and how it may have changed since it was new. Make a drawing of the object and bring it to class. Tell your class the story of this "fossil."

Finding the Relative Age of Rocks

DISCOVER • ACTIVITY

In What Order Are Sediments Deposited?

1. Make a stack of different-colored layers of clay. Each layer should be about the size and thickness of a pancake. If these flat layers are sediments, which layer of sediment was deposited first? (*Hint:* This is the oldest layer.)

2. Now form the stack into a dome by pressing it over a small rounded object, such as a small bowl. With a cheese-slicer or plastic knife, carefully cut off the top of the dome. Look at the layers that you have exposed. Which layer is the oldest?

Think It Over

Inferring If you press the stack into a small bowl and trim away the clay that sticks above the edge, where will you find the oldest layer?

Have you ever seen rock layers exposed on a cliff beside a road? Often the rock layers differ in color or texture. What are these layers, and how did they form?

The sediment that forms sedimentary rocks is deposited in flat layers one on top of the other. Over years, the sediment becomes deeply buried. Then it hardens and changes into sedimentary rock. At the same time, remains of organisms in the sediment may become fossils. Over time, many layers of sediment become different layers of rock. These rock layers provide a record of Earth's geologic history.

Relative and Absolute Ages

When you look at a rock containing a fossil, your first question may be, "How old is it?" The **relative age** of a rock is its age compared to the ages of other rocks. You have probably used the idea of relative age when comparing your age with someone else's age. For example, if you say that you are older than your brother but younger than your sister, you are describing your relative age.

The relative age of a rock does not provide its absolute age. The **absolute age** of a rock is the number of years since the rock formed. It may be impossible to know a rock's absolute age exactly. But sometimes geologists can determine a rock's absolute age to within a certain number of years.

GUIDE FOR READING

◆ How do geologists determine the relative age of rocks?

◆ How are index fossils useful to geologists?

Reading Tip Before you read, rewrite the headings in the section as *how, why,* or *what* questions. As you read, look for answers to these questions.

Kaibab limestone
250 million years old

Toroweap limestone
255 million years old

Coconino sandstone
260 million years old

Hermit shale
265 million years old

Supai sandstone
285 million years old

Younger

Older

Figure 11 More than a dozen rock layers make up the walls of the Grand Canyon. You can see five layers clearly in the photograph. *Applying Concepts In which of the labeled layers in the diagram would you find the oldest fossils? Explain.*

Sampling a Sandwich

Your teacher will give you a sandwich that represents rock layers in Earth's crust.

1. Use a round, hollow, uncooked noodle as a coring tool. Push the noodle through the layers of the sandwich.

2. Pull the noodle out of the sandwich. Break the noodle gently to remove your core sample.

3. Draw a picture coloring and labeling what you see in each layer of the core.

Observing If this were a real sample of rock layers, which layer would be the oldest? The youngest? Why do you think scientists study core samples?

The Position of Rock Layers

It can be difficult to determine the absolute age of a rock. So geologists use a method to find a rock's relative age. Geologists use the **law of superposition** to determine the relative ages of sedimentary rock layers. **According to the law of superposition, in horizontal sedimentary rock layers the oldest layer is at the bottom. Each higher layer is younger than the layers below it.** If you did the Discover activity at the beginning of this section, you have already used the law of superposition.

The walls of the Grand Canyon in Arizona illustrate the law of superposition. The sedimentary rock layers in the canyon walls represent 2 billion years of Earth's history. You can see some of the rock layers found in the Grand Canyon in Figure 11. Scientists have given names to all the layers of rock exposed on the walls of the Grand Canyon. By using the law of superposition, you should be able to determine the relative ages of these layers.

If you were to start at the top of the Grand Canyon, you would see Kaibab limestone. Because it is on top, it is the youngest layer. As you began your descent into the canyon, you would pass by Toroweap limestone. Next, you would see Coconino sandstone. The deeper you traveled into the canyon, the older the rocks would become. Your trip into the canyon is like a trip into Earth's history. The deeper you go, the older the rocks.

✓ *Checkpoint How would a geologist find the relative age of a rock?*

Other Clues to Relative Age

There are other clues to the relative ages of rocks. Geologists find some of these clues by studying extrusions and intrusions of igneous rock and faults.

Clues From Igneous Rock Igneous rock forms when magma or lava hardens. Magma is molten material beneath Earth's surface. Magma that flows onto the surface is called lava.

Lava that hardens on the surface is called an **extrusion** (eks TROO zhun). The rock layers below an extrusion are always older than the extrusion.

Beneath the surface, magma may push into bodies of rock. There, the magma cools and hardens into a mass of igneous rock called an **intrusion** (in TROO zhun). An intrusion is always younger than the rock layers around and beneath it. Figure 12A shows an intrusion. Geologists study where intrusions and extrusions formed in relation to other rock layers. This helps geologists understand the relative ages of the different types of rock.

Clues From Faults More clues come from the study of faults. A **fault** is a break in Earth's crust. Forces inside Earth cause movement of the rock on opposite sides of a fault.

A fault is always younger than the rock it cuts through. To determine the relative age of a fault, geologists find the the relative age of the most recent rock layer through which the fault slices.

Movements along faults can make it harder for geologists to determine the relative ages of rock layers. In Figure 12B you can see how the rock layers no longer line up because of movement along the fault.

Music
CONNECTION

The Grand Canyon provides one of Earth's best views of the geologic record. The American composer Ferde Grofé composed his *Grand Canyon Suite* for orchestra in 1931. The music paints a picture of desert scenery and a trip on muleback into the Grand Canyon.

In Your Journal

Listen to a recording of the *Grand Canyon Suite*. How does Grofé's music express what it's like to visit the Grand Canyon? What words would you use to describe what you heard?

Figure 12 Intrusions and faults give clues to the relative ages of rocks. **A.** An intrusion cuts through rock layers. **B.** Rock layers are broken and shifted along a fault. *Inferring Which is older, the intrusion in A or the rock layers it crosses?*

1. Sedimentary rocks form in horizontal layers.

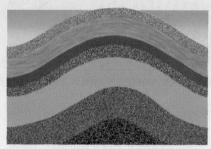

2. Folding tilts the rock layers.

Figure 13 An unconformity occurs where erosion wears away layers of sedimentary rock. Other rock layers then form on top of the eroded surface.

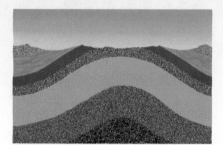

3. The surface is eroded.

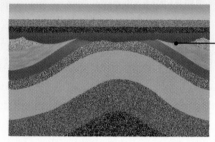

— *Unconformity*

4. New sediment is deposited, forming rock layers above the unconformity.

Gaps in the Geologic Record

The geologic record of sedimentary rock layers is not always complete. Deposition, the process by which sediments are laid down, slowly builds layers of sedimentary rock. But some of these layers may erode away, exposing an older rock surface. Then deposition begins again, building new rock layers.

The surface where new rock layers meet a much older rock surface beneath them is called an unconformity. An **unconformity** is a gap in the geologic record. An unconformity shows where some rock layers have been lost because of erosion. Figure 13 shows how an unconformity forms.

Using Fossils to Date Rocks

To date rock layers, geologists first give a relative age to a layer of rock at one location. Then they can give the same age to matching layers of rock at other locations.

Certain fossils, called index fossils, help geologists match rock layers. To be useful as an **index fossil,** a fossil must be widely distributed and represent a type of organism that existed only briefly. A fossil is considered widely distributed if it occurs in many different areas. Geologists look for index fossils in layers of rock. **Index fossils are useful because they tell the relative ages of the rock layers in which they occur.**

Geologists use particular types of organisms as index fossils—for example, certain types of trilobites. Trilobites (TRY luh byts) were a group of hard-shelled animals whose bodies had three

Figure 14 Trilobite fossils are widely distributed. Some types of trilobites serve as index fossils.

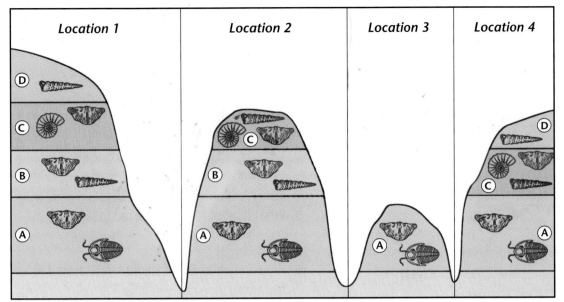

| Location 1 | Location 2 | Location 3 | Location 4 |

Figure 15 Scientists use index fossils to match up rock layers at locations that may be far apart. The trilobites in Layer A are index fossils. *Interpreting Diagrams Can you find another index fossil in the diagram?* (*Hint:* Look for a fossil that occurs in only one time period, but in several different locations.)

distinct parts. Trilobites evolved in shallow seas more than 500 million years ago. Over time, many different types of trilobites appeared. They became extinct about 245 million years ago. Trilobite fossils have been found in many different places.

To serve as an index fossil, a type of trilobite must be different in some way from other trilobites. One example is a type of trilobite with large eyes. These large-eyed trilobites survived for a time after other trilobites became extinct. Suppose a geologist finds large-eyed trilobites in a rock layer. The geologist can infer that those rocks are younger than rocks containing other types of trilobites.

You can use index fossils to match rock layers. Look at Figure 15, which shows rock layers from four different locations. Notice that two of the fossils are found in only one of these rock layers. These are the index fossils.

 Section 2 Review

1. What is the law of superposition?
2. What characteristics are necessary for a fossil to be considered an index fossil?
3. What do unconformities show?
4. **Thinking Critically Applying Concepts** Horseshoe crabs are common in the ocean along the east coast of North America. They have existed with very little change for about 200 million years. Would horseshoe crabs be useful as an index fossil? Explain why or why not.

Check Your Progress
Locate reference materials you will need to research your chosen geologic time period. Possible sources include library books, magazines, encyclopedias, and Internet articles. Also keep a list of the resources you used. As you do your research, keep in mind the pictures and facts you will need for the class time line and travel brochure. Be sure to include the organisms and environment of the time period.

CHAPTER PROJECT

You Be the Detective

Finding Clues to ROCK-LAYERS

Fossil clues give geologists a good idea of what life on Earth was like millions or even billions of years ago.

Problem

How can you use fossils and geologic features to interpret the relative ages of rock layers?

Skills Focus

interpreting data, drawing conclusions

Procedure

1. Study the rock layers at Sites 1 and 2. Write down the similarities and differences between the layers at the two sites.
2. List the kinds of fossils that are found in each rock layer of Sites 1 and 2.

Analyze and Conclude

Site 1

1. What "fossil clues" in layers A and B indicate the kind of environment that existed when these rock layers were formed? How did the environment change in layer D?
2. Which layer is the oldest? How do you know?

3. Which of the layers formed most recently? How do you know?
4. Why are there no fossils in layers C and E?
5. What kind of fossils occurred in layer F?

Site 2

6. Which layer at Site 1 might have formed at the same time as layer W at Site 2?
7. What clues show an unconformity or gap in the horizontal rock layers? Which rock layers are missing? What might have happened to these rock layers?
8. Which is older, intrusion V or layer Y? How do you know?
9. **Think About It** Working as a geologist, you find a rock containing fossils. What information would you need in order to determine this rock's age relative to one of the rock layers at Site 1?

More to Explore

Draw a sketch similar to Site 2 and include a fault that cuts across the intrusion. Have a partner then identify the relative age of the fault, the intrusion, and the layers cut by the fault.

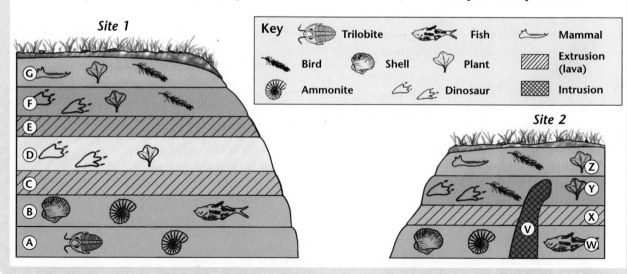

Key					
Trilobite		Fish		Mammal	
Bird		Shell		Plant	Extrusion (lava)
Ammonite		Dinosaur		Intrusion	

Site 1

Site 2

SECTION 3 Radioactive Dating

In Australia, scientists have found sedimentary rocks that contain some of the world's oldest fossils—stromatolites (stroh MAT uh lyts). Stromatolites are the remains of reefs built by organisms similar to present-day bacteria. The bacteria grew together in dense mats shaped like stacks of pancakes. The mats formed reefs in shallow water near the shores of ancient oceans. Sediment eventually covered these reefs. As the sediments changed to rock, so did the reefs.

Paleontologists have determined that some stromatolites are more than 3 billion years old. But how did scientists determine the age of these fossils? To understand the methods of absolute dating, you need to learn more about the chemistry of rocks.

Changing From One Element to Another

What do you, the air you breathe, a lemon, and a puddle of water have in common? All are kinds of matter. In fact, everything around you is made of matter. Although different kinds of matter look, feel, or smell different, all the matter you see is made of tiny particles called **atoms.** When all the atoms in a particular type of matter are the same, the matter is an **element.** Carbon, oxygen, iron, lead, and potassium are just a few of the 109 currently known elements.

Figure 16 Stromatolites were formed by clumps of one-celled organisms that lived in shallow seas more than 3 billion years ago. Similar organisms grow in the ocean near Australia today.

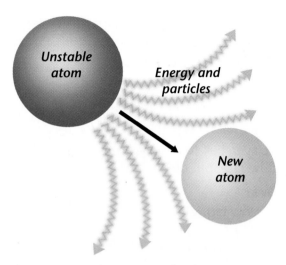

Figure 17 In the process of radioactive decay, an atom releases energy.

Most elements are stable. They do not change under normal conditions. But some elements exist in forms that are unstable. Over time, these elements break down, or decay, by releasing particles and energy in a process called **radioactive decay.** These unstable elements are said to be radioactive. **During radioactive decay, the atoms of an unstable element break down to form atoms of another element.** Radioactive elements occur naturally in igneous rocks. Scientists use the rate at which these elements decay to calculate the rock's age.

The Rate of Radioactive Decay

You have a birthday, a specific day from which you calculate your age. What's the "birthday" of a rock? For an igneous rock, that "birthday" is when it first hardens to become rock. (Recall that igneous rocks form from molten magma and lava.) As a radioactive element within the igneous rock decays, it changes into another element. So the composition of the rock changes slowly over time. The amount of the radioactive element goes down. But the amount of the new element goes up.

The rate of decay of each radioactive element is constant—it never changes. This rate of decay is the element's half-life. The **half-life** of a radioactive element is the time it takes for half of the radioactive atoms to decay. Figure 18 lists several common radioactive elements and their half-lives.

Absolute Ages From Radioactive Dating

Geologists use radioactive dating to determine the absolute ages of rocks. In radioactive dating, scientists first measure the amount of a radioactive element (the "parent" isotope) in a mineral in a rock. Then they measure the amount of the stable

Figure 18 The half-lives of different radioactive elements vary greatly. This scientist is testing a sample of material to determine how much carbon-14 it contains.

Elements Used in Radioactive Dating		
Radioactive Element	**Half-life (years)**	**Dating Range (years)**
Carbon-14	5,730	500–50,000
Potassium-40	1.3 billion	50,000–4.6 billion
Rubidium-87	47 billion	10 million–4.6 billion
Thorium-232	14.1 billion	10 million–4.6 billion
Uranium-235	713 million	10 million–4.6 billion
Uranium-238	4.5 billion	10 million–4.6 billion

Decay of Potassium-40 (Half-life = 1.3 billion years)			
Time	Amount of Potassium-40 ("Parent" Isotope)	Amount of Argon-40 ("Daughter" Isotope)	Ratio of "Parent" Isotope to "Daughter" Isotope
2.6 billion years ago	4 g	0 g	All potassium-40
1.3 billion years ago	2 g	2 g	2 : 2
Present	1 g	3 g	1 : 3

element into which the radioactive element decays (the "daughter" isotope). By calculating the ratio of the radioactive element to the stable element, scientists can determine the age of the rock.

Potassium–Argon Dating Scientists often date rocks using potassium-40. This form of potassium decays to stable argon-40 and has a half-life of 1.3 billion years. Figure 19 shows how a sample of potassium-40 breaks down into argon-40 over time. Potassium-40 is useful in dating the most ancient rocks because of its long half-life.

Carbon-14 Dating A radioactive form of carbon is carbon-14. All plants and animals contain carbon, including some carbon-14. As plants and animals grow, carbon atoms are added to their tissues. After an organism dies, no more carbon is added. But the carbon-14 in the organism's body decays. It changes to stable nitrogen-14. To determine the age of a sample, scientists measure the amount of carbon-14 that is left in the organism's remains. From this amount, they can determine its absolute age. Carbon-14 has been used to date fossils such as frozen mammoths, as well as pieces of wood and bone. Carbon-14 even has been used to date the skeletons of prehistoric humans.

Carbon-14 is very useful in dating materials from plants and animals that lived up to about 50,000 years ago. Carbon-14 has a half-life of only 5,730 years. For this reason, it can't be used to date really ancient fossils or rocks. The amount of carbon-14 left would be too small to measure accurately.

☑ *Checkpoint* **What are two types of radioactive dating?**

Figure 19 The half-life of potassium-40, a radioactive element, is 1.3 billion years. This means that half of the potassium-40 in a sample will break down into argon-40 every 1.3 billion years. *Interpreting Charts If a sample contains one fourth of the original amount of potassium-40, how old is the sample?*

Sharpen your Skills

Calculating **ACTIVITY**

A radioactive element has a half-life of 713 million years. After 2,139 million years, how many half-lives will have gone by?

Calculate how much of a 16-gram sample of the element will remain after 2,139 million years.

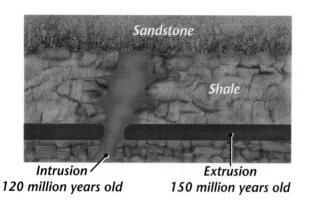

Sandstone

Shale

Intrusion
120 million years old

Extrusion
150 million years old

Figure 20 Radioactive dating has been used to determine the absolute ages of the intrusion and extrusion in the diagram. The shale lies above the extrusion and is crossed by the intrusion. Therefore the shale is younger than the extrusion, but older than the intrusion—between 150 million years old and 120 million years old. *Inferring What can you infer about the age of the sandstone?*

Radioactive Dating of Rock Layers

Radioactive dating cannot usually be used for dating rocks other than igneous rocks. As you recall, sedimentary rocks form as sediments are deposited by water or wind. The rock particles in sedimentary rocks are from other rocks, all of different ages. Radioactive dating would provide the age of the particles. It would not provide the age of the sedimentary rock.

How, then, do scientists date sedimentary rock layers? They date the igneous intrusions and extrusions near the sedimentary rock layers. Look at Figure 20. As you can see, sedimentary rock above an igneous intrusion must be younger than that intrusion.

How Old is Earth?

Radioactive dating has been used to calculate the age of Earth. The oldest rocks ever found on Earth have been dated at about 4.0 billion years old. But scientists think Earth formed even earlier than that. According to one theory, Earth and the moon are about the same age. When Earth was very young, a large object from space collided with Earth. This collision threw a large amount of material from both bodies into orbit around Earth. This material combined to form the moon. Scientists have dated moon rocks brought to Earth by astronauts during the 1970s. **Radioactive dating shows that the oldest moon rocks are about 4.6 billion years old. Scientists infer that Earth is only a little older than those moon rocks—roughly 4.6 billion years old.**

 Section 3 Review

1. Describe the process of radioactive decay.
2. What is a half-life? How is it used to determine the absolute age of a rock?
3. When do scientists use both radioactive dating and relative dating to find the age of a rock?
4. How were moon rocks used to determine the age of Earth?
5. **Thinking Critically Applying Concepts** Which of the following types of fossils can be dated using carbon-14: molds and casts, trace fossils, frozen remains, remains preserved in tar? Explain your answer.

Science at Home

Collect 10 items out of a drawer that is full of odds and ends such as keys, coins, receipts, photographs, and souvenirs. Have your family members put them in order from oldest to newest. What clues will you use to determine their relative ages? Do you remember when certain items were bought or a photograph was taken? How can you determine the oldest object of all? Make a list of the ten items in order by relative age. Are there any items for which you know the absolute age?

SECTION 4 The Geologic Time Scale

DISCOVER .... ACTIVITY ...

This Is Your Life!

1. Make a list of about 10 to 15 important events that you remember in your life.

2. On a sheet of paper, draw a time line to represent your life. Use a scale of 3.0 cm to 1 year.

3. Write each event in the correct year along the time line.

4. Now divide the time line into parts that describe major periods in your life, for example: preschool years, elementary school years, and middle school years.

Think It Over

Making Models Along which part of your time line are most of the events located? Which period of your life does this part of the time line represent? Why do you think this is so?

Imagine squeezing Earth's 4.6-billion-year history into a 24-hour day. Earth forms at midnight. About seven hours later, the earliest one-celled organisms appear. Over the next 14 hours, simple, soft-bodied organisms such as jellyfish and worms develop. A little after 9:00 P.M.—21 hours later—larger, more complex organisms evolve in the oceans. Reptiles and insects first appear about an hour after that. Dinosaurs arrive just before 11:00 P.M., but are extinct by 11:30 P.M. Modern humans don't appear until less than a second before midnight!

GUIDE FOR READING

◆ Why is the geologic time scale used to show Earth's history?

◆ What are the different units of the geologic time scale?

Reading Tip As you read, make a list of the units of geologic time scale. Write a sentence about each.

The Geologic Time Scale

Months, years, or even centuries aren't very helpful for thinking about Earth's long history. **Because the time span of Earth's past is so great, geologists use the geologic time scale to show Earth's history.** The **geologic time scale** is a record of the life forms and geologic events in Earth's history. You can see this time scale in Figure 21.

Scientists first developed the geologic time scale by studying rock layers and index fossils worldwide. With this information, scientists placed Earth's rocks in order by relative age. Later, radioactive dating helped determine the absolute age of the divisions in the geologic time scale. As geologists studied the fossil record, they found major changes in life forms at different times. They used these changes to mark where one unit of geologic time ends and the next begins. Therefore the divisions of the geologic time scale depend on events in the history of life on Earth.

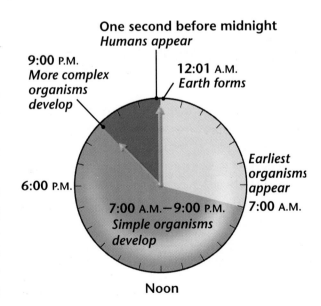

One second before midnight
Humans appear

9:00 P.M.
More complex organisms develop

12:01 A.M.
Earth forms

6:00 P.M.

Earliest organisms appear
7:00 A.M.

7:00 A.M.–9:00 P.M.
Simple organisms develop

Noon

Figure 21 If geologic time went by in a single day, all of human history would take place in less than the last second!

Geologic Time Scale

Era	Period	Millions of Years Ago	Duration (millions of years)
Cenozoic	Quaternary	– – 1.6 – – –	1.6 to present
Cenozoic	Tertiary		65
		– –66.4– –	
Mesozoic	Cretaceous		78
		– – 144 – –	
Mesozoic	Jurassic		64
		– –208– – –	
Mesozoic	Triassic		37
		– – 245 – –	
Paleozoic	Permian		41
		– –286– – –	
Paleozoic	Carboniferous		74
		– – 360 – –	
Paleozoic	Devonian		48
		– –408 – –	
Paleozoic	Silurian		30
		– –438– –	
Paleozoic	Ordovician		67
		– – 505 – –	
Paleozoic	Cambrian		39
		– – 544 – –	
Precambrian			544 million years ago–4.6 billion years ago

Figure 22 The eras and periods of the geologic time scale are used to date the events in Earth's long history.
Interpreting Diagrams How long ago did the Paleozoic Era end?

Divisions of Geologic Time

When speaking of the past, what names do you use for different spans of time? You probably use such names as *century, decade, year, month, week,* and *day.* You know that a month is longer than a week but shorter than a year. Scientists use similar divisions for the geologic time scale.

Geologic time begins with a long span of time called Precambrian Time (pree KAM bree un). Precambrian Time, which covers about 88 percent of Earth's history, ended 544 million years ago. **After Precambrian Time, the basic units of the geologic time scale are eras, periods, and epochs.**

☑ *Checkpoint* How much of Earth's history is included in Precambrian Time?

Eras, Periods, and Epochs

Geologists divide the time between Precambrian Time and the present into three long units of time called **eras.** They are the Paleozoic Era, the Mesozoic Era, and the Cenozoic Era.

Eras The Paleozoic (pay lee uh ZOH ik) began about 544 million years ago and lasted for 300 million years. The word part *paleo-* means "ancient or early," and *-zoic* means "life." Many animals that lived during the Paleozoic were animals without backbones, or **invertebrates.**

The Mesozoic (mez uh ZOH ik) began about 245 million years ago and lasted about 180 million years. The word part *meso-* means "middle." People often call the Mesozoic the Age of Dinosaurs. Yet dinosaurs were only one of the many groups of organisms that lived during this era. For example, mammals began to evolve during the Mesozoic Era.

Earth's most recent era is the Cenozoic (sen uh ZOH ik). It began about 65 million years ago and continues to the present day. The word part *ceno-* means "recent." The Cenozoic is sometimes called the Age of Mammals, because mammals became common during this time.

Periods Eras are subdivided into units of geologic time called **periods.** Geologic periods range in length from tens of millions of years to less than two million years. You can see in Figure 22 that the Mesozoic Era includes three periods: the Triassic Period, the Jurassic Period, and the Cretaceous Period.

You may wonder where the names of the geologic periods come from. Many come from places around the world where geologists first described the rocks and fossils of that period. The name Cambrian, for example, refers to Cambria, the old Roman name for Wales. Jurassic refers to the Jura Mountains in France.

The Carboniferous Period is named for the large coal deposits that formed during that period. *Carboniferous* means "carbon bearing." Geologists in the United States often divide the Carboniferous Period into the Mississippian Period (320–360 million years ago) and the Pennsylvanian Period (286–320 million years ago.)

Epochs Geologists further subdivide the periods of the Cenozoic Era into **epochs.** Why are epochs used in the time scale? The fossil record in the Cenozoic is much more complete than the fossil record of earlier eras. There are a lot more events to place in sequence, and using epochs makes this task easier.

Figure 23 The sedimentary rock layers (top) were laid down during the Ordovician period. The fossil of the plant (bottom) formed during the Carboniferous period.

Section 4 Review

1. What is the geologic time scale?
2. What are geologic periods?
3. What method of dating did geologists first use when they developed the geologic time scale? How is the scale different today?
4. **Thinking Critically Interpreting Diagrams** Which period in the Paleozoic was the longest? If you could travel back in time 100 million years, what period would you be in? What era would you be in?

Check Your Progress

CHAPTER PROJECT

Make a list of illustrations for the time line and travel brochure. Before creating the illustrations, think about what they will look like and the materials you will need to complete them. Will they be three dimensional? Will they be drawn using a computer? Begin to plan how you will use illustrations in your travel brochure. Space in a brochure is limited, so focus on the highlights of your geologic period.

As Time Goes By

Earth's history goes back 4.6 billion years. How can people grasp the vast scale of geologic time? In this lab, you will make a model to represent Earth's history.

Problem

How can you make a model of geologic time?

Materials

worksheet with 2,000 asterisks
one ream of paper

Procedure

Part 1 Table A

1. Copy Table A into your lab notebook. Figure how long ago these historic events happened and write the answers on your chart.

2. Obtain a worksheet with 2,000 asterisks printed on it. Each asterisk represents one year. The first asterisk at the top represents one year ago.

3. Starting from this asterisk, circle the asterisk that represents how many years ago each event in Table A occurred.

4. Label each circled asterisk to indicate the event.

5. Obtain a ream of copy paper. There are 500 sheets in a ream. If each sheet had 2,000 asterisks on it, there would be a total of 1 million asterisks. Therefore, each ream would represent 1 million years.

Part 2 Fill in Chart B

6. Copy Table B into your lab notebook. Determine how much paper in reams or sheets would be needed to represent the events in geologic time found in Table B. (*Hint:* Recall that each ream represents 1 million years.)

Table A Historic Events		
Event	**Date**	**Number of Years Ago**
You are born		
One of your parents is born		
Space shuttle *Challenger* explodes	1986	
Neil Armstrong first walks on the moon	1969	
World War I ends	1918	
Civil War ends	1865	
Declaration of Independence signed	1776	
Columbus crosses Atlantic	1492	
Leif Ericson visits North America	1000	

Table B Geologic Events			
Event	Number of Years Ago	Reams or Sheets of Paper	Thickness of Paper
End of the last Ice Age	10,000		
Whales evolve	50 million		
Pangaea begins to break up	225 million		
First vertebrates develop	530 million		
Multicellular organisms develop (algae)	1 billion		
First life (bacteria)	3.5 billion		
Oldest known rocks form	4.0 billion		
Age of Earth	4.6 billion		

7. Measure the thickness of a ream of paper. Use this thickness to calculate how thick a stack of paper would need to be to represent how long ago each geologic event occurred. (*Hint:* Use a calculator to multiply the thickness of the ream of paper by the number of reams.) Enter your results in Table B.

Analyze and Conclude

1. Measure the height of your classroom. How many reams of paper would you need to reach the ceiling? How many years would the height of the ceiling represent? Which geologic events listed in Table B would fall on a ream of paper inside your classroom?
2. At this scale, how many classrooms would have to be stacked on top of each other to represent the age of Earth? The time when vertebrates appeared?
3. How many times higher would the thickness of the stack be for the age of Earth than for the breakup of Pangaea?
4. On your model, how could you distinguish one era or period from another? How could you show when particular organisms evolved and when they became extinct?

5. **Think About It** Is the scale of your model practical? What would be the advantages and disadvantages of a model that fit geologic time on a time line 1 meter long?

More to Explore

This model represents geologic time as a straight line. Can you think of other ways of representing geologic time graphically? Using colored pencils, draw your own version of the geologic time scale so that it fits on a single sheet of typing paper. (*Hint:* You could represent geologic time as a wheel, a ribbon, or a spiral.)

SECTION 5 A Trip Through Geologic Time

DISCOVER · ACTIVITY

What Do Fossils Reveal About Earth's History?

1. Compare the two fossils in photos A and B. How did these organisms become fossils?

2. Work with one or two other students to study the organisms in the two photos. Think about how these organisms may have lived. Then make sketches showing what each of these organisms may have looked like.

Think It Over
Posing Questions If you were a paleontologist, what questions would you want to ask about these organisms?

GUIDE FOR READING

◆ **What were the major events in Earth's geologic history?**

◆ **What were the major events in the development of life on Earth?**

Reading Tip Preview *Exploring Life's History* on pages 188–191. Make a list of questions you have about the development of life through geologic time. Then look for answers as you read.

Your science class is going on a field trip, but this trip is a little out of the ordinary. You're going to travel back billions of years to the earliest days on Earth. Then you will move forward through time to the present. Enter the time machine and strap yourself in. Take a deep breath—you're off!

A dial on the dashboard shows the number of years before the present. You stare at the dial—it reads 4.6 billion years. You peer out the window as the time machine flies above the planet. Earth looks a little strange. Where are the oceans? Where are the continents? How will Earth change over the next billions of years? You'll answer these and other questions about Earth's history as you take this extraordinary trip.

Precambrian Time

Your journey through the first part of Earth's history will need to be very fast. Remember, Precambrian time includes most of Earth's history!

Precambrian Earth **Earth formed from a mass of dust and gas about 4.6 billion years ago.** Gravity pulled this mass together. Over time, Earth's interior became very hot and molten. Hundreds of millions of years passed. Then lava flowed over the surface, building the first continents. An atmosphere formed, and the world was covered with an ocean.

The Earliest Forms of Life Scientists cannot pinpoint when or where life began on Earth. But scientists have found fossils of single-celled organisms in rocks that formed about 3.5 billion years ago. These earliest life forms were probably similar to

184

present-day bacteria. All other forms of life on Earth evolved from these simple organisms.

About 2.5 billion years ago, organisms first began using energy from the sun to make their own food. This process is called photosynthesis. One waste product of photosynthesis is oxygen. As oxygen was released into the air, the amount of oxygen in the atmosphere slowly increased. Over time, organisms evolved that could use oxygen to produce energy from food. These organisms included animals that are like today's sponges and worms. Because they all had soft bodies, these animals left few fossils. However, the evolution of these organisms set the stage for great changes during the Paleozoic Era. You can trace the development of life in *Exploring Life's History* on pages 188–191.

The Paleozoic Era

Your time machine slows. You watch in fascination as you observe the "explosion" of life that began the Paleozoic Era.

Life Explodes During the Cambrian Period life took a big leap forward. **At the beginning of the Paleozoic Era, a great number of different kinds of organisms evolved.** Paleontologists call this event the Cambrian Explosion because so many new life forms appeared within a relatively short time. For the first time, many organisms had hard parts, including shells and outer skeletons.

At this time, all animals lived in the sea. Invertebrates such as jellyfish, worms, and sponges drifted through the water, crawled along the sandy bottom, or attached themselves to the ocean floors. Recall that invertebrates are animals that lack backbones.

Figure 24 During the early Cambrian period, Earth's oceans were home to many strange organisms unlike any animals that are alive today. The fossil above is an organism of the middle Cambrian called *Burgessia bella* from the Burgess shale.

Brachiopods and trilobites were common in the Cambrian seas. Brachiopods were small ocean animals with two shells. They resembled modern clams. Clams, however, are only distantly related to them.

During the Ordovician (awr duh VISH ee un) and Silurian (sih LOOR ee un) periods, the ancestors of the modern octopus and squid appeared. Some of these organisms, called cephalopods, grew to a length of almost 10 meters. **During this time, jawless fishes evolved. Jawless fishes were the first vertebrates.** A **vertebrate** is an animal with a backbone. These fishes had suckerlike mouths, and they soon became common in the seas.

Life Reaches Land Until the Silurian Period, only one-celled organisms lived on the land. But during the Silurian Period, plants began to grow on land. These first, simple plants grew low to the ground in damp areas. But by the Devonian Period (dih VOH nee un), plants that could grow in drier areas had evolved. Among these plants were the earliest ferns. The first insects also appeared during the Silurian Period.

Figure 25 One of the first amphibians, *Icthyostega* (center), was about 1 meter long. It lived during the late Devonian Period. Another, more fishlike amphibian, *Acanthostega* (bottom), lived at about the same time.

Both invertebrates and vertebrates lived in the Devonian seas. Even though the invertebrates were more numerous, the Devonian Period is often called the Age of Fishes. This is because every main group of fishes was present in the oceans at this time. Most fishes now had jaws, bony skeletons, and scales on their bodies. Sharks appeared in the late Devonian Period.

During the Devonian Period, animals began to invade the land. The first vertebrates to crawl onto land were lungfish with strong, muscular fins. The first amphibians evolved from these fishes. An **amphibian** (am FIB ee un) is an animal that lives part of its life on land and part of its life in water. *Ichthyostega*, shown in Figure 25, was one of the first amphibians.

Throughout the rest of the Paleozoic Era, life expanded over Earth's continents. Other groups of

Figure 26 Forests flourished during the Carboniferous Period. Insects such as dragonflies were common. *Predicting* What types of fossils would you expect to find from the Carboniferous Period?

vertebrates evolved from the amphibians. For example, small reptiles developed during the Carboniferous Period. **Reptiles** have scaly skin and lay eggs with tough, leathery shells. Some types of reptiles became very large during the later Paleozoic.

During the Carboniferous Period, winged insects evolved into many forms, including huge dragonflies and cockroaches. Giant ferns and cone-bearing plants and trees formed vast swampy forests called "coal forests." How did the coal forest get its name? The remains of the coal forest plants formed thick deposits of sediment that changed into coal over millions of years.

Figure 27 *Dimetrodon*, which lived during the Permian Period, was one of the first reptiles. This meat-eater was about 3.5 meters long.

Mass Extinction Ends the Paleozoic At the end of the Paleozoic Era, many kinds of organisms died out. This was a **mass extinction,** in which many types of living things became extinct at the same time. **The mass extinction at the end of the Paleozoic affected both plants and animals, on land and in the seas. Scientists do not know what caused the mass extinction, but as much as 95 percent of the life in the oceans disappeared.** For example, trilobites, which had existed since early in the Paleozoic, suddenly became extinct. Many amphibians also became extinct. But not all organisms disappeared. The mass extinction did not affect fishes. Many reptiles also survived.

☑ *Checkpoint* *What were three major events in the development of life during the Paleozoic Era?*

EXPLORING Life's History

Using the fossil record, paleontologists have created a picture of the different types of common organisms in each geologic period.

PRECAMBRIAN TIME
4.6 billion–544 million years ago

PALEOZOIC ERA
544–245 million years ago

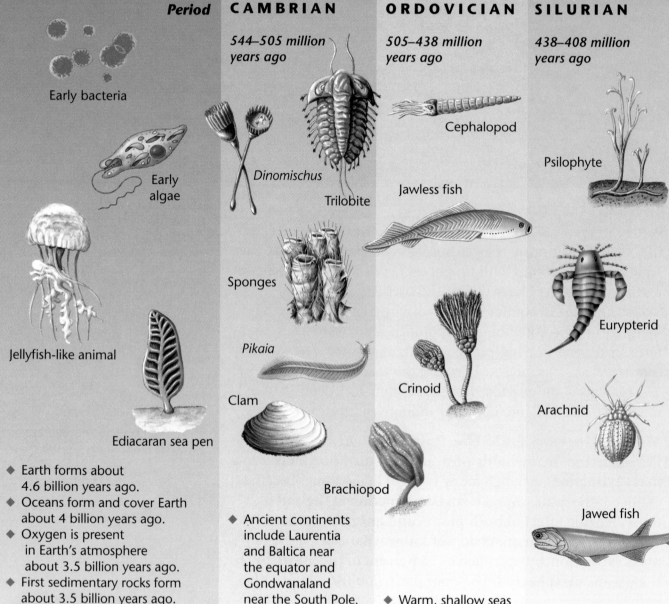

Period

CAMBRIAN
544–505 million years ago

ORDOVICIAN
505–438 million years ago

SILURIAN
438–408 million years ago

Early bacteria

Early algae

Jellyfish-like animal

Ediacaran sea pen

Dinomischus

Trilobite

Sponges

Pikaia

Clam

Cephalopod

Jawless fish

Crinoid

Brachiopod

Psilophyte

Eurypterid

Arachnid

Jawed fish

- Earth forms about 4.6 billion years ago.
- Oceans form and cover Earth about 4 billion years ago.
- Oxygen is present in Earth's atmosphere about 3.5 billion years ago.
- First sedimentary rocks form about 3.5 billion years ago.
- Bacteria appear about 3.5 billion years ago.
- Earth's first ice age occurs about 2.3 billion years ago.
- Soft-bodied, multicellular organisms develop late in the Precambrian.
- First mass extinction probably occurs near the end of the Precambrian.

- Ancient continents include Laurentia and Baltica near the equator and Gondwanaland near the South Pole.
- Shallow seas cover much of the land.
- Great "explosion" of invertebrate life occurs in seas.
- Invertebrates with shells appear, including trilobites, mollusks, and brachiopods.

- Warm, shallow seas cover much of Earth.
- Ice cap covers what is now North Africa.
- Invertebrates dominate the oceans.
- Early vertebrates— jawless fish— become common.

- Early continents Laurentia and Baltica collide.
- Coral reefs develop.
- Fish with jaws develop.
- Land plants appear.
- Insects and spiders appear.

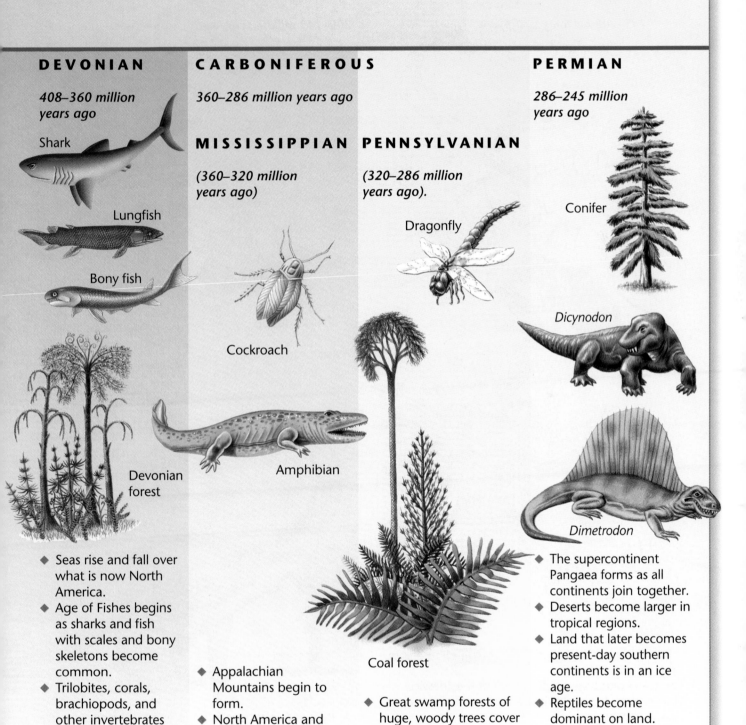

DEVONIAN

408–360 million years ago

Shark

Lungfish

Bony fish

Devonian forest

- ◆ Seas rise and fall over what is now North America.
- ◆ Age of Fishes begins as sharks and fish with scales and bony skeletons become common.
- ◆ Trilobites, corals, brachiopods, and other invertebrates flourish in the oceans.
- ◆ Lungfish develop.
- ◆ First amphibians reach land.
- ◆ Forests grow in swampy areas.

CARBONIFEROUS

360–286 million years ago

MISSISSIPPIAN

(360–320 million years ago)

Cockroach

Amphibian

- ◆ Appalachian Mountains begin to form.
- ◆ North America and Northern Europe lie in warm, tropical region.
- ◆ Cold conditions are present in what is now South America and Africa.

PENNSYLVANIAN

(320–286 million years ago).

Dragonfly

Coal forest

- ◆ Great swamp forests of huge, woody trees cover eastern North America and parts of Europe.
- ◆ First true reptiles appear.
- ◆ Insects become abundant.
- ◆ Winged insects appear.

PERMIAN

286–245 million years ago

Conifer

Dicynodon

Dimetrodon

- ◆ The supercontinent Pangaea forms as all continents join together.
- ◆ Deserts become larger in tropical regions.
- ◆ Land that later becomes present-day southern continents is in an ice age.
- ◆ Reptiles become dominant on land.
- ◆ Warm-blooded reptiles appear.
- ◆ Mass extinction causes many marine invertebrates, including trilobites, to disappear.

MESOZOIC ERA
245–65 million years ago

Period TRIASSIC

245–208 million years ago

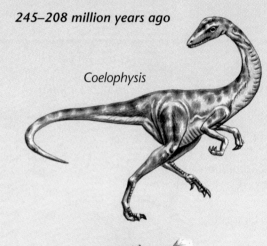

Coelophysis

Morganucodon

Cycad

- ◆ Pangaea holds together for much of the Triassic.
- ◆ Hot, dry conditions dominate center of Pangaea.
- ◆ Age of Reptiles begins.
- ◆ First dinosaurs appear.
- ◆ First mammals, which evolve from warm-blooded reptiles, appear.
- ◆ First turtles and crocodiles appear.
- ◆ Conifers, palmlike trees, and ginkgo trees dominate forests.

JURASSIC

208–144 million years ago

Stegosaurus

Megazostrodon

Archaeopteryx

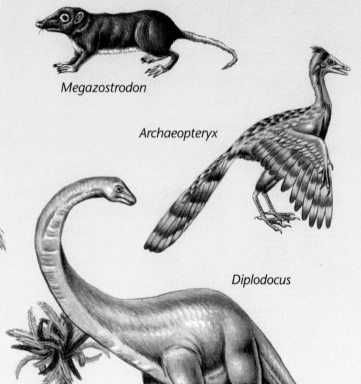

Diplodocus

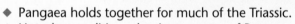

- ◆ Pangaea continues to break apart as North America separates from Africa and South America.
- ◆ Sea levels rise in many parts of the world.
- ◆ Largest dinosaurs thrive, including *Stegosaurus, Diplodocus,* and *Apatosaurus.*
- ◆ First birds appear.
- ◆ First flying reptiles, pterosaurs, appear.

CRETACEOUS

144–65 million years ago

Magnolia

Tyrannosaurus rex

Creodonts

Triceratops

- Continents move toward their present-day positions, as South America splits from Africa.
- Widespread volcanic activity occurs.
- First flowering plants appear.
- Dinosaurs dominate, including *Tyrannosaurus rex*.
- First snakes appear.
- Mass extinction at end causes disappearance of many land and marine life forms, including dinosaurs.

TERTIARY

65–1.6 million years ago

Uintatherium

Hyracotherium

Plesiadapis

- The Rocky Mountains, Alps, Andes, and Himalayas form.
- Continents move into present-day positions.
- Continental glacier covers Antarctica about 25 million years ago.
- Flowering plants thrive.
- First grasses appear.
- Age of Mammals begins.
- Modern groups such as horses, elephants, bears, rodents, and primates appear.
- Mammals return to the seas in the forms of whales and dolphins.
- Ancestors of humans evolve.
- Continental glaciers repeatedly cover part of North America beginning about 2.5 million years ago.

QUATERNARY

1.6 million years ago to the present

Saber-toothed cat

Megatherium

Homo sapiens

- Thick glaciers advance and retreat over much of North America and Europe, parts of South America and Asia, and all of Antarctica.
- The Great Lakes form.
- Giant mammals flourish in parts of North America and Eurasia not covered by ice. But they become extinct when the Ice Age ends about 10,000 years ago.
- Mammals, flowering plants, and insects dominate land.
- Modern humans evolve in Africa about 100,000 years ago.

260 million years ago

Figure 28 The supercontinent Pangaea began to break apart about 225 million years ago. *Observing How have North America and South America moved in relation to Africa and Europe?*

Present

The Supercontinent Pangaea

Scientists aren't sure what caused the mass extinction at the end of the Paleozoic. One theory is that Earth's climate changed. But what caused this climate change? Scientists hypothesize that it may have been caused by the slow movement of the continents.

During the Permian period, about 260 million years ago, Earth's continents moved together to form a great landmass, or supercontinent, called Pangaea (pan JEE uh). The formation of Pangaea caused deserts to expand in the tropics. At the same time, sheets of ice covered land closer to the South Pole. Many organisms could not survive the new climate. After Pangaea formed, it broke apart again. Figure 28 shows how the continents moved toward their present-day positions. They moved very slowly—only a few centimeters per year.

The movement of continents is sometimes called continental drift. But the continents don't really "drift." The continents move slowly over Earth's surface because of forces inside Earth.

✓ *Checkpoint* *What was Pangaea?*

The Mesozoic Era

Millions of years flash by. Your time machine cruises above Pangaea and the landmasses that formed when it broke apart. Watch out—there's a dinosaur! You're observing an era that you've read about in books and seen in movies.

The Triassic Period Some living things survived the Permian mass extinction. These organisms became the main forms of life early in the Triassic Period (try AS ik). Plants and animals that survived included fish, insects, reptiles, and cone-bearing plants called conifers. **Reptiles were so successful during the Mesozoic Era that this time is often called the Age of Reptiles.**

About 225 million years ago, the first dinosaurs appeared. One of the earliest dinosaurs, *Coelophysis*, was a meat eater that had light, hollow bones and ran swiftly on its hind legs. It was about 2.5 meters long.

Mammals also first appeared during the Triassic Period. A **mammal** is a warm-blooded vertebrate that feeds its young milk. Mammals probably evolved from warm-blooded reptiles. The mammals of the Triassic Period were very small, about the size of a mouse or shrew. From these first small mammals, all mammals that live today evolved.

The Jurassic Period During the Jurassic Period (joo RAS ik), dinosaurs became the dominant animal on land. Scientists have identified several hundred different kinds of dinosaurs. Some were plant eaters, while others were meat eaters. Dinosaurs "ruled" Earth for about 150 million years, but different types lived at different times. At 20 meters long, *Dicraeosaurus* was one of the larger dinosaurs of the Jurassic Period. The smallest known dinosaur, *Compsognathus,* was only about 50 centimeters long when fully grown.

Figure 29 *Dicraeosaurus* was a plant-eating dinosaur that lived during the late Jurassic Period.

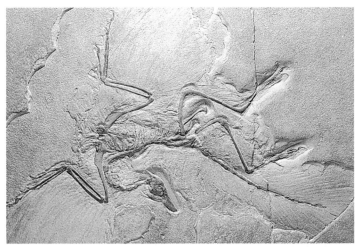

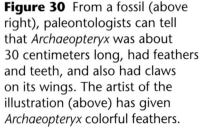

Figure 30 From a fossil (above right), paleontologists can tell that *Archaeopteryx* was about 30 centimeters long, had feathers and teeth, and also had claws on its wings. The artist of the illustration (above) has given *Archaeopteryx* colorful feathers.

One of the first birds, called *Archaeopteryx*, appeared during the Jurassic Period. The name *Archaeopteryx* means "ancient wing thing." Many paleontologists now think that birds evolved from dinosaurs. During the 1990s, scientists discovered fossils in China with the skulls and teeth of dinosaurs. But these creatures had birdlike bodies and feathers.

The Cretaceous Period Reptiles were still the dominant vertebrates throughout the Cretaceous Period (krih TAY shus). Dinosaurs, such as the meat-eating *Tyrannosaurus rex*, ruled the land. But mammals continued to evolve. Flying reptiles and birds competed for places in the sky. The hollow bones and feathers of birds made them better adapted to their environment than the flying reptiles, which became extinct during the Cretaceous Period. In the seas, reptiles such as turtles and crocodiles swam among fishes and marine invertebrates.

The Cretaceous Period also brought new forms of life. Flowering plants evolved. These included leafy trees, shrubs, and small flowering plants like the ones you see today. Unlike the conifers, flowering plants produce seeds that are inside a fruit. The fruit helps the seeds survive.

Another Mass Extinction At the close of the Cretaceous

INTEGRATING SPACE SCIENCE

Period, about 65 million years ago, another mass extinction occurred. **Scientists hypothesize that this mass extinction occurred when an object from space struck Earth.** This object was probably an asteroid. Asteroids are rocky masses that orbit the sun between Mars and Jupiter. On rare occasions, the orbits of certain asteroids come dangerously close to Earth. Once in many millions of years, an impact may occur.

When the asteroid hit Earth, the impact threw huge amounts of dust and water vapor into the atmosphere. Many organisms on land and in the oceans died immediately. Dust and heavy clouds blocked sunlight around the world for years. Without sunlight, plants died, and plant-eating animals starved. This mass extinction wiped out over half of all plant and animal groups. No dinosaurs survived. Many other kinds of reptiles also became extinct.

Not all scientists agree that an asteroid impact caused the mass extinction. Some scientists think that climate changes caused by increased volcanic activity were responsible.

☑ *Checkpoint* *What major groups of organisms developed during the Mesozoic Era?*

Figure 31 Scientists hypothesize that during the Cretaceous an asteroid hit Earth near the present-day Yucatán Peninsula, in southeastern Mexico.
Relating Cause and Effect How did the asteroid impact affect life on Earth?

The Cenozoic Era

Your voyage through time continues through the Cenozoic Era toward the present. Paleontologists often call the Cenozoic Era the Age of Mammals. During the Mesozoic Era, mammals had a hard time competing with dinosaurs for food and places to live. **The extinction of dinosaurs created an opportunity for mammals. During the Cenozoic Era, mammals evolved adaptations that allowed them to live in many different environments—on land, in water, and even in the air.**

The Tertiary Period During the Tertiary Period, Earth's climates were generally warm and mild. In the oceans, many types of mollusks appeared. Marine mammals such as whales and dolphins evolved. On land, flowering plants, insects, and mammals flourished. When grasses evolved, they provided a food source for grazing mammals. These were the ancestors of today's cattle, deer, sheep, and other grass-eating mammals. Some mammals became very large, as did some birds.

Figure 32 This extinct mammal was related to present-day horses. The fossil formed during the Tertiary Period between 36 and 57 million years ago.

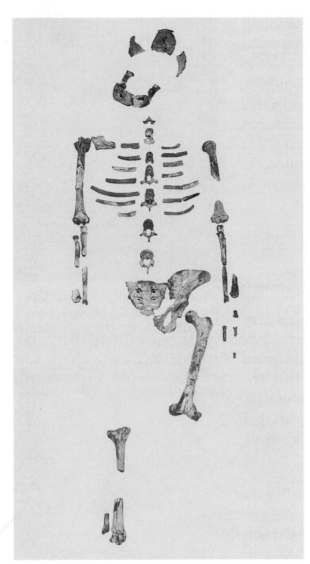

Figure 33 Scientists nicknamed this fossil skeleton Lucy. An early ancestor of modern humans, Lucy lived about 3.3 million years ago.

The Quaternary Period The mammals that had evolved during the Tertiary Period eventually faced a changing environment. **Earth's climate cooled, causing a series of ice ages during the Quaternary Period.** Repeatedly, thick continental glaciers advanced and retreated over parts of Europe and North America.

So much of Earth's water was frozen in continental glaciers that the level of the oceans fell by more than 100 meters. Then, about 20,000 years ago, Earth's climate began to warm. Over thousands of years, the continental glaciers melted. This caused sea level to rise again.

In the oceans, algae, coral, mollusks, fish, and mammals thrived. Insects and birds shared the skies. On land, flowering plants and mammals such as bats, cats, dogs, cattle, and humans—just to name a few—became common.

The fossil record suggests that human ancestors appeared about 3.5 million years ago. Modern humans, or *Homo sapiens,* may have evolved as early as 100,000 years ago. By about 12,000 to 15,000 years ago, humans had migrated around the world to every continent except Antarctica.

Your time machine has now arrived back in the present. You and all organisms on Earth are living in the Quaternary Period of the Cenozoic Era. Is this the end of evolution and the changing of Earth's surface? No, these processes will continue as long as Earth exists. But you'll have to take your time machine into the future to see just what happens!

Section 5 Review

1. What is the "Cambrian explosion"? Why is it important to the history of life on Earth?
2. What was Pangaea? When did it form?
3. How did the extinction of dinosaurs affect the evolution of mammals?
4. What do scientists think was the source of the oxygen in Earth's atmosphere?
5. **Thinking Critically Making Generalizations** How do you think mass extinctions have affected evolution?

Check Your Progress
CHAPTER PROJECT

Create illustrations of your portion of the time line. How will you show animals, plants, and environments of that time? When you have finished your illustrations, place them on the time line. Then make a rough draft of your travel brochure. Have a classmate or teacher edit your rough draft before you write the final draft. Do you have all the information about your geologic period that will make a person want to travel there?

SECTION 1 Fossils

Key Ideas

◆ The rock cycle is the series of processes on and beneath Earth's surface that changes rocks from one type of rock to another.
◆ The major kinds of fossils include petrified remains, molds, casts, carbon films, trace fossils, and preserved remains.

Key Terms

rock   petrified fossil
igneous rock   mold
sedimentary rock   cast
metamorphic rock   carbon film
rock cycle   trace fossil
paleontologist

SECTION 2 Finding the Relative Age of Rocks

Key Ideas

◆ The law of superposition can be used to determine the relative ages of rock layers.
◆ Scientists also study faults, intrusions, and extrusions to find the relative ages of rock layers.
◆ Index fossils are useful in dating rock layers because they are easily recognized, occur in many different areas, and represent organisms that lived during only one short period of Earth's history.

Key Terms

relative age   intrusion
absolute age   fault
law of superposition unconformity
extrusion   index fossil

SECTION 3 Radioactive Dating

INTEGRATING CHEMISTRY

Key Ideas

◆ During radioactive decay, the atoms of one element decay into atoms of another element.
◆ Scientists use radioactive dating to determine the absolute ages of rocks.

Key Terms

atom   radioactive decay
element   half-life

SECTION 4 The Geologic Time Scale

Key Ideas

◆ Scientists use the geologic time scale because the time span of Earth's history is so great.
◆ The basic divisions of the geologic time scale are eras, periods, and epochs.

Key Terms

geologic time scale   invertebrate   epoch
era   period

SECTION 5 A Trip Through Geologic Time

Key Ideas

◆ A great number of different kinds of living things evolved during the "Cambrian explosion" at the beginning of the Paleozoic Era.
◆ During the Permian Period, Earth's continents joined together and formed the supercontinent called Pangaea.
◆ The extinction of the dinosaurs at the end of the Mesozoic Era created an opening for mammals, which evolved to live in most environments on land, in water, and in the air.

Key Terms

vertebrate   reptile   mammal
amphibian   mass extinction

USING THE INTERNET

ACTIVITY

www.science-explorer.phschool.com

C H A P T E R 6 A S S E S S M E N T

California Test Prep: Reviewing Content

Multiple Choice

Choose the answer that best completes each sentence.

1. The rock that forms when particles of other rocks or the remains of plants and animals are pressed and cemented together is called a(n)
   a. metamorphic rock.
   b. extrusion.
   c. sedimentary rock.
   d. igneous rock.

2. A hollow area in sediment in the shape of all or part of an organism is called a
   a. mold.   b. cast.
   c. trace fossil.   d. carbon film.

3. A gap in the geologic record formed when sedimentary rocks cover an eroded surface is called a(n)
   a. intrusion.   b. unconformity.
   c. fault.   d. extrusion.

4. When a radioactive element decays, it releases
   a. atoms.
   b. potassium-40.
   c. particles and energy.
   d. carbon-14.

5. Eras of geologic time are subdivided into
   a. epochs.   b. centuries.
   c. decades.   d. periods.

True or False

If the statement is true, write true. If it is false, change the underlined word or words to make the statement true.

6. A dinosaur footprint in rock is an example of a <u>trace fossil</u>.

7. A <u>carbon film</u> is a fossil in which minerals have replaced all or part of an organism.

8. The <u>relative age</u> of something is the exact number of years since an event occurred.

9. A <u>period</u> is the time required for half of the atoms of a radioactive element to decay.

10. The <u>Paleozoic Era</u> is often called the Age of Reptiles.

Checking Concepts

11. How does a petrified fossil form?

12. Describe how the rock cycle can change igneous rock into sedimentary rock and sedimentary rock into metamorphic rock. (*Hint:* Use granite, sandstone, and quartzite as examples.)

13. Describe a process that could cause an unconformity.

14. What evidence would a scientist use to determine the absolute age of a fossil found in a sedimentary rock?

15. What era is often called the Age of Mammals? Why is this appropriate?

16. **Writing to Learn** Imagine that your time machine comes to a halt just as a big event occurs at the end of the Mesozoic Era. Describe what you see, and then describe how this event affects the life you see on Earth.

Thinking Visually

17. **Concept Map** Copy the concept map about fossils onto a piece of paper. Then complete it and add a title. (For more on concept maps, see the Skills Handbook.)

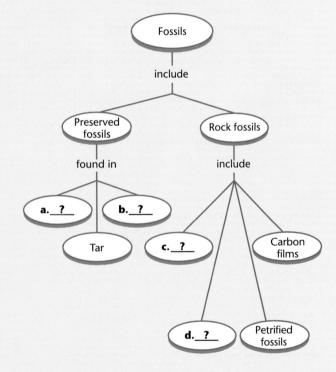

Test Prep: Skills

Use the diagram of rock layers below to answer Questions 18–21.

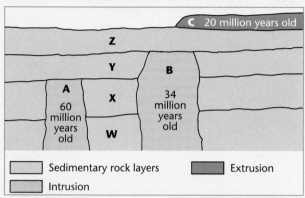

C 20 million years old

Z

Y

B
34 million years old

A
60 million years old

X

W

☐ Sedimentary rock layers
☐ Intrusion
☐ Extrusion

18. Inferring Which is the oldest layer of sedimentary rock? Which is the youngest? How do you know?

🔵 **19. Measuring** What method did a scientist use to determine the age of the intrusion and extrusion?

20. Interpreting Data What is the relative age of layer Y (*Hint:* With what absolute ages can you compare it?)

21. Interpreting Data What is the relative age of layer Z?

Thinking Critically

22. Applying Concepts Suppose that paleontologists found a certain kind of trilobite in a rock layer at the top of a hill in South America. Then they found the same kind of trilobite in a rock layer at the bottom of a cliff in Africa. What could the paleontologists conclude about the two rock layers?

23. Making Judgments If you see a movie in which early humans fight giant dinosaurs, how would you judge the scientific accuracy of that movie? Give reasons for your judgment.

24. Relating Cause and Effect When Pangaea formed, the climate changed and the land on Earth became drier. Why do you think that this climate change favored reptiles over amphibians?

25. Problem Solving Carbon-14 has a half-life of 5,730 years, while uranium-235 has a half-life of 713 million years. Which would be better to use in dating a fossil from Precambrian time? Explain.

Performance Assessment

CHAPTER PROJECT

Wrap Up

Present Your Project You have completed your illustrations for the time line and travel brochure. Now you are ready to present the story of the geologic time period you researched. Be sure to include the wonderful and awesome things people will see when they travel to this time period. Don't forget to warn them of any dangers that await them.

Reflect and Record In your journal, reflect on what you have learned about Earth's history. What were the most interesting things you found out? If you could travel back in time, how far back would you go?

Getting Involved

In Your Community Brainstorm with your class about places in your community where you might find fossils. Fossils may be found in sedimentary rocks exposed at the surface or in the sandstone and limestone used in buildings. Accompanied by an adult, visit one of these locations. Sketch or photograph any fossil you find. What type of organism does the fossil represent? How did the fossil form? Make a display showing the fossil that you found and your conclusions about it.

Mammals of the JURASSIC PERIOD

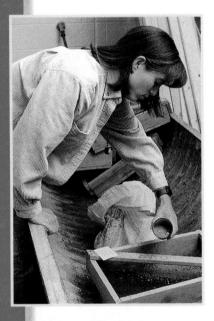

Kelli Trujillo, 31, is a graduate student in vertebrate paleontology at the University of Wyoming. During the summer, she splits her time between several fossil digs. Kelli is a musician as well as an outdoor enthusiast. She plays guitar, flute, and piano.

Spending half your summer alone in a tiny trailer in a deserted part of Wyoming may not sound like fun. But for Kelli Trujillo, a graduate student in paleontology (pay lee un TAHL uh jee), it's a dream come true. As a paleontologist, she studies the remains of ancient living things.

Kelli Trujillo is working near Como Bluff, Wyoming, one of the most famous dinosaur graveyards in the United States. But she is not searching for dinosaur bones. Kelli is looking for the remains of mammals that lived during the late Jurassic Period, about 150 million years ago.

During the Jurassic Period, southeast Wyoming was flat and dotted with lakes and streams. The Rocky Mountains had not yet formed. Small animals lived in the shadows of the dinosaurs. Among these small animals were some of the earliest mammals: mouselike and shrewlike creatures. Very little is known about these mammals. Their bones are tiny, so finding them is difficult. "If I find a mammal tooth, that's a big deal, because those discoveries are still really rare," says Kelli.

Apatosaurus and small mammals lived in the same period.

Talking with Kelli Trujillo

Q *How did you get interested in science?*

A My dad was a history teacher, but he had a passion for geology, so we always had rocks around the house. We spent a lot of time outside, camping and hiking and looking at rocks. I knew what quartz and mica were before I even went to school.

Q *How did you choose geology?*

A In high school I took a geology class with a really great teacher who helped develop my interest, especially in fossils. But I didn't think I could be a geologist because you have to take algebra. Algebra was difficult for me. It scared me. So I got a degree in veterinary technology, which didn't require any math. I worked in that field for three years, but I just didn't like it. So I decided to go back to college and take the math classes I needed for a science degree.

Q *Why did you specialize in paleontology?*

A I got started as a volunteer on some fossil digs. The first was a student project near Gunnison, Colorado. A couple of students there had dug up more than 900 bone fragments from an *Apatosaurus*, a large four-legged dinosaur. Later, I helped a friend dig out an *Allosaurus*, a big meat-eating dinosaur, near Medicine Bow, Wyoming.

Q *What have you found at your fossil sites so far?*

A There are a lot of turtle shell fragments, about four or five square centimeters in size, with bumps and ridges in them. I've got lots of crocodile teeth and some lungfish teeth. I also have some salamander vertebrae—spinal column bones— and several vertebrae and jaw fragments from a small lizard called *Cteniogenys*. I've found twenty mammal teeth.

Q *How did those fragments happen to be preserved?*

A The animals probably lived in or near a small lake. When they died, their bodies got buried in sediments—layers of soil—at the bottom of the lake. The remains of these animals stayed buried for 150 million years.

Q *What can you infer about an organism from teeth or bone fragments?*

A You can usually tell a lot about animals from their teeth. That's because animals with different diets have different types of teeth. For instance, meat-eaters don't need grinding teeth like those that plant-eaters have. Crocodile and lizard teeth are pretty easy to identify. Mammal teeth are very specialized. In fact, these

▲ **Kelli looks for mammal fragments at this site in Wyoming (above). Kelli and a co-worker examine a fossil from the Jurassic Period (right).**

◄ **Kelli worked at some of the mammal and dinosaur sites located on this map.**

specialized teeth are one of the things that separate mammals from other animals.

With bones, it really depends. If you have the entire bone, you can usually make a good guess about what type of animal it came from. But often you just find unidentifiable fragments.

Q *How does the rock where the fossil is found provide clues to the age of the fossil?*

A It's difficult to get an absolute age on sedimentary rocks. Often we just go by the rule that younger rocks are on top of older rocks. If we're really lucky, there will be a volcanic ash layer in the rocks, or certain crystals or iron minerals that we know how to date. In Wyoming, I'm working in a layer of rocks known as the Morrison Formation, which has been dated to the late Jurassic Period.

Q *How do scientists know where to dig for fossils?*

A Usually you see something on the surface, some scraps of bone sticking out from the rock. Bone has a different shape and texture and is often a different color. So if you know what you're looking for, a bone catches your eye.

Q *What tools do you use?*

A One of my most useful tools is a broom. I use it to clean the rocks so I can see their surfaces clearly. When you're digging out big bones, you use everything from picks and shovels to power tools like jackhammers and air drills. For small or delicate pieces, you need hand tools, like rock hammers and chisels, and a screen box. A screen box is basically a wooden box with a screen bottom. You put a couple of handfuls of rock in it and put the box

Dinosaur and Mammal Teeth

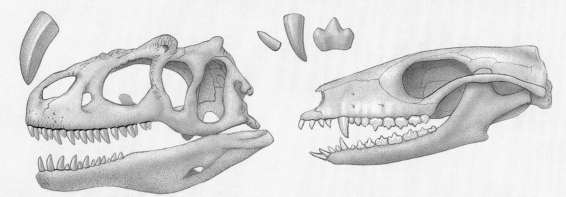

The strong jaws and long pointed teeth of *Allosaurus* (above) worked like a saw to tear apart smaller dinosaurs. *Allosaurus* was a large, meat-eating dinosaur of the Jurassic Period.

Mammal teeth are different from dinosaur teeth. The teeth of Jurassic mammals (above) are specialized for different functions. The combination of canines, incisors, and molars allowed the mammal to tear, shred, and grind.

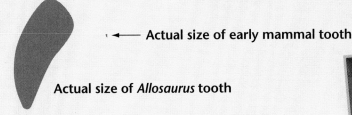

◄— Actual size of early mammal tooth

Actual size of *Allosaurus* tooth

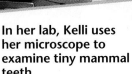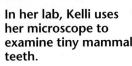

In her lab, Kelli uses her microscope to examine tiny mammal teeth.

in a big trough of water. You let the water wash the rock off the fossil. If you have the right kind of rock, it will wash away. But some rock never dissolves, and you're just out of luck.

Q How do you recover the small mammal fossils?

A I collect a couple of bags of rocks and bring them back to the lab. Then I wash them in the screen box, dry what's left, and search through it. The fossils are very small—some of them fit on the head of a pin! So you have to look at everything under a microscope, grain by grain, to see if you've got any fossils mixed in with the rock. It takes an awful lot of patience.

Q What do you hope to find?

A Usually teeth are all that's left of early mammals, but I'm hopeful this site will yield skulls and other bones, like arms or legs or vertebrae. I was

pretty excited when I found those twenty mammal teeth.

Q Do you ever get discouraged or lonely out in the field?

A When I'm out working at the site, the time goes so fast I don't even think about it. Being outside all day is wonderful. The bugs and wind aren't so good, but I'm in the middle of nowhere, and it's absolutely beautiful.

In Your Journal

Kelli Trujillo's work as a paleontologist involves a number of different steps. At each step, from searching a site for fossils to drawing conclusions in the lab, Kelli uses a wide range of skills. Make a two column list. In one column list the steps Kelli follows. In the second column describe the skills Kelli uses at each step.

The following California Science Content Standards are addressed in this chapter:

1. All living organisms are composed of cells, from just one to many trillions, whose details usually are visible only through a microscope.

   a. Cells function similarly in all living organisms.

   f. As multicellular organisms develop, their cells differentiate.

3. Biological evolution accounts for the diversity of species developed through gradual processes over many generations.

   a. Both genetic variation and environmental factors are causes of evolution and diversity of organisms.

   c. How independent lines of evidence from geology, fossils, and comparative anatomy provide a basis for the theory of evolution.

   d. How to construct a simple branching diagram to classify living groups of organisms by shared derived characteristics, and expand the diagram to include fossil organisms.

4. Evidence from rocks allows us to understand the evolution of life on Earth.

Mystery Object

Suppose that you visited a location like the one in this scene. Imagine yourself standing perfectly still, all your senses alert to the things around you. You wonder which of the things around you are alive. The newt clearly is, but what about the rest? Is the pink thing alive? Are the other things living or nonliving?

In this chapter, you will learn that it is not always easy to determine whether something is alive. This is because living things share some characteristics with nonliving things. To explore this idea firsthand, you will be given a mystery object to observe. How can you determine if your object is a living thing? What signs of life will you look for?

Your Goal To study an object for several days to determine whether or not it is alive.

To complete this project successfully, you must

◆ care for your object following your teacher's instructions
◆ observe your object each day, and record your data
◆ determine whether your object is alive, and if so, which kingdom it belongs in
◆ follow the safety guidelines in Appendix A

Get Started With a few classmates, brainstorm a list of characteristics that living things share. Can you think of any nonliving things that share some of these characteristics? Which characteristics on your list can help you conclude whether or not your mystery object is alive?

Check Your Progress You'll be working on this project as you study this chapter. To keep your project on track, look for Check Your Progress boxes at the following points.

Section 1 Review, page 213: Carry out your tests.
Section 2 Review, page 217: Record your observations daily.
Section 4 Review, page 232: Classify the object as living or nonliving.

Wrap Up At the end of the chapter (page 235), you will display your object and present evidence for whether or not it is alive. Be prepared to answer questions from your classmates.

Both the beautiful pink coral fungus and the newt sitting beside it are alive.

a. Earth processes today are similar to those that occurred in the past and slow geologic processes have large cumulative effects over long periods of time.

d. Evidence from geologic layers and radioactive dating indicate the Earth is approximately 4.6 billion years old, and that life has existed for more than 3 billion years.

e. Fossils provide evidence of how life and environmental conditions have changed.

7. Scientific progress is made by asking meaningful questions and conducting careful investigations.

a. Select and use appropriate tools and technology to perform tests, collect data, and display data.

c. Communicate the logical connection among hypothesis, science concepts, tests conducted, data collected, and conclusions drawn from the scientific evidence.

e. Communicate the steps and results from an investigation in written reports and verbal presentations.

① What Is Life?

DISCOVER ·······································ACTIVITY···

Is It Living or Nonliving?

1. Your teacher will give you and a partner a wind-up toy.

2. With your partner, decide who will find evidence that the toy is alive and who will find evidence that the toy is not alive.

3. Observe the wind-up toy. Record the characteristics of the toy that support your position about whether or not the toy is alive.

4. Share your lists of living and nonliving characteristics with your classmates.

Think It Over

Forming Operational Definitions Based on what you learned from the activity, create a list of characteristics that living things share.

GUIDE FOR READING

◆ What characteristics do all living things share?

◆ What do living things need to survive?

Reading Tip As you read, use the headings to make an outline of the characteristics and needs of living things.

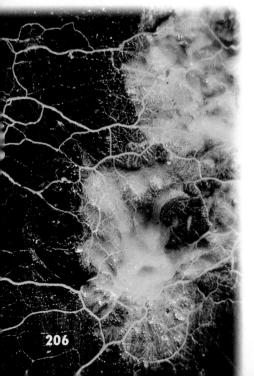

Looking like the slimy creatures that star in horror movies, the "blobs" appeared in towns near Dallas, Texas, in the summer of 1973. Jellylike masses, like the ones in Figure 1, overran yards and porches all over the towns. The glistening blobs oozed slowly along the ground. Terrified homeowners didn't know what the blobs were. Some people thought that they were life forms from another planet. People around Dallas were worried until biologists, scientists who study living things, put their minds at ease. The blobs were slime molds—living things usually found on damp, decaying material on a forest floor. The unusually wet weather around Dallas that year provided ideal conditions for the slime molds to grow in people's yards.

The Characteristics of Living Things

If you were asked to name some living things, or **organisms,** you might name yourself, a pet, and maybe some insects or plants. But you would probably not mention a moss growing in a shady spot, the mildew on bathroom tiles, or the slime molds that oozed across the lawns in towns near Dallas. But all of these things are also organisms that share six important characteristics

Figure 1 Slime molds similar to these grew in yards and porches in towns near Dallas, Texas, one summer.

◀ **Animal cells**

◀ **Plant cells**

Figure 2 Like all living things, the butterfly and the leaf are made of cells. Although the cells of different organisms are not identical, they share important characteristics. *Making Generalizations In what ways are cells similar?*

with all other living things. **All living things have a cellular organization, contain similar chemicals, use energy, grow and develop, respond to their surroundings, and reproduce.**

Cellular Organization All organisms are made of small building blocks called cells. A **cell** is the basic unit of structure and function in an organism. The smallest cells are so tiny that you could fit over a million of them on the period at the end of this sentence. To see most cells, you need a microscope—a tool that uses lenses, like those in eyeglasses, to magnify small objects.

Organisms may be composed of only one cell or of many cells. **Unicellular,** or single-celled organisms, include bacteria (bak TEER ee uh), the most numerous organisms on Earth. A bacterial cell carries out all of the functions necessary for the organism to stay alive. **Multicellular** organisms are composed of many cells. The cells of many multicellular organisms are specialized to do certain tasks. For example, you are made of trillions of cells. Specialized cells in your body, such as muscle and nerve cells, work together to keep you alive. Nerve cells carry messages from your surroundings to your brain. Other nerve cells then carry messages to your muscle cells, making your body move.

The Chemicals of Life The cells of all living things are composed of chemicals. The most abundant chemical in cells is water. Other chemicals called carbohydrates (kahr boh HY drayt) are a cell's energy source. Two other chemicals, proteins (PROH teenz) and lipids (LIP idz), are the building materials of cells, much like wood and bricks are the building materials of houses. Finally, nucleic (noo KLEE ik) acids are the genetic material—the chemical instructions that direct the cell's activities.

Figure 3 Over time, a tiny acorn develops into a giant oak tree. A great deal of energy is needed to produce the trillions of cells that make up the body of an oak tree. *Comparing and Contrasting* *In what way does the seedling resemble the oak tree? In what ways is it different?*

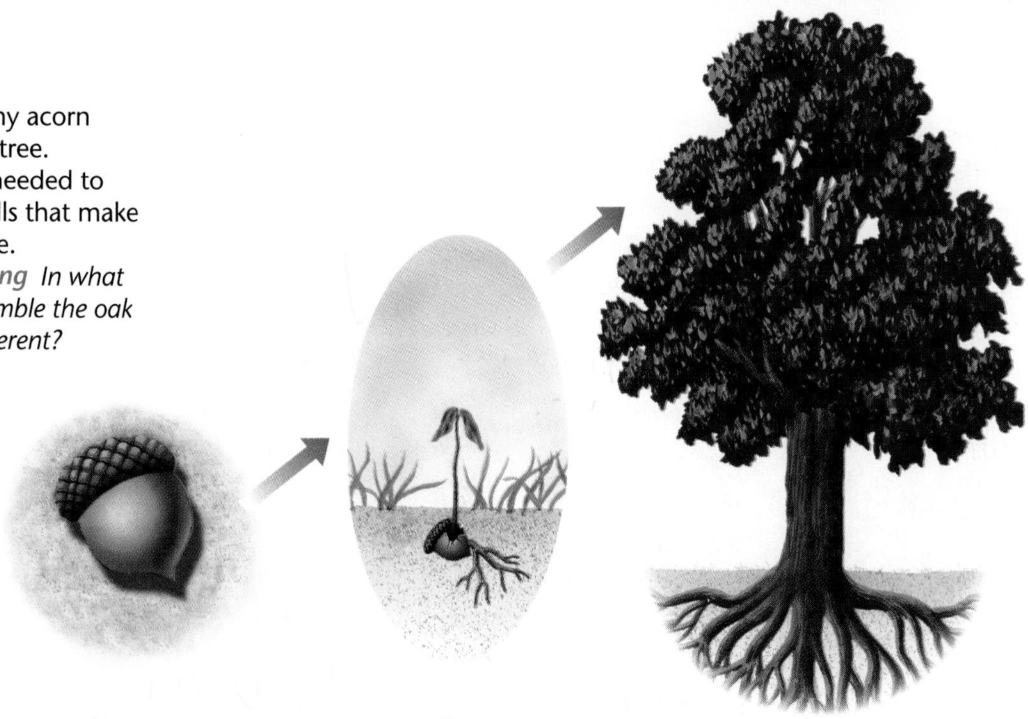

Acorn *Seedling* *Oak tree*

TRY THIS

React! ACTIVITY

In this activity, you will test your responses to three different stimuli.

1. Have a partner clap his or her hands together about six inches in front of your face. Describe how you react.
2. Look at one of your eyes in a mirror. Cover the eye with your hand for a minute. While looking in the mirror, remove your hand. Observe how the size of your pupil changes.
3. Bring a slice of lemon close to your nose and mouth. Describe what happens.

Classifying For each action performed, name the stimulus and the response.

Energy Use The cells of organisms use energy to do what living things must do, such as grow and repair injured parts. An organism's cells are always hard at work. For example, as you read this paragraph, your eye and brain cells are busy. The cells of your stomach and intestine are digesting food. Your blood cells are moving chemicals around your body. If you've hurt yourself, some of your cells are repairing the damage.

Growth and Development Another characteristic of living things is that they grow and develop. Growth is the process of becoming larger. **Development** is the process of change that occurs during an organism's life to produce a more complex organism. For example, as multicellular organisms develop, their cells differentiate, or become specialized. To grow and develop, organisms use energy to create new cells. Look at Figure 3 to see how an acorn develops as it grows into an oak tree.

You may argue that some nonliving things grow and change as they age. For example, a pickup truck rusts as it ages. Icicles grow longer as more water freezes on their tips. But pickup trucks and icicles do not use energy to change and grow. They also don't become more complex over time.

Response to Surroundings If you've ever seen a plant in a sunny window, you may have observed that the plant's stems have bent so that the leaves face the sun. Like a plant bending toward the light, all organisms react to changes in their environment. A change in an organism's surroundings that causes the organism to react is called a **stimulus** (plural *stimuli*). Stimuli include changes in temperature, light, sound, and other factors.

An organism reacts to a stimulus with a **response**—an action or change in behavior. For example, has someone ever leapt out at you from behind a door? If so, it's likely that you jumped or screamed. Your friend's sudden motion was the stimulus that caused your startled response. Nonliving things, such as rocks, do not react to stimuli as living things do.

Reproduction Another characteristic of organisms is the ability to **reproduce,** or produce offspring that are similar to the parents. Robins lay eggs that develop into young robins that closely resemble their parents. Sunflowers produce seeds that develop into sunflower plants, which in turn make more seeds. Bacteria produce other bacteria exactly like themselves.

☑ *Checkpoint* How do growth and development differ?

Life Comes From Life

Today, when people observe young plants in a garden or see a litter of puppies, they know that these new organisms are the result of reproduction. Four hundred years ago, however, people believed that life could appear suddenly from nonliving material. For example, when people saw flies swarming around decaying meat, they concluded that flies could arise from rotting meat. When frogs appeared in muddy puddles after heavy rains, people concluded that frogs could sprout from the mud in ponds. The mistaken idea that living things arise from nonliving sources is called **spontaneous generation.**

It took hundreds of years of experiments to convince people that spontaneous generation does not occur. One scientist who did some of these experiments was an Italian doctor, Francesco Redi. In the mid-1600s, Redi designed a controlled experiment to show that flies do not spontaneously arise from decaying meat. In a **controlled experiment**, a scientist carries out two tests that are identical in every respect except for one factor. The one factor that the scientist changes is called the **variable.** The scientist can conclude that any differences in the results of the two tests must be due to the variable.

Even after Redi's work, many people continued to believe that spontaneous generation occurred in bacteria. In the mid-1800s,

Figure 4 All organisms respond to changes in their surroundings. This willow ptarmigan's feathers have turned white in response to its snowy surroundings.This Alaskan bird's plumage will remain white until spring.

the French chemist Louis Pasteur designed some controlled experiments that finally disproved spontaneous generation. The controlled experiments of Francesco Redi and Louis Pasteur helped to convince people that living things do not arise from nonliving material. Look at *Exploring the Experiments of Redi and Pasteur* to learn more about the experiments they performed.

✓ *Checkpoint* **What is a controlled experiment?**

The Needs of Living Things

Imagine yourself biking through a park on a warm spring day. As you ride by a tree, you see a squirrel running up the tree trunk. Although it may seem that squirrels and trees do not have the

EXPLORING the Experiments of Redi and Pasteur

Redi designed one of the first controlled experiments. By Pasteur's time, controlled experiments were standard procedure. As you explore, identify the variable in each experiment.

FRANCESCO REDI

REDI'S EXPERIMENT

1 Redi placed meat in two identical jars. He left one jar uncovered. He covered the other jar with a cloth that let in air.

2 After a few days, Redi saw maggots (young flies) on the decaying meat in the open jar. There were no maggots on the meat in the covered jar.

3 Redi reasoned that flies had laid eggs on the meat in the open jar. The eggs hatched into maggots. Because flies could not lay eggs on the meat in the covered jar, there were no maggots there. Therefore, Redi concluded that the decaying meat did not produce maggots.

210

same basic needs as you, they do. All organisms need four things to stay alive. **Living things must satisfy their basic needs for energy, water, living space, and stable internal conditions.**

Energy You read earlier that organisms need a source of energy to live. They use food as their energy source. Organisms differ in the ways they obtain their energy. Some organisms, such as plants, capture the sun's energy and use it along with carbon dioxide, a gas found in Earth's atmosphere, and water to make their own food. Organisms that make their own food are called **autotrophs** (AW tuh trawfs). *Auto-* means "self" and *-troph* means "feeder." Autotrophs use the food they make as an energy source to carry out their life functions.

PASTEUR'S EXPERIMENT

1 In one experiment, Pasteur put clear broth into two flasks with curved necks. The necks would let in oxygen but keep out bacteria from the air. Pasteur boiled the broth in one flask to kill any bacteria in the broth. He did not boil the broth in the other flask.

2 In a few days, the unboiled broth became cloudy, showing that new bacteria were growing. The boiled broth remained clear. Pasteur concluded that bacteria do not spontaneously arise from the broth. New bacteria appeared only when living bacteria were already present.

LOUIS PASTEUR

Later, Pasteur took the curve-necked flask containing the broth that had remained clear and broke its long neck. Bacteria from the air could now enter the flask. In a few days, the broth became cloudy. This evidence confirmed Pasteur's conclusion that new bacteria appear only when they are produced by existing bacteria.

Figure 5 All organisms need a source of energy to live. **A.** *Volvox* is an autotroph that lives in fresh water, where it uses the sun's energy to make its own food. **B.** This American lobster, a heterotroph, is feeding on a herring it has caught. *Applying Concepts How do heterotrophs depend on autotrophs for energy?*

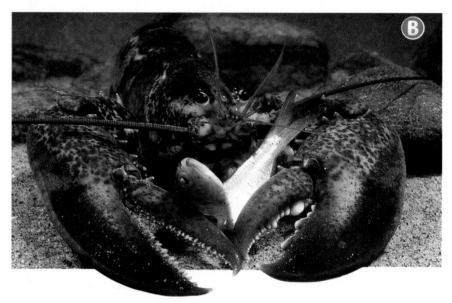

Organisms that cannot make their own food are called **heterotrophs** (HET uh roh trawfs). *Hetero-* means "other." A heterotroph's energy source is also the sun—but in an indirect way. Heterotrophs either eat autotrophs and obtain the energy in the autotroph's stored food, or they consume other heterotrophs that eat autotrophs. Animals, mushrooms, and slime molds are examples of heterotrophs.

Water All living things need water to survive—in fact, most organisms can live for only a few days without water. Organisms need water to do things such as obtain chemicals from their surroundings, break down food, grow, move substances within their bodies, and reproduce.

INTEGRATING CHEMISTRY One important property of water that is vital to living things is its ability to dissolve more chemicals than any other substance on Earth. In your body, for example, water makes up 92 percent of the liquid part of your blood. The oxygen and food that your cells need dissolve in the blood and are transported throughout your body. Carbon dioxide and other waste also dissolve in the blood. Your body's cells also provide a watery environment in which chemicals are dissolved. In a sense, you can think of yourself as a person-shaped sack of water in which other substances are dissolved. Fortunately, your body contains some substances that do not dissolve in water, and so you hold your shape.

Sharpen your Skills

Designing an Experiment ACTIVITY

Your teacher will give you a slice of potato. Predict what percentage of the potato's mass is water. Then come up with a plan to test your prediction. For materials, you will be given a hairdryer and a balance. Obtain your teacher's approval before carrying out your plan. How does your result compare with your prediction?

Living Space All organisms need a place to live—a place to get food and water and find shelter. Because there is a limited amount of living space on Earth, some organisms may compete for space. Plants, for example, occupy a fixed living space. Above the ground, their branches and leaves compete for living space with those of other plants. Below ground, their roots compete for water and minerals. Unlike plants, organisms such as animals move around. They may either share living space with others or compete for living space.

Stable Internal Conditions Because conditions in their surroundings can change significantly, organisms must be able to keep the conditions inside their bodies constant. The maintenance of stable internal conditions despite changes in the surroundings is called **homeostasis** (hoh mee oh STAY sis). You know that when you are healthy your body temperature stays constant despite temperature changes in your surroundings. Your body's regulation of temperature is an example of homeostasis.

Other organisms have different mechanisms for maintaining homeostasis. For example, imagine that you are a barnacle attached to a rock at the edge of the ocean. At high tide, the ocean water covers you. At low tide, however, your watery surroundings disappear, and you are exposed to hours of sun and wind. Without a way to keep water in your cells, you'd die. Fortunately, a barnacle can close up its hard outer plates, trapping a bubble of water inside. In this way, the barnacle can keep its body moist until the next high tide.

Figure 6 A tree trunk provides these mushrooms with food, water, and shelter.

Section 1 Review

1. Name six characteristics that you have in common with a tree.
2. List the four things that all organisms need to stay alive.
3. How did Pasteur's experiment show that bacteria do not arise spontaneously in broth?
4. **Thinking Critically** Applying Concepts You see a crowd of gulls fighting over an object on the wet sand at the ocean's edge. You investigate. The object is a vase-shaped, pink blob about as round as a dinner plate. How will you decide if it is a living thing?

Check Your Progress
CHAPTER PROJECT
At this point, you should be ready to carry out your tests for signs of life following your teacher's directions. Before you start, examine your mystery object carefully, and record your observations. Also, decide whether you need to revise the list of life characteristics you prepared earlier. (*Hint:* Do not be fooled by the object's appearance—some organisms appear dead during a certain stage of their life.)

Controlling Variables

Please Pass the Bread!

In this lab, you will control variables in an investigation into the needs of living things.

Problem

What factors are necessary for bread molds to grow?

Materials

paper plates
plastic dropper
bread without preservatives
sealable plastic bags
tap water
packing tape

Procedure

1. Brainstorm with others to predict which factors might affect the growth of bread mold. Record your ideas.
2. To test the effect of moisture on bread mold growth, place two slices of bread of the same size and thickness on separate, clean plates.
3. Add drops of tap water to one bread slice until the whole slice is moist. Keep the other slice dry. Expose both slices to the air for 1 hour.
4. Put each slice into its own sealable bag. Press the outside of each bag to remove the air. Seal the bags. Then use packing tape to seal the bags again. Store the bags in a warm, dark place.
5. Copy the data table into your notebook.

6. Every day for at least 5 days, briefly remove the sealed bags from their storage place. Record whether any mold has grown. Estimate the area of the bread where mold is present. **CAUTION:** *Do not unseal the bags. At the end of the experiment, give the sealed bags to your teacher.*
7. Choose another factor that may affect mold growth, such as temperature or the amount of light. Set up an experiment to test the factor you choose. Remember to keep all conditions the same except for the one you are testing.

Analyze and Conclude

1. What conclusions can you draw from each of your experiments?
2. What was the variable in the first experiment? In the second experiment?
3. What basic needs of living things were demonstrated in this lab? Explain.
4. **Think About It** What is meant by "controlling variables"? Why is it necessary to control variables in an experiment?

Design an Experiment

Suppose that you lived in Redi's time. A friend tells you that living things such as molds just suddenly appear on bread. Design an experiment that might convince your friend that the new mold comes from existing mold.

DATA TABLE

	Moistened Bread Slice		Unmoistened Bread Slice	
	Mold Present?	Area with Mold	Mold Present?	Area with Mold
Day 1				
Day 2				

SECTION 2 The Origin of Life

DISCOVER ·ACTIVITY· · ·

How Can the Composition of Air Change?

1. 🐭 🌱 Your teacher will give you two covered, plastic jars. One contains a plant and one contains an animal.

2. Observe the organisms in each jar. Talk with a partner about how you think each organism affects the composition of the air in its jar.

3. Write a prediction about how the amount of oxygen in each jar would change over time if left undisturbed.

4. Return the jars to your teacher.

Think It Over

Inferring Scientists hypothesize that Earth's early atmosphere was different from today's atmosphere. What role might early organisms have played in bringing about those changes?

You stare out the window of your time machine. You have traveled back to Earth as it was 3.6 billion years ago. The landscape is rugged, with bare, jagged rocks and little soil. You search for a hint of green, but there is none. You see only blacks, browns, and grays. Lightning flashes all around you. You hear the rumble of thunder, howling winds, and waves pounding the shore.

You neither see nor hear any living things. However, you know that this is the time period when scientists think that early life forms arose on Earth. You decide to explore. To be safe, you put on your oxygen mask. Stepping outside, you wonder what kinds of organisms could ever live in such a place.

Earth's Early Atmosphere

You were smart to put on your oxygen mask before exploring early Earth. Scientists think that early Earth had a different atmosphere than it has today. **Nitrogen, water vapor, carbon dioxide, and methane were probably the most abundant gases in Earth's atmosphere 3.6 billion years ago. Although all these gases are still found in the atmosphere today, the major gases are nitrogen and oxygen.** You, like most of today's organisms, could not have lived on Earth 3.6 billion years ago, because there was no oxygen in the air. However, scientists think that life forms appeared on Earth at that time.

GUIDE FOR READING

◆ How was the atmosphere of early Earth different from today's atmosphere?

◆ How do scientists hypothesize that life arose on early Earth?

Reading Tip Before you read, preview Figure 7. List some ways that you think early Earth differed from today's Earth.

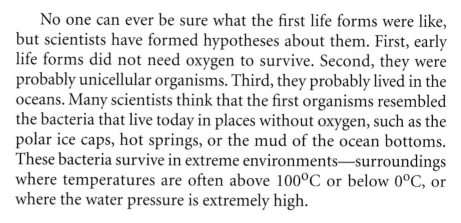

Figure 7 The atmosphere of early Earth had little oxygen. There were frequent volcanic eruptions, earthquakes, and violent weather.
Inferring What conditions on early Earth would have made it impossible for modern organisms to survive?

No one can ever be sure what the first life forms were like, but scientists have formed hypotheses about them. First, early life forms did not need oxygen to survive. Second, they were probably unicellular organisms. Third, they probably lived in the oceans. Many scientists think that the first organisms resembled the bacteria that live today in places without oxygen, such as the polar ice caps, hot springs, or the mud of the ocean bottoms. These bacteria survive in extreme environments—surroundings where temperatures are often above 100°C or below 0°C, or where the water pressure is extremely high.

Life's Chemicals

One of the most intriguing questions that scientists face is explaining how early life forms arose. Although Redi and Pasteur demonstrated that living things do not spontaneously arise on today's Earth, scientists reason that the first life forms probably did arise from nonliving materials.

Two American scientists, Harold Urey and Stanley Miller, provided the first clue as to how organisms might have arisen on Earth. In 1953, they designed an experiment in which they re-created the conditions of early Earth in their laboratory. They placed water (to represent the ocean), and a mixture of the gases thought to compose Earth's early atmosphere into a flask. They were careful to keep oxygen and unicellular organisms out of the mixture. Then, they sent an electric current through the mixture to simulate lightning. Within a week, the mixture darkened. In the dark fluid, Miller and Urey found some small chemical units that, if joined together, could form proteins—one of the building blocks of life.

☑ *Checkpoint* *What did Harold Urey and Stanley Miller model in their experiment?*

The First Cells

In experiments similar to Miller and Urey's, other scientists succeeded in producing chemical units that make up carbohydrates and nucleic acids. **From the results of these experiments, scientists hypothesized that the small chemical units of life formed gradually over millions of years in Earth's waters.** Some of these units joined to form the large chemical building blocks that are found in cells. Eventually, some of these large chemicals accumulated and became the forerunners of the first cells.

These hypotheses are consistent with evidence from fossils. **Fossils** are traces of ancient organisms that have been preserved in rock or other substances. The fossils in Figure 8 are of bacteria-like organisms that were determined to be between 3.4 and 3.5 billion years old. Scientists think that these ancient cells may be evidence of Earth's earliest life forms.

The first cells could not have needed oxygen to survive. They probably were heterotrophs that used the chemicals in their surroundings for energy. As they grew and reproduced, their numbers increased. In turn, the amount of chemicals available to them decreased. At some point, some of the cells may have developed the ability to make their own food. These early ancestors of today's autotrophs had an important effect on the atmosphere. As they made their own food, they produced oxygen as a waste product. As the autotrophs thrived, oxygen accumulated in Earth's atmosphere. Over millions of years, the amount of oxygen increased to its current level.

No one will ever know for certain how life first appeared on Earth. However, scientists will continue to ask questions, construct models, and look for both experimental and fossil evidence about the origin of life on Earth.

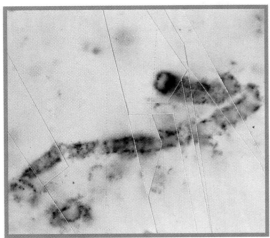

Figure 8 This fossil of bacteria-like cells was found in western Australia. It is the oldest fossil known—about 3.5 billion years old.

Section 2 Review

1. Explain why you could not have survived in the atmosphere of early Earth.
2. Describe how scientists think that life could have arisen on Earth.
3. Describe Urey and Miller's experiment.
4. **Thinking Critically Inferring** How is the existence of organisms in hot springs today consistent with the scientific hypothesis of how life forms arose on Earth?

Check Your Progress

CHAPTER PROJECT

Observe your object at least once a day. Record your observations in a data table. Draw accurate diagrams. (*Hint:* Measuring provides important information. Take measurements of your object regularly. If you cannot measure it directly, make estimates.)

SECTION 3 Classifying Organisms

DISCOVER

•••ACTIVITY••••

Can You Organize a Junk Drawer?

1. Your teacher will give you some items that you might find in the junk drawer of a desk. Your job is to organize the items.

2. Examine the objects and decide on three groups into which you can sort them.

3. Place each object into one of the groups based on how the item's features match the characteristics of the group.

4. Compare your grouping system with those of your classmates.

Think It Over
Classifying Explain which grouping system seemed most useful.

GUIDE FOR READING

◆ Why do scientists organize living things into groups?

◆ What is the relationship between classification and evolution?

Reading Tip Before you read, make a list of the boldfaced vocabulary terms. As you read, write the meaning of each term in your own words.

Suppose you had only ten minutes to run into a supermarket to get what you need—milk and tomatoes. Could you do it? In most supermarkets this would be an easy task. First, you might go to the dairy aisle and find the milk. Then you'd go to the produce aisle and find the tomatoes. Finally, you'd pay for the items and leave the store.

Now imagine shopping for these same items in a market where the shelves were organized in a random manner. To find what you need, you'd have to search through boxes of cereal, cans of tuna, bins of apples, and much more. You could be there for a long time!

Why Do Scientists Classify?

Just as shopping can be a problem in a disorganized store, finding information about one of the millions of kinds of organisms can also be a problem. Today, scientists have identified at least 2.5 million kinds of organisms on Earth. This number includes all forms of life, from plants and animals to bacteria. It is important for biologists to have all these living things organized.

People organize a lot of things into groups. For example, if a friend asks you what kind of music you like, you might say that you like country or rap music. Although you may not know it, you have grouped the music you like. **Classification** is the process of grouping things based on their similarities.

218

Biologists use classification to organize living things into groups so that the organisms are easier to study. The scientific study of how living things are classified is called **taxonomy** (tak SAHN uh mee). Taxonomy is useful because once an organism is classified, a scientist knows a lot about that organism. For example, if you know that crows are classified as birds, you know that crows have wings, feathers, and a beak.

INTEGRATING EARTH SCIENCE Biologists aren't the only scientists who classify things. For example, geologists—scientists who study the structure and history of Earth—classify rocks. Geologists separate rocks into three groups according to how they formed. By classifying rocks in this way, geologists can make sense of the variety of rocks on Earth.

Early Classification Systems

The first scientist to develop a classification system for organisms was the Greek scholar Aristotle. In the fourth century B.C., Aristotle observed many animals. He recorded each animal's appearance, behavior, and movement. Then he divided animals into three groups: those that fly, those that swim, and those that walk, crawl, or run.

Aristotle could see that even though organisms in a group moved in a similar way, they were different in many other ways. So he used their differences to divide each group into subgroups—smaller groups of organisms that shared other similarities.

Aristotle's method of using careful observations as the basis for classification and his idea of creating subgroups are still used today. However, organisms are no longer classified into large groups on the basis of how they move or where they live.

☑ *Checkpoint* *What were the three major groups of animals in Aristotle's system of classification?*

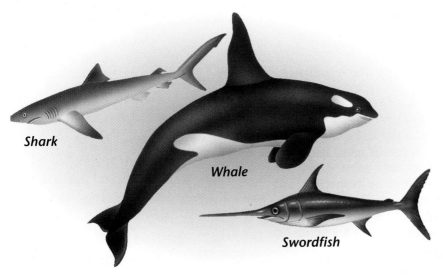

Shark

Whale

Swordfish

Figure 9 Aristotle would have classified this shark, whale, and swordfish together. However, he would have separated them into subgroups because they differ from each other in many ways. *Classifying List two differences that would place these animals into separate subgroups.*

What's In a Name?

You don't have to know Latin to understand the meaning of a scientific name. Just hearing the name *Ursus horribilis* should tell you that you don't want to meet that organism up close. *Ursus horribilis* is commonly known as a grizzly bear. The Latin word *ursus* means "bear" and *horribilis* means "horrible or feared."

A species name describes an organism like an adjective describes the noun it modifies. Some names describe a specific trait; others tell who discovered the organism. For example, *Pheidole fullerae* is the name of a species of ants discovered by an office worker named Fuller. Other names tell you where the organism was discovered or where it lives. Guess where you'd find the plant *Viola missouriensis*.

In Your Journal

Look in dictionaries or other reference books to find the meaning of these species names: *Musca domestica, Hirudo medicinalis,* and *Cornus florida.* Then try to identify English words that are derived from the Latin terms.

The Classification System of Linnaeus

In the 1750s, a Swedish scientist named Carolus Linnaeus expanded on Aristotle's ideas of classification. Like Aristotle, Linnaeus used observations as the basis of his system. He wrote descriptions of organisms from his observations, and placed organisms in groups based on their observable features.

Linnaeus also used his observations to devise a naming system for organisms. In Linnaeus's naming system, called **binomial nomenclature** (by NOH mee ul NOH men klay chur), each organism is given a two-part name.

The first part of an organism's scientific name is its genus. A **genus** (JEE nus) (plural *genera*) is a classification grouping that contains similar, closely related organisms. For example, pumas, ocelots, and house cats are all classified in the genus *Felis*. Organisms that are classified in the genus *Felis* share characteristics such as sharp, retractable claws and behaviors such as hunting other animals.

The second part of an organism's scientific name is its species name. A **species** (SPEE sheez) is a group of similar organisms that can mate and produce fertile offspring in nature. A species name sets one species in a genus apart from another. The species name often describes a distinctive feature of an organism, such as where it lives or its color. For example, the scientific name for many pumas, or mountain lions, is *Felis concolor*. *Concolor* means "the same color" in Latin. The scientific name for some ocelots is *Felis pardalis*. The word *pardalis* means "spotted like a panther" in Latin. The scientific name for house cats is *Felis domesticus*. The species name *domesticus* means "of the house" in Latin.

Figure 10 These animals belong to the genus *Felis*. The species names of the animals distinguish them from each other. **A.** This puma's coat is one color, which is indicated by its species name *concolor*. **B.** This ocelot has a spotted coat, which is described by its species name *pardalis*. **C.** The species name of this kitten is *domesticus*, which indicates that it is a house cat.

Linnaeus's system might remind you of the way you are named because you, also, have a two-part name made up of your first name and your family name. Your two-part name distinguishes you from others. In a similar way, binomial nomenclature ensures that a combination of two names distinguishes one kind of organism from another. Together, a genus and a species name identify one kind of organism.

Notice that both the genus and species names are Latin words. Linnaeus used Latin words in his naming system because Latin was the language that scientists communicated in during that time. Notice also that a complete scientific name is written in italics. The genus is capitalized while the species name begins with a small letter.

Binomial nomenclature makes it easy for scientists to communicate about an organism because everyone uses the same name for the same organism. Look at the organism in Figure 11. This photograph shows one type of pine tree that grows in the southern United States. People call this tree by any one of a number of common names: loblolly pine, longstraw pine, or Indian pine. Fortunately, this tree has only one scientific name, *Pinus taeda*.

☑ *Checkpoint* Which part of a scientific name is like your first name? Your family name?

Figure 11 Although there are many common names for this tree, it has only one scientific name.
Making Generalizations What is the advantage of having scientific names for organisms?

Levels of Classification

The classification system that scientists use today is based on the contributions of Aristotle and Linnaeus. But today's classification system uses a series of seven levels to classify organisms. To help you understand the levels in classification, imagine a room filled with everybody who lives in your state. First, all of the people who live in your *town* raise their hands. Then, those who live in your *neighborhood* raise their hands. Then, those who live on your *street* raise their hands. Finally, those who live in your *house* raise their hands. Each time, fewer people raise their hands. But you'd be in all of the groups. The most general group you belong to is the state. The most specific group is the house. The more levels you share with others, the more you have in common with them.

The Seven Levels of Classification Modern biologists classify organisms into the seven levels shown in Figure 12. Of course, organisms are not grouped by where they live but rather by their shared characteristics. First an organism is placed in a broad group, which in turn is divided into more specific groups.

A kingdom is the broadest level of organization. Within a kingdom, there are phyla (FY luh) (singular *phylum*). Within each phylum are classes. Each class is divided into orders. Each order contains families, and each family contains at least one genus. Finally, within a genus, there are species. The more classification levels that two organisms share, the more characteristics they have in common.

Classifying an Owl Take a closer look at Figure 12 to see how the levels of classification apply to the great horned owl, a member of the animal kingdom. Look at the top row of the figure. As you can see, a wide variety of organisms also belong to the animal kingdom. Now, look at the phylum, class, and order levels. Notice that as you move down the levels in the figure, there are fewer kinds of organisms in each group. More importantly, the organisms in each group have more in common with each other. For example, the class Aves includes all birds, while the order Strigiformes only includes owls. Different owls have more in common with each other than they do with other birds.

☑ *Checkpoint* *List the seven levels of classification from the broadest to the most specific.*

Kingdom Animalia

Phylum Chordata

Class Aves

Order Strigiformes

Family Strygidae

Genus *Bubo*

Species *Bubo virginianus*

Figure 12 Scientists use seven levels to classify organisms such as the great horned owl. Notice that, as you move down the levels, the number of organisms decreases. The organisms at lower levels share more characteristics with each other. *Interpreting Diagrams How many levels do a robin and the great horned owl share?*

Figure 13 These three species of finches that live on the Galapagos Islands may have arisen from a single species. Notice the differences in these birds' appearances, especially their beaks. **A.** This cactus finch uses its pointed beak to pierce the outer covering of cactus plants. **B.** The warbler finch uses its needlelike beak to trap insects. **C.** The large-billed ground finch cracks open large seeds with its strong, wide beak.

Evolution and Classification

At the time that Linnaeus developed his classification system, people thought that species never change. They could see that some organisms were similar. They thought that these organisms had always been similar, yet distinct from each other. In 1859, a British naturalist named Charles Darwin published a theory about how species can change over time. Darwin's theory has had a major impact on how species are classified.

Darwin collected much of the data for his theory on the Galapagos Islands off the western coast of South America. As he studied the islands' finches, he observed that some species of finches were similar to each other but different from finches living in South America. Darwin hypothesized that some members of a single species of finch flew from South America to the islands. Once on the islands, the species changed little by little over a long time until it was very different from the species remaining in South America. In this way, two groups of a single species can accumulate enough differences over a long time to become two separate species. This process by which species gradually change over time is called **evolution**.

✓ *Checkpoint* *Where did Darwin collect much of his data?*

Classification Today

The theory of evolution changed the way biologists think about classification. Today, scientists understand that certain organisms are similar because they share a common ancestor. For example, Darwin hypothesized that the finches that lived on the Galapagos Islands shared a common ancestor with the finches that live in South America. When organisms share a common ancestor, they share an evolutionary history. Today's system of classification considers the history of a species when classifying the species. **Species with similar evolutionary histories are classified more closely together.**

How do scientists get information about the evolutionary history of a species? One way is by studying fossils. Scientists compare the body structures as well as the chemical makeup of fossils to each other and to modern organisms. This information adds to their knowledge of evolutionary relationships among organisms.

Scientists also obtain clues about the evolutionary history of a species by comparing the body structures of living organisms. For example, look at the organisms in Figure 14. Notice that the bones in the flipper of a whale are similar to the bones in the wing of a bat and in the arm of a human. This similarity indicates that whales, bats, and humans have a similar evolutionary history.

Additional information about evolutionary history can be learned by comparing the early development of different organisms. Humans and rabbits, for example, go through similar stages in their early development before birth. The similarity provides evidence that humans and rabbits may share some evolutionary history.

Figure 14 Compare the bones in the limbs of the bat, whale, and human. Although a bone may differ in size and shape, it is in a similar location in each of the limbs.
Inferring What do the bones in the limbs suggest about the animals' evolutionary history?

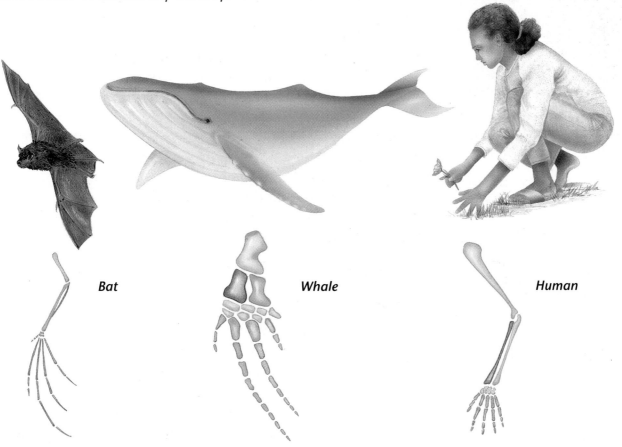

Bat   *Whale*   *Human*

Figure 15 Scientists analyze the chemical makeup of an organism's cells to learn about its evolutionary history. By comparing the chemicals in the cells of weasels, top, and skunks, bottom, scientists learned that these organisms are not as closely related as once thought.

Today, scientists rely primarily on information about the chemical makeup of cells to determine evolutionary history. The more closely two species are related, the more similar the chemicals that make up their cells. The skunk and weasel had been classified in the same family for 150 years. Recently, however, scientists compared some nucleic acids from the cells of skunks and weasels. Surprisingly, they found many differences, suggesting that these organisms are not as closely related as they had thought. Some scientists propose changing the classification of skunks. They suggest removing skunks from the family Mustelidae, which contains members of the weasel family. They want to reclassify skunks into a family called Mephitidae, which means "noxious gas" in Latin.

☑ *Checkpoint* *How do scientists use fossils to learn about the evolutionary history of organisms?*

Using the Classification System

You may be wondering why you should care about taxonomy. Suppose you wake up and feel something tickling your ankle. You fling back the covers and stare at a tiny creature crouching in the sheets by your right foot. Although it's only the size of a small melon seed, you don't like the looks of its two claws waving at you. Then, in a flash, it's gone—darting off under the safety of your covers.

How could you learn the identity of the organism that tickled you awake? One way to identify the organism would be to use a field guide. Field guides are books with illustrations that highlight differences between similar-looking organisms.

Another tool you could use to identify the organism is called a taxonomic key. A **taxonomic key** is a series of paired statements that describe the physical characteristics of different organisms.

Taxonomic Key

Step 1

1a. Has 8 legs	Go to Step 2.
1b. Has more than 8 legs	Go to Step 3.

Step 2

2a. Has one oval-shaped body region	Go to Step 4.
2b. Has two body regions	Go to Step 5.

Step 3

3a. Has one pair of legs on each body segment	Centipede
3b. Has two pairs of legs on each body segment	Millipede

Step 4

4a. Is less than 1 millimeter long	Mite
4b. Is more than 1 millimeter long	Tick

Step 5

5a. Has clawlike pincers	Go to Step 6.
5b. Has no clawlike pincers	Spider

Step 6

6a. Has a long tail with a stinger	Scorpion
6b. Has no tail or stinger	Pseudoscorpion

The taxonomic key in Figure 16 can help you identify the organism in your bed. To use the key, start by reading the two paired statements numbered 1a and 1b. Notice that the two statements are opposites. Decide which of the statements applies to the organism. Follow the direction at the end of that statement. For example, if the organism has 8 legs, follow the direction at the end of statement 1a, which says "Go to Step 2." Continue this process until you learn the organism's identity.

Figure 16 A taxonomic key is a series of paired statements that describe the physical characteristics of different organisms. There are six pairs of statements in this key. *Drawing Conclusions What is the identity of the organism shown in the picture?*

Section 3 Review

Science at Home

1. Why is it important for biologists to classify organisms into groups?
2. How is an organism's evolutionary history related to the way in which it is classified?
3. Explain Linnaeus's contribution to modern taxonomy.
4. **Thinking Critically Applying Concepts** Create a taxonomic key that could help identify a piece of fruit as either an apple, an orange, a strawberry, or a banana.

With a family member, go on a "classification hunt" in the kitchen. Look in your cabinets, refrigerator, and drawers to discover what classification systems your family uses to organize items. Discuss the advantages of organizing items in your kitchen in the way that you do. Then explain to your family member the importance of classification in biology.

Living Mysteries

In this lab, you will discover how some familiar mammals are classified.

Problem

How does a taxonomic key help you classify living things?

Skills Focus

observing, inferring, classifying

Materials

pencil   paper

Procedure

1. Observe the five organisms labeled A through E. All of these organisms belong to the class known as mammals, a group that includes you and many of the animals that are most familiar to you. Each of these mammals belongs to a different order of mammals.

2. Examine the paired statements in the taxonomic key for mammals. Begin at Step 1 to identify the order to which the mammal in photograph A belongs. Because the animal in photograph A does not have five digits or hands with flexible thumbs, go to Step 2. Keep following the key until you identify this mammal's order.

3. Use the key to identify the order to which the mammals in photographs B through E belong.

Taxonomic Key for Mammals

Step 1		
1a.	Have five digits on all limbs, and hands with flexible thumbs	Primates (includes monkeys, chimpanzees, and humans)
1b.	Do not have five digits on all limbs, and hands with flexible thumbs	Go to Step 2.
Step 2		
2a.	Have limbs with claws or nails, not hooves	Go to Step 3.
2b.	Have limbs with hooves, not claws or nails	Go to Step 4.
Step 3		
3a.	Have long muscular trunks	Proboscidea (includes all types of elephants)
3b.	Have sharp teeth for biting and tearing flesh	Carnivora (includes lions, bears, and raccoons)
Step 4		
4a.	Have limbs with an even number of hooved toes	Artiodactyla (includes antelopes, sheep and cows)
4b.	Have limbs with an odd number of hooved toes	Perissodactyla (includes horses and rhinoceroses)

Ⓐ

Analyze and Conclude

1. For each organism in the photographs, name the order of mammals to which it belongs.
2. Why is it important that the pair of statements at Step 1 be opposites?
3. Could you use this taxonomic key to classify animals that are not mammals? Explain.
4. Could you use this key to classify different types of carnivores, such as foxes, skunks, and walruses? Explain.

5. **Think About It** Based on your answers to questions 3 and 4, what can you infer about the limits of specific taxonomic keys?

More to Explore

Try making a taxonomic key to sort four or five everyday objects such as writing implements or shoes. Try out your key on a partner to test it. Make any necessary changes. Then, exchange keys with a classmate. Use the keys to sort the selected objects.

SECTION 4 The Six Kingdoms

DISCOVER • ACTIVITY

Which Organism Goes Where?

1. Your teacher will give you some organisms to observe. Two of the organisms are classified in the same kingdom.

2. Observe the organisms. Decide which organisms might belong in the same kingdom. Write the reasons for your decision. Wash your hands after handling the organisms.

3. Discuss your decision and reasoning with your classmates.

Think It Over

Forming Operational Definitions What characteristics do you think define the kingdom into which you placed the two organisms?

GUIDE FOR READING

◆ What are the six kingdoms into which all organisms are grouped?

Reading Tip Before you read the section, make a list of the headings. As you read, list the characteristics of organisms in each kingdom.

When Linnaeus developed his system of classification, there were two kingdoms: plant and animal. But, the use of the microscope led to the discovery of new organisms and the identification of differences among cells. A two-kingdom system was no longer useful. **Today, the system of classification includes six kingdoms: archaebacteria, eubacteria, protists, fungi, plants, and animals.** Organisms are placed into kingdoms based on their type of cells, their ability to make food, and the number of cells in their bodies.

Archaebacteria

In 1983, scientists took a water sample from a spot deep in the Pacific Ocean where hot gases and molten rock boiled into the ocean from Earth's interior. To their surprise, they discovered unicellular organisms in the sample. Today, scientists classify these organisms in a kingdom called Archaebacteria (ahr kee bak TEER ee uh), which means "ancient bacteria."

Archaebacteria can be either autotrophic or heterotrophic. Some live on the ocean floor, some in salty water, and some in hot springs. Don't be alarmed, but some even live in your intestines.

Figure 17 Heat-loving archaebacteria thrive in this hot spring in Yellowstone National Park.

Archaebacteria are **prokaryotes** (proh KAR ee ohtz), organisms whose cells lack a nucleus. A **nucleus** (NOO klee us) (plural *nuclei*) is a dense area in a cell that contains nucleic acids—the chemical instructions that direct the cell's activities. In prokaryotes, nucleic acids are not contained within a nucleus.

Eubacteria

What do the bacteria that produce yogurt have in common with the bacteria that give you strep throat? They both belong to the kingdom known as Eubacteria (yoo bak TEER ee uh). Like archaebacteria, eubacteria are unicellular prokaryotes. And like archaebacteria, some eubacteria are autotrophs while others are heterotrophs. Eubacteria are classified in their own kingdom, however, because their chemical makeup is different from that of archaebacteria.

Unlike some eubacteria, such as those that cause strep throat, most eubacteria are helpful. Some produce vitamins, some produce foods like yogurt, and some recycle essential chemicals, such as nitrogen.

☑ *Checkpoint* *How are eubacteria similar to archaebacteria? How do they differ?*

Protists

Slime molds, like the ones that frightened people near Dallas, are protists (PROH tists). The protist kingdom is sometimes called the "odds and ends" kingdom because its members are so different from one another. For example, some protists are autotrophs, while others are heterotrophs. Also, although most protists are unicellular, some, such as the organisms that are commonly called seaweeds, are multicellular.

You may be wondering why those protists that are unicellular are not classified in one of the kingdoms of bacteria. It is because, unlike bacteria, protists are **eukaryotes** (yoo KAR ee ohtz)—organisms with cells that contain nuclei.

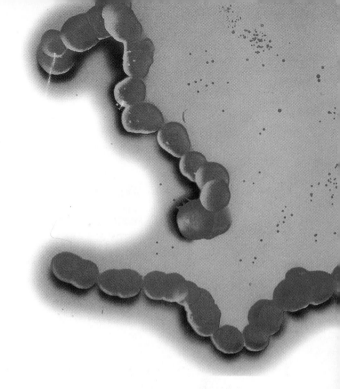

Figure 18 Most eubacteria are helpful. However, these eubacteria are *Streptococci,* which can give you strep throat! *Classifying What characteristics do eubacteria share?*

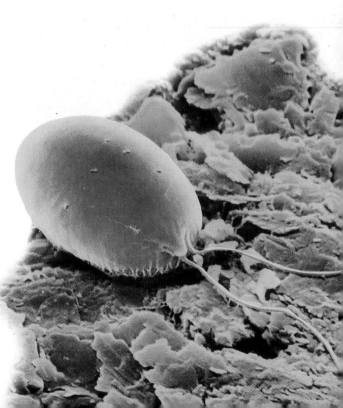

Figure 19 The protist kingdom contains diverse organisms. This unicellular green protist, which lives in fresh water, is called *Chlamydomonas.*

Figure 20 The animal you see peeking out of this cuplike fungus is a poison arrow frog. These organisms live in the forests of Central America. *Interpreting Photographs* Which organisms in the photograph are heterotrophs?

Fungi

If you have ever seen mushrooms, you have seen fungi (FUN jy). Mushrooms, molds, and mildew are all fungi. Most fungi are multicellular eukaryotes. A few, such as yeast, are unicellular eukaryotes. Fungi are found almost everywhere on land, but only a few live in fresh water. All fungi are heterotrophs. Most fungi feed on dead or decaying organisms. The cuplike fungus you see in Figure 20 obtains its food from the parts of plants that are decaying in the soil.

Plants

Dandelions on a lawn, mosses in a forest, and tomatoes in a garden are familiar kinds of plants. Plants are all multicellular eukaryotes. In addition, plants are autotrophs that make their own food. Without plants, life on Earth would not exist. Plants feed almost all of the heterotrophs on Earth. The plant kingdom includes a variety of organisms. Some plants produce flowers, while others do not. Some plants, such as a giant sequoia tree, can grow very tall. Others, like mosses, never grow taller than a few centimeters.

Animals

A dog, a flea on the dog's ear, and a rabbit the dog chases have much in common because all are animals. All animals are multicellular eukaryotes. In addition, all animals are heterotrophs. Animals have different adaptations that allow them to locate food, capture it, eat it, and digest it. Members of the animal kingdom are found in diverse environments on Earth.

Section 4 Review

1. List the six kingdoms into which all organisms are classified.
2. Which two kingdoms include only prokaryotes?
3. Which kingdoms include only heterotrophic organisms?
4. **Thinking Critically Classifying** In a rain forest, you see an unfamiliar green organism. As you watch, an ant walks onto one of its cuplike leaves. The leaf closes and traps the ant. Do you have enough information to classify this organism? Why or why not?

Check Your Progress
CHAPTER PROJECT

Now that you have completed your observations, analyze your data. Conclude whether your object is alive. Then review what you learned about the six kingdoms. Which kingdom does your object belong in or most resemble? (*Hint:* Recall that an organism's nutrition is an important distinction among some of the kingdoms. How did your mystery object obtain its food?)

SECTION 1 What Is Life?

Key Ideas

◆ All living things have a cellular organization, contain similar chemicals, use energy, grow and develop, respond to their surroundings, and reproduce.

◆ Organisms arise from other organisms similar to themselves.

◆ All living things must satisfy their basic needs for energy, water, living space, and stable internal conditions.

Key Terms

organism	variable
cell	autotroph
unicellular	heterotroph
multicellular	homeostasis
development	
stimulus	
response	
reproduce	
spontaneous generation	
controlled experiment	

SECTION 2 The Origin of Life

INTEGRATING EARTH SCIENCE

Key Ideas

◆ Nitrogen, water vapor, carbon dioxide, and methane were probably the most abundant gases in Earth's atmosphere 3.6 billion years ago. Today the major gases are nitrogen and oxygen.

◆ Scientists hypothesize that over millions of years, the small chemical units of life formed in Earth's oceans. Some joined to form the large chemical building blocks found in cells.

Key Term
fossil

SECTION 3 Classifying Organisms

Key Ideas

◆ Biologists use classification to organize living things into groups so that the organisms are easy to study.

◆ Carolus Linnaeus devised a system of naming organisms called binomial nomenclature.

◆ Today, organisms are classified into seven levels: kingdom, phylum, class, order, family, genus, and species.

◆ Species with similar evolutionary histories are classified more closely together.

Key Terms

classification
taxonomy
binomial
   nomenclature
genus
species
evolution
taxonomic key

SECTION 4 The Six Kingdoms

Key Ideas

◆ All organisms are grouped into six kingdoms: archaebacteria, eubacteria, protists, fungi, plants, and animals.

◆ Some characteristics used to classify organisms into kingdoms are cell structure, the way organisms obtain food, and the number of cells in organisms.

Key Terms

prokaryote	nucleus	eukaryote

USING THE INTERNET

www.science-explorer.phschool.com

California Test Prep: Reviewing Content

Multiple Choice

Choose the letter of the answer that best completes each statement.

1. The idea that life could spring from nonliving matter is called
   a. development.
   b. spontaneous generation.
   c. homeostasis.
   d. evolution.

2. Which gas was not part of Earth's atmosphere 3.6 billion years ago?
   a. methane   b. nitrogen
   c. oxygen   d. water vapor

3. The science of placing organisms into groups based on shared characteristics is called
   a. development.   b. biology.
   c. taxonomy.   d. evolution.

4. A genus is divided into
   a. species.   b. phyla.
   c. families.   d. classes.

5. Which organisms have cells that do not contain nuclei?
   a. protists   b. archaebacteria
   c. plants   d. fungi

True or False

If the statement is true, write true. If it is false, change the underlined word or words to make the statement true.

6. Your first teeth fall out and are replaced by permanent teeth. This is an example of <u>development</u>.

7. When you eat salad, you are acting like an <u>autotroph</u>.

8. The first organisms on Earth were probably <u>heterotrophs</u>.

9. <u>Aristotle</u> devised a system of naming organisms that is called binomial nomenclature.

10. The process by which organisms gradually change over a long period of time is called <u>evolution</u>.

Checking Concepts

11. Your friend thinks that plants are not alive because they do not move. How would you respond to your friend?

12. Describe where Earth's early organisms lived, and how they obtained food.

13. What are the advantages of identifying an organism by its scientific name?

14. What evidence do scientists use to learn about the evolutionary history of a species?

15. What is the major difference between fungi and plants?

16. **Writing to Learn** Write a paragraph that describes how your pet, or a friend's pet, meets its needs as a living thing.

Thinking Visually

17. **Concept Map** Copy the concept map about the needs of organisms onto a separate sheet of paper. Then complete it and add a title. (For more on concept maps, see the Skills Handbook.)

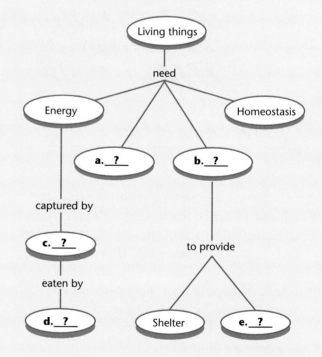

Test Prep: Skills

A student designed an experiment to test how light affects the growth of plants. Refer to the illustrations below to answer Questions 18–21.

18. **Controlling Variables** Is this a controlled experiment? If not, why not? If so, identify the variable.
19. **Developing Hypotheses** What hypothesis might this experiment be testing?

20. **Predicting** Based on what you know about plants, predict how each plant will have changed after two weeks.
21. **Designing Experiments** Design a controlled experiment to determine whether the amount of water that a plant receives affects its growth.

Thinking Critically

22. **Applying Concepts** How do you know that a robot is not alive?
23. **Classifying** Which two of the following organisms are most closely related: *Entamoeba histolytica, Escherichia coli, Entamoeba coli?* Explain your answer.
24. **Relating Cause and Effect** When people believed that spontaneous generation occurred, there was a recipe for making mice: Place a dirty shirt and a few wheat grains in an open pot; wait three weeks. List the reasons why this recipe might have worked. How could you demonstrate that spontaneous generation was not responsible for the appearance of mice?

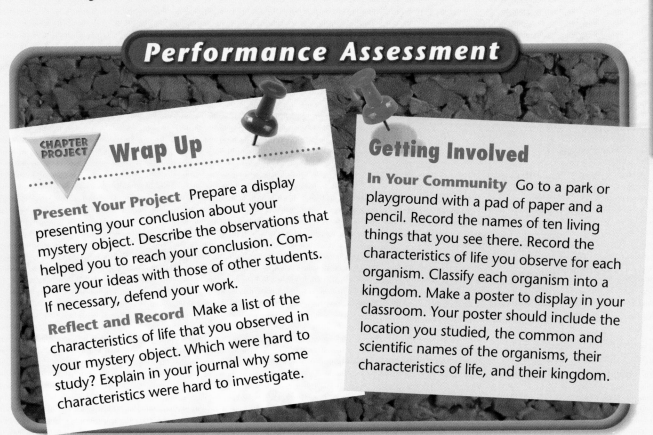

Performance Assessment

CHAPTER PROJECT Wrap Up

Present Your Project Prepare a display presenting your conclusion about your mystery object. Describe the observations that helped you to reach your conclusion. Compare your ideas with those of other students. If necessary, defend your work.

Reflect and Record Make a list of the characteristics of life that you observed in your mystery object. Which were hard to study? Explain in your journal why some characteristics were hard to investigate.

Getting Involved

In Your Community Go to a park or playground with a pad of paper and a pencil. Record the names of ten living things that you see there. Record the characteristics of life you observe for each organism. Classify each organism into a kingdom. Make a poster to display in your classroom. Your poster should include the location you studied, the common and scientific names of the organisms, their characteristics of life, and their kingdom.

CHAPTER 7 ASSESSMENT

CHAPTER
8 Viruses and Bacteria

> If you've ever had chicken pox, this virus was responsible for your illness.

CALIFORNIA SCIENCE CONTENT STANDARDS

The following California Science Content Standards are addressed in this chapter:

1. All living organisms are composed of cells, from just one to many trillions, whose details usually are visible only through a microscope.

   e. Cells divide to increase their numbers through a process of mitosis, which results in two daughter cells with identical sets of chromosomes.

2. A typical cell of any organism contains genetic instructions that specify its traits. Those traits may be modified by environmental influences.

   a. The differences between the life cycles and reproduction of sexual and asexual organisms.

3. Biological evolution accounts for the diversity of species developed through gradual processes over many generations.

   a. Both genetic variation and environmental factors are causes of evolution and diversity of organisms.

5. The anatomy and physiology of plants and animals illustrate the complementary nature of structure and function.

236

Be a Disease Detective

The virus pictured on this page may look harmless, but it's not. If you've ever had chicken pox, you've experienced it firsthand. Soon after the virus enters your body, red blotches appear on your skin, and you begin to itch. The chicken pox virus as well as many other viruses and bacteria cause diseases that pass from person to person. In this chapter, you will learn about viruses and bacteria, and how they affect other living things.

Not too long ago, catching certain viral and bacterial "childhood diseases" was a routine part of growing up. Those diseases included chicken pox, mumps, and pertussis (whooping cough), and others. In this project, you will select one childhood disease to investigate.

Your Goal To survey people of different ages to find out what they know about a childhood disease.

To complete this project successfully, you must
◆ select and research one disease to learn more about it
◆ prepare a questionnaire to survey people about their knowledge and experience with the disease
◆ question a total of 30 people in different age groups, and report any patterns that you find

Get Started With several classmates, make a list of childhood diseases. Choose one disease for your survey. Do some research to find out more about the disease. Also write down the steps involved in carrying out a survey. What questions will you need to ask? How will you select the people for your survey? Draft your questionnaire.

Check Your Progress You'll be working on this project as you study this chapter. To keep your project on track, look for Check Your Progress boxes at the following points.
Section 1 Review, page 244: Write your questionnaire, and identify the people to survey.
Section 3 Review, page 263: Analyze your survey results and look for patterns.

Wrap Up At the end of the chapter (page 267), you will present your survey results to your classmates.

---

b. Organ systems function because of the contributions of individual organs, tissues, and cells. The failure of any part can affect the entire system.

7. Scientific progress is made by asking meaningful questions and conducting careful investigations.

a. Select and use appropriate tools and technology to perform tests, collect data, and display data.

b. Utilize a variety of print and electronic resources (including the World Wide Web) to collect information as evidence as part of a research project.

c. Communicate the logical connection among hypothesis, science concepts, tests conducted, data collected, and conclusions drawn from the scientific evidence.

d. Construct scale models, maps and appropriately labeled diagrams to communicate scientific knowledge.

SECTION
1 Viruses

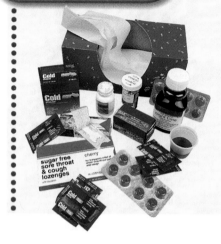

Can You Cure a Cold?

1. Look at the cold medications that your teacher displays. You may have used some of these products when you had a cold.

2. Read the ingredient labels on the products. Read the product claims.

3. Decide which medication you would use if you had a cold. Record the reasons for your choice of product.

Think It Over

Inferring Do medications cure colds? Explain your answer.

GUIDE FOR READING

◆ Why are viruses considered to be nonliving?

◆ What is the basic structure of a virus?

◆ How do viruses multiply?

Reading Tip As you read, use the headings to outline information about the characteristics of viruses.

It is a dark and quiet night. An enemy spy slips silently across the border. Invisible to the guards, the spy creeps cautiously along the edge of the road, heading toward the command center. Undetected, the spy sneaks by the center's security system and reaches the door. Breaking into the control room, the spy takes command of the central computer. The enemy is in control.

Moments later the command center's defenses finally activate. Depending on the enemy's strength and cunning, the defenses may squash the invasion before much damage is done. Otherwise the enemy will win and take over the territory.

What Is a Virus?

Although this spy story may read like a movie script, it describes events that can occur in your body. The spy acts very much like a virus invading an organism. A **virus** is a small, nonliving particle that invades and then reproduces inside a living cell.

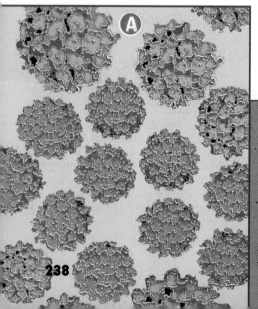

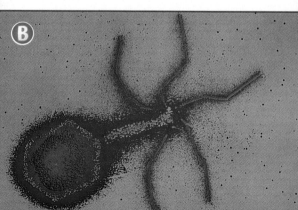

Biologists consider viruses to be nonliving because viruses are not cells. Viruses do not use energy to grow or to respond to their surroundings. Viruses also cannot make food, take in food, or produce wastes.

The only way in which viruses are like organisms is in their ability to multiply. But, although viruses can multiply, they do so differently than organisms. Viruses can only multiply when they are inside a living cell. The organism that a virus enters and multiplies inside is called a host. A **host** is a living thing that provides a source of energy for a virus or an organism. Organisms that live on or in a host and cause harm to the host are called **parasites** (PA ruh syts). Almost all viruses act like parasites because they destroy the cells in which they multiply.

No organisms are safe from viruses. Viruses can infect the organisms of all six kingdoms—archaebacteria, eubacteria, protists, fungi, plants, and animals. Each virus, however, can enter, or infect, only a few types of cells in a few specific species. For example, most cold viruses only infect cells in the nose and throat of humans. The tobacco mosaic virus only infects the leaf cells of tobacco plants.

☑ *Checkpoint* *When you have a cold, are you the host or the parasite?*

Naming Viruses

Because viruses are not alive, scientists do not use binomial nomenclature to name them. Instead, scientists may name a virus, such as the polio virus, after the disease it causes. Other viruses are named for the organisms they infect, as is the case with the tomato mosaic virus, which infects tomato plants. Scientists named the Ebola virus after the place in Africa where it was first found. And scientists sometimes name viruses after people. The Epstein-Barr virus, for example, was named for the two scientists who first identified the virus that causes the disease known as infectious mononucleosis.

Figure 1 Viruses are tiny nonliving particles that invade and reproduce inside living cells. Viruses can infect the organisms of all six kingdoms. **A.** Papilloma viruses cause warts to form on human skin. **B.** This virus, called a bacteriophage, infects bacteria. **C.** Tobacco mosaic viruses infect tobacco plants. **D.** The rabies virus infects nerve cells in certain animals. **E.** The blue circles in this photo are viruses that cause German measles in humans.

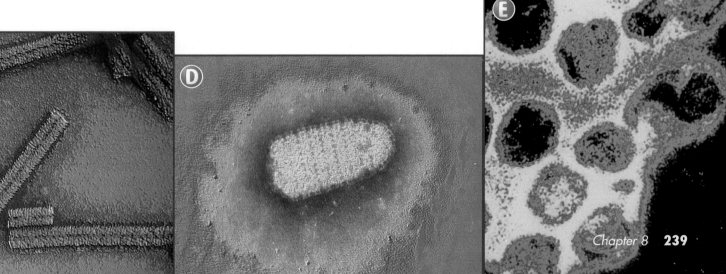

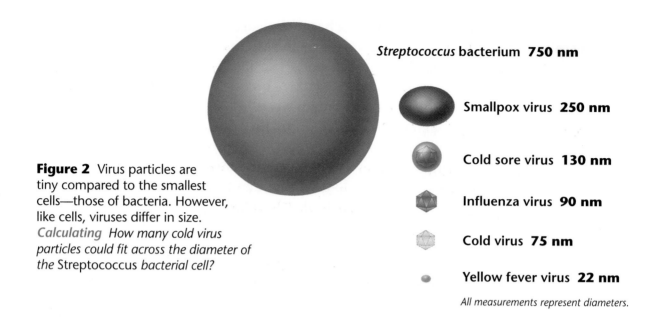

Streptococcus bacterium **750 nm**

Smallpox virus 250 nm

Cold sore virus 130 nm

Influenza virus 90 nm

Cold virus 75 nm

Yellow fever virus 22 nm

All measurements represent diameters.

Figure 2 Virus particles are tiny compared to the smallest cells—those of bacteria. However, like cells, viruses differ in size. *Calculating How many cold virus particles could fit across the diameter of the* Streptococcus *bacterial cell?*

The Shapes and Sizes of Viruses

As you can see from the photographs in Figure 1, viruses vary widely in shape. Some viruses are round, while some others are rod-shaped. Other viruses have bricklike, threadlike, or bulletlike shapes. There are even some viruses, such as the bacteriophage in Figure 1B, that have complex, robotlike shapes. A **bacteriophage** (bak TEER ee oh fayj) is a virus that infects bacteria. In fact, its name means "bacteria eater."

Just as viruses vary in shape, they also vary in size. Viruses are smaller than cells and cannot be seen with the microscopes you use in school. Viruses are so small that they are measured in units called nanometers (nm). One nanometer is one billionth of a meter (m). The smallest viruses, such as yellow fever viruses, are about 22 nanometers in diameter. The largest viruses, such as smallpox viruses, are about 250 nanometers in diameter. Most viruses measure between 50 and 60 nanometers in diameter. The smallest cells, those of bacteria, are much larger than the average virus, as you can see in Figure 2.

Structure of Viruses

Although the viruses in Figure 1 may look very different, they all have a similar structure. **All viruses have two basic parts: an outer coat that protects the virus and an inner core made of genetic material.** A virus's genetic material contains the instructions for making new viruses. Figure 3 shows the basic structure of a virus. The structure might remind you of a chocolate-covered candy. The outer coat of a virus is like the chocolate on the outside of a candy. The inner core is like the gooey filling inside the candy.

Genetic material

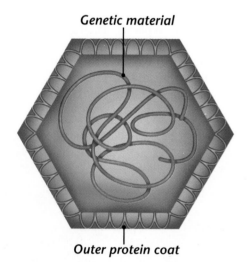

Outer protein coat

Figure 3 All viruses have a similar structure. They have an outer coat made of protein and an inner core that contains genetic material.

240

The coat of a virus plays an important role during the invasion of a host cell. This coat is made of proteins. Each virus contains unique proteins in its coat. The shape of the proteins allows the virus's coat to attach to, or lock onto, certain cells in the host. Like keys, a virus's proteins only fit into certain "locks," or proteins, on the surface of a host's cells. Figure 4 shows how the lock-and-key action works. Because this action is highly specific, a certain virus will attach to only one or a few types of cells. For example, the human immunodeficiency virus, or HIV, can only attach to specific cells in the human body. These human cells have proteins on their surfaces that complement, or "fit," those on the virus.

✓ *Checkpoint* *Why does a virus only invade a specific kind of cell?*

How Viruses Multiply

After a virus attaches to a cell, it enters the cell. **Once inside, a virus's genetic material takes over the cell's functions. The genetic material directs the cell to produce the virus's proteins and genetic material. These proteins and genetic material are then assembled into new viruses.** Some viruses take over the cell's functions immediately. Other viruses wait for a while.

Active Viruses After entering a cell, an active virus immediately goes into action. The virus's genetic material takes over the cell's functions, and the cell quickly begins to produce the virus's proteins and genetic material. Then these parts assemble into new viruses. Like a photocopy machine left in the "on" position, the invaded cell makes copy after copy of new viruses. When it

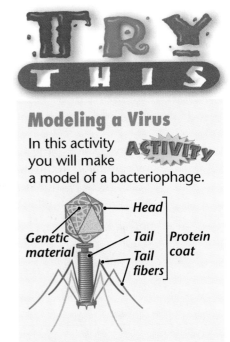

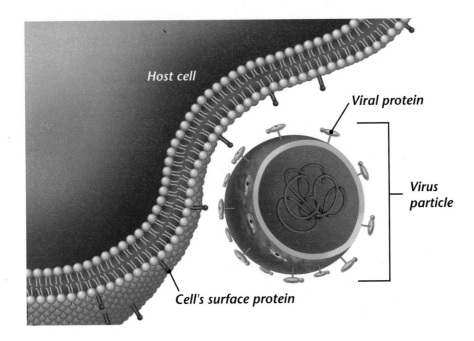

Host cell

Viral protein

Virus particle

Cell's surface protein

Figure 4 The shape of the proteins in a virus's coat determines what type of cell the virus will infect. The proteins fit together with the cell's proteins in the same way that a key fits a lock. Once attached, the virus can release its genetic material into the cell.

is full of new viruses, the host cell bursts open and releases the new viruses. In *Exploring How Viruses Multiply*, you can follow how an active virus multiplies.

Hidden Viruses Some viruses function differently than active viruses after entering a cell—at least for a while. The genetic material of these viruses enters a host cell. Then, instead of going into action like an active virus does, the virus's genetic material becomes part of the cell's genetic material. The virus does not appear to affect the cell's functions. The virus's genetic material may stay in this inactive state for a long time. Then, for reasons that scientists do not yet fully understand, the virus's genetic material suddenly becomes active. It takes over the cell's

EXPLORING *How Viruses Multiply*

Active viruses enter cells and immediately begin to multiply, leading to the quick death of the invaded cells. Other viruses "hide" for a while inside the host cells before they become active.

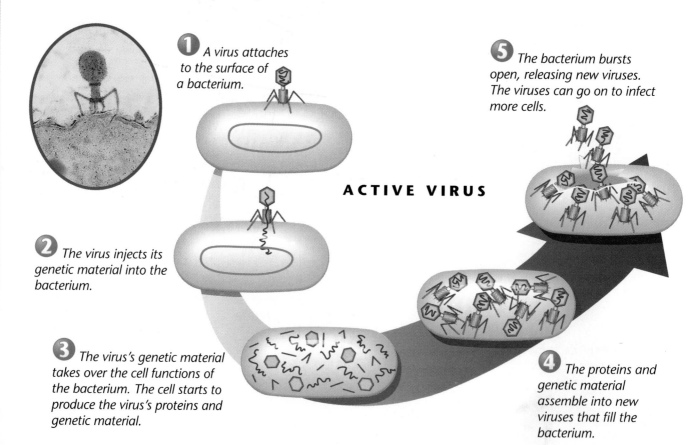

1 A virus attaches to the surface of a bacterium.

2 The virus injects its genetic material into the bacterium.

3 The virus's genetic material takes over the cell functions of the bacterium. The cell starts to produce the virus's proteins and genetic material.

ACTIVE VIRUS

4 The proteins and genetic material assemble into new viruses that fill the bacterium.

5 The bacterium bursts open, releasing new viruses. The viruses can go on to infect more cells.

functions in much the same way that active viruses do. In a short time, the cell is full of new viruses, and it bursts open to release them. Look at *Exploring How Viruses Multiply* to see how a hidden virus multiplies.

The virus that causes cold sores in humans is an example of a hidden virus. The virus can remain inactive for months or years inside the nerve cells in the face. While hidden, the virus causes no symptoms. When it becomes active, the virus causes a swollen, painful sore to form near the mouth. Strong sunlight and stress are two factors that scientists believe may activate a cold sore virus. After an active period, the virus once again "hides" in the nerve cells until it becomes active once again.

☑ *Checkpoint* **Give one example of a hidden virus.**

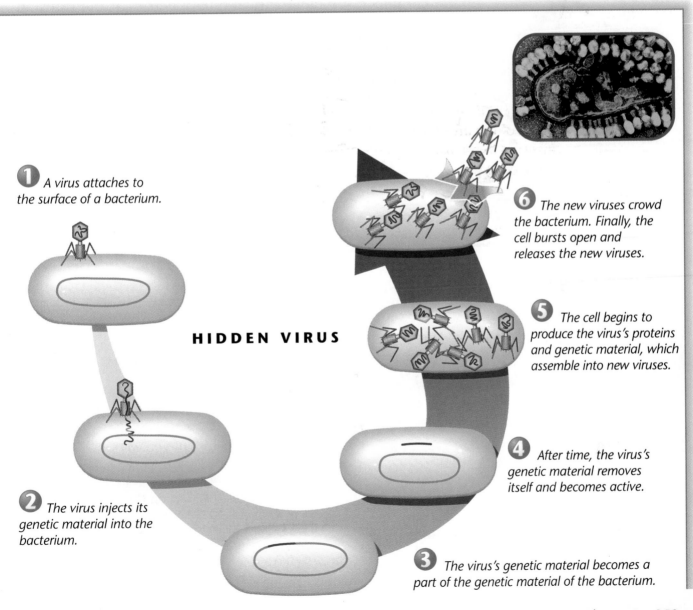

HIDDEN VIRUS

1 *A virus attaches to the surface of a bacterium.*

2 *The virus injects its genetic material into the bacterium.*

3 *The virus's genetic material becomes a part of the genetic material of the bacterium.*

4 *After time, the virus's genetic material removes itself and becomes active.*

5 *The cell begins to produce the virus's proteins and genetic material, which assemble into new viruses.*

6 *The new viruses crowd the bacterium. Finally, the cell bursts open and releases the new viruses.*

Viruses and the Living World

If you've ever had a cold sore or been sick with a cold or flu, you know that viruses can cause disease in organisms. Some diseases, such as colds, are mild—people are sick for a short time but soon recover. Other diseases, such as acquired immunodeficiency syndrome, or AIDS, can cause death.

Viruses also cause diseases in organisms other than humans. For example, the rice dwarf virus stunts the growth of rice plants, resulting in lower yields of this food crop. Alfalfa mosaic disease kills alfalfa plants, an important food source for horses, cattle, and other farm animals. House pets, such as dogs and cats, can get a deadly viral disease called distemper. Dogs, foxes, and raccoons are a few of the animals that rabies viruses can infect. If a rabid animal bites a person, it can transmit rabies to the person.

 INTEGRATING TECHNOLOGY By now you might be thinking that viruses do no good. But the news about viruses isn't all bad. Scientists are putting viruses to use in a new technique called gene therapy. In gene therapy, scientists take advantage of a virus's ability to get inside a host cell. They add important genetic material to a virus and then use the virus as a "messenger service" to deliver the genetic material to cells that need it. Scientists have used gene therapy on people with disorders such as cystic fibrosis (SIS tik fy BRO sis). People with cystic fibrosis do not have the genetic material they need to keep their lungs functioning properly. Gene therapy shows some promise to become a medical treatment for cystic fibrosis and other disorders.

Figure 5 The beautiful striped pattern on this Rembrandt tulip was originally caused by the tulip mosaic virus.

Section 1 Review

1. Explain why biologists consider viruses to be nonliving.
2. Describe the basic structure of a virus.
3. Compare the two ways that viruses can multiply.
4. **Thinking Critically Inferring** Scientists hypothesize that viruses could not have existed on Earth before organisms, such as bacteria, appeared. Use what you know about viruses to support this hypothesis.

Check Your Progress

CHAPTER PROJECT

By now, you should have a draft of the questions you will ask in your survey. Have your teacher review your questions. Then begin your survey. (*Hint*: Design the questionnaire so that you can easily record and tally the responses. Test your survey on a few people you know to make sure the questions are clear.)

How Many Viruses Fit on a Pin?

In this lab, you will make models to help you investigate the size of viruses.

Problem

How many viruses could fit on the head of a pin?

Materials

straight pin
pencil
scissors
calculator (optional)

long strips of paper
meter stick
tape

Procedure

1. Examine the head of a straight pin. Write a prediction about the number of viruses that could fit on the pinhead. **CAUTION:** *Avoid pushing the pin against anyone's skin.*

2. Assume that the pinhead has a diameter of about 1 mm. If the pinhead were enlarged 10,000 times, its diameter would measure 10 m. Create a model of the pinhead by cutting and taping together narrow strips of paper to make a strip that is 10 m long. The strip of paper represents the diameter of the enlarged pinhead.

3. Lay the 10-m strip of paper on the floor of your classroom or in the hall. Imagine creating a large circle that had the strip as its diameter. The circle would be the pinhead at the enlarged size. Calculate the area of the enlarged pinhead using this formula:

$$\text{Area} = \pi \times \text{radius}^2$$

Remember that you can find the radius by dividing the diameter by 2.

4. A virus particle may measure 200 nm on each side (1 nm equals a billionth of a meter). If the virus were enlarged 10,000 times, each side would measure 0.002 m. Cut out a square 0.002 m by 0.002 m to serve as a model for a virus. *(Hint:* 0.002 m = 2 mm)

5. Next, find the area in meters of one virus particle at the enlarged size. Remember that the area of a square equals side × side.

6. Now divide the area of the pinhead that you calculated in Step 3 by the area of one virus particle to find out how many viruses could fit on the pinhead.

7. Exchange your work with a partner, and check each other's calculations. Make any corrections that are necessary.

Analyze and Conclude

1. Approximately how many viruses can fit on the head of a pin?

2. How did your calculation compare with your prediction? If the two numbers were very different, explain why they were different.

3. What did you learn about the size of viruses by magnifying both the viruses and pinheads to 10,000 times their actual size?

4. **Think About It** Why do scientists sometimes make and use enlarged models of very small things such as viruses?

More to Explore

Think of another everyday object that you could use to model some other facts about viruses, such as their shapes or how they infect cells. Describe your model and explain why the object would be a good choice.

SECTION
2 Bacteria

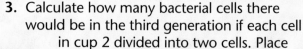

DISCOVER

How Quickly Can Bacteria Multiply?

1. Your teacher will give you some beans and paper cups. Number the cups 1 through 8. Each bean will represent a bacterial cell.

2. Put one bean into cup 1 to represent the first generation of bacteria. Approximately every 20 minutes, a bacterial cell reproduces by dividing into two cells. Put two beans into cup 2 to represent the second generation of bacteria.

3. Calculate how many bacterial cells there would be in the third generation if each cell in cup 2 divided into two cells. Place the correct number of beans in cup 3.

4. Repeat Step 3 five more times. All the cups should now contain beans. How many cells are in the eighth generation? How much time has elapsed since the first generation?

Think It Over

Inferring Based on this activity, explain why the number of bacteria can increase rapidly in a short period of time.

GUIDE FOR READING

◆ How are the cells of bacteria different from those of all other organisms?

◆ What positive roles do bacteria play in people's lives?

Reading Tip Before you read, make a list of the boldfaced vocabulary words in the section. Predict the meaning of each word. As you read, check your predictions.

Y ou may not know it, but seconds after you were born, tiny organisms surrounded and invaded your body. Today, millions of these organisms coat your skin. As you read this page, they swarm inside your nose, throat, and mouth. In fact, there are more of these organisms living in your mouth than there are people who are living on Earth. You don't see or feel these organisms because they are very small. But you cannot escape them. They are found nearly everywhere on Earth—in soil, rocks, Arctic ice, volcanoes, and in all living things. These organisms are bacteria.

The Bacterial Cell

Although there are many bacteria on Earth, they were not discovered until the late 1600s. A Dutch businessman named Anton van Leeuwenhoek (LAY vuhn hook) found them by accident. Leeuwenhoek had a rather unusual hobby—making microscopes. One day, while he was using one of his microscopes to look at scrapings from his teeth, he saw some tiny organisms in the sample. However, because his microscopes were not very powerful, Leeuwenhoek could not see any details inside these tiny organisms.

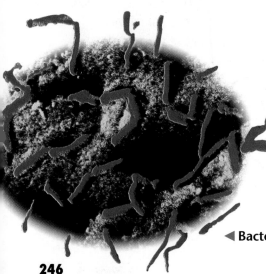

◄ Bacteria on the surface of a human tooth

If Leeuwenhoek had owned one of the high-powered microscopes in use today, he would have seen the single-celled organisms that are known as **bacteria** (singular *bacterium*) in detail. As you learned in Chapter 7, the cells of bacteria differ from the cells of other organisms in many ways. **Bacteria are prokaryotes. The genetic material in their cells is not contained in a nucleus.** In addition to lacking a nucleus, the cells of prokaryotes also lack many other structures that are found in the cells of eukaryotes. However, regardless of the structure of their cells, prokaryotes accomplish all tasks necessary for life. That is, each bacterial cell uses energy, grows and develops, responds to its surroundings, and reproduces.

Cell Shapes If you were to look at bacterial cells under a microscope, you would notice that bacterial cells have one of three basic shapes: spherical, rodlike, or spiral shaped. The shape of a bacterial cell helps scientists identify the type of bacteria. For example, bacteria that cause strep throat are spherical. Figure 6 shows the different shapes of bacterial cells.

Cell Structures The shape of a bacterial cell is determined by the chemical makeup of its outermost structure—the cell wall. Cell walls surround most bacterial cells. A bacterium's rigid cell wall helps to protect the cell.

Inside the cell wall is the cell membrane, which controls what materials pass into and out of the cell. The region inside the cell membrane, called the **cytoplasm** (SY toh plaz um), contains a gel-like material. Tiny structures called ribosomes are located in the cytoplasm. **Ribosomes** (RY buh sohmz) are chemical factories where proteins are produced. The cell's genetic material, which looks like a thick, tangled string, is also located in the cytoplasm. If you could untangle the genetic material, you would see that it forms a circular shape. The genetic material contains the instructions for all the cell's functions, such as how to produce proteins on the ribosomes.

Figure 6 Bacteria have three basic shapes. **A.** Like the bacteria that cause strep throat, these *Staphylococcus aureus* bacteria are spherical. They represent over 30 percent of the bacteria that live on your skin. **B.** *Escherichia coli* bacteria have rodlike shapes. These bacteria are found in your intestines. **C.** *Borrelia burgdorferi* bacteria, which cause Lyme disease, are spiral-shaped.

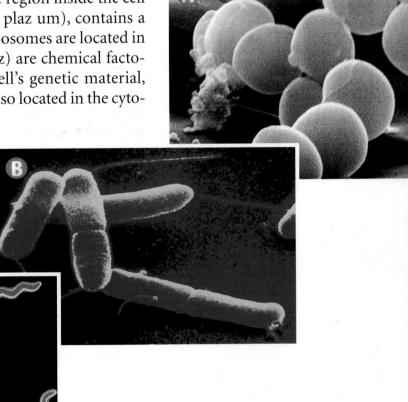

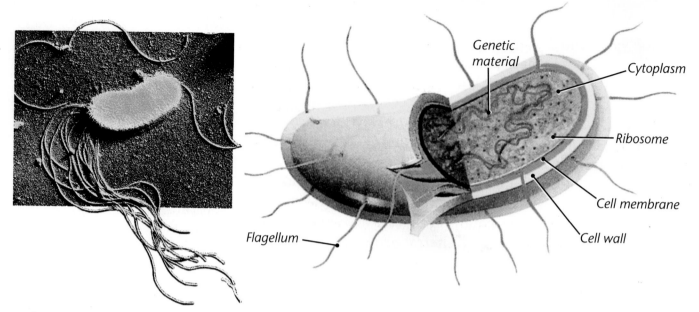

Genetic material

Cytoplasm

Ribosome

Cell membrane

Cell wall

Flagellum

Figure 7 The diagram shows the structures found in a typical bacterial cell. *Interpreting Photographs Which structures can you locate in the photograph of the bacterium? What roles do these structures play?*

You can see the cell wall, cytoplasm, ribosomes, and genetic material in the bacterial cell in Figure 7. Another structure you see is a flagellum. A **flagellum** (fluh JEL um) (plural *flagella*) is a long, whiplike structure that extends from the cell membrane and passes out through the cell wall. A flagellum helps a cell to move by spinning in place like a propeller. A bacterial cell can have many flagella, one, or none. Most bacteria that do not have flagella cannot move on their own. Instead, they depend on air, water currents, clothing, and other objects to carry them from one place to another.

Two Kingdoms of Bacteria

Until recently, biologists grouped all bacteria together in a single kingdom on the basis of their similar cellular structure. However, although all bacteria look similar, some differ chemically. After analyzing the chemical differences, scientists have reclassified bacteria into two separate kingdoms—archaebacteria and eubacteria.

Archaebacteria As you learned in Chapter 7, the word *archaebacteria* means "ancient bacteria." And these bacteria are ancient! Archaebacteria already existed on Earth for billions of years before dinosaurs appeared. Scientists think that today's archaebacteria closely resemble Earth's first life forms.

Many archaebacteria live in extreme environments. They are found in such places as hot springs, where some thrive in water that is as hot as 110°C. Others live in environments that are as acidic as lemon juice. Some archaebacteria live in salty waters, such as Utah's Great Salt Lake. Archaebacteria also live in the intestines of animals, the mud at the bottom of swamps, and in sewage. They are the bacteria that produce the foul odors that you may associate with these places.

Eubacteria Unlike archaebacteria, most eubacteria do not live in extreme environments. However, they live everywhere else. For example, millions of eubacteria live on and in your body. Eubacteria coat your skin and swarm in your nose. Don't be alarmed. Most of them are either useful or harmless to you.

INTEGRATING EARTH SCIENCE Eubacteria help maintain some of Earth's physical conditions and thus help other organisms to survive. For example, some eubacteria are autotrophs that float near the surfaces of Earth's waters. These bacteria use the sun's energy to produce food and oxygen. Scientists think that billions of years ago autotrophic bacteria were responsible for adding oxygen to Earth's atmosphere. Today, the distant offspring of those bacteria help to keep Earth's current level of oxygen at 20 percent.

☑ *Checkpoint* *Why are archaebacteria and eubacteria placed in separate kingdoms?*

Reproduction in Bacteria

When bacteria have plenty of food, the right temperature, and other suitable conditions, they thrive and reproduce frequently. Under these ideal conditions, some bacteria can reproduce as often as once every 20 minutes. Fortunately, growing conditions for bacteria are rarely ideal. Otherwise, there would soon be no room on Earth for other organisms!

Asexual Reproduction Bacteria reproduce by **binary fission**, a process in which one cell divides to form two identical cells. Binary fission is a form of **asexual reproduction.** Asexual reproduction is a reproductive process that involves only one parent and produces offspring that are identical to the parent. In binary fission, the cell first duplicates its genetic material and then divides into two separate cells. Each new cell gets its own complete copy of the parent cell's genetic material as well as some of the parent's ribosomes and cytoplasm. Figure 8 shows a parent cell forming two new cells by binary fission.

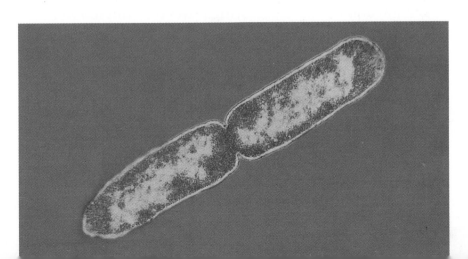

Figure 8 Bacteria, such as this *Escherichia coli,* reproduce by binary fission. Each new cell is identical to the parent cell.

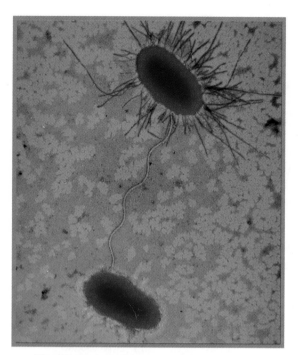

Figure 9 In conjugation, one bacterium transfers some of its genetic material into another bacterium. *Observing What structure allows the cells to transfer genetic material?*

Sexual Reproduction Some bacteria, such as the ones in Figure 9, may at times undergo a simple form of sexual reproduction called conjugation. **Sexual reproduction** involves two parents who combine their genetic material to produce a new organism, which differs from both parents. During **conjugation** (kahn juh GAY shun), one bacterium transfers some of its genetic material into another bacterial cell through a thin, threadlike bridge that joins the two cells. After the transfer, the cells separate.

Conjugation results in bacteria with new combinations of genetic material. When these bacteria divide by binary fission, the new genetic material passes to the new cells. Conjugation does not increase the number of bacteria. However, it does result in the production of new bacteria, which are genetically different than the parent cells.

Survival Needs

From the bacteria that live inside the craters of active volcanoes to those that live in the pores of your skin, all bacteria need certain things to survive. Bacteria must have a source of food, a way of breaking down the food to release the food's energy, and survival techniques when conditions in their surroundings become unfavorable.

Obtaining Food Some bacteria are autotrophs and make their own food. Autotrophic bacteria make food in one of two ways. Some autotrophic bacteria make food by capturing and using the sun's energy as plants do. Other autotrophic bacteria, such as those that live deep in the ocean, do not use the sun's energy. Instead, these bacteria use the energy from chemical substances in their environment to make their food.

Some bacteria are heterotrophs that obtain food by consuming autotrophs or other heterotrophs. Heterotrophic bacteria may consume a variety of foods—from milk and meat, which you might also eat, to the decaying leaves on a forest floor.

Respiration Like all organisms, bacteria need a constant supply of energy to carry out their functions. This energy comes from food. The process of breaking down food to release its energy is called **respiration**. Like many other organisms, most bacteria need oxygen to break down their food. But a few kinds of bacteria do not need oxygen for respiration. In fact, those bacteria die if oxygen is present in their surroundings. For them, oxygen is a poison that kills!

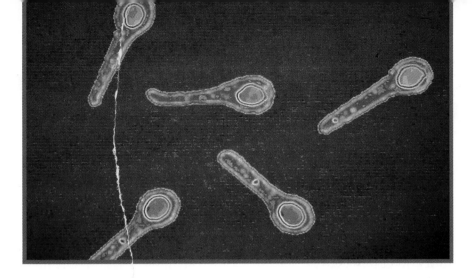

Figure 10 When conditions in the environment become unfavorable for growth, some bacteria form endospores. These endospores of *Clostridium tetani* can survive for years.

Endospore Formation Sometimes the conditions in the environment become unfavorable for the growth of bacteria. For example, food sources can disappear or wastes can poison the bacteria. Some bacteria can survive these harsh conditions by forming endospores like the ones you see in Figure 10. An **endospore** is a small, rounded, thick-walled, resting cell that forms inside a bacterial cell. It contains the cell's genetic material and some of its cytoplasm. Because endospores can resist freezing, heating, and drying, they can survive for many years. Endospores are also light—a breeze can lift and carry them to new places. If an endospore lands in a place where conditions are suitable, it opens up. Then the bacterium can begin to grow and multiply.

☑ *Checkpoint* *How do autotrophic bacteria obtain energy to make food?*

Bacteria and The Living World

When you hear the word *bacteria*, you may think about getting sick. After all, strep throat, many ear infections, and other diseases are caused by bacteria. It is true that some bacteria cause diseases and other harmful effects. However, most bacteria are either harmless or helpful to people. In fact, in many ways, people depend on bacteria. **Bacteria are involved in fuel and food production, environmental recycling and cleanup, and the production of medicines.**

Fuel The next time you use natural gas to boil an egg, grill a hamburger, or heat your house, think of archaebacteria. The archaebacteria that live in oxygen-free environments, such as the thick mud at the bottom of lakes and swamps, produce a gas called methane during respiration. The methane produced by archaebacteria that died millions of years ago is the major component in about 20 percent of Earth's deposits of natural gas.

Bacteria for Breakfast

In this activity, you will observe helpful bacteria in a common food.

1. Put on your apron. Add water to plain yogurt to make a thin mixture.

2. With a plastic dropper, place a drop of the mixture on a glass slide.

3. Use another plastic dropper to add one drop of methylene blue dye to the slide. **CAUTION:** *This dye can stain your skin.*

4. Put a coverslip on the slide.

5. Observe the slide under both the low and high power lenses of a microscope.

Observing Draw a diagram of what you see under high power. Label any cell structures that you see.

Food Do you like cheese, yogurt, and apple cider? What about olives and sauerkraut? The activities of helpful bacteria produce all of these foods and more. For example, bacteria that grow in a liquid poured around fresh cucumbers turn the cucumbers into pickles. Bacteria that grow in apple cider change the cider to vinegar. Bacteria that grow in milk produce dairy products such as buttermilk, sour cream, yogurt, and cheeses.

However, some bacteria cause food to spoil when they break down the food's chemicals. Spoiled food usually smells or tastes foul and can make you very sick. Since ancient times, people have

SCIENCE & History

Bacteria and Foods of the World

Ancient cultures lacked refrigeration and other modern methods of preventing food spoilage. People in these cultures developed ways to use bacteria to preserve foods. You may enjoy some of these foods today.

1000 B.C. China

The Chinese salted vegetables and packed them in containers. Naturally-occurring bacteria fed on the vegetables and produced a sour taste. The salt pulled water out of the vegetables and left them crisp. These vegetables were part of the food rations given to workers who built the Great Wall of China.

3000 B.C.	2000 B.C.	1000 B.C.

2300 B.C. Egypt

Ancient Egyptians made cheese from milk. Cheesemaking begins when bacteria feed on the sugars in milk. The milk separates into solid curds and liquid whey. The curds are processed into cheeses, which keep longer than milk.

500 B.C. Mediterranean Sea Region

People who lived in the regions around the Mediterranean Sea chopped meat, seasoned it with salt and spices, rolled it, and hung it to dry. Bacteria in the drying meat gave unique flavors to the food. The rolled meat would keep for weeks in cool places.

developed ways to slow down food spoilage. They have used such methods as heating, refrigerating, drying, salting, or smoking foods. These methods help to preserve food by preventing the bacteria that cause spoiling from growing in the food.

Environmental Recycling Do you recycle plastic, glass, and other materials? If you do, you have something in common with some heterotrophic eubacteria. These bacteria, which live in the soil, are **decomposers**—organisms that break down large chemicals in dead organisms into small chemicals. Decomposers are

In Your Journal

Find out more about one of these ancient food production methods and the culture that developed it. Write a report about the importance of the food to the culture.

A.D. 1500
The West Indies

People in the West Indies mixed beans from the cocoa plant with bacteria and other microorganisms, then dried and roasted them. The roasted beans were then brewed to produce a beverage with a chocolate flavor. The drink was served cold with honey, spices, and vanilla.

A.D. 1   A.D. 1000   A.D.. 2000

A.D. 500
China

The Chinese crushed soybeans with wheat, salt, bacteria, and other microorganisms. The microorganisms fed on the proteins in the wheat and soybeans. The salt pulled water out of the mixture. The protein-rich soy paste that remained was used to flavor foods. The soy sauce you may use today is made in a similar manner.

A.D. 1850
United States of America

Gold prospectors in California ate a bread called sourdough bread. The bacteria *Lactobacillus san francisco* gave the bread its sour taste. Each day before baking, cooks would set aside some dough that contained the bacteria to use in the next day's bread.

Figure 11 Bacteria live in the swellings on the roots of this soybean plant. The bacteria convert nitrogen from the air into substances the plant needs. *Applying Concepts Why might farmers plant soybeans in a field that is low in nitrogen?*

"nature's recyclers"—they return basic chemicals to the environment for other living things to reuse. For example, in the fall, the leaves of many trees die and fall to the ground. Decomposing bacteria spend the next months breaking down the chemicals in the dead leaves. The broken-down chemicals mix with the soil, and can then be absorbed by the roots of nearby plants.

Other recycling eubacteria live in swellings on the roots of some plants, such as peanuts, peas, and soybeans. There, they convert nitrogen gas from the air into nitrogen compounds that the plants need to grow. The plants cannot convert nitrogen from the air into the nitrogen compounds they need. Therefore, the bacteria that live in the roots of plants help the plants to survive.

Environmental Cleanup Some bacteria help to clean up  Earth's land and water. Can you imagine having a bowl of oil for dinner instead of soup? Well, there are some bacteria that prefer the oil. They convert the dangerous chemicals in oil into harmless substances. Scientists have put these bacteria to work cleaning up oil spills in oceans and gasoline leaks in the soil under gas stations.

Health and Medicine You may find it hard to believe that many of the bacteria living in your body actually keep you healthy. In your digestive system, for example, your intestines teem with bacteria. This is a natural and healthy situation. Some of the bacteria help you digest your food. Some make vitamins that your body needs. Others compete for space with disease-

Figure 12 Scientists use bacteria such as these *Ochrobactrum anthropi* to help clean up oil spills.

Figure 13 Today, bacteria can be used to produce medicines. The bacteria can be grown in huge numbers in vats like these.

causing organisms. They prevent the harmful bacteria from attaching to your intestines and making you sick.

 INTEGRATING TECHNOLOGY Scientists have put some bacteria to work making medicines and other substances. People can use these substances to live healthy lives. The first medicine-producing bacteria were made in the 1970s. By manipulating the genetic material of bacteria, scientists engineered bacteria to produce human insulin. Although healthy people can make their own insulin, people with diabetes cannot. Many people with diabetes need to take insulin on a daily basis. Thanks to their fast rate of reproduction, large numbers of insulin-making bacteria can be grown in huge vats. The human insulin they produce is then purified and made into medicine.

Section 2 Review

1. How is a bacterial cell different from the cells of other kinds of organisms?
2. List four ways in which bacteria are helpful to people.
3. What happens during binary fission?
4. Describe how a bacterium can survive when conditions are unfavorable for growth.
5. **Thinking Critically Applying Concepts** Why are some foods, such as milk, heated to high temperatures before they are bottled?

Science at Home

With a family member, look around your kitchen for foods that are made using bacteria. Read the labels on the foods to see if the role of bacteria in the food's production is mentioned. Discuss with your family member the helpful roles that bacteria play in the lives of people.

Do Disinfectants Work?

When your family goes shopping, you may buy cleaning products called disinfectants. Disinfectants kill microorganisms such as bacteria, which may cause infection or decay. In this lab, you will compare the effects of two different disinfectants.

Problem

How well do disinfectants control the growth of bacteria?

Skills Focus

observing, inferring, drawing conclusions

Materials

clock
2 plastic droppers
2 household disinfectants
3 plastic petri dishes with sterile nutrient agar
wax pencil
transparent tape

Procedure

1. Copy the data table into your notebook.
2. Work with a partner. Obtain 3 petri dishes containing sterile agar. Without opening them, use a wax pencil to label the bottoms "A," "B," and "C." Write your initials beside each letter.

3. Wash your hands thoroughly with soap, then run a fingertip across the surface of your worktable. Your partner should hold open the cover of petri dish A, while you run that fingertip gently across the agar in a zig-zag motion. Close the dish immediately.
4. Repeat Step 3 for dishes B and C.
5. Use a plastic dropper to transfer 2 drops of one disinfectant to the center of petri dish A. Open the cover just long enough to add the disinfectant to the dish. Close the cover immediately. Record the name of the disinfectant in your data table. **CAUTION:** *Do not inhale vapors from the disinfectant.*
6. Repeat Step 5 for dish B but add 2 drops of the second disinfectant. **CAUTION:** *Do not mix any disinfectants together.*
7. Do not add any disinfectant to dish C.
8. Tape down the covers of all 3 petri dishes so that they will remain tightly closed. Allow the 3 dishes to sit upright on your work surface for at least 5 minutes. **CAUTION:** *Do not open the petri dishes again.* Wash your hands with soap and water.
9. As directed by your teacher, store the petri dishes in a warm, dark place where they can remain for at least 3 days. Remove them only to make a brief examination each day.

Petri Dish	Disinfectant	Day 1	Day 2	Day 3
A				
B				
C				

DATA TABLE

10. After one day, observe the contents of each dish without removing the covers. Estimate the percentage of the agar surface that shows any changes. Record your observations. Return the dishes to their storage place when you have finished making your observations. Wash your hands with soap.

11. Repeat Step 10 after the second day and again after the third day.

12. After you and your partner have made your last observations, return the petri dishes to your teacher unopened.

Analyze and Conclude

1. How did the appearance of dish C change during the lab?

2. How did the appearance of dishes A and B compare with dish C? Explain any similarities or differences.

3. How did the appearance of dishes A and B compare with each other? How can you account for any differences?

4. Why was it important to set aside one petri dish that did not contain any disinfectant?

5. **Apply** Based on the results of this lab, what recommendation would you make to your family about the use of disinfectants? Where in the house do you think these products would be needed most?

Design an Experiment

Go to a store and look at soap products that claim to be "antibacterial" soaps. How do their ingredients differ from other soaps? How do their prices compare? Design an experiment to test how well these products control the growth of bacteria.

SECTION 3 Viruses, Bacteria, and Your Health

DISCOVER ·ACTIVITY· · ·

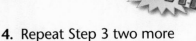

How Do Infectious Diseases Spread?

1. Put on goggles and plastic gloves. Your teacher will give you a plastic dropper and a plastic cup half filled with a liquid. Do not taste, smell, or touch the liquid.

2. In this activity, you will model how some diseases spread. Your teacher will signal the start of a "talking" period. Choose a classmate to talk with briefly. As you talk, exchange a dropperful of the liquid in your cup with your classmate.

3. At your teacher's signal, talk to another classmate. Exchange a dropperful of liquid.

4. Repeat Step 3 two more times.

5. Your teacher will add a few drops of a liquid to each student's cup. If your fluid turns pink, it indicates that you have "contracted a disease" from one of your classmates. Wash your hands when you have finished the activity.

Think It Over

Predicting How many more rounds would it take for everyone in your class to "become infected"? Use your prediction to explain why some diseases can spread quickly through a population.

GUIDE FOR READING

◆ How do infectious diseases spread from person to person?

Reading Tip Before you read, rewrite the section's headings as questions. As you read, write answers to the questions.

It started last night with a tickle in the back of your throat. This morning, when you woke up, your nose felt stuffy. By lunchtime, your muscles started to ache. By the time the big game started after school, your mouth felt dry and your throat was scratchy. Now, in the seventh inning of the game, you feel awful. You're sneezing and talking like you have a clothespin on your nose. You can't seem to get warm, and you're shivering on the bench. You've caught a cold—or maybe more accurately, a cold has caught you!

How Infectious Diseases Spread

Have you ever wondered how you catch a cold, a strep throat, or even the chicken pox? These and many other diseases are called **infectious diseases**—illnesses that pass from one organism to another. **Infectious diseases can spread in one of four ways: through contact with either an infected person, a contaminated object, an infected animal, or an environmental source.** Once contact occurs, some disease-causing agents may enter a person through breaks in the skin, or they may be inhaled or swallowed. Others may enter the body through the moist linings of the eyes, ears, nose, mouth, or other body openings.

Contact With an Infected Person Direct contact such as touching, hugging, or kissing an infected person can spread some infectious diseases. For example, kissing an infected person can transmit cold sores. Many other infectious diseases can be spread by indirect contact with an infected person. A common form of indirect contact is inhaling the tiny drops of moisture that an infected person sneezes or coughs into the air. This is because the drops of moisture contain disease-causing organisms. For example, the flu can be spread by inhaling drops of moisture that contain the flu virus.

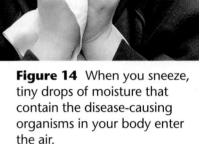

Figure 14 When you sneeze, tiny drops of moisture that contain the disease-causing organisms in your body enter the air.

Contact With a Contaminated Object Some viruses and bacteria can survive for a while outside a person's body. They can be spread via objects, such as eating utensils, or in contaminated food or water. For example, drinking from a cup used by an infected person can spread diseases such as strep throat and mononucleosis. If you touch an object that an infected person has sneezed or coughed on, you may transfer some viruses or bacteria to yourself if you then touch your mouth or eyes. If you drink water or eat food that an infected person has contaminated, you may get sick. Drinking water that contains small amounts of sewage is a common way that disease is spread in many areas of the world.

Contact With an Animal The bites of animals can transmit some serious infectious diseases to humans. For example, the deadly disease rabies can be transferred through the bite of an infected dog, raccoon, or some other animals. The bites of ticks can transmit the bacteria that cause Lyme disease. The bites of mosquitoes can spread the virus that causes encephalitis—a serious disease in which the brain tissues swell.

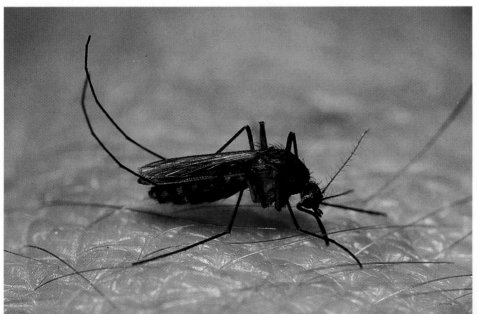

Figure 15 This mosquito, *Culex nigripalpus,* is feeding on human blood. If this mosquito contains the virus that causes encephalitis, it can transmit the disease through its bite. *Applying Concepts What other diseases are spread by animal bites?*

Social Studies
CONNECTION

ALASKA

Nome

Nenana

Iditarod

Anchorage

BERING SEA

Gulf of Alaska

KEY

—— Antitoxin Run   —— Iditarod Trail

Contact With Environmental Sources Some viruses and bacteria live in food, water, and soil, or on the surfaces of objects. The places where they are naturally found are environmental sources of disease. For example, poultry, eggs, and meat often contain salmonella bacteria. Eating foods that contain these bacteria can lead to one type of food poisoning. Cooking the foods thoroughly kills the bacteria. A soil bacterium called *Clostridium botulinum* can grow in improperly processed canned foods. It produces a poison known as a **toxin**, which soaks into the food. Eating the food causes a serious, often deadly disease known as botulism. *Clostridium tetani*, another soil-dwelling bacteria, can enter a person's body through a wound and cause the deadly disease tetanus.

✓ *Checkpoint* *What is one thing you can do to reduce the risk of food poisoning?*

Common Infectious Diseases

There are thousands of kinds of infectious diseases. Some are common in one part of the world but rare or absent in other places. Many infectious diseases are caused by viruses and bacteria. Others are caused by protists and fungi, which you will learn about in the next chapter. Figure 17 provides important information about some common viral and bacterial diseases in this country.

Figure 16 Today, an event called the Iditarod Trail Dog Sled Race takes place in March each year. Sled-dog teams compete in a 1,930-kilometer race to celebrate the history of the Iditarod Trail.

Common Infectious Diseases

Disease	Disease-Causing Agent	Symptoms	How Spread	Treatment	Prevention
Acquired immuno-deficiency syndrome (AIDS)	Virus	Weight loss; chronic fatigue; fever; diarrhea; frequent infections	Sexual contact; contact with blood; pregnancy, birth, and breast-feeding	Drugs to slow viral multiplication	Avoid contact with infected body fluids
Chicken Pox	Virus	Fever; red itchy rash	Contact with rash; inhale droplets	Antiviral drug (for adults)	Vaccine
Influenza (flu)	Virus	High fever; sore throat; headache; cough	Contact with contaminated objects; inhale droplets	Bed rest; fluids	Vaccine (mainly for high-risk ill, elderly, and young)
Measles	Virus	High fever; sore throat; cough; white spots on cheek lining; rash; puffy eyelids	Inhale droplets	Bed rest, cough medicine	Vaccine
Poliomyelitis (polio)	Virus	Fever; muscle weakness; headache; difficulty swallowing	Inhale droplets	Bed rest	Vaccine
Rabies	Virus	Drooling; skin sensitivity; alternating periods of rage and calm; difficulty swallowing	Animal bite	Vaccine	Avoid wild animals and pets that act abnormally; keep track of pets outside
Food poisoning	Various bacteria	Vomiting; cramps; diarrhea; fever	Eating foods containing the bacteria	Antitoxin medicines; rest	Properly cook and store foods; avoid foods in rusted and swollen cans
Lyme disease	Bacterium	Rash at site of tick bite; chills; fever; body aches; joint swelling	Animal bite	Antibiotic	Tuck pants into socks; wear long-sleeved shirt
Strep throat	Bacterium	Fever; sore throat; swollen glands	Inhale droplets; contact with infected object	Antibiotic	Avoid contact with infected people
Tetanus (lockjaw)	Bacterium	Stiff jaw and neck muscles; spasms; difficulty swallowing	Deep puncture wound	Antibiotic; opening and cleaning wound	Vaccine
Tuberculosis (TB)	Bacterium	Fatigue; mild fever; weight loss; night sweats; cough	Inhale droplets	Antibiotic	Vaccine (for those in high risk occupations only)

Figure 17 Many common infectious diseases are caused by viruses and bacteria. Much is known about how these diseases are spread and how they can be treated or prevented. *Interpreting Charts Which diseases are spread by inhaling droplets in the air?*

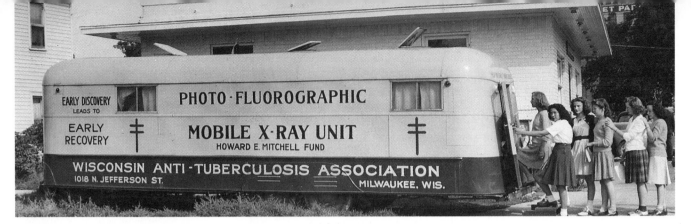

Figure 18 Before antibiotics were available to treat tuberculosis, the deadly disease spread easily. People visited mobile X-ray vans to be screened for tuberculosis. *Relating Cause and Effect How has antibiotic resistance affected the number of tuberculosis cases?*

Treating Infectious Diseases

Once you start to have symptoms of an infectious disease, your attention probably turns quickly to helping yourself feel better. For most infectious diseases, the best treatment is bedrest. Indeed, resting, drinking lots of fluids, and eating well-balanced meals may be all you can do while you recover from some infectious diseases.

Viral Diseases Unfortunately, there are no medications that can cure viral infections. However, while no cures exist, there are many over-the-counter medications that treat the symptoms. These medications are available without a prescription. Over-the-counter medications can make you feel better. But, they can also delay your recovery if you resume your normal routine while you are still sick. They can also hide symptoms that would normally cause you to go to a doctor.

Bacterial Diseases Unlike viral diseases, many bacterial diseases can be cured with medications known as antibiotics. An **antibiotic** is a chemical that can kill bacteria without harming a person's cells. Antibiotics are made naturally by some bacteria and fungi. Today, antibiotics such as penicillin are made in large quantities in factories. Penicillin works by weakening the cell walls of some bacteria and causing the cells to burst.

If you have ever had a strep throat infection, you know that the infection makes swallowing feel like you have a throat full of barbed wire. But soon after you begin taking the antibiotic that your doctor prescribes, your throat feels better. This is because the antibiotic quickly kills the bacteria that cause strep throat.

Unfortunately, antibiotics are less effective today than they once were. This is because many bacteria have become resistant to antibiotics over the years. Resistant bacteria are able to survive in the presence of an antibiotic. The recent increase in tuberculosis cases demonstrates the impact of antibiotic resistance. Between 1950 and 1980, the number of cases of tuberculosis dropped significantly as patients took antibiotics. Unfortunately, there were always a few tuberculosis bacteria that were resistant to the antibiotics. Those bacteria survived and reproduced, producing more bacteria like themselves. Today, many resistant bacteria exist. Since the mid-1980s, the number of tuberculosis cases has been on the rise despite the use of antibiotics.

Preventing Infectious Diseases

One important tool that helps to prevent the spread of infectious diseases is vaccines. A **vaccine** is a substance that stimulates the body to produce chemicals that destroy viruses or bacteria. A vaccine may be made from dead or altered viruses or bacteria. The viruses or bacteria in the vaccine do not cause disease, but instead activate the body's natural defenses. In effect, the altered viruses or bacteria put the body "on alert." If that virus or bacterium ever invades the body, it is destroyed before it can produce disease. You may have been vaccinated against diseases such as tetanus, pertussis (whooping cough), measles, mumps, and polio. Now there is also a vaccine available for the viral disease chicken pox.

Staying Healthy

The best way to protect against infectious diseases is to keep your body healthy. You need to eat nutritious food, as well as get plenty of rest, fluids, and exercise. You can also protect yourself by washing your hands often and by not sharing eating utensils or drink containers. You should also make sure that you have all recommended vaccinations. Storing food properly, keeping kitchen equipment and surfaces clean, and cooking meats well can prevent food poisoning.

Unfortunately, despite your best efforts, you'll probably get infectious diseases, such as colds, from time to time. When you do get ill, get plenty of rest, follow your doctor's recommendations, and try not to infect others.

Figure 19 By exercising and keeping your body healthy, you can help protect yourself from infectious diseases.

Section 3 Review

1. List four ways that infectious diseases can be spread.
2. What is an antibiotic? What types of infectious diseases do antibiotics cure?
3. What is a vaccine?
4. **Thinking Critically Inferring** Why is washing your hands an effective way to prevent the spread of some infectious diseases?

Check Your Progress

CHAPTER PROJECT

By now you should have nearly all of your questionnaires answered. You should be ready to tally your responses. Begin to think about how you will use graphs or other visual ways to organize your results. (*Hint:* You may need to review the research you did earlier to help you make sense of some survey data.)

Antibiotic Resistance—An Alarming Trend

Penicillin, the first antibiotic, became available for use in 1943. Soon afterward, antibiotics became known as the "wonder drugs." Over the years, they have reduced the occurrence of many bacterial diseases and saved millions of lives. But each time an antibiotic is used, a few bacteria—those resistant to the drug—survive. They pass on their resistance to the next generation of bacteria. As more and more patients take antibiotics, the number of resistant bacteria increases.

In 1987, penicillin killed more than 99.9 percent of a type of bacteria that causes ear infections. By 1995, 25 percent of those bacteria were resistant to penicillin. Diseases such as tuberculosis are on the increase due in part to growing antibiotic resistance.

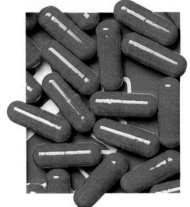

The Issues

What Can Doctors and Patients Do?

In a typical year, about 6 billion dollars worth of antibiotics are sold to drugstores and hospitals in the United States. One way to slow down the process that leads to resistance is to decrease the amount of antibiotics people use. About one out of five prescriptions for antibiotics is written for colds and other viral illnesses. Antibiotics, however, do not kill viruses. If doctors could better identify the cause of an infection, they could avoid prescribing unnecessary antibiotics.

Patients can also play an important role. If a doctor prescribes a ten-day course of antibiotics, all of the prescription should be taken. If a patient stops taking the antibiotic, the resistant bacteria will survive and reproduce. Then, a second antibiotic may be necessary. Patients also need to learn that some illnesses are best treated with rest and not with antibiotics.

Limiting Non-medical Uses of Antibiotics

About forty percent of the antibiotics used each year are not given to people. Instead, the drugs are fed to food animals, such as cattle and chickens, to prevent illness and increase growth. Reducing this type of use would limit the amount of the drugs in food animals and in the people who eat them. But these actions might increase the risk of disease in animals and lead to higher meat prices.

Finding New Antibiotics

Another way to slow the increase of antibiotic resistance might be through more research. Scientists are trying to identify new antibiotics. With more kinds of antibiotics, scientists hope that bacteria will not develop resistances as quickly.

You Decide

1. Identify the Problem

Describe how the use of antibiotics can eventually make these medicines not work as well.

2. Analyze the Options

List all the ways to fight the development of antibiotic resistance in bacteria. For each action, tell who would carry it out and how it would work. Mention any costs or drawbacks.

3. Find a Solution

Make a persuasive poster about one way to deal with antibiotic resistance. Support your viewpoint with sound reasons. Target the group who could make the change.

SECTION 1 Viruses

Key Ideas

◆ Viruses are considered to be nonliving because viruses are not cells, and they do not use energy to grow and develop, or to respond to their surroundings.

◆ All viruses have two basic parts: an outer coat that protects the virus and an inner core made of genetic material.

◆ Once inside a cell, a virus uses the host cell's functions to make its own proteins and genetic material. The proteins and genetic material assemble into new viruses, which burst out, destroying the host.

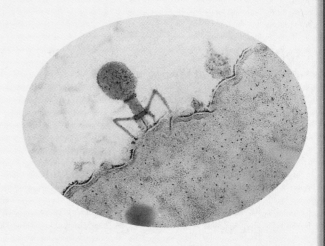

Key Terms

virus	parasite
host	bacteriophage

SECTION 2 Bacteria

Key Ideas

◆ Bacteria are prokaryotes. Their cells do not have nuclei that contain the cell's genetic material. Instead, the genetic material floats freely in the cytoplasm.

◆ Bacteria reproduce asexually by binary fission, which results in the production of two cells exactly like the parent cell. Some bacteria have a simple form of sexual reproduction called conjugation. This process results in a cell with a new combination of genetic information.

◆ Bacteria play positive roles in the lives of humans. Bacteria are involved in fuel and food production, in environmental recycling and cleanup, and in the production of medicines.

Key Terms

bacterium	asexual reproduction
cytoplasm	conjugation
ribosome	respiration
flagellum	endospore
binary fission	decomposer
sexual reproduction	

SECTION 3 Viruses, Bacteria, and Your Health

INTEGRATING HEALTH

Key Ideas

◆ Infectious disease can spread through contact with an infected person, a contaminated object, an infected animal, or an environmental source.

◆ There is no cure for viral diseases. Bacterial diseases can be cured through the use of antibiotics. Vaccines can prevent some viral and bacterial diseases.

Key Terms

infectious disease	antibiotic
toxin	vaccine

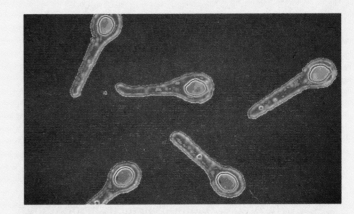

USING THE INTERNET ACTIVITY

www.science-explorer.phschool.com

CHAPTER 8 ASSESSMENT

California Test Prep: Reviewing Content

Multiple Choice

Choose the letter of the best answer.

1. Bacteriophages are viruses that attack and destroy
   a. other viruses.   **b.** bacteria.
   c. plants.   **d.** humans.

2. Which part of a virus determines which host cells it can infect?
   a. genetic material   **b.** ribosomes
   c. flagellum   **d.** outer coat

3. Viruses multiply
   a. by conjugation.
   b. by binary fission.
   c. by taking over a cell's functions.
   d. both asexually and sexually.

4. Most bacteria are surrounded by a rigid protective structure called the
   a. cell wall.   **b.** cell membrane.
   c. protein coat.   **d.** flagellum.

5. Which of the following statements about infectious diseases is *not* true?
   a. Some can be spread by contact with an infected person.
   b. Some can be spread by contact with animals.
   c. All can be treated with antibiotics.
   d. Some can be prevented with vaccines.

True or False

If the statement is true, write true. If it is false, change the underlined word or words to make the statement true.

6. <u>Hidden viruses</u> enter a cell and immediately begin to multiply.

7. In gene therapy, scientists take advantage of a <u>bacteria's</u> ability to get inside a host cell.

8. Most <u>archaebacteria</u> live in extreme environments.

9. Bacteria form <u>endospores</u> to survive unfavorable conditions in their surroundings.

10. A <u>vaccine</u> is a chemical that can kill bacteria without harming a person's cells.

Checking Concepts

11. List three ways that viruses are different from cells.

12. Explain why a certain virus will attach to only one or a few types of cells.

13. Describe how a bacteriophage multiplies.

14. What are the parts of a bacterial cell? Explain the role of each part.

15. Describe how bacteria reproduce.

16. How do the bacteria that live in your intestines help you?

17. Explain how antibiotics kill bacteria.

18. How do vaccines prevent the spread of some infectious diseases?

19. **Writing to Learn** Imagine you are a cold virus. The student you infected just sneezed you into the air in the cafeteria. Write a description of what happens to you until you finally attach to a cell in another student.

Thinking Visually

20. Copy the Venn diagram comparing viruses and bacteria onto a separate sheet of paper. Then complete the Venn diagram. (For more on Venn diagrams, see the Skills Handbook.)

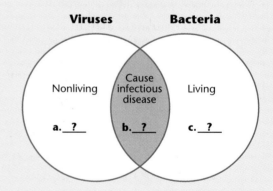

Test Prep: Skills

The graph shows how the number of bacteria that grow on a food source changes over time. Use the graph to answer Questions 21–23.

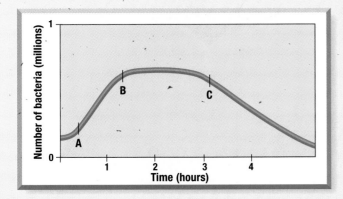

21. Interpreting Data Explain what is happening between points A and B.

22. Developing Hypotheses Develop a hypothesis that explains why the number of bacteria stays constant between points B and C.

23. Designing Experiments How could you test the hypothesis you developed in Question 22? What would your results show?

Thinking Critically

24. Classifying You know that viruses vary in shape, size, and the kinds of organisms they infect. Which one of these three characteristics would you use as a basis for a classification system for viruses? Explain your answer.

25. Comparing and Contrasting Describe the similarities and differences between active and hidden viruses.

26. Problem Solving Bacteria will grow in the laboratory on a gelatin-like substance called agar. Viruses will not grow on agar. If you needed to grow viruses in the laboratory, what kind of substance would you have to use? Explain.

Performance Assessment

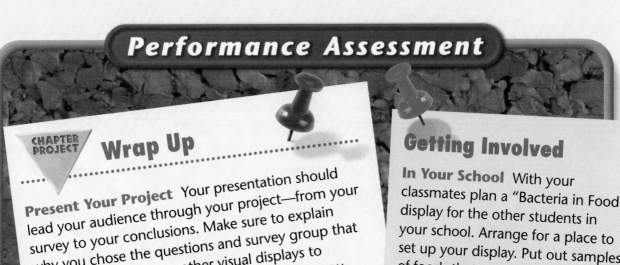

CHAPTER PROJECT Wrap Up

Present Your Project Your presentation should lead your audience through your project—from your survey to your conclusions. Make sure to explain why you chose the questions and survey group that you did. Use graphs or other visual displays to highlight important similarities or differences you found. Make sure that you support your conclusions with data.

Reflect and Record Do you think that a survey like this one is similar to a science experiment? What makes them alike or different? In your journal, describe what you did to make your survey accurate and complete.

Getting Involved

In Your School With your classmates plan a "Bacteria in Food" display for the other students in your school. Arrange for a place to set up your display. Put out samples of foods that require bacteria for their production. Make posters and models to inform students how bacteria are involved in each food's production. Be prepared to answer questions about the foods and about the bacteria that are used to make the foods.

CALIFORNIA
SCIENCE CONTENT STANDARDS

The following California Science Content Standards are addressed in this chapter:

1. All living organisms are composed of cells, from just one to many trillions, whose details usually are visible only through a microscope.

    a. Cells function similarly in all living organisms.

    b. The characteristics that distinguish plant cells from animal cells, including chloroplasts and cell walls.

    d. Mitochondria liberate energy for the work that cells do, and chloroplasts capture sunlight energy for photosynthesis.

2. A typical cell of any organism contains genetic instructions that specify its traits. Those traits may be modified by environmental influences.

    a. The differences between the life cycles and reproduction of sexual and asexual organisms.

3. Biological evolution accounts for the diversity of species developed through gradual processes over many generations.

    a. Both genetic variation and environmental factors are causes of evolution and diversity of organisms.

A Mushroom Farm

Have you ever seen mushrooms growing in a local park or on a forest floor? Over the centuries, people have been curious about these organisms because they seem to sprout up without warning, often after a rainfall. Mushrooms are the most familiar type of fungi. In some ways, they resemble plants, often growing near or even on them like small umbrellas. But mushrooms are very different from plants in some important ways. In this project, you'll learn these differences.

As you read the chapter, you'll also learn about other fungi and about the diverse kingdom known as protists. You'll find out how these organisms carry out their life activities and how important they are to people and to the environment.

Your Goal To determine the conditions needed for mushrooms to grow.

To complete this project successfully, you must
◆ choose one variable, and design a way to test how it affects mushroom growth
◆ make daily observations, and record them in a data table
◆ prepare a poster that describes the results of your experiment
◆ follow the safety guidelines in Appendix A

Get Started With your partners, brainstorm possible hypotheses about the way variables such as light or moisture could affect the growth of mushrooms. Write your own hypothesis and the reasons why you chose it. Write out a plan for testing the variable that you chose. Then start growing your mushrooms!

Check Your Progress You'll be working on this project as you study the chapter. To keep your project on track, look for Check Your Progress boxes at the following points.

Section 2 Review, page 282: Make observations and collect data.

Section 3 Review, page 294: Plan a poster about your discoveries.

Wrap Up At the end of the chapter (page 297), you will display your poster that details what you learned about mushroom growth.

Although these scarlet waxy cap mushrooms are quite tasty, beware. There are poisonous mushrooms that look just like them.

---

5. The anatomy and physiology of plants and animals illustrate the complementary nature of structure and function.

   b. Organ systems function because of the contributions of individual organs, tissues, and cells. The failure of any part can affect the entire system.

7. Scientific progress is made by asking meaningful questions and conducting careful investigations.

   c. Communicate the logical connection among hypothesis, science concepts, tests conducted, data collected, and conclusions drawn from the scientific evidence.

   d. Construct scale models, maps and appropriately labeled diagrams to communicate scientific knowledge.

   e. Communicate the steps and results from an investigation in written reports and verbal presentations.

SECTION

① Protists

ACTIVITY

What Lives in a Drop of Pond Water?

1. Use a plastic dropper to place a drop of pond water on a microscope slide.

2. Put the slide under your microscope's low-power lens. Focus on the objects you see.

3. Find at least three different objects that you think might be organisms. Observe them for a few minutes.

4. Draw the three organisms in your notebook. Below each sketch, describe the movements or behaviors of the organism. Wash your hands thoroughly when you have finished.

Think It Over

Observing What characteristics did you observe that made you think that each organism was alive?

GUIDE FOR READING

◆ What are the characteristics of animal-like, funguslike, and plantlike protists?

Reading Tip As you read, use the headings to make an outline of the different kinds of protists.

Look at the objects in Figure 1. What do they look like to you? Jewels? Stained glass windows? Crystal ornaments? You might be surprised to learn that these beautiful, delicate structures are the walls of unicellular organisms called diatoms. Diatoms live in both salt water and fresh water. These tiny organisms are at the base of the food web that provides food for some of Earth's largest organisms—whales.

What Is a Protist?

Diatoms are only one type of organism classified in the protist kingdom. Protists are so different from each other that you can think of this kingdom as the "junk drawer" kingdom. You may have a drawer in your room where you store ticket stubs, postcards, and other odds and ends. Just as these items don't really fit anywhere else in your room, protists don't really fit into any other biological kingdom. Protists do share some characteristics. They are all eukaryotes, or organisms that have cells with nuclei. In addition, all protists live in moist surroundings.

Despite these common characteristics, the word that best describes the protist kingdom is diversity. For example, most protists are unicellular like the diatoms. On the other hand, some

Figure 1 These delicate-looking diatoms are classified in the protist kingdom.

protists are multicellular. In fact, the protists known as giant kelps can be over 100 meters long. Protists also vary in how they obtain food—some are heterotrophs, some are autotrophs, and others are both. Some protists cannot move, while others zoom around their moist surroundings.

Because of the great variety of protists, scientists have proposed different ways of grouping these organisms. One useful way of grouping protists is to divide them into three categories: animal-like protists, funguslike protists, and plantlike protists.

☑ *Checkpoint* *What characteristics do all protists share?*

Animal-like Protists

What image pops into your head when you think of an animal? A tiger chasing its prey? A snake slithering onto a rock? Most people immediately associate animals with movement. In fact, movement is often involved with an important characteristic of animals—obtaining food. All animals are heterotrophs that must obtain food by consuming other organisms.

Like animals, animal-like protists are heterotrophs. And most animal-like protists, or **protozoans** (proh tuh ZOH unz), are able to move from place to place to obtain their food. Unlike animals, however, protozoans are unicellular. Some scientists distinguish between four types of protozoans based on the way these organisms move and live.

Protozoans With Pseudopods The ameba in *Exploring Protozoans* on the next page belongs to the group of protozoans called sarcodines. Sarcodines move and feed by forming **pseudopods** (SOO doh pahdz)—temporary bulges of the cell membrane that fill with cytoplasm. The word *pseudopod* means "false foot." Pseudopods form when the cell membrane pushes outward in one location. The cytoplasm flows into the bulge

Figure 2 The protist kingdom includes animal-like, plantlike, and funguslike organisms. **A.** These shells contained unicellular, animal-like protists called foraminifera. **B.** This red alga is a multicellular, plantlike protist found on ocean floors. **C.** This yellow slime mold is a funguslike protist. *Comparing and Contrasting In what way are animal-like protists similar to animals? How do they differ?*

and the rest of the organism follows. Pseudopods enable sarcodines to move in response to changes in the environment. For example, amebas use psuedopods to move away from bright light. Sarcodines also use pseudopods to trap food. The organism extends a pseudopod on each side of the food particle. The two pseudopods then join together, trapping the particle inside.

Organisms that live in fresh water, such as amebas, have a problem. Small particles, like those of water, pass easily through the cell membrane into the cytoplasm. If the excess water were to build up inside the cell, the ameba would burst. Fortunately, amebas have a **contractile vacuole** (kun TRAK til VAK yoo ohl), a structure that collects the extra water and then expels it from the cell.

EXPLORING *Protozoans*

Amebas are sarcodines that live either in water or soil. They feed on bacteria and smaller protists in the surroundings. Paramecia are ciliates that live mostly in fresh water. Like amebas, paramecia feed on bacteria and smaller protists.

AMEBA

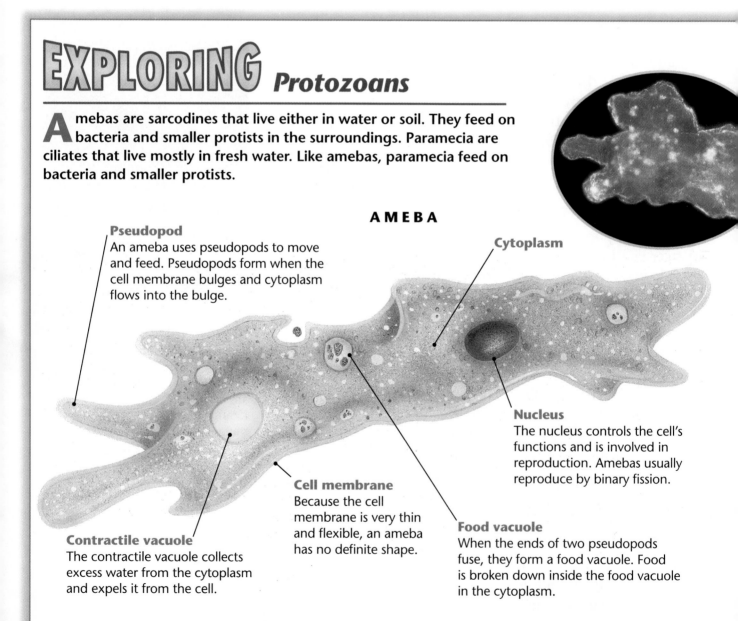

Pseudopod
An ameba uses pseudopods to move and feed. Pseudopods form when the cell membrane bulges and cytoplasm flows into the bulge.

Cytoplasm

Nucleus
The nucleus controls the cell's functions and is involved in reproduction. Amebas usually reproduce by binary fission.

Cell membrane
Because the cell membrane is very thin and flexible, an ameba has no definite shape.

Food vacuole
When the ends of two pseudopods fuse, they form a food vacuole. Food is broken down inside the food vacuole in the cytoplasm.

Contractile vacuole
The contractile vacuole collects excess water from the cytoplasm and expels it from the cell.

Protozoans With Cilia The second type of animal-like protist is the ciliate. Ciliates have structures called **cilia** (SIL ee uh) which are hairlike projections from cells that move with a wavelike pattern. They use cilia to move, obtain food, and sense the environment. Cilia act something like tiny oars to move a ciliate. Their movement sweeps food into the organism.

Ciliates have complex cells. In *Exploring Protozoans*, you see a ciliate called a paramecium. Notice that the paramecium has two nuclei. The large nucleus controls the everyday tasks of the cell. The small nucleus functions in reproduction. Paramecia usually reproduce asexually by binary fission. Sometimes, they reproduce by conjugation. This occurs when two paramecia join together and exchange genetic material.

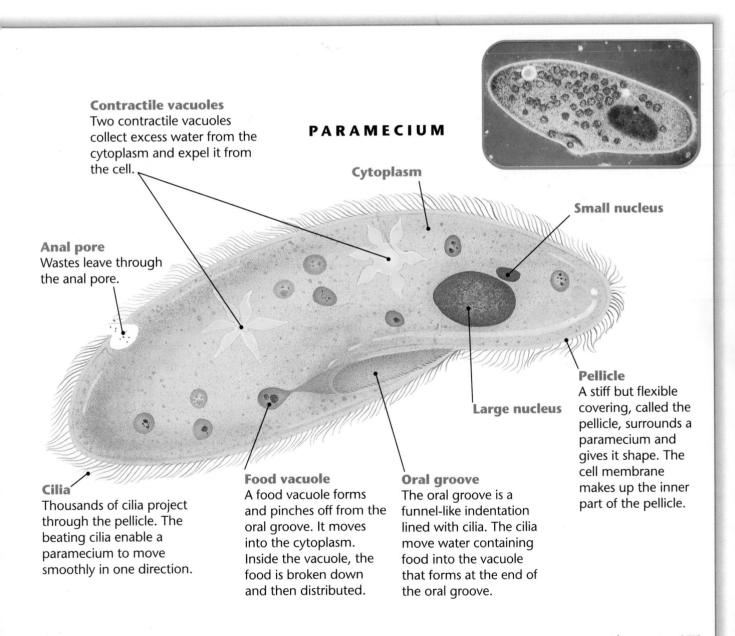

PARAMECIUM

Contractile vacuoles
Two contractile vacuoles collect excess water from the cytoplasm and expel it from the cell.

Cytoplasm

Small nucleus

Anal pore
Wastes leave through the anal pore.

Pellicle
A stiff but flexible covering, called the pellicle, surrounds a paramecium and gives it shape. The cell membrane makes up the inner part of the pellicle.

Large nucleus

Cilia
Thousands of cilia project through the pellicle. The beating cilia enable a paramecium to move smoothly in one direction.

Food vacuole
A food vacuole forms and pinches off from the oral groove. It moves into the cytoplasm. Inside the vacuole, the food is broken down and then distributed.

Oral groove
The oral groove is a funnel-like indentation lined with cilia. The cilia move water containing food into the vacuole that forms at the end of the oral groove.

Figure 3 When people drink from freshwater streams and lakes, they can get hiker's disease. Below you see the organism responsible for the disease, a protozoan called *Giardia lamblia*.

Feeding Paramecia

In this activity you will feed *Chlorella*, a plantlike protist, to paramecia.

1. Use a plastic dropper to place one drop of paramecium culture on a microscope slide. Add some cotton fibers to slow down the paramecia.

2. Use the microscope's low-power objective to find some paramecia.

3. Add one drop of *Chlorella* to the paramecium culture on your slide.

4. Switch to high power and locate a paramecium. Observe what happens. Then wash your hands.

Inferring What evidence do you have that paramecia are heterotrophs? That *Chlorella* are autotrophs?

Protozoans With Flagella The third type of protozoans are called zooflagellates (zoh uh FLAJ uh lits)—animal-like protists that use flagella to move. Most zooflagellates have one to eight long, whiplike flagella that help them move.

Many zooflagellates live inside the bodies of other organisms. For example, one type of zooflagellate lives in the intestines of termites. The zooflagellates digest the wood that the termites eat, producing sugars for themselves and for the termites. In turn, the termites protect the zooflagellates. The interaction between these two species is an example of **symbiosis** (sim bee OH sis)— a close relationship where at least one of the species benefits. When both partners benefit from living together, the relationship is a type of symbiosis called **mutualism.**

INTEGRATING HEALTH Sometimes a zooflagellate harms the animal in which it lives. In Figure 3 you see a zooflagellate called *Giardia*. This zooflagellate is a parasite in humans. Wild animals, such as beavers, deposit *Giardia* organisms in freshwater streams, rivers, and lakes. When a person drinks water containing *Giardia*, the zooflagellates attach to the person's intestine, where they feed and reproduce. The person develops a serious intestinal condition commonly called hiker's disease.

Other Protozoans The fourth type of protozoans, the sporozoans, are characterized more by the way they live than by the way they move. Sporozoans are parasites that feed on the cells and body fluids of their hosts. They move in a variety of ways. Some have flagella and some depend on hosts for transport. One even slides from place to place on a layer of slime that it produces.

Many sporozoans have more than one host. For example, *Plasmodium* is a sporozoan that causes malaria, a serious disease of the blood. Two hosts are involved in *Plasmodium's* life cycle—humans and a species of mosquitoes found in tropical areas. The disease spreads when a healthy mosquito bites a person with malaria, becomes infected, and then bites a healthy person. Symptoms of malaria include high fevers that alternate with severe chills. These symptoms can last for weeks, then disappear, only to reappear a few months later.

☑ *Checkpoint* *What structures do protozoans use to move?*

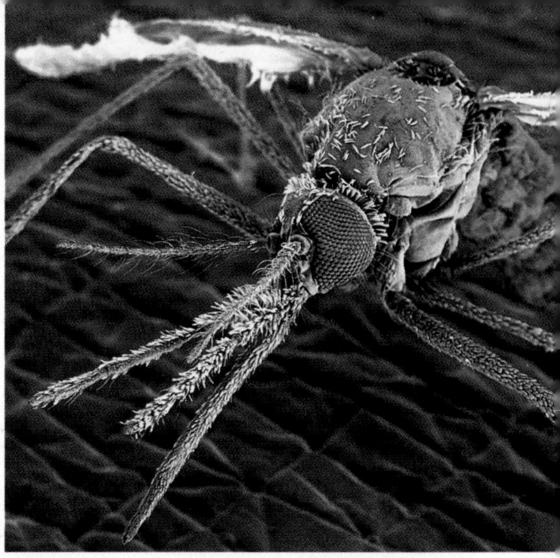

Funguslike Protists

The second group of protists are the funguslike protists. Recall from Chapter 7 that fungi include organisms such as mushrooms and yeast. Until you learn more about fungi in Section 3, you can think of fungi as the "sort of like" organisms. Fungi are "sort of like" animals because they are heterotrophs. They are "sort of like" plants because their cells have cell walls. In addition, most fungi use spores to reproduce. A **spore** is a tiny cell that is able to grow into a new organism.

Like fungi, funguslike protists are heterotrophs, have cell walls, and use spores to reproduce. Unlike fungi, however, all funguslike protists are able to move at some point in their lives. The three types of funguslike protists are water molds, downy mildews, and slime molds.

Water Molds and Downy Mildews Most water molds and downy mildews live in water or in moist places. These organisms grow as tiny threads that look like a fuzzy covering. Figure 5 shows a fish attacked by a water mold.

Water molds and downy mildews also attack food crops, such as potatoes, cabbages, corn, and grapes. A water mold destroyed the Irish potato crops in 1845 and 1846. The loss of these crops led to a famine that resulted in the deaths of over one million Irish people. Many others left Ireland and moved to other countries, such as Canada and the United States.

Figure 4 *Anopheles* mosquitoes can carry a sporozoan, *Plasmodium*, which causes malaria in people. *Relating Cause and Effect Why do you think it is difficult to control the spread of malaria?*

Figure 5 This threadlike water mold is a parasite that grows on fish. The water mold eventually kills the fish.

Figure 6 Slime molds, like the chocolate tube slime mold (left), feed on microorganisms on the surfaces of decaying materials. When food runs low, they grow stalks that produce spores (right).

Slime Molds Slime molds live in moist soil and on decaying plants and trees. Slime molds are often beautifully colored. Many are bright yellow, like the one in Figure 6. Their glistening bodies creep over fallen logs and dead leaves on shady, moist forest floors. They move in an amebalike way by forming pseudopods and oozing along the surfaces of decaying materials. Slime molds feed on bacteria and other microorganisms.

Some slime molds are large enough to be seen with the naked eye. Many, however, are so small that you need a microscope to see them. When the food supply decreases or other conditions change, some tiny slime molds creep together and form a multicellular mass. Spore-producing structures grow out of the mass and release spores, which can develop into a new generation of slime molds.

✓ *Checkpoint* *In what environments are slime molds found?*

Plantlike Protists

If you've ever seen seaweed at a beach, then you are familiar with a type of plantlike protist. Plantlike protists, which are commonly called **algae** (AL jee), are even more varied than the animal-like and funguslike protists. **The one characteristic that all algae share is that, like plants, they are autotrophs.**

Some algae live in the soil, others live on the barks of trees, and still others live in fresh water and salt water. Algae that live on the surface of ponds, lakes, and oceans are an important food source for other organisms in the water. In addition, most of the oxygen in Earth's atmosphere is made by these algae.

Algae range greatly in size. Some algae, such as diatoms, are unicellular. Others are groups of unicellular organisms that live together in colonies. Still others, such as seaweeds, are multicellular. Recall from Chapter 7 that a unicellular organism carries out all the functions necessary for life. But the cells of a multi-cellular organism are specialized to do certain tasks. When single-celled algae come together to form colonies, some of the cells may become specialized to perform certain functions, such as reproduction. However, most cells in a colony continue to carry out all functions. Colonies can contain from four up to thousands of cells.

Algae exist in a wide variety of colors because they contain many types of **pigments**—chemicals that produce color. Depending on their pigments, algae can be green, yellow, red, brown, orange, or even black. Read on to learn about the types of algae that live on Earth.

Euglenoids Euglenoids are green, unicellular algae that are found mostly in fresh water. Unlike other algae, euglenoids have one animal-like characteristic—they can be heterotrophs under certain conditions. When sunlight is available, euglenoids are autotrophs that produce their own food. However, when sunlight is not available, euglenoids will act like heterotrophs by finding and taking in food from their environment.

In Figure 7 you see a euglena, which is a common euglenoid. Notice the long whiplike flagellum that helps the organism move. Locate the eyespot near the flagellum. Although the eyespot is not really an eye, it contains pigments. These pigments are sensitive to light and help a euglena recognize the direction of a light source. You can imagine how important this response is to an organism that needs light to make food.

Figure 7 Euglenas are unicellular algae that live in fresh water. In sunlight, euglenas make their own food. Without sunlight, they obtain food from their environment. *Interpreting Diagrams What structures help a euglena find and move toward light?*

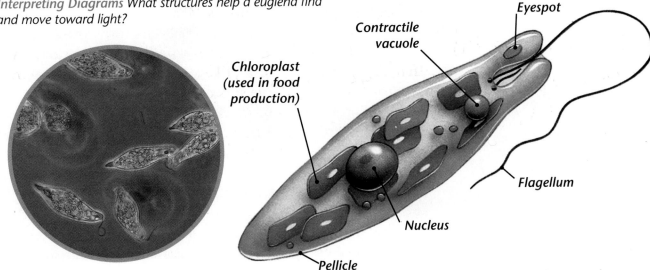

Contractile vacuole

Eyespot

Chloroplast (used in food production)

Flagellum

Nucleus

Pellicle

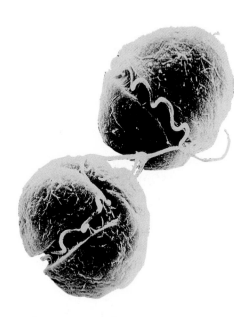

Dinoflagellates Dinoflagellates are unicellular algae covered by stiff plates that look like a suit of armor. Because they have different amounts of green, red, and other pigments, dinoflagellates exist in a variety of colors.

All dinoflagellates have two flagella held in grooves between their plates. When the flagella beat, the dinoflagellates twirl like toy tops through the water. Many glow in the dark and look like miniature fireflies dancing on the ocean's surface at night.

Figure 8 Dinoflagellates, such as these *Gonyaulax*, have rigid plates for protection. They use flagella to move through the water.

Diatoms Diatoms are unicellular protists with beautiful glasslike cell walls. Some float on the surface of freshwater and saltwater environments. Others attach to objects such as rocks in shallow water. Diatoms move by oozing chemicals out of slits in their cell walls. They then glide in the slime. Diatoms are a food source for heterotrophs in the water.

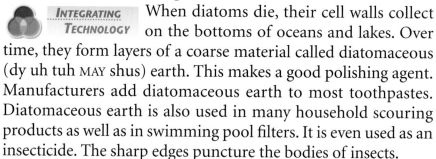

When diatoms die, their cell walls collect on the bottoms of oceans and lakes. Over time, they form layers of a coarse material called diatomaceous (dy uh tuh MAY shus) earth. This makes a good polishing agent. Manufacturers add diatomaceous earth to most toothpastes. Diatomaceous earth is also used in many household scouring products as well as in swimming pool filters. It is even used as an insecticide. The sharp edges puncture the bodies of insects.

Green Algae As their name suggests, all green algae contain green pigments. Otherwise, green algae are quite diverse, as you can see in Figure 9. Although most green algae are unicellular, some form colonies, and a few are multicellular. You might have seen multicellular green algae, or green seaweed, washed up on a beach. Most green algae live in either freshwater or saltwater surroundings. The few that live on land are found along the bases of trees or in moist soils.

Figure 9 Green algae range in size from unicellular organisms to multicellular seaweeds. **A.** The multicellular sea lettuce, *Ulva*, lives in oceans. **B.** This unicellular algae, *Closterium*, lives in fresh water.

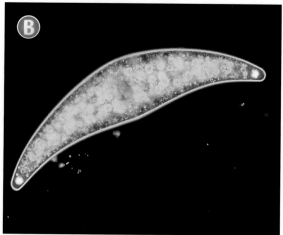

Red Algae Almost all red algae are multicellular seaweeds. Divers have found red algae growing at depths greater than 260 meters below the ocean's surface. Their red pigments are especially good at absorbing the small amount of light that enters deep ocean waters.

Red algae are used by humans in a variety of ways. Carrageenan (kar uh JEE nun), a substance extracted from red algae, is used in products such as ice creams and hair conditioners. For people in many Asians cultures, red algae is a nutrient-rich delicacy that is eaten fresh, dried, or toasted.

Brown Algae Many of the organisms that are commonly called seaweeds are brown algae. In addition to their brown pigment, brown algae also contain green, yellow, and orange pigments. As you can see in Figure 10, a typical brown alga has many plantlike structures. Holdfasts anchor the alga to rocks. Stalks support the blades, which are the leaflike structures of the alga. Brown algae also have gas-filled sacs called bladders that allow the algae to float upright in the water.

Brown algae flourish in cool, rocky waters. Brown algae called rockweed live along the Atlantic coast of North America. Giant kelps, which can grow to 100 meters in length, live in some Pacific coastal waters. The giant kelps form large underwater "forests" where many organisms, including sea otters and abalone, live. Some people eat brown algae for their nutrients. Substances called algins are extracted from brown algae and used as thickeners in foods such as puddings and salad dressings.

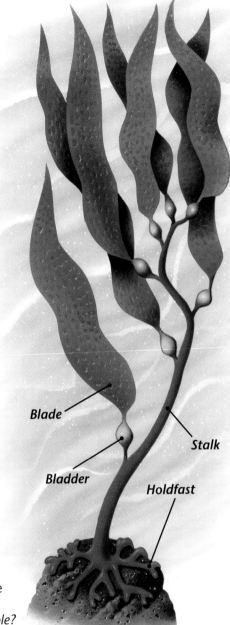

Blade

Stalk

Bladder

Holdfast

Figure 10 Giant kelps have many plantlike structures. *Applying Concepts What plant structures do the holdfasts and blades resemble?*

Section 1 Review

1. What characteristic do all protozoans share?
2. What are three characteristics of the funguslike protists?
3. What characteristic do algae share with plants?
4. **Thinking Critically Making Judgments** Would you classify euglena as an animal-like protist or as a plantlike protist? Explain your answer.

Science at Home

Look through your kitchen with a family member to find products that contain substances made from algae. Look at both food and non-food items. Before you begin, tell your family member that words such as diatomaceous earth, algin, and carrageenan are substances that come from algae. Make a list of the products and the algae-based ingredient they contain. Share your list with the class.

SECTION 2 Algal Blooms

Over a five week period one year, the bodies of 14 humpback whales washed up along beaches on Cape Cod, Massachusetts. The whales showed no outward signs of sickness. Their stomachs were full of food. Their bodies contained plenty of blubber to insulate them from changes in water temperature. What caused such healthy-looking animals to die?

When biologists examined the dead whales' tissues, they identified the cause of the puzzling deaths. The whales' cells contained a deadly toxin produced by a dinoflagellate called *Alexandrium tamarense*. For reasons that scientists don't fully understand, the population of these algae grew rapidly in the ocean waters through which the whales were migrating. When the whales fed on the toxin-producing algae or on fishes that had eaten the algae, the toxins reached a deadly level and killed the whales.

Algae are common in both saltwater and freshwater environments on Earth. They float on the surface of the waters and use sunlight to make food. The rapid growth of a population of algae is called an **algal bloom.** The deaths of the humpbacks is one example of the damage that an algal bloom can cause.

◄ A humpback whale

Figure 11 Rapid algae growth has caused a red tide in this small bay off the coast of California. *Relating Cause and Effect What organisms are most often responsible for causing red tides?*

Saltwater Blooms

In Figure 11, you see an algal bloom in ocean water. Saltwater algal blooms are commonly called **red tides.** This is because the algae that grow rapidly often contain red pigments and turn the color of the water red. But red tides do not always look red. Some red tides are brown, green, or colorless depending on the species of algae that blooms. Dinoflagellates and diatoms are two algae that frequently bloom in red tides.

Scientists are not sure why some saltwater algal populations increase rapidly at times. But red tides occur most often when there is an increase in nutrients in the water. Increases in ocean temperature due to climate changes also affect the occurrence of red tides. Some red tides occur regularly in certain seasons. The cold bottom layers of the ocean contain a lot of nutrients. When the cold water mixes with the surface waters, more nutrients become available to surface organisms. With excess nutrients present in the surface waters, blooms of algae occur.

Red tides are dangerous when the toxins that the algae produce become concentrated in the bodies of organisms that consume the algae. Shellfish feed on large numbers of the algae and store the toxins in their cells. Fishes may also feed on the algae and store the toxins. When people or other large organisms eat these shellfish and fishes, it may lead to serious illness or even death. Public health officials close beaches in areas of red tides and prohibit people from gathering shellfish or fishing.

INTEGRATING TECHNOLOGY Red tides occur more frequently worldwide today than they did a decade ago. Scientists cannot yet predict when red tides will occur. They use images taken by satellites in space to track how red tides move with ocean currents. Satellite images can also detect increases in ocean temperatures, which may put an area at risk for red tide.

✓ *Checkpoint* *Why are red tides often red in color?*

Figure 12 Increased nutrient levels in lakes and ponds can lead to algal blooms. The thick layer of algae on the surface can threaten other organisms in the water. *Problem Solving Outline a series of steps that could help slow down the rapid growth of algae in a lake.*

Freshwater Blooms

Algal blooms also occur in bodies of fresh water. Have you ever seen a pond or lake that looked as if it was coated with a layer of green paint? The green layer of surface scum usually consists of huge numbers of unicellular green algae.

Lakes and ponds undergo natural processes of change over time. In a process called **eutrophication** (yoo troh fih KAY shun), nutrients, such as nitrogen and phosphorus, build up in a lake or pond over time, causing an increase in the growth of algae.

Certain natural events and human activities can increase the rate of eutrophication. For example, when farmers spread fertilizers on fields, some of these chemicals can run off into nearby lakes and ponds. In addition, poorly designed or aging septic systems can leak their contents into the soil. The nutrients make their way from the soil into water that leads into lakes and ponds. These events cause a rapid increase in algae growth.

The rapid growth of algae in a pond or lake triggers a series of events with serious consequences. First, the layer of algae prevents sunlight from reaching plants and other algae beneath the surface. Those organisms die and sink to the bottom. Then organisms, such as bacteria, which break down the bodies of the dead plants and algae, increase in number. Soon the bacteria use up the oxygen in the water. Fishes and other organisms in the water die without the oxygen they need to survive. About the only life that survives is the algae on the surface.

Algal blooms in fresh water can be easier to control than those in salt water because lakes and ponds have definite boundaries. To slow eutrophication, scientists first need to find the sources of the excess nutrients and then eliminate them. If the source can be eliminated and the nutrients used up, eutrophication slows to its natural rate.

Section 2 Review

1. Why are red tides dangerous?
2. What causes a freshwater bloom?
3. How does the death of bottom plants in a shallow pond affect the rest of the pond?
4. **Thinking Critically** **Problem Solving** A new housing development is to be built along a recreational lake. What factors should the developers consider to protect the lake from rapid eutrophication?

Check Your Progress
By now, you should have your teacher's approval for your plan, and you should have started growing your mushrooms. Make careful observations of growth every day. Include sketches and measurements as appropriate. Use a data table to organize the data you collect. *(Hint: As you make your observations, be careful not to disturb the experiment or introduce any new variables.)*

CHAPTER PROJECT

AN EXPLOSION OF LIFE

Living things are interconnected with their surroundings in many ways. In this lab, you will investigate how one change in a freshwater environment can affect everything that lives in that environment.

Problem

How does the amount of fertilizer affect algae growth?

Skills Focus

controlling variables, predicting, drawing conclusions

Materials

4 glass jars with lids   marking pen
aged tap water   aquarium water
graduated cylinder   liquid fertilizer

Procedure

1. Read through the steps in the procedure. Then write a prediction describing what you think will happen in each of the four jars.
2. Copy the data table into your notebook. Be sure to allow enough lines to make entries for a two-week period.
3. Label four jars A, B, C, and D. Fill each jar half full with aged tap water.
4. Add aquarium water to each jar until the jar is three-fourths full.
5. Add 3 mL of liquid fertilizer to jar B; 6 mL to jar C; and 12 mL to jar D. Do not add any fertilizer to jar A. Loosely screw the lid on each jar. Place all the jars in a sunny location where they will receive the same amount of direct sunlight.

DATA TABLE

Date	Observations			
	Jar A no fertilizer	Jar B 3 mL fertilizer	Jar C 6 mL fertilizer	Jar D 12 mL fertilizer
Day 1				
Day 2				

6. Observe the jars every day for two weeks. Compare the color of the water in the four jars. Record your observations in your data table.

Analyze and Conclude

1. How did the color in the four jars compare at the end of the two-week period? How can you account for any differences that you observed?
2. What was the purpose of jar A?
3. Describe the process that led to the overall color change in the water. What organisms were responsible for causing that color change?
4. Predict what would have happened if you placed the four jars in a dark location instead of in sunlight. Explain your prediction.
5. **Apply** What do you think might happen to fish and other living organisms when fertilizer gets into a body of fresh water? What are some ways that fertilizer might get into a body of water?

Design an Experiment

Some detergents contain phosphates, which are an ingredient in many kinds of fertilizer. Design an experiment to compare how regular detergent and low-phosphate detergent affect the growth of algae.

Eutrophication — The Threat to Clear, Clean Water

Weiss Lake, on the Georgia-Alabama border, is a popular vacation area. People come to this lake to fish, boat, and swim. But every year about 2 million pounds of phosphorus pour into Weiss Lake from rivers. These excess nutrients are threatening the lake's good fishing and clean, clear water.

Weiss Lake is just one of thousands of lakes and ponds in the United States threatened by eutrophication. The threat is not just to recreation. Drinking water for nearly 70 percent of Americans comes from lakes, reservoirs, and other surface water.

The Issues

Where Does the Pollution Come From?
The two main sources of excess nutrients are wastes and fertilizers from farms and wastewater from sewage treatment plants. When farmers fertilize crops, the plants absorb only some of these nutrients. The excess nutrients can be washed with soil into lakes and ponds. When wastewater from homes and factories is treated, large amounts of nutrients still remain in the water. For example, about 380 million liters of treated wastewater flow toward Weiss Lake daily. This treated wastewater still contains large amounts of phosphorus produced by many factories.

What Are the Costs of Eutrophication?
People who live near Weiss Lake depend on the lake for jobs and money. But as the fish die in the oxygen-poor waters, swimming and boating in the murky water become less appealing and possibly unsafe. Over 4,000 jobs and millions of dollars each year would be lost if Weiss Lake were to close down. But upgrading or building new water-treatment plants would cost millions of dollars in higher taxes to citizens.

What Can Be Done? Even as cities, farms, and factories grow, the amount of nutrients reaching lakes and ponds can be reduced. Factories can install water-treatment facilities that remove more nitrogen and phosphorus from their wastewater. Farmers can often reduce the use of fertilizers. People can plant trees along the banks of lakes to reduce the amount of soil entering the lake. These solutions can cost millions of dollars, but they can reverse the problem.

You Decide

1. Identify the Problem

In your own words, describe the eutrophication issues that affect Weiss Lake.

2. Analyze the Options

Make a chart of different ways to slow the eutrophication process. How would each work? What groups of people would be affected?

3. Find a Solution

Create a "prevention plan" advising town leaders how to reduce eutrophication in lakes and ponds.

SECTION 3 Fungi

DISCOVER  ACTIVITY

Do All Molds Look Alike?

1. Your teacher will give you two sealed, clear plastic bags—one containing moldy bread and another containing moldy fruit. **CAUTION:** *Do not open the sealed bags at any time.*

2. Examine each mold. In your notebook, describe what you see.

3. Then, use a hand lens to examine each mold. Sketch each mold in your notebook and list its characteristics.

4. Return the sealed bags to your teacher. Wash your hands.

Think It Over
Observing How are the molds similar? How do they differ?

Unnoticed, a speck of dust lands on a cricket's back. But this is no ordinary dust—it is alive! Tiny glistening threads emerge from the dust and begin to grow into the cricket's moist body. As they grow, the threads release chemicals that slowly dissolve the cricket's living tissues. The threads continue to grow deeper into the cricket's body. Within a few days, the cricket's body is little more than a hollow shell filled with a tangle of the deadly threads. Then the threads begin to grow up and out of the dead cricket. They produce long stalks with knobs at their tips. When one of the knobs breaks open, it will release thousands of dustlike specks, which the wind can carry to new victims.

What Are Fungi?

The strange cricket-killing organism is a member of the fungi kingdom. Although you may not have heard of a cricket-killing fungus before, you are probably familiar with other kinds of fungi. For example, the molds that grow on stale bread or on decaying fruit are all fungi. Mushrooms that sprout in forests or yards are also fungi.

GUIDE FOR READING

◆ What characteristics do fungi share?

◆ How do fungi obtain food?

◆ What roles do fungi play in the living world?

Reading Tip Before you read, preview the headings. Record them in outline form, leaving space for writing notes.

▼ A bush cricket attacked by a killer fungus

Fungi vary in size from the unicellular yeasts to the multicellular fungi, such as mushrooms and the bracket fungi that look like shelves growing on tree trunks. **Most fungi share three important characteristics: They are eukaryotes, use spores to reproduce, and are heterotrophs that feed in a similar way.** In addition, fungi need moist, warm places in which to grow. They thrive on moist foods, damp tree barks, lawns coated with dew, damp forest floors, and even wet bathroom tiles.

Cell Structure

Except for yeast cells, which are unicellular, the cells of fungi are arranged in structures called hyphae. **Hyphae** (HY fee) (singular *hypha*) are the branching, threadlike tubes that make up the bodies of multicellular fungi. The hyphae of some fungi are continuous threads of cytoplasm that contain many nuclei. Substances move quickly and freely through the hyphae.

The appearance of a fungus depends on how its hyphae are arranged. In some fungi, the threadlike hyphae are loosely tangled. Fuzzy-looking molds that grow on old foods have loosely tangled hyphae. In other fungi, hyphae are packed tightly together. For example, the stalk and cap of the mushrooms in Figure 13 are made of hyphae packed so tightly that they appear solid. Underground, however, a mushroom's hyphae form a loose, threadlike maze in the soil.

☑ *Checkpoint* *What structures make up the bodies of multicellular fungi?*

Cap

Gills

Stalk

Hyphae

Underground hyphae

Figure 13 The hyphae in the stalk and cap of a mushroom are packed tightly to form very firm structures. Underground hyphae, on the other hand, are arranged loosely. *Inferring* *What function do you think the underground hyphae perform?*

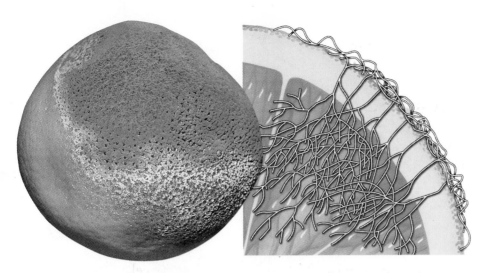

Figure 14 The mold *Penicillium* often grows on old fruits such as this orange. Notice that some hyphae grow deep inside the orange. These hyphae digest the food and absorb the smaller chemicals.

How Do Fungi Obtain Food?

Although fungi are heterotrophs, they do not take food into their bodies as you do. Instead fungi absorb food through hyphae that grow into the food source.

Look at Figure 14 to see how a fungus feeds. **First, the fungus grows hyphae into a food source. Then digestive chemicals ooze from the tips of the hyphae into the food. The digestive chemicals break down the food into small substances that can be absorbed by the hyphae.** Imagine yourself sinking your fingers down into a chocolate cake and dripping digestive chemicals out of your fingertips. Then imagine your fingers absorbing the digested particles of the cake. That's how a fungus feeds.

Some fungi feed on the remains of dead organisms. Other fungi are parasites that break down the chemicals in living organisms. For example, athlete's foot is a disease caused by a fungus that feeds on chemicals in a person's skin. Dutch elm disease is caused by a fungus that feeds on elm trees and eventually kills the trees.

Reproduction in Fungi

Like it or not, fungi are everywhere. The way they reproduce guarantees their survival and spread. Fungi usually reproduce by producing lightweight spores that are surrounded by a protective covering. Spores can be carried easily through air or water to new sites. Fungi produce many more spores than will ever grow into new fungi. Only a few of the thousands of spores that a fungus releases will fall where conditions are right for them to grow into new organisms.

Making Spore Prints

In this activity, you will examine the reproductive structures of a mushroom. **ACTIVITY**

1. Place a fresh mushroom cap, gill side down, on a sheet of white paper. **CAUTION:** *Do not eat the mushroom.*

2. Cover the mushroom cap with a plastic container. Wash your hands with soap.

3. After two days, carefully remove the container and then the cap. You should find a spore print on the paper.

4. Examine the print with a hand lens. Then wash your hands with soap.

Predicting Use your spore print to estimate how many spores a mushroom could produce. Where would spores be most likely to grow into new mushrooms?

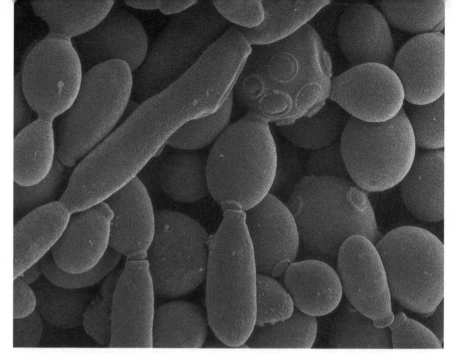

Figure 15 Budding is a form of asexual reproduction that occurs in yeast. The small yeast cell that grows from the body of a parent cell is identical to the parent.

Fungi produce spores in structures called **fruiting bodies,** which are reproductive hyphae that grow out of a fungus. The appearances of fruiting bodies vary from one type of fungus to another. For some fungi, such as mushrooms and puffballs, the part of the fungus that you see is the fruiting body. In other fungi, such as bread molds, the stalklike fruiting bodies grow upward from the hyphae on the surface of the bread. The knoblike structure, or spore case, at the tip of a stalk contains the spores.

Asexual Reproduction Most fungi reproduce both asexually and sexually. When there is adequate moisture and food, most fungi reproduce asexually by growing fruiting bodies that release thousands of spores.

Unicellular yeast cells undergo a form of asexual reproduction called **budding.** In budding, no spores are produced. Instead, a small yeast cell grows from the body of a large, well-fed parent cell in a way that might remind you of a bud forming on the branch of a tree. The new cell then breaks away and lives on its own.

Sexual Reproduction When growing conditions become unfavorable, fungi may reproduce sexually. In sexual reproduction, the hyphae of two fungi grow together. A new spore-producing structure grows from the joined hyphae. The new structure produces spores, which can develop into fungi that differ from either parent.

Checkpoint *What is a fruiting body?*

Classification of Fungi

Fungi are classified into groups based on the shape of the spore-producing structures and on their ability to reproduce sexually. The four groups of fungi—the threadlike fungi, the sac fungi, the club fungi, and the imperfect fungi—are shown in Figure 16.

▲ **Threadlike Fungi**

This group contains about 600 different species of molds, including many common bread molds, such as this *Rhizopus*. These fungi produce spores in their threadlike hyphae.

▲ **Sac Fungi**

This group contains over 30,000 diverse species of fungi, including yeast, morels, truffles, and some fungi that cause plant diseases, such as Dutch elm disease. They are called sac fungi because they produce spores in structures that look like sacks. The sac fungi in the photo are called bird's nest fungi.

◄ **Club Fungi**

This group includes about 25,000 species of mushrooms, bracket fungi, plant parasites, and puffballs. Club fungi produce spores in structures that look like clubs. One of the puffballs in the photo is shooting out its spores.

▲ **Imperfect Fungi**

The 25,000 species in this group include this *Penicillium*, the source of an important antibiotic. The fungi in this group are not known to reproduce sexually.

Figure 16 The four groups of fungi differ in the appearance of their spore-producing structures and in how they reproduce.
Classifying *To which group do mushrooms belong?*

What's for Lunch?

In this lab, you will draw conclusions about the effects of two substances on the activity of yeast.

Problem

How does the presence of sugar or salt affect the activity of yeast?

Materials

marking pen
5 plastic straws
salt
beaker
graduated cylinder
5 small narrow-necked bottles
5 round balloons
sugar
warm water (40–45°C)
dry powdered yeast

Procedure

1. Copy the data table into your notebook. Then read over the entire procedure to see how you will test the activity of the yeast cells in bottles A through E. Write a prediction about what will happen in each bottle.

2. Gently stretch each of the 5 balloons so that they will inflate easily.

3. Using the marking pen, label the bottles A, B, C, D, and E.

4. Use a beaker to fill each bottle with the same amount of warm water. **CAUTION:** *Glass is fragile. Handle the bottles and beaker gently to avoid breakage. Do not touch broken glass.*

5. Put 5 mL of salt into bottle B.

6. Put 5 mL of sugar into bottles C and E.

7. Put 30 mL of sugar into bottle D.

8. Put 2 mL of powdered yeast into bottle A, and stir the mixture with a clean straw. Remove the straw and discard it.

9. Immediately place a balloon over the opening of bottle A. Make sure that the balloon opening fits very tightly around the neck of the bottle.

10. Repeat Steps 8 and 9 for bottle B, bottle C, and bottle D.

DATA TABLE

Bottle	Contents	Prediction	Observations
A	Yeast alone		
B	Yeast and 5 mL of salt		
C	Yeast and 5 mL of sugar		
D	Yeast and 30 mL of sugar		
E	No yeast and 5 mL of sugar		

11. Place a balloon over bottle E without adding yeast to the bottle.

12. Place the 5 bottles in a warm spot away from drafts. Observe and record what happens.

Analyze and Conclude

1. Which balloons changed in size during this lab? How did they change?

2. Explain why the balloon changed size in some bottles and not in others. What caused that change in size?

3. Do yeast cells use sugar as a food source? How do you know?

4. Do yeast cells use salt as a food source? How do you know?

5. What did the results from bottle C show, compared with the results from bottle D?

6. **Think About It** If you removed bottle E from your experiment, would you be able to conclude whether or not sugar is a food source for the yeast cells? Why or why not?

Design an Experiment

Develop a hypothesis about whether yeast cells need light to carry out their life activities. Then design an experiment to test your hypothesis. Obtain your teacher's permission before you carry out the experiment.

Fungi and the Living World

Fungi affect humans and other organisms in many ways. **Fungi play an important role as decomposers on Earth. In addition, many fungi provide foods for people. Some cause disease and some fight disease. Still other fungi live in symbiosis with other organisms.**

Environmental Recycling Like bacteria, fungi are decomposers—organisms that break down the chemicals in dead organisms. For example, many fungi live in the soil and break down the chemicals in dead plant matter. This process returns important nutrients to the soil. Without fungi and bacteria, Earth would be buried under dead plants and animals.

Food and Fungi When you eat a slice of bread, you benefit from the work of yeast. Bakers add yeast to bread dough to make it rise. Yeast cells use the sugar in the dough for food and produce carbon dioxide gas as they feed. The gas forms bubbles, which cause the dough to rise. You see these bubbles as holes in a slice of bread. Without yeast, bread would be flat and solid. Yeast is also used to make wine from grapes. Yeast cells feed on the sugar in the grapes and produce carbon dioxide and alcohol.

Other fungi are also important sources of foods. Molds are used in the production of foods such as some cheeses. The blue streaks in blue cheese, for example, are actually growths of *Penicillium roqueforti*. People enjoy eating mushrooms in salads and soups and on pizza. Because some mushrooms are poisonous, however, you should never pick or eat wild mushrooms.

☑ *Checkpoint* *What are three foods that fungi help to produce?*

Disease-Causing Fungi Many fungi cause serious diseases in plants that result in huge crop losses every year. Corn smut and wheat rust are two club fungi that cause diseases in important food crops. Fungal plant diseases also affect other crops, including rice, cotton, and soybeans.

INTEGRATING HEALTH Some fungi cause diseases in humans as well. Athlete's foot causes an itchy irritation in the damp places between toes. Ringworm, another fungal disease, causes an itchy, circular rash on the skin. Because the fungi that cause these

Figure 17 Many food crops are lost each year due to fungal diseases. The ear of corn in the photo has been attacked by a fungus called corn smut. *Making Generalizations Why is the spread of fungal diseases difficult to control?*

diseases produce spores at the site of infection, the diseases can spread easily from person to person. Both diseases can be treated with antifungal medications.

Disease-Fighting Fungi   In 1928 a Scottish biologist, Alexander Fleming, was examining petri dishes in which he was growing bacteria. To his surprise, Fleming noticed a spot of a bluish-green mold growing in one dish. Curiously, no bacteria were growing near the mold. Fleming hypothesized that the mold, a fungus named *Penicillium*, produced a substance that killed the bacteria growing near it. Fleming's work led to the development of the first antibiotic, penicillin. It has saved the lives of millions of people with bacterial infections. Since the discovery of penicillin, many additional antibiotics have been isolated from both fungi and eubacteria.

Fungus-Plant Root Associations   Some fungi help plants grow larger and healthier when their hyphae grow among the plant's roots. The hyphae spread out underground and absorb water and nutrients from the soil for the plant. With more water and nutrients, the plant grows larger than it would have grown without its fungal partner. The plant is not the only partner that benefits. The fungi get to feed on the extra food that the plant makes and stores.

Many plants are so dependent on their fungal partners that they cannot survive well without them. For example, orchids cannot grow without their fungal partners.

Language Arts CONNECTION

Folk tales are ancient stories that were passed down by word of mouth over many generations. Folk tales often involve magical elements, such as fairies—supernatural beings with powers to become invisible, change form, and affect the lives of people.

The circle of mushrooms in Figure 18 was often mentioned in folk tales. These circles were said to be the footprints of fairies who danced there at midnight. These mushroom circles were given the name "fairy rings"—a name that is still used today. People believed that the area inside a fairy ring was a magical location. Cutting down the tree inside a fairy ring was believed to bring bad luck.

In Your Journal

A type of mushroom called a toadstool is mentioned in some folk tales. Write a paragraph that could be part of a folk tale that reveals how toadstools got their name.

Figure 18 The fruiting bodies of these mushrooms have emerged in an almost perfect circular pattern. This pattern is called a fairy ring. The mushrooms share the same network of underground hyphae.

Figure 19 Lichens consist of a fungus living together with either algae or autotrophic bacteria. **A.** This lichen—a British soldier—probably gets its name from its scarlet red tops, which stand upright. **B.** The lichens covering these rocks are slowly breaking down the rocks to create soil.

Lichens A **lichen** (LY kun) consists of a fungus and either algae or autotrophic bacteria that also live together in a mutualistic relationship. You have probably seen some familiar lichens—irregular, flat, crusty patches that grow on tree barks or rocks. The fungus benefits from the food produced by the algae or bacteria. The algae or bacteria, in turn, obtain water and minerals from the fungus.

INTEGRATING EARTH SCIENCE Lichens are often called "pioneer" organisms because they are the first organisms to appear on the bare rocks in an area after a volcano, fire, or rock slide has occurred. Over time, the lichens break down the rock into soil in which other organisms can grow. Lichens are also useful as indicators of air pollution. Many species of lichens are very sensitive to pollutants and die when pollution levels rise. By monitoring the growth of lichens, scientists can assess the air quality in an area.

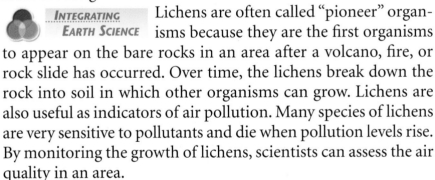

Section 3 Review

1. List three characteristics that fungi share.
2. Explain how a fungus feeds. What do fungi feed on?
3. Describe three roles that fungi play in the world.
4. **Thinking Critically Classifying** Explain why mushrooms are classified as fungi rather than as plants.

Check Your Progress

CHAPTER PROJECT

Continue to observe your mushrooms and collect data. Begin to review your data to see which conditions favored mushroom growth. How do your results compare with your hypothesis? Begin to plan your poster now. Think about how you can use graphs and diagrams to display your results. *(Hint:* Draw a rough sketch of your poster, and show it to your teacher. Include a labeled drawing of a mushroom.)

SECTION 1 Protists

Key Ideas

◆ Animal-like protists, or protozoans, include sarcodines, ciliates, zooflagellates, and sporozoans. Like animals, these protists are heterotrophs. Most protozoans move by using pseudopods, cilia, or flagella.

◆ Funguslike protists include water molds, downy mildews, and slime molds. Like fungi, these protists are heterotrophs, have cell walls, and use spores to reproduce.

◆ Plantlike protists, or algae, include euglenoids, dinoflagellates, diatoms, green algae, red algae, and brown algae. Like plants, these organisms are autotrophs.

Key Terms

protozoan	mutualism
pseudopod	spore
contractile vacuole	algae
cilia	pigment
symbiosis	

SECTION 2 Algal Blooms

INTEGRATING ENVIRONMENTAL SCIENCE

Key Ideas

◆ Red tides occur when a population of algae increases quickly in ocean waters. Some algae can secrete toxins that poison animals.

◆ Nutrients in a lake or pond build up over time, causing an increase in the numbers of algae. An accelerated rate of eutrophication can lead to the deaths of many organisms in the lake or pond.

Key Terms

algal bloom	eutrophication
red tide	

SECTION 3 Fungi

Key Ideas

◆ Most fungi are eukaryotes, use spores to reproduce, and are heterotrophs.

◆ Most fungi feed by absorbing food through their hyphae. The hyphae secrete digestive chemicals into a food source, which is broken down into small substances that are absorbed by the hyphae.

◆ Fungi produce spores in structures called fruiting bodies. The majority of fungi reproduce both asexually and sexually.

◆ Fungi are decomposers that recycle Earth's chemicals. In addition, some fungi cause disease while some fight disease. Many produce important foods for people. Some fungi live in symbiotic relationships with other organisms.

Key Terms
hypha
fruiting body
budding
lichen

USING THE INTERNET ACTIVITY

www.science-explorer.phschool.com

California Test Prep: Reviewing Content

Multiple Choice

Choose the letter of the best answer.

1. Which of the following characteristics describes *all* protists?
   a. They are unicellular.
   b. They can be seen with the unaided eye.
   c. Their cells have nuclei.
   d. They are unable to move on their own.

2. Which protist uses cilia to move?
   a. euglena
   b. ameba
   c. paramecium
   d. diatom

3. Which statement is true of slime molds?
   a. They are always unicellular.
   b. They are autotrophs.
   c. They are animal-like protists.
   d. They use spores to reproduce.

4. An overpopulation of saltwater algae is called a(n)
   a. pigment.
   b. lichen.
   c. red tide.
   d. eutrophication.

5. A lichen is a symbiotic association between which of the following?
   a. fungi and plant roots
   b. algae and fungi
   c. algae and bacteria
   d. protozoans and algae

True or False

If the statement is true, write true. If it is false, change the underlined word or words to make the statement true.

6. Sarcodines use <u>flagella</u> to move.

7. <u>Eutrophication</u> is the process by which nutrients in a lake build up over time, causing an increase in the growth of algae.

8. Most fungi are made up of threadlike structures called <u>hyphae</u>.

9. All mushrooms are classified as <u>sac</u> fungi.

10. Most fungi that live among the roots of plants are <u>beneficial</u> to the plants.

Checking Concepts

11. Describe how an ameba obtains its food.

12. How do algae differ in terms of size?

13. Compare how animal-like, funguslike, and plantlike protists obtain food.

14. How does sexual reproduction occur in fungi?

15. Explain how both organisms in a lichen benefit from their symbiotic relationship.

16. **Writing to Learn** Imagine you are a spore in a ripe puffball. An animal passing by punctures the outer covering of your spore case. Describe what happens to you next.

Thinking Visually

17. **Flowchart** Copy this flowchart about changes in a lake onto a separate sheet of paper. Then complete the flowchart and add a title. (For more on flowcharts, see the Skills Handbook.)

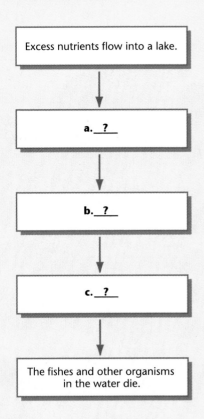

Excess nutrients flow into a lake.

a. ___?___

b. ___?___

c. ___?___

The fishes and other organisms in the water die.

Test Prep: Skills

When yeast is added to bread dough, the yeast cells produce carbon dioxide, which causes the dough to rise. The graph below shows how temperature affects the amount of carbon dioxide that is produced. Use the graph to answer Questions 18–20.

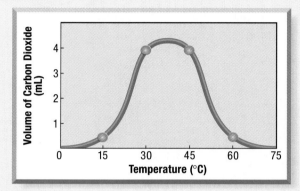

18. Interpreting Data Explain how temperature affects the amount of carbon dioxide that the yeast cells produce.

19. Inferring Use the graph to explain why yeast is dissolved in warm water rather than cold water when it is used to make bread.

20. Predicting Based on the graph, would you expect bread dough to continue to rise if it were placed in a refrigerator (about 2°–5°C)? Explain.

Thinking Critically

21. Comparing and Contrasting How are amebas and paramecia similar to one another? How are they different?

22. Relating Cause and Effect You see a layer of green scum growing on the walls of your aquarium at home. List some possible reasons why this growth has occurred.

23. Predicting If algae disappeared from Earth's waters, what would happen to living things on Earth? Explain your answer.

24. Problem Solving What actions could homeowners take to discourage the growth of mildew in their basement? Explain why these actions might help solve the problem.

Performance Assessment

CHAPTER PROJECT Wrap Up

Present Your Project Now it's time to finalize your poster. Be sure to include your hypothesis, and describe the conditions that produced the best mushroom growth. Make sure you have described your investigation clearly and that your graph is easy to understand. Check that your drawing of a mushroom is correct and clearly labeled.

Reflect and Record What did you learn about mushrooms from this project? Did you encounter and solve any problems? Did the project raise new questions for you? If so, how could you answer those questions?

Getting Involved

In Your School With your classmates, plan a display to show some of the roles that protists and fungi play in people's lives. Arrange for a place to set up your display. Include colorful posters, models, and samples of materials that contain protists and fungi. Check with your teacher about the proper way to display live samples of organisms. Be prepared to answer questions about your display.

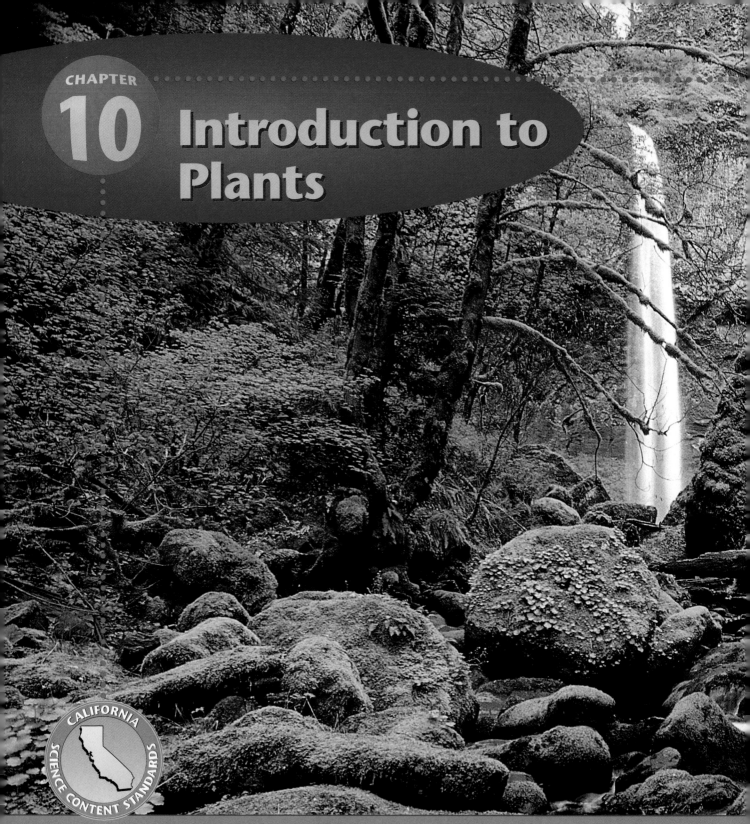

The following California Science Content Standards are addressed in this chapter:

1. All living organisms are composed of cells, from just one to many trillions, whose details usually are visible only through a microscope.

   b. The characteristics that distinguish plant cells from animal cells, including chloroplasts and cell walls.

   c. The nucleus is the repository for genetic information in plant and animal cells.

   d. Mitochondria liberate energy for the work that cells do, and chloroplasts capture sunlight energy for photosynthesis.

2. A typical cell of any organism contains genetic instructions that specify its traits. Those traits may be modified by environmental influences.

   a. The differences between the life cycles and reproduction of sexual and asexual organisms.

3. Biological evolution accounts for the diversity of species developed through gradual processes over many generations.

   a. Both genetic variation and environmental factors are causes of evolution and diversity of organisms.

PROJECT 10

Become a Moss Expert

In a shady valley, mosses cover the banks of a stream. Overhead, trees stretch their branches toward the light. Each type of plant has its own requirements for growth. In this project, you'll care for one type of plant, a moss similar to the ones growing on these rocks. By the time you're finished, you'll be able to tell others what conditions are needed for mosses to grow.

Your Goal To create a brochure titled "How to Raise Mosses" to share with an audience of your choice.

To successfully complete this project you must
- grow moss in a terrarium you construct from a 2-liter bottle
- observe the moss daily, and keep a log of the amount of light, water, and other conditions you provide for it
- publish information about caring for mosses
- follow the safety guidelines in Appendix A

Get Started In a small group, create a list of places where you've seen mosses growing. Compare the list your group makes with those from other groups. What are some locations that many groups identified? What do you notice about the environments where mosses are found? List possible ways to create a similar environment in a terrarium. Start to write out a plan for making the terrarium.

Check Your Progress You'll be working on this project as you study this chapter. To keep your project on track, look for Check Your Progress boxes at the following points.
   Section 1 Review, page 307: Plan your terrarium.
   Section 3 Review, page 318: Provide the proper conditions as you care for your moss.
   Section 4 Review, page 324: Plan and produce your brochure.

Wrap Up At the end of the chapter (page 327), you'll share your brochure about mosses with your audience.

Mosses carpet the rocks along this stream in Pennsylvania's Pocono Mountains.

---

5. The anatomy and physiology of plants and animals illustrate the complementary nature of structure and function.

a. Plants and animals have levels of organization for structure and function, including cells, tissues, organs, organ systems, and the whole organism.

6. Physical principles underlie biological structures and functions.

e. White light is a mixture of many wavelengths (colors).

f. Light interacts with matter by transmission, absorption, or scattering.

7. Scientific progress is made by asking meaningful questions and conducting careful investigations.

c. Communicate the logical connection among hypothesis, science concepts, tests conducted, data collected, and conclusions drawn from the scientific evidence.

SECTION 1 The Plant Kingdom

What Do Leaves Reveal About Plants?

1. Your teacher will give you two leaves from plants that grow in two very different environments: a desert and an area with average rainfall.

2. Carefully observe the color, size, shape, and texture of the leaves. Touch the surfaces of each leaf. Examine each leaf with a hand lens. Record your observations in your notebook.

3. When you have finished, wash your hands thoroughly with soap and water.

Think It Over

Inferring Use your observations to determine which plant lives in the desert and which does not. Give at least one reason to support your inference.

GUIDE FOR READING

◆ What characteristics do all plants share?

◆ What do plants need to live successfully on land?

Reading Tip Before you read, list the boldfaced vocabulary words in your notebook. Leave space to add notes as you read.

Imagine a forest where a thick growth of fungi, mosses, and ferns carpets the floor. Because there is no bare soil, seedlings start their lives on fallen logs. Ferns hang like curtains from the limbs of giant hemlock trees. Douglas fir trees grow taller than 20-story buildings. Other plants with strange names—scouler willow, vanilla leaf, self-heal, and licorice fern—also grow in the forest.

Such a forest exists on the western slopes of the Olympic Mountains in Washington State. Native Americans named the forest *Hoh*, which means "fast white water," after a river there. In some areas of the forest, over 300 centimeters of rain fall each year, which makes the area a rain forest. But unlike rain forests in the tropics, the most common trees in the Hoh rain forest are maples, spruces, red cedars, and firs.

▼ The Hoh rain forest

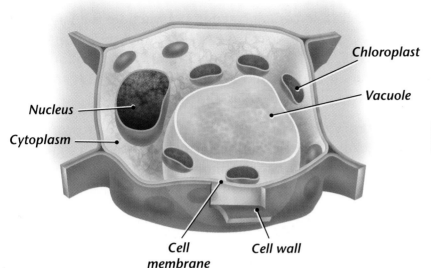

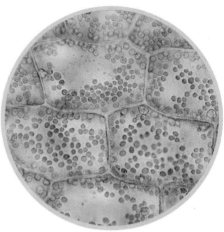

Figure 1 Plants have eukaryotic cells that are enclosed by a cell wall. *Interpreting Photographs Which plant cell structures can you find in the photograph on the right? What roles do these structures play?*

What Is a Plant?

You would probably recognize many of the plants that grow in the Hoh rain forest. You encounter other familiar plants when you pick flowers, run across freshly cut grass, or eat vegetables such as carrots. Members of the plant kingdom share some important characteristics. **Plants are autotrophs that produce their own food. In addition, all plants are eukaryotes that contain many cells.**

Plants Are Autotrophs You can think of a plant as a sun-powered, food-making factory. The process by which plants make food is called **photosynthesis** (foh toh SIN thuh sis). The word *photosynthesis* comes from two Greek words. *Photo* means "light," and *synthesis* means "to make." During photosynthesis, a plant uses carbon dioxide gas and water to make food and oxygen. The process occurs in a series of complex chemical reactions. Sunlight provides the energy that powers the entire process. You will learn more about the process of photosynthesis in the next section.

Plant Cells If you were to look at a plant's cells under a microscope, you would see that plants are eukaryotes. But unlike the cells of some other eukaryotes, a plant's cells are enclosed by a cell wall. The **cell wall** is a boundary that surrounds the cell membrane and separates the cell from the environment. Plant cell walls are made mostly of **cellulose** (SEL yuh lohs), a chemical that makes the walls rigid. Because of the rigid cell walls, plant cells look something like boxes, as Figure 1 shows.

Plant cells also contain many structures called chloroplasts. **Chloroplasts** (KLAWR uh plasts), which look similar to green jelly beans, are the structures in which food is made. The Greek word *chloro* means "green."

Plant cells also contain vacuoles. A **vacuole** is a large, sack-like storage area. The vacuole stores many substances, including water, wastes, and food. A vacuole expands like a balloon when water enters it and shrinks when water leaves it. If too much water leaves a plant's vacuoles, the plant wilts.

Plants Are Multicellular You don't need a microscope to see plants because they are multicellular. Plants do vary greatly in size, however. For example, mosses are among the smallest plants—many are only a few millimeters tall. But some redwood trees can grow over 80 meters tall.

No matter how large or small a plant is, its cells are organized into **tissues**—groups of similar cells that perform a specific function in an organism. For example, most plants that live on land have tissues that transport materials throughout their bodies. You will learn about some important plant tissues later in this chapter.

☑ *Checkpoint* *What is the function of the vacuole in a plant cell?*

Origin of Plants

Which organisms were the ancestors of today's plants? To answer this question, biologists study fossils, the traces of ancient life forms preserved in rock and other substances. The oldest plant fossils are about 400 million years old. These fossils show that early plants resembled small algae.

Other clues to the origin of plants come from analyzing the chemical makeup of plants. In particular, biologists study a green pigment called **chlorophyll** (KLAWR uh fil), which is found in the chloroplasts of plants as well as in algae and some bacteria. Like ice cream, chlorophyll comes in different "flavors," or forms, that have slightly different chemical structures. Scientists have found that plants and green algae contain the same form of chlorophyll. For this reason, biologists infer that ancient green algae were the ancestors of today's plants.

Figure 2 These fossils are from two plants that lived about 300 million years ago. The larger fossil is of a fern's leaf. The small star-shaped fossil is of a plant called a horsetail. *Inferring What organisms do scientists think gave rise to today's plants?*

Living on Land

Unlike algae, most plants live on land. How is living on land different from living in water? Imagine multicellular green algae floating in the ocean. Their bodies are held up toward the sunlight by the water around them. The algae obtain water and other materials directly from their watery surroundings. When algae reproduce, sperm cells swim to egg cells through the water.

Now imagine the same green algae living on land. Would the algae be able to stand upright? Could they absorb water and other materials from their surroundings? Could their sperm cells swim to egg cells? The answer to all of these questions is no. **For plants to survive on land, they must have ways to obtain water and other materials from their surroundings, retain water, transport materials throughout the plant, support their bodies, and reproduce successfully.** In *Exploring Plant Adaptations* on the next page, you can see some of the ways in which plants are adapted to live on land.

Obtaining Water and Other Materials Recall that all organisms need water to survive. Obtaining water is easy for algae because water surrounds them. To live on land, though, plants need adaptations for obtaining water from the soil. Plants must also have ways of obtaining other nutrients from the soil.

Retaining Water Have you ever noticed that a puddle of rainwater gradually shrinks and then disappears after the rain stops? This happens because there is more water in the puddle than in the air. As a result, the water evaporates into the air. The same principle explains why a plant on land can dry out. Because there is more water in plant cells than in air, water evaporates into the air. Plants need adaptations to reduce water loss to the air. One common adaptation is a waxy, waterproof layer called the **cuticle** that covers the leaves of most plants.

Interpreting Data

The table shows how much water a certain plant loses during the hours listed.

Time	Water Loss (grams)
7 to 8 AM	190
9 to 10 AM	209
11 to Noon	221
1 to 2 PM	233
3 to 4 PM	227
5 to 6 PM	213
7 to 8 PM	190
9 to 10 PM	100
11 to Midnight	90

When does the plant lose the most water? The least water? How could you account for the pattern you see?

EXPLORING *Plant Adaptations*

Today, plants are found in almost every environment on Earth—deserts, lakes, jungles, and even the polar regions. As you read about each plant, notice how it is adapted to living in its specific environment.

◄ Pasque Flower
Pasque flowers, such as this *Anemone patens,* often grow on cold, rocky mountain slopes. The flower's petals trap sunlight, keeping the flower up to 10° C warmer than the surrounding air. This feature enables the plant to survive in cold environments.

Staghorn Fern ►
Staghorn ferns do not grow in soil. Instead, they cling to the bark of trees in tropical areas. The leaves that hug the bark store water and nutrients. The leaves that hang down are involved in reproduction.

▲ Bristlecone Pine
Because the needles of bristlecone pines live more than 15 years, the trees survive long periods of drought. Bristlecone pine trees can live more than 4,000 years. This is because they grow slowly in high altitude areas where there are few harmful insects or other disease-causing organisims.

◄ Water Lily
Water lilies live only in fresh water. Large, flat leaves and sweet-smelling flowers float on the water's surface. The plants have long stems under the water. Roots anchor the plant in the mud at the bottom of the pond.

Rafflesia ▶
The rafflesia plant produces the largest flowers on Earth. This flower that grew in Borneo measures over 83 centimeters in diameter. Rafflesia flowers have a foul odor—something like rotting meat. The odor attracts insects that help the plant reproduce.

▲ Mangrove
Mangrove trees, such as these on Guadalcanal Island in the Pacific Ocean, grow in salt water in tropical areas. The tree's huge root system makes the tree appear as if it is on stilts. The roots trap soil and sand around them, providing a material in which to anchor as they grow.

◀ Date Palm
Date palms, such as these growing on a date farm in southern California, grow in warm climates. These flowering trees can grow up to 23 meters tall. The leaves are long and narrow, reducing the amount of surface area for evaporation. The female trees produce dates that hang from the stems in large clusters.

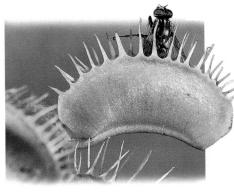

◀ Venus Fly Trap
The Venus fly trap can grow in soil that is low in nitrogen. This is because the plant obtains its nitrogen by digesting insects that it traps. When an insect touches sensitive hairs on the inner surface of a leaf, the two parts of the leaf quickly snap shut. It takes about ten days for the plant to digest an insect.

Figure 4 The vascular tissue in these tree ferns transports water and nutrients inside the plants. Vascular tissue also strengthens and supports the plants' stems and leaves.

Transporting Materials A plant needs to transport food, water, minerals, and other materials from one part of its body to another. In general, water and minerals are taken up by the bottom part of the plant. Food is made in the top part. But all the plant's cells need water, minerals, and food. To supply all cells with the materials they need, water and minerals must be transported up to the top of the plant. Then food must be transported throughout the plant.

Some plants have transporting tissue called **vascular tissue.** Vascular tissue is an internal system of tubelike structures through which water and food move inside the plant. Plants that have vascular tissue are called vascular plants. Vascular plants can grow quite tall because they have an effective way of transporting substances to distant cells.

Support While algae are supported by the surrounding water, a plant on land must support its own body. Because plants need sunlight for photosynthesis, the food-making parts of the plant must be exposed to as much sunlight as possible. In vascular plants, vascular tissue strengthens and supports the large bodies of the plants.

Reproduction All plants undergo sexual reproduction that involves fertilization. **Fertilization** occurs when a sperm cell unites with an egg cell. The fertilized egg is called a **zygote.** For algae and some plants, fertilization can only occur if there is water in the environment. This is because sperm cells swim through the water to egg cells. Other plants, however, have an adaptation that make it possible for fertilization to occur in dry environments. You will learn more about this adaptation in the next chapter.

☑ *Checkpoint* *Why do plants need adaptations to prevent water loss?*

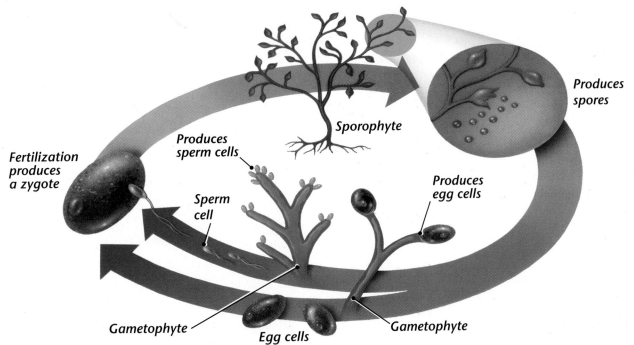

Fertilization produces a zygote

Produces sperm cells

Sporophyte

Produces spores

Sperm cell

Produces egg cells

Gametophyte

Egg cells

Gametophyte

Figure 5 Plants have complex life cycles that consist of two stages—the sporophyte stage and the gametophyte stage. *Interpreting Diagrams During which stage are sperm and egg cells produced?*

Complex Life Cycles

Unlike most animals, plants have complex life cycles that are made up of two different stages, or generations. In one stage, called the **sporophyte** (SPAWR uh fyt), the plant produces spores, the tiny cells that can grow into new organisms. A spore develops into the plant's other stage, called the gametophyte. In the **gametophyte** (guh MEE tuh fyt) stage, the plant produces two kinds of sex cells, or **gametes**—sperm cells and egg cells.

Figure 5 shows a typical plant life cycle. A sperm cell and egg cell join to form a zygote. The zygote then develops into a sporophyte. The sporophyte produces spores, which develop into the gameophyte. Then the gameophyte produces sperm cells and egg cells and the cycle starts again. The sporophyte of a plant usually looks quite different than the gametophyte.

Section 1 Review

1. List three characteristics that all plants share.
2. What are five adaptations that plants need to survive on land?
3. What evidence led scientists to think that green algae were the ancestors of plants?
4. **Thinking Critically Classifying** Suppose you found a tall plant living in the desert. Do you think it would be a vascular plant? Explain.

Designing Experiments

Eye on Photosynthesis

I n this lab, you'll design an experiment to investigate what substances and conditions are needed for photosynthesis.

Problem

What raw materials and conditions are involved in photosynthesis?

Materials

Elodea plants	2 test tubes
water (boiled, then cooled)	2 wax pencils
wide-mouthed container	lamp (optional)
sodium bicarbonate solution	

Procedure

Part 1 Observing Photosynthesis

1. Use a wax pencil to label two test tubes *1* and *2*. Fill test tube 1 with sodium bicarbonate solution, which provides a source of carbon dioxide.

2. Fill the container about three-fourths full of sodium bicarbonate solution.

3. Hold your thumb over the mouth of test tube 1. Turn the test tube over, and lower the tube to the bottom of the container. Do not let in any air. If necessary, repeat this step so that test tube 1 contains no air pockets. **CAUTION:** *Glass test tubes are fragile. Handle the test tubes carefully. Do not touch broken glass.*

4. Fill test tube 2 with sodium bicarbonate solution. Place an *Elodea* plant in the tube with the cut stem at the bottom. Put your thumb over the mouth of the test tube, and lower it into the container without letting in any air. Wash your hands.

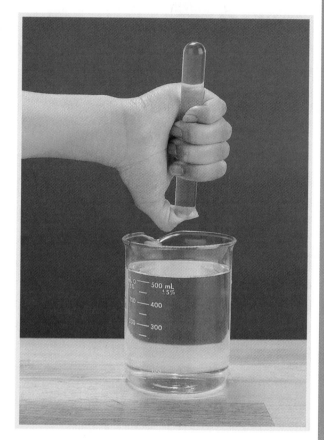

5. Place the container with the two test tubes in bright light. After a few minutes, examine both test tubes for bubbles.

6. If bubbles form in test tube 2, observe the *Elodea* stem to see if it is producing the bubbles. The bubbles are oxygen bubbles. The production of oxygen signals that photosynthesis is taking place.

7. Leave the setup in bright light for thirty minutes. Observe what happens to any bubbles that form. Record your observations.

Part 2 Is Carbon Dioxide Needed for Photosynthesis?

8. Your teacher will provide a supply of water that has been boiled and then cooled. Boiling drives off gases that are dissolved in the water, including carbon dioxide.

9. Based on what you learned in Part 1, design an experiment to show whether or not carbon dioxide is needed for photosynthesis. Obtain your teacher's approval before carrying out your experiment. Record all your observations.

Part 3 What Other Conditions Are Needed for Photosynthesis?

10. Make a list of other factors that may affect photosynthesis. For example, think about conditions such as light, the size of the plant, and the number of leaves.

11. Choose one factor from your list. Then design an experiment to show how the factor affects photosynthesis. Obtain your teacher's approval before carrying out your experiment. Record all your observations.

Analyze and Conclude

1. What process produced the bubbles you observed in Part 1?
2. In Part 1, what was the purpose of test tube 1?
3. Based on your results in Part 2, is carbon dioxide necessary for photosynthesis?
4. Explain what you learned about photosynthesis from the investigation you did in Part 3.
5. **Think About It** For the experiments you carried out in Parts 2 and 3, identify the manipulated variable and the responding variable. Explain whether or not your experiments were controlled experiments.

More to Explore

A small animal in a closed container will die, even if it has enough water and food. A small animal in a closed container with a plant, water, and food will not die. Use what you have learned from this experiment to explain those facts.

SECTION 2 Photosynthesis and Light

DISCOVER ••• ACTIVITY••••

What Colors Make Up Sunlight?

1. Glue a piece of white paper onto the inside bottom of a shoebox.

2. Place the box on its side near a window or outside in a sunny area.

3. 🛠 Hold a mirror in front of the open side of the box. Adjust the mirror until it reflects sunlight onto the paper in the box. **CAUTION:** *Do not direct the sunlight into your eyes.*

4. Hold a prism between the mirror and the box as shown in the photo. Adjust the location of the prism so that sunlight passes through the prism.

5. Describe what you see on the paper in the box.

Think It Over

Observing What did you learn about light by carrying out this investigation?

GUIDE FOR READING

◆ What happens when light strikes a green leaf?

◆ How do scientists describe the overall process of photosynthesis?

Reading Tip As you read, make a list of the main ideas and the supporting details about photosynthesis.

The year was 1883. T. W. Engelmann, a German biologist, was at work in his laboratory. He peered into the microscope at some strands of algae on a slide. The microscope had a prism located between the light source and the algae. As Engelmann watched the algae, he saw gas bubbles forming in the water around some of the cells. Curiously, no gas bubbles formed around other cells. Although Engelmann did not know it at the time, his experiment provided a clue about how light is involved in photosynthesis. To understand what Engelmann observed, you need to know more about the nature of light.

The Nature of Light

The sun is the source of energy on Earth. If you take a walk outside on a sunny day, you feel the sun's energy as the sun heats your skin. You see the energy in the form of light on objects around you. The light that you see is called white light. But when white light passes through a prism, you can see that it is made up of the colors of the rainbow—red, orange, yellow, green, blue, and violet. Scientists refer to these colors as the visible spectrum.

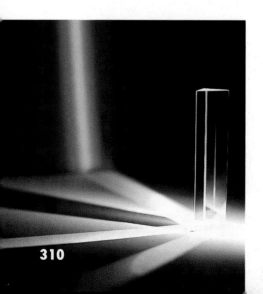

Figure 6 When sunlight passes through a prism, it separates into its parts—the colors of the rainbow.

In addition to prisms, white light strikes many other objects. Some objects such as glass and other transparent materials transmit light, or allow the light to pass through. Shiny surfaces such as mirrors reflect, or bounce back, light. Dark objects such as street pavements absorb, or take in and hold, light.

Most objects, however, reflect some colors of the visible spectrum while they absorb other colors. For example, when white light strikes a red shirt, the shirt absorbs most of the light's colors. However, the shirt reflects red light. The shirt looks red because your eyes see the reflected color.

☑ *Checkpoint* *What are the colors of the visible spectrum?*

Plants and Light

Like red shirts and most other objects around you, plants absorb some colors of the visible spectrum and reflect others. **When light strikes the green leaves of a plant, most of the green part of the spectrum is reflected. Most of the other colors of light are absorbed.**

Plant Pigments When light strikes a leaf, it is absorbed by pigments found in the chloroplasts of the cells. Chlorophyll, the most abundant pigment in plants, absorbs most of the blue and red light. Green light, on the other hand, is reflected rather than absorbed. This explains why chlorophyll appears green in color, and why plants appear green.

Other pigments, called **accessory pigments,** include yellow, orange, and red pigments. These pigments absorb colors of light that chlorophyll does not. Most accessory pigments are not visible in plants for most of the year because they are masked by the chlorophyll. However, in some areas during the fall season, cool temperatures break down the chlorophyll in many plants. The colors of the accessory pigments become visible and produce the beautiful orange, red, and yellow colors of fall leaves.

Figure 7 When chlorophyll breaks down in some trees in the fall, the accessory pigments in the leaves become visible. *Applying Concepts Which colors do the accessory pigments in leaves reflect?*

Capturing Energy Because light is a form of energy, a substance that absorbs light absorbs energy. Just as a car requires the energy in gasoline to move, the process of photosynthesis in plants requires energy in the form of light. Photosynthesis begins when light strikes the chlorophyll in the chloroplasts of the plant's cells. The light energy that is absorbed powers the process of photosynthesis.

☑ *Checkpoint* *What colors of light does chlorophyll absorb?*

Unraveling the Mysteries of Photosynthesis

What do plants need to make their own food? What substances do plants produce in the process of photosynthesis? Over time, the work of many scientists has provided answers to these questions.

1771
Joseph Priestley

When Joseph Priestley, an English scientist, placed a burning candle in a covered jar, the flame went out. When he placed both a plant and a candle in a covered jar, the candle kept burning. Priestley concluded that the plant released something into the air that kept the candle burning. Today we know that plants produce oxygen, a product of photosynthesis.

1650   **1750**

1643
Jean-Baptiste Van Helmont

A Dutch scientist, Jean-Baptiste Van Helmont, planted a willow tree in a tub of soil. After five years of adding only water, the tree gained 74 kilograms. Van Helmont concluded that trees need only water to grow. Today it is known that water is one of the raw materials of photosynthesis.

1779
Jan Ingenhousz

Jan Ingenhousz, a Dutch scientist, placed branches with leaves in water. In sunlight, the leaves produced oxygen bubbles. In the dark, the leaves produced no oxygen. Ingenhousz concluded that plants need sunlight to produce oxygen, a product of photosynthesis.

The Chemistry of Photosynthesis

INTEGRATING CHEMISTRY Light energy is just one of the things that plants need to carry out photosynthesis. Just as you need flour and eggs to make cookies, a plant also needs raw materials to make its own food. Plants use carbon dioxide gas and water as raw materials for photosynthesis.

During photosynthesis, plants use the energy absorbed by the chlorophyll to power a series of complex chemical reactions.

In Your Journal

Find out more about the experiments conducted by one of these scientists. Then write a summary of one experiment as it might appear in a front-page newspaper story of the time. Be sure to give your story a headline.

1883
T. W. Engelmann

T. W. Engelmann studied how different colors of light affect photosynthesis in green algae. He found that cells bathed in blue and red light had the fastest rates of photosynthesis. Today scientists know that the chlorophyll in both green algae and plants absorbs mostly blue and red light.

1850

1950

1864
Julius Sachs

A German biologist, Julius Sachs, observed living leaf cells under a microscope. As he watched, he tested the cells for the presence of carbohydrates. Sachs discovered that plants produce carbohydrates during photosynthesis.

1948
Melvin Calvin

The American scientist Melvin Calvin traced the chemical path that the carbon from carbon dioxide follows during photosynthesis. By doing this, Calvin learned about the complex chemical reactions of photosynthesis.

Figure 8 In photosynthesis, the energy in sunlight is used to make sugar and oxygen from carbon dioxide and water. *Classifying Which substances are the raw materials of photosynthesis? Which are the products?*

In these reactions, carbon dioxide from the air and water from the soil combine to produce sugar, a type of carbohydrate. Another product, oxygen gas, is also produced. The events of photosynthesis are pictured in Figure 8.

One way that scientists describe chemical reactions is to write equations. A chemical equation shows the raw materials and the products. **The many chemical reactions of photosynthesis can be summarized by the following equation.**

$$\text{carbon dioxide} + \text{water} \xrightarrow{\text{light energy}} \text{sugar} + \text{oxygen}$$
$$(CO_2) \qquad (H_2O) \qquad\qquad (C_6H_{12}O_6) \quad (O_2)$$

Carbon dioxide and water combine in the presence of light to produce sugar and oxygen.

Like all organisms, plants need a steady supply of energy to grow and develop, respond, and reproduce. Some of the food made by plants supplies the energy for these activities. The excess food is stored by the plants in their roots, stems, or leaves. Carrot plants, for example, store excess food in their roots. When you eat a carrot, you are eating the plant's stored food.

Section 2 Review

1. Describe what happens when light strikes a green leaf.
2. What is the overall equation for photosynthesis? What information does the equation provide?
3. What happens when light passes through a prism? What does this reveal about white light?
4. **Thinking Critically** **Relating Cause and Effect** Sometimes you see a rainbow during a rain shower. What might act as a prism to separate the light into its colors?

Science at Home

With a family member, look around your kitchen for objects that transmit, reflect, and absorb white light. Explain to your family member what happens to white light when it strikes each type of object. Then use one object to explain why you see it as the color you do.

3 Mosses, Liverworts, and Hornworts

Will Mosses Absorb Water?

1. Place 20 milliliters (mL) of sand into a plastic graduated cylinder. Place 20 mL of peat moss into a second plastic graduated cylinder.

2. Predict what would happen if you were to slowly pour 10 mL of water into each of the two graduated cylinders and then wait five minutes.

3. To test your prediction, use a third graduated cylinder to slowly add 10 mL of water to the sand. Then add 10 mL of water to the moss. After 5 minutes, record your observations.

Think It Over
Predicting How did your prediction compare with your results? What did you learn about moss from this investigation?

I f you enjoy gardening, you know that a garden requires time, effort, and knowledge. Before you start to plant your garden, you need to know how much water and sun your plants will need. You also need to know whether the soil in your garden can supply the plants with the water and nutrients they need.

Many gardeners add peat moss to the soil in their gardens. Peat moss improves the texture of soil and increases the soil's ability to hold water. When peat moss is added to claylike soil, it loosens the soil so that the plant's roots can easily grow through it. When peat moss is added to sandy soil, the soil stays moist for a longer time after it is watered.

Characteristics of Nonvascular Plants

Peat moss contains one type of **nonvascular plant.** Some other nonvascular plants are liverworts and hornworts. **All nonvascular plants are low-growing plants that lack vascular tissue.**

GUIDE FOR READING

◆ What characteristics do nonvascular plants share?

Reading Tip As you read, make a table comparing and contrasting mosses, liverworts, and hornworts.

Nonvascular plants do not have vascular tissue—a system of tubelike structures that transport water and other materials. Nonvascular plants can only pass materials from one cell to the next. That means that the materials do not travel very far or very quickly. Also, these plants have only their rigid cell walls to provide support. With this type of structure, these plants cannot grow very wide or tall. As a result, nonvascular plants are small and grow low to the ground.

Like all plants, nonvascular plants require water to survive. These plants lack roots, but they can obtain water and minerals directly from their surroundings. Many nonvascular plants live where water is plentiful. But even nonvascular plants that live in drier areas need enough water to let the sperm cells swim to the egg cells during reproduction.

Mosses

Have you ever seen mosses growing in the crack of a sidewalk, on a tree trunk, or on rocks that are misted by waterfalls? With over 10,000 species, mosses are by far the most diverse group of nonvascular plants.

The Structure of a Moss If you were to look closely at a moss, you would see a plant that looks something like the one in Figure 9. The familiar green fuzzy moss is the gametophyte generation of the plant. Structures that look like tiny leaves grow off a small stemlike structure. Thin rootlike structures called **rhizoids** anchor the moss and absorb water and nutrients from the soil. The sporophyte generation grows out of the gametophyte. It consists of a slender stalk with a capsule at the end. The capsule contains spores.

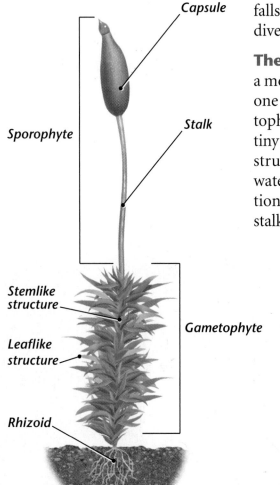

Capsule

Sporophyte

Stalk

Stemlike structure

Leaflike structure

Gametophyte

Rhizoid

Figure 9 A moss gametophyte is low-growing and has structures that look like roots, stems, and leaves. The stalklike sporophyte generation remains attached to the gametophyte. *Interpreting Diagrams What structure anchors the gametophyte in the soil?*

The Importance of Mosses Many people use peat moss in agriculture and gardening. The peat moss that gardeners use contains sphagnum (SFAG num) moss. Sphagnum moss grows in a type of wetland called a **bog.** The still water in a bog is so acidic that decomposing organisms cannot live in the water. Thus when the plants die, they do not decay. Instead, the dead plants accumulate at the bottom of the bog. Over time, the mosses become compressed into layers and form a blackish-brown material called **peat.** Large deposits of peat exist in North America, Europe, and Asia. In Europe and Asia, people use peat as a fuel to heat homes and to cook food.

INTEGRATING EARTH SCIENCE Like the lichens you learned about in Chapter 9, many mosses are pioneer plants. They are among the first organisms to grow in areas destroyed by volcanoes or in burnt-out forests. Like lichens, mosses trap wind-blown soil. Over time, enough soil accumulates to support the growth of other plants whose spores or seeds are blown there.

☑ *Checkpoint* *What does a moss sporophyte look like?*

Figure 10 The sphagnum moss that grew in this bog is being harvested as peat.

Figure 11 Like mosses, liverworts and hornworts are nonvascular plants. **A.** Liverworts grow flat along the ground on moist soil and rocks. **B.** Hornworts grow only in soil and are often found growing among grasses.

Liverworts and Hornworts

Figure 11 shows examples of two other groups of nonvascular plants—liverworts and hornworts. There are more than 8,000 species of liverworts. This group of plants is named for the shape of the plant's body, which looks somewhat like a human liver. *Wort* is an old English word for "plant." Liverworts are often found growing as a thick crust on moist rocks or soil along the sides of a stream. Unlike mosses, most liverworts grow flat along the ground. In Figure 11, you can see the gametophyte generation of one type of liverwort.

There are fewer than 100 species of hornworts. At first glance, these plants resemble liverworts. But if you look closely, you can see slender, curved structures that look like horns growing out of the gametophytes. These hornlike structures, which give these plants their names, are the sporophytes. Unlike mosses or liverworts, hornworts are seldom found on rocks or tree trunks. Instead, hornworts live in moist soil, often mixed in with grass plants.

Section 3 Review

1. Describe two characteristics that nonvascular plants share. Explain how the two characteristics are related.
2. Describe the structure of a moss plant.
3. How does peat form?
4. **Thinking Critically Comparing and Contrasting** In what ways are mosses, liverworts, and hornworts similar? How do they differ?

Check Your Progress CHAPTER PROJECT
You should now be caring for your moss, and providing the best conditions for its survival and growth. Be sure to keep in mind how mosses differ from other familiar kinds of plants. (*Hint:* Keep your terrarium warm, but not hot, and make sure it remains moist.)

Masses of Mosses

I n this lab, you will look closely at some tiny members of the plant kingdom.

Problem

How is a moss plant adapted to carry out its life activities?

Materials

clump of moss	hand lens
metric ruler	toothpicks
plastic dropper	water

Procedure

1. Your teacher will give you a clump of moss. Examine the clump from all sides. Draw a diagram of what you see. Measure the size of the overall clump and the main parts of the clump. Record your observations.
2. Using toothpicks, gently separate five individual moss plants from the clump. Be sure to pull them totally apart so that you can observe each plant separately. If the moss plants appear to dry up as you are working, moisten them with a few drops of water.
3. Measure the length of the leaflike, stemlike, and rootlike structures on each plant. If brown stalks and capsules are present, measure them. Find the average length of each structure.
4. Make a life-size drawing of a moss plant. Label the parts, give their sizes, and record the color of each part. When you are finished observing the moss, return it to your teacher. Wash your hands thoroughly.

5. Obtain class averages for the sizes of the structures you measured in Step 3. Also, if the moss that you observed had brown stalks and capsules, share your observations about those structures.

Analyze and Conclude

1. Describe the typical size of the leaflike portion of moss plants, the typical height of the stemlike portion, and the typical length of the rootlike portion.
2. In which part(s) of the moss does photosynthesis occur? How do you know?
3. Why are mosses unable to grow very tall?
4. **Think About It** What did you learn by observing a moss up close and in detail?

More to Explore

Select a moss plant with stalks and capsules. Use toothpicks to release some of the spores, which can be as small as dust particles. Examine the spores under a microscope.

SECTION
4 Ferns and Their Relatives

DISCOVER

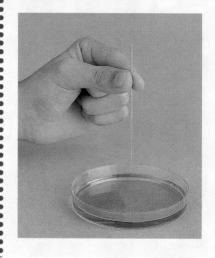

How Quickly Can Water Move Upward?

1. Put on your goggles. Your teacher will give you a plastic petri dish as well as a narrow glass tube that is open at both ends.

2. Fill the petri dish half full of water. Add a drop of food coloring to the water.

3. Stand the tube on end in the water and hold it upright. Observe what happens. Record your observations.

Think It Over

Inferring Why might it be an advantage for the transporting cells of plants to be arranged in a tubelike way?

GUIDE FOR READING

◆ What are the main characteristics of seedless vascular plants?

Reading Tip As you read, create a table comparing ferns, club mosses, and horsetails.

The time is 340 million years ago—long before the dinosaurs lived. The place is somewhere in the forests that covered most of Earth's land. If you could have walked through one of these ancient forests, it would have looked very strange to you. You might have recognized the mosses and liverworts that carpeted the moist soil. But overhead you would have seen odd-looking trees, some towering 25 meters above the ground. Among the trees were ancient ferns—huge versions of the ferns you find in today's florist shops. Other trees resembled giant stick figures with leaves up to one meter long. The huge leaves hugged the branches, looking something like the scales that cover a fish.

INTEGRATING EARTH SCIENCE As the trees and other plants died, they formed thick layers and partially decomposed. Over millions of years, the layers became compressed under the weight of the layers above them. Eventually, these layers became the coal deposits that we use for fuel today.

Characteristics of Seedless Vascular Plants

The odd-looking plants in the ancient forests were the ancestors of three groups of plants that are alive today—ferns, club mosses, and horsetails. **Ferns and their relatives share two characteristics. They have vascular tissue and use spores to reproduce.**

Vascular Tissue What adaptations allowed plants to grow very tall? Unlike the mosses, the ancient trees were **vascular plants**—plants that have vascular tissue. Vascular plants are better suited to life on land than are nonvascular plants. This is because vascular tissue solves the problems of support and transportation. Vascular tissue transports water quickly and efficiently throughout the plant's body. It also transports the food produced in the leaves to other parts of the plant, including the roots.

In addition, vascular tissue strengthens the plant's body. Imagine a handful of drinking straws bundled together with rubber bands. The bundle of straws would be stronger and more stable than a single straw would be. In a similar way, vascular tissue provides strength and stability to a plant.

Figure 12 Ferns and their relatives dominated the ancient forests on Earth.

1.  Your teacher will give you a fern plant to observe.

2. Draw a diagram of the plant and label the structures that you see.

3. Use a hand lens to observe the top and lower surfaces of the leaf. Run a finger over both surfaces.

4. With a plastic dropper, add a few drops of water to the top surface of the leaf. Note what happens.

Inferring Use your observations to explain how ferns are adapted to life on land.

Spores for Reproduction Ferns, club mosses, and horsetails still need to grow in moist surroundings. This is because the plants release spores into their surroundings, where they grow into gametophytes. When the gametophytes produce egg cells and sperm cells, there must be enough water available for fertilization to occur.

☑ *Checkpoint* **What adaptation allowed plants to grow tall?**

Ferns

Fossil records indicate that ferns first appeared on land about 400 million years ago. There are over 12,000 species of ferns alive today. They range in size from tiny plants about the size of this letter "M" to large tree ferns that grow up to 5 meters tall in moist, tropical areas.

The Structure of Ferns Like other vascular plants, ferns have true stems, roots, and leaves. The stems of most ferns are underground. Leaves grow upward from the top side of the stems, and roots grow downward from the bottom of the stems. Roots are structures that anchor the fern to the ground and absorb water and nutrients from the soil. These substances enter the root's vascular tissue and travel through the tissue into the stems and leaves. In Figure 13 you can see the fern's structure.

Frond

Stem

Root

Figure 13 Most ferns have underground stems in addition to underground roots. The leaves, or fronds, grow above ground.

Figure 14 Spores are produced on the undersides of mature fronds.
Applying Concepts What happens to spores that are released?

Look closely at the fern's leaves, or **fronds.** Notice that the frond is divided into many smaller parts that look like small leaves. Many other ferns have a similar divided-leaf structure. The upper surface of each frond is coated with a cuticle that helps the plant retain water. In many types of ferns, the developing leaves are coiled at first. Because they resemble the top of a violin, these young leaves are often called fiddleheads. As they mature, the fiddleheads uncurl.

Reproduction in Ferns The familiar fern with its visible fronds is the sporophyte stage of the plant. On the underside of mature fronds, spores develop in tiny spore cases. When the spores are released, wind and water can carry them great distances. If a spore lands in moist, shaded soil, it develops into a gametophyte. Fern gametophytes are tiny plants that grow low to the ground.

The Importance of Ferns Ferns are useful to people in many ways. They are popular houseplants because they are attractive and easy to grow. Ferns are also used to grow other kinds of houseplants. For example, orchids are often grown on the tangled masses of fern roots.

People eat some ferns. During the spring, fiddleheads are sold in supermarkets and farm stands. Fiddleheads make a nutritious vegetable dish. But because some ferns are not safe to eat, you should never gather wild fiddleheads for food.

In Southeast Asia, farmers grow a small aquatic fern alongside rice plants in their rice fields. Tiny pockets in the fern's leaves provide a home for some bacteria. The bacteria produce a natural fertilizer that helps the rice plants grow.

Figure 15 Fiddleheads are the developing leaves of a fern.

Figure 16 Club mosses and horse-tails are other seedless vascular plants. **A.** This club moss looks like a tiny pine tree. **B.** These horsetail plants have jointed stems. Needle-like branches grow out of each joint.

Club Mosses and Horsetails

Two other groups of seedless, vascular plants are the club mosses and horsetails. Like ferns, club mosses and horsetails have true leaves, stems, and roots. They also have a similar life cycle. However, there are relatively few species of club mosses and horsetails alive today.

Unlike their larger ancestors, today's club mosses are small. Do not be confused by the name *club mosses*. Unlike the true mosses, the club mosses have vascular tissue. You may be familiar with the club moss you see in Figure 16. The plant, which looks like the small branch of a pine tree, is sometimes called ground pine or princess pine. It grows in moist woodlands and near streams.

There are 30 species of horsetails on Earth today. As you can see in Figure 16, the stems of horsetails are jointed. Long, coarse, needlelike branches grow in a circle around each joint. Small leaves grow flat against the stem just above each joint. The stems contain silica, a gritty substance also found in sand. During colonial times, Americans called horsetails "scouring rushes" because they used the plants to scrub their pots and pans.

Section 4 Review

1. What two characteristics do ferns, club mosses, and horsetails share? How do these characteristics differ from those of mosses?
2. Describe the structure of a fern plant. What do its leaves, stems, and roots look like?
3. List three ways that ferns are useful to people today.
4. **Thinking Critically Applying Concepts** Although ferns have vascular tissue, they still must live in moist, shady environments. Explain why this is true.

Check Your Progress CHAPTER PROJECT

Begin planning your brochure as you continue caring for your moss. What's the best way to give clear directions for making a terrarium? What must you say about the amount of light, water, and other conditions that mosses need to survive? (*Hint:* Be sure to include important information about mosses, such as how tall they grow and how they reproduce.)

SECTION 1 The Plant Kingdom

Key Ideas

◆ Plants are autotrophs. All plants are also multicellular eukaryotes.

◆ Plant cells have cell walls that are made mostly of cellulose. Plant cells contain chloroplasts, in which food is made, and vacuoles that store water, food, and other substances.

◆ All plants have complex life cycles. In the sporophyte stage, plants produce spores. In the gametophyte stage, plants produce sperm cells and egg cells.

◆ For plants to survive on land, they need ways to obtain water and other materials from their surroundings, retain moisture, support their bodies, transport materials throughout the plant, and reproduce successfully.

Key Terms

photosynthesis	cuticle	sporophyte
cell wall	vascular tissue	gametophyte
cellulose	fertilization	gamete
chloroplast	zygote	
vacuole		
tissue		
chlorophyll		

SECTION 2 Photosynthesis and Light

INTEGRATING PHYSICS

Key Ideas

◆ White light is made up of the different colors of the rainbow—red, orange, yellow, green, blue, and violet.

◆ Most of the light that strikes a leaf is absorbed by pigments in the chloroplasts of the cells. Chlorophyll, the main pigment, absorbs red and blue light. Light energy powers the process of photosynthesis.

◆ In photosynthesis, carbon dioxide and water are converted into sugars and oxygen using the light energy.

Key Term

accessory pigment

SECTION 3 Mosses, Liverworts, and Hornworts

Key Ideas

◆ Nonvascular plants are small, low-growing plants that lack vascular tissue. Most nonvascular plants transport materials by passing them from one cell to the next. They live in areas where there is enough moisture for them to survive.

◆ Mosses, liverworts, and hornworts are three types of nonvascular plants.

Key Terms

nonvascular plant	bog
rhizoid	peat

SECTION 4 Ferns and Their Relatives

Key Ideas

◆ Seedless vascular plants have vascular tissue and use spores to reproduce. These plants include ferns, club mosses, and horsetails.

◆ Although seedless vascular plants grow taller than nonvascular plants, they still need to live in moist places. The plants' spores are released into the environment, where they grow into gametophytes.

Key Terms

vascular plant	frond

USING THE INTERNET

ACTIVITY

www.science-explorer.phschool.com

California Test Prep: Reviewing Content

Multiple Choice
Choose the letter of the best answer.

1. Mosses and ferns are both
   a. vascular plants.
   b. nonvascular plants.
   c. seed plants.
   d. plants.
2. The ancestors of plants were probably
   a. fungi.
   b. brown algae.
   c. green algae.
   d. bacteria.
3. When visible light strikes a green leaf, green light is
   a. reflected.
   b. absorbed.
   c. transmitted.
   d. stored.
4. The familiar green, fuzzy moss is the
   a. frond.
   b. rhizoid.
   c. gametophyte.
   d. sporophyte.
5. The leaves of ferns are called
   a. rhizoids.
   b. sporophytes.
   c. fronds.
   d. cuticles.

True or False
If the statement is true, write true. If it is false, change the underlined word or words to make the statement true.

6. Plants are <u>autotrophs</u>.
7. In the fall, leaves turn colors because <u>accessory pigments</u> become visible as the chlorophyll breaks down.
8. <u>Carbon dioxide and water</u> are the products of photosynthesis.
9. Mosses are <u>vascular</u> plants.
10. The young leaves of <u>liverworts</u> are known as fiddleheads.

Checking Concepts

11. Describe three structures that characterize the eukaryotic cells of plants. Explain the role of each structure.
12. In what two ways is vascular tissue important to a plant?
13. Briefly describe the life cycle of a typical plant.
14. Explain why a yellow school bus appears yellow.
15. What role does chlorophyll play in photosynthesis?
16. In what ways do mosses and club mosses differ from each other? In what ways are they similar?
17. **Writing to Learn** Imagine that you are a beam of white light traveling through the air. Write a paragraph to explain what happens to you when a green leaf gets in your way.

Thinking Visually

18. **Compare/Contrast Table** Copy the table comparing mosses and ferns onto a separate sheet of paper. Complete the table by filling in the missing information. Then add a title. (For more on compare/contrast tables, see the Skills Handbook.)

Characteristic	Moss	Fern
Size	a. ?	Can be tall
Environment	Moist	b. ?
Body parts	Rootlike, stemlike, and leaflike	c. ?
Familiar generation	d. ?	sporophyte
Vascular tissue present?	e. ?	f. ?

Test Prep: Skills

A scientist exposed a green plant to different colors of light. She then measured how much of each light the plant absorbed. Use the data to answer Questions 19–22.

Absorption of Light by a Plant	
Color of Light	**Percentage of Light Absorbed**
Red	55
Orange	10
Yellow	2
Green	1
Blue	85
Violet	40

19. Graphing Construct a bar graph using the information in the data table. (For information on constructing bar graphs, see the Skills Handbook.)

20. Drawing Conclusions List the three colors of light that are most important for photosynthesis in this plant.

21. Predicting If the plant were exposed only to yellow light, how might the plant be affected? Explain.

22. Inferring If a plant with reddish leaves were used in a similar experiment, how might the results differ? Explain.

Thinking Critically

23. Applying Concepts A friend tells you that he has seen moss plants that are about 2 meters tall. Is your friend correct? Explain.

24. Comparing and Contrasting How does the sporophyte generation of a plant differ from the gametophyte generation?

25. Relating Cause and Effect People have observed that mosses tend to grow on the north side of a tree rather than the south side. Why do you think this is so?

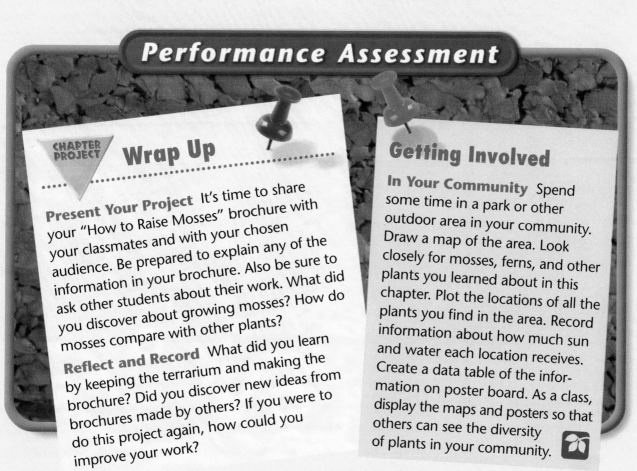

Performance Assessment

CHAPTER PROJECT ▾ Wrap Up

Present Your Project It's time to share your "How to Raise Mosses" brochure with your classmates and with your chosen audience. Be prepared to explain any of the information in your brochure. Also be sure to ask other students about their work. What did you discover about growing mosses? How do mosses compare with other plants?

Reflect and Record What did you learn by keeping the terrarium and making the brochure? Did you discover new ideas from brochures made by others? If you were to do this project again, how could you improve your work?

Getting Involved

In Your Community Spend some time in a park or other outdoor area in your community. Draw a map of the area. Look closely for mosses, ferns, and other plants you learned about in this chapter. Plot the locations of all the plants you find in the area. Record information about how much sun and water each location receives. Create a data table of the information on poster board. As a class, display the maps and posters so that others can see the diversity of plants in your community.

CALIFORNIA
SCIENCE CONTENT STANDARDS

The following California Science Content Standards are addressed in this chapter:

1. All living organisms are composed of cells, from just one to many trillions, whose details usually are visible only through a microscope.

   b. The characteristics that distinguish plant cells from animal cells, including chloroplasts and cell walls.

   d. Mitochondria liberate energy for the work that cells do, and chloroplasts capture sunlight energy for photosynthesis.

   f. As multicellular organisms develop, their cells differentiate.

2. A typical cell of any organism contains genetic instructions that specify its traits. Those traits may be modified by environmental influences.

   a. The differences between the life cycles and reproduction of sexual and asexual organisms.

3. Biological evolution accounts for the diversity of species developed through gradual processes over many generations.

   a. Both genetic variation and environmental factors are causes of evolution and diversity of organisms.

Cycle of a Lifetime

How long is a seed plant's life? Redwood trees can live for thousands of years. Tomato plants die after one growing season. Can organisms that seem so different have anything in common? In this chapter, you'll find out. Some answers will come from this chapter's project. In this project, you'll grow some seeds, then care for the plants until they, in turn, produce their own seeds.

Your Goal To care for and observe a plant throughout its life cycle. To complete this project successfully you must

◆ grow a plant from a seed
◆ observe and describe key parts of your plant's life cycle, such as seed germination and pollination
◆ harvest and plant the seeds that your growing plant produces
◆ follow the safety guidelines in Appendix A

Get Started Observe the seeds that your teacher gives you. In a small group, discuss what conditions the seeds might need to grow. What should you look for after you plant the seeds? What kinds of measurements could you make? Will it help to make drawings? When you are ready, plant your seeds.

Thistle plants depend on bees for pollination.

Check Your Progress You'll be working on this project as you study this chapter. To keep your project on track, look for Check Your Progress boxes at the following points.

Section 1 Review, page 339: Observe the developing seedlings.
Section 3 Review, page 351: Pollinate your flowers.
Section 5 Review, page 360: Collect the seeds from your plant and plant some of them.

Wrap Up At the end of the chapter (page 363), you'll present an exhibit showing the plant's life cycle.

---

5. The anatomy and physiology of plants and animals illustrate the complementary nature of structure and function.

   a. Plants and animals have levels of organization for structure and function, including cells, tissues, organs, organ systems, and the whole organism.

   b. Organ systems function because of the contributions of individual organs,

tissues, and cells. The failure of any part can affect the entire system.

   f. The structures and processes by which flowering plants generate pollen and ovules, seeds, and fruit.

7. Scientific progress is made by asking meaningful questions and conducting careful investigations.

   a. Select and use appropriate tools and technology to perform tests, collect data, and display data.

   c. Communicate the logical connection among hypothesis, science concepts, tests conducted, data collected, and conclusions drawn from the scientific evidence.

SECTION 1 The Characteristics of Seed Plants

DISCOVER .... ACTIVITY

Which Plant Part Is It?

1. With a partner, carefully observe the items of food your teacher gives you.

2. Make a list of the food items.

3. For each food item, write the name of the part of the plant—root, stem, or leaf—from which you think the food is obtained.

Think It Over

Classifying Classify the items into groups depending on the plant part from which the food is obtained. Compare your groupings with those of your classmates.

GUIDE FOR READING

◆ What characteristics do seed plants share?

◆ What are the main parts of a seed?

◆ What are the functions of leaves, stems, and roots?

Reading Tip As you read, make a list of the boldfaced terms. Write a definition for each term in your own words.

Chances are you've seen dandelions. But how much do you know about these common plants? For example, do you know that dandelion blossoms open only in sunlight? Or that each blossom is made up of hundreds of tube-shaped flowers? Do you know that a seed develops in each of these tiny flowers? And that, just like apple seeds, dandelion seeds are enclosed in structures that biologists call fruits?

The next time you see a dandelion's fluffy "seed head," examine it closely. It is made up of hundreds of individual fruits, each containing a seed. Each fruit has a hooklike structure at one end. Like tiny parachutes, the fruits ride in currents of air. When one hooks into moist soil, the seed inside can grow into a new dandelion plant.

What Is a Seed Plant?

Dandelions are seed plants. So are most of the other plants on Earth. In fact, seed plants outnumber seedless plants by more than ten to one. You eat many seed plants—rice, tomatoes, peas, and squash, for example. You may also eat the meat of animals that eat seed plants. You wear clothes made from seed plants, such as cotton and flax. You may even live in a home built from seed plants—oak, pine, or maple trees. In addition, seed plants produce much of the oxygen you breathe.

Figure 1 Some of these dandelions are releasing tiny parachute-like fruits, which carry the seeds inside to new areas.

All seed plants share two characteristics. They have vascular tissue and use seeds to reproduce. In addition, they all have body plans that include leaves, stems, and roots. Like seedless plants, seed plants have complex life cycles that include the sporophyte and the gametophyte. In seed plants, the plants that you see are the sporophytes. The gametophytes are microscopic.

Vascular Tissue

Most seed plants live on land. Recall from Chapter 10 that land plants face many challenges, including standing upright and supplying all their cells with water and food. Like ferns, seed plants meet these two challenges with vascular tissue. The thick walls of the cells in the vascular tissue help support the plants. In addition, water, food, and nutrients are transported throughout the plants in vascular tissue.

There are two types of vascular tissue. **Phloem** (FLOH um) is the vascular tissue through which food moves. When food is made in the plant's leaves, it enters the phloem and travels to the plant's stems and roots. Water and nutrients, on the other hand, travel in the vascular tissue called **xylem** (ZY lum). The plant's roots absorb water and nutrients from the soil. These materials enter the root's xylem and move upward into the plant's stems and leaves.

☑ *Checkpoint* *What material travels in phloem? What materials travel in xylem?*

Figure 2 Seed plants are diverse and live in many environments. **A.** Wheat is an important food for people. **B.** Organpipe cacti, here surrounded by other flowering plants, live in deserts. **C.** Lodgepole pines thrive in the mountains of the western United States.
Applying Concepts *What two roles does vascular tissue play in these plants?*

The In-Seed Story

1. Your teacher **ACTIVITY** will give you a hand lens and two different seeds that have been soaked in water.

2. Carefully observe the outside of each seed. Draw what you see.

3. Gently remove the coverings of the seeds. Then carefully separate the parts of each seed. Use a hand lens to examine the inside of each seed. Draw what you see.

Observing Based on your observations, label the parts of each seed. Then describe the function of each part next to its label.

Seeds

One reason why seed plants are so numerous is that they produce seeds. **Seeds** are structures that contain a young plant inside a protective covering. As you learned in Chapter 10, seedless plants need water in the surroundings for fertilization to occur. Seed plants do not need water in the environment to reproduce. This is because the sperm cells are delivered directly to the regions near the eggs. After sperm cells fertilize the eggs, seeds develop and protect the young plant from drying out.

If you've ever planted seeds in a garden, you know that seeds look different from each other. Despite their differences, however, all seeds have a similar structure. **A seed has three important parts—an embryo, stored food, and a seed coat.**

The young plant that develops from the zygote, or fertilized egg, is called the **embryo.** As you can see in Figure 3, the embryo already has the beginnings of roots, stems, and leaves. In the seeds of most plants, the embryo stops growing when it is quite small. When the embryo begins to grow again, it uses the food stored in the seed until it can make its food. In some plants, food is stored inside one or two seed leaves, or **cotyledons** (kaht uh LEED unz). You can see the cotyledons in the seeds in Figure 3.

The outer covering of a seed is called the seed coat. Some familiar seed coats are the "skins" on lima beans, peanuts, and peas. The seed coat acts like plastic wrap, protecting the embryo and its food from drying out. This allows a seed to remain inactive for a long time. For example, after finding some 10,000-year-old seeds in the Arctic, scientists placed them in warm water. Two days later, the seeds began to grow!

☑ *Checkpoint* *What is the function of the seed coat?*

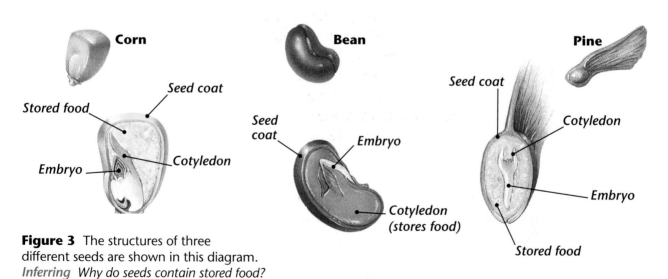

Figure 3 The structures of three different seeds are shown in this diagram. *Inferring Why do seeds contain stored food?*

Figure 4 Plants have different ways of dispersing their seeds. **A.** Both grass seeds and spiny parsley seeds are hitching a ride on this dog's fur. **B.** Water transports coconut palm seeds to new areas. **C.** The wind carries milkweed seeds through the air. **D.** Witch hazel plants shoot out seeds when their pods explode.

Seed Dispersal

To develop into a new plant, a seed needs light, water, and nutrients. After seeds have formed, they are usually scattered, sometimes far from where they were produced. When seeds land in a suitable area, they can sprout, or begin to grow.

The scattering of seeds is called seed dispersal. Seeds, or the fruits that enclose the seeds, are dispersed in many ways. One method involves animals. Some animals eat fruits, such as cherries and grapes. The seeds inside pass through the animal's digestive system and are deposited in new areas. Other seeds are enclosed in barblike structures that hook onto an animal's fur or a person's clothes. The structures then fall off in a new area. Water disperses other seeds when the seeds float in oceans, rivers, and streams. The seeds inside coconuts, for example, are carried from one area to another by ocean currents.

A third dispersal method involves wind. Wind disperses lightweight seeds, such as those of milkweed plants and pine trees. Finally, some plants shoot out their seeds, in a way that might remind you of popping popcorn. For example, the seedpods of wisteria and impatiens plants burst suddenly. The force scatters the seeds away from the pods in many directions.

Figure 5 The embryo in this peanut seed uses stored food to germinate. **A.** The peanut's root is the first structure to begin growing. **B.** After the root anchors the germinating plant, the peanut's stem and first two leaves emerge from the seed.

Germination

After seeds are dispersed, they may remain inactive for a while, or they may begin to grow immediately. **Germination** (jur muh NAY shun) is the early growth stage of the embryo. Germination begins when the seed absorbs water from the environment. Then the embryo uses its stored food to begin to grow. First, the embryo's roots grow downward, then its leaves and stem grow upward.

Seeds that are dispersed far away from the parent have a better chance of survival. This is because these young plants do not have to compete with their parent for light, water, and nutrients as they begin to grow.

☑ *Checkpoint* *What must happen before germination can begin?*

Leaves

The most numerous parts on many plants are their leaves. Plant leaves vary greatly in size and shape. Pine trees, for example, have needle-shaped leaves. Birch trees have small rounded leaves with jagged edges. Yellow skunk cabbages, which grow in the northwestern United States, have oval leaves that can be more than one meter wide. No matter what their shape, leaves play an important role in a plant. **Leaves capture the sun's energy and carry out the food-making process of photosynthesis.**

The Structure of a Leaf If you were to cut through a leaf and look at the edge under a microscope, you would see the structures in *Exploring a Leaf.* The leaf's top and bottom surface layers protect the cells inside. Between the layers of cells inside the leaf are veins that contain xylem and phloem. The underside of the leaf has small openings, or pores, called **stomata** (STOH muh tuh) (singular *stoma*). The Greek word *stoma* means "mouth"—and stomata do look like tiny mouths. The stomata open and close to control when gases enter and leave the leaf. When the stomata are open, carbon dioxide enters the leaf and oxygen and water vapor exit.

The Leaf and Photosynthesis The structure of a leaf is ideal for carrying out photosynthesis. Recall from Chapter 10 that photosynthesis occurs in the chloroplasts of plant cells. The cells that contain the most chloroplasts are located near the leaf's upper surface, where they are exposed to the sun. The chlorophyll in the chloroplasts traps the sun's energy.

Carbon dioxide enters the leaf through open stomata. Water, which is absorbed by the plant's roots, travels up the stem to the leaf through the xylem. During photosynthesis, sugar and oxygen are produced from the carbon dioxide and water. Oxygen passes out of the leaf through the open stomata. The sugar enters the phloem and then travels throughout the plant.

EXPLORING *a Leaf*

A leaf is a well-adapted food factory. Each structure helps the leaf produce food.

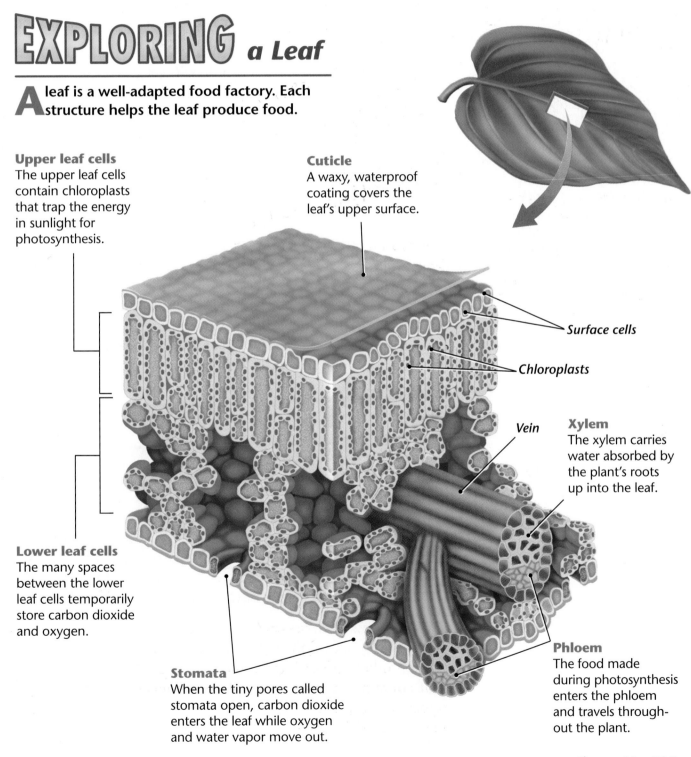

Upper leaf cells
The upper leaf cells contain chloroplasts that trap the energy in sunlight for photosynthesis.

Cuticle
A waxy, waterproof coating covers the leaf's upper surface.

Surface cells

Chloroplasts

Vein

Xylem
The xylem carries water absorbed by the plant's roots up into the leaf.

Lower leaf cells
The many spaces between the lower leaf cells temporarily store carbon dioxide and oxygen.

Stomata
When the tiny pores called stomata open, carbon dioxide enters the leaf while oxygen and water vapor move out.

Phloem
The food made during photosynthesis enters the phloem and travels through-out the plant.

In this activity you will calculate the speed at which fluid moves up a celery stalk.

1. Put on your apron. Fill a plastic container halfway with water. Stir in a drop of red food coloring.

2. Place the freshly cut end of a celery stalk in the water. Lean the stalk against the container's side.

3. After 20 minutes, remove the celery. Use a metric ruler to measure the height of the water in the stalk.

4. Use the measurement and the following formula to calculate how fast the water moved up the stalk.

$$\text{Speed} = \frac{\text{Height}}{\text{Time}}$$

Based on your calculation, predict how far the water would move in 2 hours. Then test your prediction.

Controlling Water Loss Because such a large area of a leaf is exposed to the air, water can quickly evaporate, or be lost, from a leaf into the air. The process by which water evaporates from a plant's leaves is called **transpiration.** A plant can lose a lot of water through transpiration. A corn plant, for example, can lose as much as 3.8 liters of water on a hot summer day. Without a way to slow down the process of transpiration, a plant would shrivel up and die.

Fortunately, plants have ways to slow down transpiration. One way that plants retain water is by closing the stomata. The stomata often close when the temperature is very hot.

☑ *Checkpoint* *How does carbon dioxide get into a leaf?*

Stems

The stem of a plant has two important functions. **The stem carries substances between the plant's roots and leaves. The stem also provides support for the plant and holds up the leaves so they are exposed to the sun.** In addition, some stems, such as those of asparagus, also store food.

Stems vary in size and shape. Some stems, like those of the baobab trees in Figure 6, are a prominent part of the plant. Other stems, like those of cabbages, are short and hidden.

The Structure of a Stem Stems can be either herbaceous (hur BAY shus) or woody. Herbaceous stems are soft. Dandelions, dahlias, peppers, and tomato plants have herbaceous stems.

Figure 6 This road in Madagascar is called Baobab Avenue. Tall, fat stems and stubby branches give baobab trees an unusual appearance.

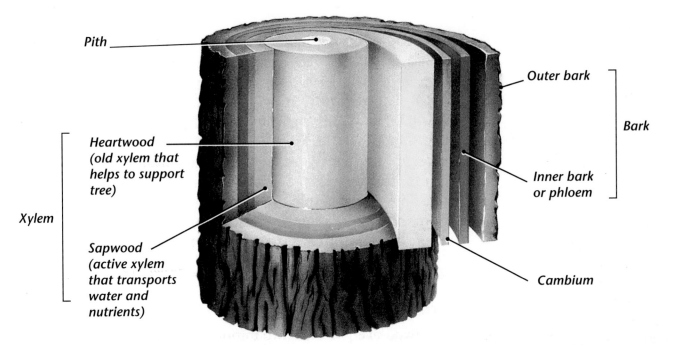

Pith

Outer bark

Bark

Heartwood
(old xylem that
helps to support
tree)

Inner bark
or phloem

Xylem

Sapwood
(active xylem
that transports
water and
nutrients)

Cambium

Figure 7 A typical woody stem is made up of many cell layers. *Interpreting Diagrams Where is the cambium located? What is the function of this layer of cells?*

In contrast, woody stems are hard and rigid. Maple trees, pine trees, and roses all have woody stems.

Herbaceous and woody stems consist of phloem and xylem tissue as well as many other supporting cells. However, unlike herbaceous stems, woody stems have an outer layer of material called bark, which helps protect the cells inside it, and inner layers of heartwood for additional support.

In Figure 7 you can see the inner structure of a woody stem. Bark covers the outer part of the stem. Just inside the outer bark layer is the phloem. Inside the phloem is a layer of cells called the **cambium** (KAM bee um). The cells of the cambium divide to produce new phloem and xylem. This process increases the stem's width. Just inside the cambium is a layer of active xylem that transports water and nutrients. Inside that layer is a layer of xylem cells that no longer carries water and nutrients. This layer, which is called heartwood, strengthens the stem, providing it with additional support. In the center of the stem is a material called the pith. In young trees, the pith stores food and water.

Annual Rings Have you ever looked at a tree stump and seen a pattern of circles that looks something like a target? These circles are called annual rings because they represent one year of a tree's growth. Annual rings are made of xylem. Xylem cells that form in the spring are large and have thin walls because they grow rapidly. They produce a wide, light brown ring. Xylem cells that form in the summer grow slowly and, therefore, are small and have thick walls. They produce a thin, dark ring. One pair of

light and dark rings represents one year's growth. You can estimate a tree's age by counting its annual rings.

INTEGRATING EARTH SCIENCE The width of a tree's annual rings can provide important clues about past weather conditions, such as rainfall. In rainy years, more xylem is produced, so the tree's annual rings are wide. In dry years, rings are narrow. By examining a tree's annual rings, scientists can make inferences about the weather conditions during the tree's life. For example, when scientists examined annual rings from trees in the southwestern United States, they inferred that severe droughts occurred in the years 840, 1067, 1379, and 1632.

☑ *Checkpoint* *What function does bark perform?*

Figure 8 Tree rings tell more than just the age of a tree. For example, thick rings that are far apart indicate years in which growing conditions were favorable. *Interpreting Photographs What was the weather like during the early years of this locust tree's life?*

Roots

Have you ever tried to pull a dandelion out of the soil? It's not easy, is it? That is because most roots are good anchors. **Roots anchor a plant in the ground and absorb water and nutrients from the soil.** The more root area a plant has, the more water and nutrients it can absorb. The roots of an oak tree, for example, may be twice as long as the aboveground tree. In addition, for plants such as carrots and beets, roots function as a storage area for food.

Types of Roots As you can see in Figure 9, there are two types of root systems: taproot and fibrous. A taproot system consists of a long, thick main root. Thin, branching roots grow off the main root. Turnips, radishes, dandelions, and cacti have taproots. In contrast, fibrous root systems consist of several main roots that branch

Figure 9 A plant's roots anchor the plant and absorb substances from the soil. **A.** A taproot grows deep into the soil. The plant is hard to pull out of the ground. **B.** Fibrous roots consist of several main roots that repeatedly branch. They take soil with them when you pull them out of the ground.

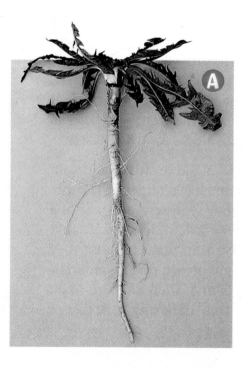

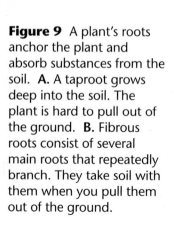

repeatedly to form a tangled mass of roots and soil. Lawn grass, corn, and most trees have fibrous roots.

The Structure of a Root In Figure 10 you see the structure of a typical root. Notice that the tip of the root is rounded and is covered by a structure called the **root cap.** The root cap, which contains dead cells, protects the root from injury from rocks as the root grows through the soil. Behind the root cap are the cells that divide to form new root cells.

Root hairs grow out of the root's surface. These hairs increase the surface area of the root that touches the soil. When more surface area is in contact with the soil, more water and nutrients can be absorbed. The root hairs also help to anchor the plant in the soil.

Locate the vascular tissue in the center of the root. The water and nutrients that are absorbed from the soil quickly move into the xylem. From there, these substances are transported upward to the plant's stems and leaves.

Phloem tissue transports food manufactured in the leaves to the root. The root tissues may then use the food for growth or store it for future use by the plant. The root also contains a layer of cambium, which produces new xylem and phloem.

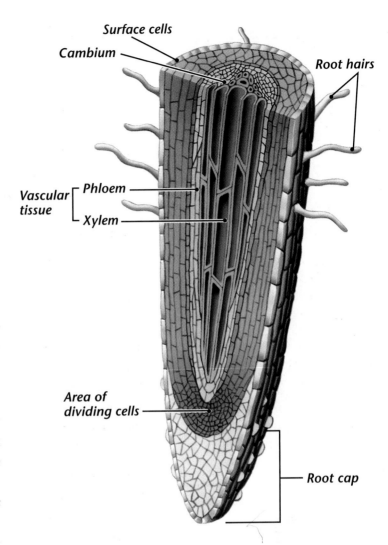

Figure 10 The root cap protects the root as it grows into the soil. Root hairs absorb water and nutrients, which are transported through the root's vascular tissue.

Section 1 Review

1. What two characteristics do all seed plants share?
2. List the three main parts of a seed. Describe the function of each part in producing a new plant.
3. What are the main functions of a plant's leaves, stems, and roots?
4. **Thinking Critically Predicting** Predict what would happen to a plant if you were to coat the underside of each leaf with wax. Explain your prediction.

Check Your Progress
CHAPTER PROJECT
If your seeds haven't germinated yet, they soon will. For the next few days keep a close watch on your young plants to see how they grow. How do they change in height? How do the leaves appear and grow? (*Hint:* Consider using drawings or photographs as part of your record keeping.)

DISCOVER

Are All Leaves Alike?

1. Your teacher will give you a hand lens, a ruler, and the leaves from some seed plants.

2. Using the hand lens, examine each leaf. Sketch each leaf in your notebook.

3. Measure the length and width of each leaf. Record your measurements in your notebook.

Think It Over

Classifying Divide the leaves into two groups on the basis of your observations. Explain why you grouped the leaves as you did.

GUIDE FOR READING

◆ What are the characteristics of gymnosperms?

◆ How do gymnosperms reproduce?

Reading Tip Before you read, preview *Exploring the Life Cycle of a Gymnosperm* on page 344. List any unfamiliar terms. As you read, write definitions for the terms.

Have you ever seen a tree that has grown wider than a car? Do trees this huge really exist? The answer is yes. Some giant sequoia trees, which grow almost exclusively in central California, are over ten meters wide. You can understand why giant sequoias are commonly referred to as "big trees." It takes a long time for a tree to grow so big. Scientists think that the largest giant sequoias may be about 2,000 years old. One reason they live so long is because their bark is fire-resistant.

What Are Gymnosperms?

The giant sequoia trees belong to the group of seed plants known as gymnosperms. A **gymnosperm** (JIM nuh spurm) is a seed plant that produces naked seeds. The seeds of gymnosperms are "naked" because they are not enclosed by any protective covering.

Every gymnosperm produces naked seeds. In addition, many gymnosperms also have needlelike or scalelike leaves, and deep-growing root systems. Although a few kinds of gymnosperms are shrubs or vines, most are trees.

◀ **A giant sequoia in California**

Types of Gymnosperms

Gymnosperms are the oldest type of seed plant. According to fossil evidence, gymnosperms first appeared on Earth about 360 million years ago. Fossils also indicate that there were many more species of gymnosperms in the past than today. Today, gymnosperms are classified into four groups—the cycads, the ginkgo, the gnetophytes, and the conifers.

Cycads About 175 million years ago, the majority of plants on Earth were cycads (SY kadz). Today, cycads are found only in tropical areas. As you can see in Figure 11, cycads look like palm trees with cones. A cycad cone can grow as large as a football. In Mexico people grind seeds from the cones of one cycad to make a type of flour for tortillas.

Ginkgo Like cycads, ginkgoes (GING kohz) are also hundreds of millions of years old. Only one species of ginkgo, *Ginkgo biloba*, exists today. It probably survives only because the Chinese and Japanese cared for the species in their gardens. Ginkgoes can grow as tall as 25 meters. Today, ginkgo trees are planted along many city streets because they can tolerate the air pollution produced by city traffic.

Gnetophytes Gnetophytes (NEE tuh fyts) are the gymnosperms that you are least likely to see. These gymnosperms live only in the hot, dry deserts of southern Africa, the deserts of the western United States, and the tropical rain forests. Some gnetophytes are trees, some are shrubs, and others are vines.

Figure 11 Gymnosperms are the oldest seed plants. **A.** Cycads, similar to this sago palm, were quite common during the age of dinosaurs. **B.** Only one kind of ginkgo, *Ginkgo biloba*, lives today. **C.** Gnetophytes, such as *Welwitschia mirabilis* shown here, grow in the very dry deserts of west Africa.

Figure 12 Ponderosa pines (A) are conifers that grow in the Rocky Mountains. Both male cones (B) and female cones (C) are produced on a single tree. *Comparing and Contrasting How do the male and female cones differ?*

Conifers Conifers (KAHN uh furz), or cone-bearing plants, are the largest and most diverse group of gymnosperms on Earth today. Most conifers, such as pines, redwoods, cedars, hemlocks, and junipers, are evergreen plants. Evergreen plants keep their leaves, or needles, year round. Old needles drop off and are replaced by new ones throughout the life of the plant.

If someone were to write a Book of Records for plants, conifers would get many awards. As you already know, giant sequoia trees would win the widest tree on Earth award. New Zealand pygmy pines, in contrast, are among the shortest trees on Earth. They grow only 8 centimeters tall. A bristlecone pine tree in Nevada holds the record for being the oldest organism on Earth. Its annual rings indicate that the tree is about 4,900 years old!

Reproduction

Most gymnosperms have reproductive structures called **cones.** Cones are covered with scales. Most gymnosperms produce two types of cones: male cones and female cones. Usually, a single plant produces both male and female cones. In some types of gymnosperms, however, individual trees produce either male cones or female cones. A few types of gymnosperms produce no cones at all.

Figure 12 shows the male and female cones of a Ponderosa pine. Notice that the male cones are smaller than the female cones. Male cones produce tiny grains of pollen. **Pollen** contains the microscopic cells that will later become sperm cells. Male cones produce so many pollen grains that they can overflow the spaces between the cone's scales.

Female cones contain at least one ovule at the base of each scale. An **ovule** (OH vyool) is a structure that contains an egg cell. After fertilization occurs, the ovule develops into a seed.

You can learn how gymnosperms reproduce in *Exploring the Life Cycle of a Gymnosperm* on the next page. **First, pollen falls from a male cone onto a female cone. In time, a sperm cell and an egg cell join together in an ovule on the female cone.** After fertilization occurs, the zygote develops into the embryo part of the seed.

Pollination and Fertilization   The transfer of pollen from a male reproductive structure to a female reproductive structure is called **pollination.** In gymnosperms, wind often carries the pollen from the male cones to the female cones. The pollen collects in a sticky substance produced by each ovule. The scales of the female cone close and seal in the pollen. Inside the closed scale, fertilization occurs. The seed then develops on the scale.

Female cones stay on the tree until the seeds mature. It can take up to two years for the seeds of some gymnosperms to mature. Male cones, however, usually fall off the tree after they have shed their pollen.

Seed Dispersal   As the seeds develop, the female cone increases in size. The cone's position on the branch may change as well. Cones that contain immature seeds point upward, while cones that contain mature seeds point downward. When the seeds are mature, the scales open. The wind shakes the seeds out of the cone and carries them away. Only a few seeds will land in a suitable place and grow into new plants.

☑ *Checkpoint*   *What is pollen and where is it produced?*

The Scoop on Cones

In this activity, **ACTIVITY** you will observe the structure of a female cone.

1. Use a hand lens to look closely at the female cone. Gently shake the cone over a piece of white paper. Observe what happens.

2. Break off one scale from the cone. Examine its base. If the scale contains a seed, remove the seed.

3. With a hand lens, examine the seed from Step 2, or examine a seed that fell on the paper in Step 1.

4. Wash your hands.

Inferring How does the structure of the cone protect the seeds?

EXPLORING the Life Cycle of a Gymnosperm

Pine trees have a typical life cycle for a gymnosperm. Follow the steps of pollination, fertilization, and seed development in the pine tree.

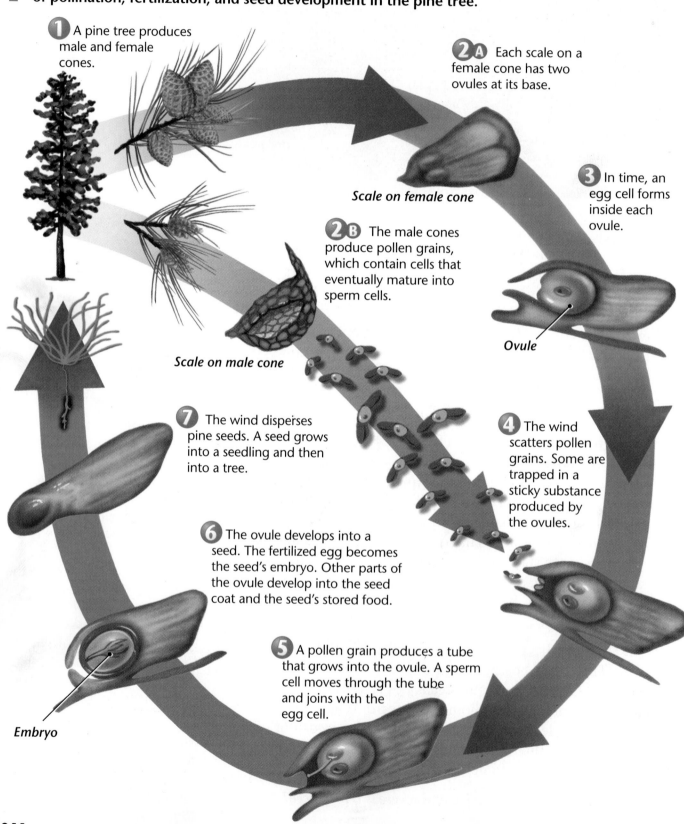

1 A pine tree produces male and female cones.

2A Each scale on a female cone has two ovules at its base.

Scale on female cone

3 In time, an egg cell forms inside each ovule.

Ovule

2B The male cones produce pollen grains, which contain cells that eventually mature into sperm cells.

Scale on male cone

7 The wind disperses pine seeds. A seed grows into a seedling and then into a tree.

4 The wind scatters pollen grains. Some are trapped in a sticky substance produced by the ovules.

6 The ovule develops into a seed. The fertilized egg becomes the seed's embryo. Other parts of the ovule develop into the seed coat and the seed's stored food.

5 A pollen grain produces a tube that grows into the ovule. A sperm cell moves through the tube and joins with the egg cell.

Embryo

Figure 13 Conifers provided the lumber for this playground.

Gymnosperms and the Living World

Paper and other wood products, such as the lumber used to build homes, come from conifers. Conifers are also used to make the rayon fibers in clothes as well as the cellophane wrappers on some food products. Other products, such as turpentine and the rosin used by baseball pitchers and musicians, are made from the sap produced by some conifers.

INTEGRATING ENVIRONMENTAL SCIENCE Because conifers are so useful to humans, they are grown in large forests in many regions of the United States. One method that is sometimes used to obtain lumber is called clear cutting. In this method all of the trees in a large area of a forest are cut down at once. This practice can leave forest animals homeless and cause the soil to be washed away by rains. Sometimes, other less-damaging cutting methods are used. For example, loggers may cut down trees in a long, narrow strip and then plant new trees in the strips. This method allows forests to regrow more quickly without the loss of soil and homes for wildlife.

Section 2 Review

1. What are three characteristics of gymnosperms?
2. Describe how gymnosperms reproduce.
3. List four products that are produced from gymnosperms. Which group of gymnosperms are used to make the products in your list?
4. **Thinking Critically Comparing and Contrasting** Compare the functions of male and female cones.

Science at Home

With a family member, make a list of things in your home that are made from gymnosperms. Then describe the characteristics of gymnosperms to your family member. What gymnosperms grow where you live?

SECTION
3 Angiosperms

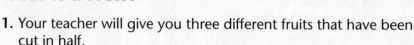

DISCOVER

ACTIVITY

What Is a Fruit?

1. Your teacher will give you three different fruits that have been cut in half.

2. Use a hand lens to carefully observe the outside of each fruit. For each fruit, record its color, shape, size, and external features. Record your observations in your notebook.

3. Carefully observe the structures inside the fruit. Record your observations.

Think It Over
Forming Operational Definitions Based on your observations, how would you define the term *fruit*?

GUIDE FOR READING

◆ What characteristics do angiosperms share?

◆ How do angiosperms reproduce?

Reading Tip Before you read, preview the photographs in this section. Predict how angiosperms differ from gymnosperms.

▼ Kudzu vines

Americans who visited the Japanese pavilion at the United States Centennial Exhibition in 1876 were introduced to kudzu, an attractive Asian vine. Soon, many Americans began planting kudzu in their communities. Little did they know that this creeping vine would become a huge problem.

Kudzu is one of the world's fastest-growing plants. Although it is nicknamed the "mile-a-minute vine," kudzu really does not grow that fast. But it can grow as much as 30 centimeters a day. In the southern United States, kudzu now covers an area twice the size of Connecticut. Unfortunately, there is no effective way to control the growth of this fast-growing plant.

What Are Angiosperms?

Kudzu is a type of seed plant known as an angiosperm. An **angiosperm** (AN jee uh spurm) is a plant that produces seeds that are enclosed in a fruit. The word *angiosperm* comes from two Greek words that mean "seed in a vessel." The protective "vessel"

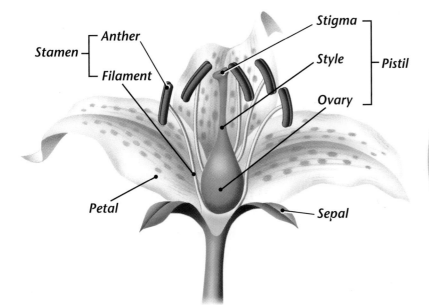

Figure 14 Like most flowers, this lily contains both male and female reproductive structures. *Interpreting Photographs What structures in the diagram can you find in the photograph?*

where seeds develop is called the **ovary.** The ovary is located within an angiosperm's **flower**—the reproductive structure of an angiosperm. **Two characteristics of angiosperms are that they produce flowers and fruits.**

Most of the familiar plants around you are angiosperms. Angiosperms live almost everywhere on Earth. They grow in frozen areas in the Arctic, tropical jungles, and barren deserts. A few angiosperms, such as mangrove trees and some sea grasses, even live in the oceans.

The Structure of Flowers

Like the plants that produce them, flowers come in all sorts of shapes, sizes, and colors. But all flowers have the same function— reproduction. Look at Figure 14 to see the parts of a typical flower. As you read about the parts, keep in mind that the description does not apply to all flowers. For example, some flowers have only male reproductive parts, and some flowers lack **petals**—the colorful structures that you see when flowers open.

When a flower is still a bud, it is enclosed by leaflike structures called **sepals** (SEE pulz). Sepals protect the developing flower. After the sepals fold back, the petals are revealed. The colors and shapes of the petals and the odors produced by the flower attract insects and other animals. These organisms ensure that pollination occurs.

Within the petals are the flower's male and female reproductive parts. Locate the thin stalks topped by small knobs inside the flower in Figure 14. These are the **stamens** (STAY munz), the male reproductive parts. The thin stalk is called the filament. Pollen is produced in the knob, or anther, at the top of the stalk.

The American artist Georgia O'Keeffe (1887–1986) is best known for her paintings of the landscape and wildlife in the western United States. Below you see an O'Keeffe painting of a red poppy. O'Keeffe painted the flower with accurate detail. Look carefully at the red poppy. At first it may not appear to have a lot of detail. But if you look more closely, you can see such structures as petals and reproductive parts.

In Your Journal

Write a paragraph describing the red poppy's adaptations for attracting animals for pollination.

The female parts, or **pistils** (PIS tulz), are usually found in the center of the flower. Some flowers have two or more pistils; others have only one. The sticky tip of the pistil is called the stigma. A slender tube, called a style, connects the stigma to a hollow structure at the base of the flower. This hollow structure is the ovary, which contains one or more ovules.

Reproduction

You can learn how angiosperms reproduce in *Exploring the Life Cycle of an Angiosperm*. **First, pollen falls on a stigma. In time, the sperm cell and egg cell join together in the flower's ovule. The zygote develops into the embryo part of the seed.**

Pollination and Fertilization A flower is pollinated when a grain of pollen falls on the stigma. Like gymnosperms, some angiosperms are pollinated by the wind. But most angiosperms rely on birds, bats, or insects for pollination. Nectar, a sugar-rich food, is located deep inside a flower. When an animal enters a flower to obtain the nectar, it brushes against the anthers and becomes coated with pollen. Some of the pollen can drop onto the flower's stigma as the animal leaves the flower. The pollen can also be brushed onto the sticky stigma of the next flower the animal visits. If the pollen falls on the stigma of a similar plant, fertilization can occur. The zygote then begins to develop into the seed's embryo. Other parts of the ovule develop into the rest of the seed.

Seed Dispersal As the seed develops, the ovary changes into a **fruit**—a ripened ovary and other structures that enclose one or more seeds. Apples and cherries are fruits. So are many foods you usually call vegetables, such as tomatoes and squash. For an angiosperm, a fruit is a way to disperse its seeds. Animals that eat fruits help to disperse their seeds.

☑ *Checkpoint* *What attracts pollinators to angiosperms?*

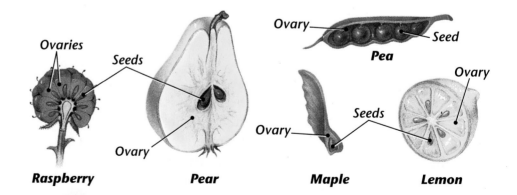

Figure 15 The seeds of angiosperms are enclosed within fruits, which protect and disperse the seed.

Raspberry — Ovaries, Seeds, Ovary

Pear — Seeds, Ovary

Maple — Ovary, Seeds

Pea — Ovary, Seed

Lemon — Ovary

EXPLORING the Life Cycle of an Angiosperm

All angiosperms have a similar life cycle. Follow the steps of pollination, fertilization, and fruit development in this typical angiosperm.

1 The angiosperm produces flowers.

2Ⓐ Inside the ovary, an egg cell is produced in each ovule.

Ovule

Ovary

2Ⓑ The cells in the anther produce pollen grains.

Anther

3 Pollen grains are trapped on the stigma.

Sperm cells

Pollen tube

7 A seed grows into a new plant.

6 The ovary and other structures develop into a fruit that encloses the seeds. The fruit helps in seed dispersal.

Embryo

4 The pollen grain produces a pollen tube that grows into the ovule. A sperm cell moves through the pollen tube and joins with the egg cell.

5 The ovule develops into a seed. The fertilized egg becomes the seed's embryo. Other parts of the ovule develop into the seed coat and the seed's stored food.

Monocots

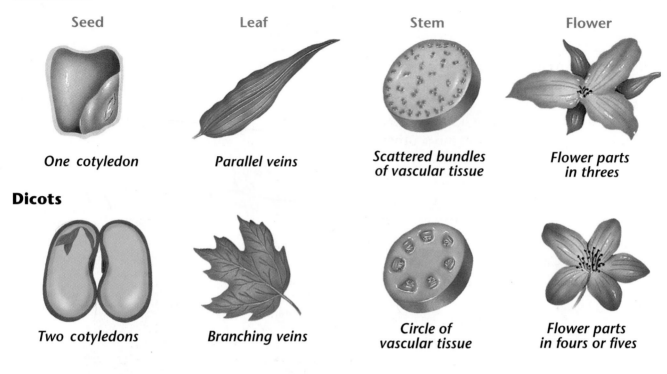

Seed — One cotyledon

Leaf — Parallel veins

Stem — Scattered bundles of vascular tissue

Flower — Flower parts in threes

Dicots

Seed — Two cotyledons

Leaf — Branching veins

Stem — Circle of vascular tissue

Flower — Flower parts in fours or fives

Figure 16 Monocots and dicots are the two groups of angiosperms. The groups differ in the number of cotyledons, the arrangement of veins and vascular tissue, and the number of petals.
Classifying Would a plant whose flowers have 20 petals be a monocot or a dicot?

Types of Angiosperms

Angiosperms are divided into two major groups: monocots and dicots. "Cot" is short for *cotyledon*. Recall from Section 1 that the cotyledon, or seed leaf, provides food for the embryo. *Mono* means "one" and *di* means "two". **Monocots** are angiosperms that have only one seed leaf. **Dicots,** on the other hand, produce seeds with two seed leaves. Look at Figure 16 to compare the characteristics of monocots and dicots.

Monocots Grasses, including corn, wheat, and rice, and plants such as lilies and tulips are monocots. The flowers of a monocot usually have either three petals or a multiple of three petals. Monocots usually have long, slender leaves with veins that run parallel to one another like train rails. The bundles of vascular tissue in monocot stems are usually scattered randomly throughout the stem.

Dicots Dicots include plants such as roses and violets, as well as dandelions. Both oak and maple trees are dicots, as are food plants such as beans and apples. The flowers of dicots often have either four or five petals or multiples of these numbers. The leaves are usually wide, with veins that branch off from one another. Dicot stems usually have bundles of vascular tissue arranged in a circle.

Checkpoint *How do the petals of monocots and dicots differ in number?*

Angiosperms and the Living World

Angiosperms are an important source of food, clothing, and medicine for other organisms. Plant-eating animals, such as cows, elephants, and beetles, eat flowering plants such as grasses as well as the leaves of trees. People eat vegetables, fruits, and cereals, all of which are angiosperms.

People also produce clothing and other products from angiosperms. For example, the seeds of cotton plants, like the ones you see in Figure 17, are covered with cotton fibers. The stems of flax plants provide linen fibers. The sap of tropical rubber trees is used to make rubber for tires and other products. Furniture is often made from the wood of maple, cherry, and oak trees.

 INTEGRATING HEALTH Some angiosperms are used in the making of medicine. For example, aspirin was first made from a substance found in the leaves of willow trees. Digitalis, a heart medication, comes from the leaves of the foxglove plant. Cortisone is a medicine made from the roots of the Mexican yam. It is used to treat arthritis and other joint problems. These medicines have helped improve the health of many people.

Figure 17 Cotton seeds, which develop in structures called bolls, are covered with fibers that are manufactured into cotton fabric.

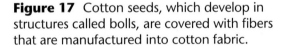

Section 3 Review

1. What two characteristics do all angiosperms share? Explain the importance of those characteristics.
2. Give a brief description of how reproduction occurs in angiosperms.
3. List the parts of a typical flower. What is the function of each part?
4. **Thinking Critically Inferring** A certain plant has small, dull-colored flowers with no scent. Do you think the plant is pollinated by animals or by the wind? Explain.

Check Your Progress

CHAPTER PROJECT

Your plants should now have, or will soon have, flowers. Make a diagram of the flower's structure. When the flowers open, you'll have to pollinate them. This work is usually done by insects or birds. After pollination, watch how the flower changes. (*Hint:* Discuss with your teacher and classmates how to pollinate the flowers.)

A Close Look at Flowers

In this lab, you will examine a flower in order to understand how it works.

Problem

What is the function of a flower, and what roles do its different parts play?

Skills Focus

observing, measuring, inferring

Materials

paper towels	plastic dropper
hand lens	microscope
slide	large flower
coverslip	scalpel
tape	water
metric ruler	lens paper

Procedure

Part 1 The Outer Parts of the Flower

1. Tape 4 sheets of paper towel on your work area. Obtain a flower from your teacher. While handling the flower gently, observe its shape and color. Use the ruler to measure it. Notice whether the petals have any spots or other markings. Does the flower have a scent? Record your observations with sketches and descriptions.

2. Observe the sepals. How many are there? How do they relate to the rest of the flower? (*Hint:* The sepals are often green, but not always.) Record your observations.

3. Use a scalpel to carefully cut off the sepals without damaging the structures beneath them. **CAUTION:** *Scalpels are sharp. Cut in a direction away from yourself and others.*

4. Observe the petals. How many are there? Are all the petals the same, or are they different? Record your observations.

Part 2 The Male Part of the Flower

5. Carefully pull off the petals to examine the male part of the flower. Try not to damage the structures beneath the petals.

6. Observe the stamens. How many are there? How are they shaped? How tall are they? Record your observations.

7. Use a scalpel to carefully cut the stamens away from the rest of the flower without damaging the structures beneath them. Lay the stamens on the paper towel.

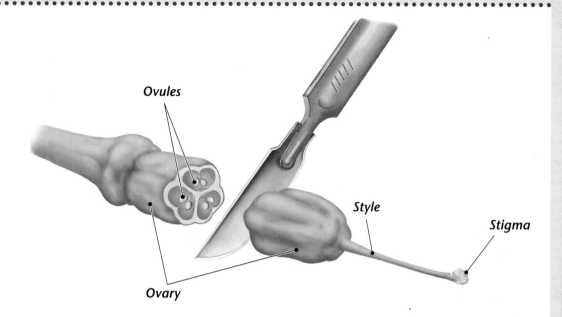

Ovules

Style

Stigma

Ovary

8. Obtain a clean slide and coverslip. Hold a stamen over the slide, and gently tap some pollen grains from the anther onto the slide. Add a drop of water to the pollen. Then place the coverslip over the water and pollen.

9. Observe the pollen under both the low-power objective and the high-power objective of a microscope. Draw and label a pollen grain.

Part 3 The Female Part of the Flower

10. Use a scalpel to cut the pistil away from the rest of the flower. Measure the height of the pistil. Examine its shape. Observe the top of the pistil. Determine if that surface will stick to and lift a tiny piece of lens paper. Record your observations.

11. Lay the pistil on the paper towel. Holding it firmly at its base, use a scalpel to cut the pistil in half at its widest point, as shown in the diagram above. **CAUTION:** *Cut away from your fingers.* How many compartments do you see? How many ovules do you see? Record your observations.

Analyze and Conclude

1. Based on your observations, describe how the petals, pistils, sepals, and stamens of a flower are arranged.

2. What is the main function of a flower? How are the sepals, petals, stamens, and pistil involved in that function?

3. How does a flower produce seeds?

4. Did your flower show any patterns in the number of sepals, petals, stamens, or other structures? If so, describe that pattern. Is your flower a monocot or a dicot?

5. **Apply** How do you think the flower you examined is pollinated? Use your observations, including the heights of the pistil and stamens, to support your answer.

More to Explore

Some kinds of flowers do not have all the parts found in the flower in this lab. Obtain a different flower. Find out which parts this flower has, and which parts are missing. Get your teacher's approval before carrying out this investigation.

SECTION
4 Plant Responses and Growth

DISCOVER ·············· ACTIVITY

Can a Plant Respond to Touch?

1. Your teacher will give you two plants. Observe the first plant. Gently touch a leaf and observe what happens over the next three minutes. Record your observations.

2. Repeat Step 1 with the second plant.

3. Wash your hands with soap and water.

Think It Over
Inferring What advantage might a plant have if its leaves responded to touch?

GUIDE FOR READING

◆ What are three stimuli that produce plant responses?

◆ What functions do plant hormones control?

Reading Tip As you read, use the headings to make an outline about plant responses and growth.

▼ A floating bladderwort

The bladderwort is a freshwater plant with small yellow flowers. Attached to its floating stems are structures called bladders. When a water flea touches a sensitive hair on a bladder, the bladder flicks open. Faster than you can blink, the water flea is sucked inside and the bladder snaps shut. The plant then digests the trapped flea.

A bladderwort responds quickly—faster than many animals respond to a similar stimulus. You may be surprised to learn that some plants have lightning-quick responses. In fact, you might have thought that plants do not respond to stimuli at all. But plants do respond to some stimuli, although they usually do so more slowly than the bladderwort.

Tropisms

Animals usually respond to stimuli by moving. Unlike animals, plants commonly respond by growing either toward or away from a stimulus. A plant's growth response toward or away from a stimulus is called a **tropism** (TROH pihz uhm). If a plant grows toward the stimulus, it is said to show a positive tropism. If a plant grows away from a stimulus, it shows a negative tropism. **Touch, light, and gravity are three important stimuli to which plants respond.**

Touch Some plants, such as bladderworts, show a response to touch called thigmotropism. The term *thigmo* comes from a Greek word that means "touch." The stems of many vines, such as grapes and morning glories, show a positive thigmotropism. As the vines grow, they coil around any object that they touch.

Light All plants exhibit a response to light called phototropism. The leaves, stems, and flowers of plants grow toward light, showing a positive phototropism. For example, sunflower plants exhibit a strong positive phototropism. As the sun's position changes during the day, sunflowers move on their stalks so that they are always facing the sun.

Gravity Plants also respond to gravity. This response is called gravitropism. Roots show positive gravitropism—they grow downward, with the pull of gravity. Stems, on the other hand, show negative gravitropism—they grow upward.

Plant Hormones

Plants are able to respond to light, gravity, and touch because they produce hormones. A **hormone** produced by a plant is a chemical that affects how the plant grows and develops. **In addition to tropisms, plant hormones also control germination, the formation of flowers, stems, and leaves, the shedding of leaves, and the development and ripening of fruit.**

One important plant hormone is named **auxin** (AWX sin). Auxin speeds up the rate at which a plant's cells grow. Auxin controls a plant's response to light. When light shines on one side of a plant's stem, auxin moves to the shaded side of the stem. The cells on that side begin to grow faster. Eventually, the cells on the stem's shady side are longer than those on its sunny side. So the stem bends toward the light.

✓ *Checkpoint* *What role does the hormone auxin play in a plant?*

Life Spans of Angiosperms

If you've ever planted a garden, you know that many flowering plants grow, flower, and die in a single year. Flowering plants that complete a life cycle within one growing season are called annuals. The word annual comes from the Latin word *annus,* which means "year." Most annuals have herbaceous stems. Annuals include many garden plants, such as marigolds, petunias, and pansies. Wheat, tomatoes, and cucumbers are also annuals.

Angiosperms that complete their life cycle in two years are called biennials (by EN ee ulz). The Latin prefix *bi* means "two."

Figure 18 The face of this sunflower turns on its stalk throughout the day so that it always faces the sun. *Making Generalizations How does a positive phototropism help a plant survive?*

Figure 19 A flowering plant is classified as an annual, biennial, or perennial depending on the length of its life cycle. **A.** These morning glories are annuals. **B.** Foxglove, like this *Digitalis purpurea*, is a biennial. **C.** This peony, a perennial, will bloom year after year.

In the first year, biennials germinate and grow roots, very short stems, and leaves. During their second year, biennials grow new stems and leaves and then produce flowers and seeds. Once the flowers produce seeds, the plant dies. Parsley, celery, and foxglove are biennials.

Flowering plants that live for more than two years are called perennials. The Latin word *per* means "through." Perennials usually live through many years. Some perennials, such as peonies and asparagus, have herbaceous stems. The leaves and stems above the ground die each winter. New ones are produced each spring. Most perennials, however, have woody stems. Bristlecone pines, oak trees, and honeysuckle are examples of woody perennials.

Section 4 Review

1. Name three stimuli to which plants respond.
2. What is a plant hormone? List four processes that a plant's hormones control.
3. Suppose you are growing a plant on a windowsill. After a few days, you notice that the plant's leaves and flowers are facing the window. Explain why this has occurred.
4. **Thinking Critically** **Applying Concepts** Is the grass that grows in most lawns an annual, a biennial, or a perennial? Explain.

Science at Home

With a family member, soak some corn seeds or lima bean seeds in water overnight. Then push them gently into some soil in a paper cup until they are just covered. Keep the soil moist. When you see the stems break through the soil, place the cup in a sunny window. After a few days, explain to your family member why the plants responded the way they did.

Which Way is Up?

In this lab, you will use your knowledge of germination to develop a hypothesis about seedlings and gravity.

Problem

How is the growth of a seed affected by gravity?

Materials

4 corn seeds
paper towels
water
marking pencil

plastic petri dish
scissors
masking tape
clay

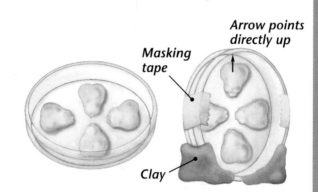

Masking tape

Arrow points directly up

Clay

Procedure

1. With your classmates, discuss how gravity affects objects. Then, with your group, develop a hypothesis that explains how gravity affects the direction of seedling growth.
2. Arrange four seeds that have been soaked in water for 24 hours in a petri dish. The pointed ends of the seeds should face the center of the dish, as shown in the illustration.
3. Place a circle cut from a paper towel over the seeds. Moisten one or more paper towels with water so that they are wet but not dripping. Pack them in the dish to hold the seeds firmly in place. Cover the dish, and seal it with tape.
4. Lay the dish upside-down so the seeds show. Use a marking pencil to draw a small, outward-facing arrow over one of the seeds, as shown in the illustration. Turn the dish over and write your name and the date on it.
5. Use clay to stand up the petri dish so that the arrow points upward. Put the petri dish in a dark place.

6. Once a day for a week, remove the petri dish and check it. Do not open the dish. Observe and sketch the seeds. Note the seeds' direction of growth. Then return the dish, making sure that the arrow points upward.

Analyze and Conclude

1. What new structures emerged as the seeds developed? How did the direction of growth compare from seed to seed?
2. Did your results confirm your hypothesis? If not, describe any differences between your hypothesis and your results.
3. Why was it necessary to grow these seeds in the dark?
4. **Think About It** What evidence or ideas did you consider when you wrote your hypothesis? Did any of your ideas change as a result of this experiment? Explain.

Design an Experiment

How will your seedlings respond if you now allow them to grow in the light? Design an experiment to find out. Obtain your teacher's approval before carrying out your experiment.

SECTION 5 Feeding the World

DISCOVER ⋯⋯⋯⋯⋯⋯⋯⋯⋯⋯⋯⋯⋯⋯⋯⋯ ACTIVITY ⋯

Will There Be Enough to Eat?

1. Choose a numbered tag from the bag that your teacher provides. If you pick a tag with the number 1 on it, you're from a wealthy country. If you pick a tag with the number 2, you're from a middle-income country. If you pick a tag with the number 3, you're from a poor country.

2. Find classmates that have the same number on their tag. Sit down as a group.

3. Your teacher will serve your group a meal. The amount of food you receive will depend on the number on your tag.

4. As you eat, observe the people in your group and in the other groups. After you eat, record your observations. Also, record how you felt and what you were thinking during the meal.

Think It Over

Predicting Based on this activity, predict what effect an increase in the world's population would have on the world's food supply.

GUIDE FOR READING

◆ What methods may help farmers produce more crops?

Reading Tip As you read, make a list of the technologies being used to increase Earth's food supply.

Today, about six billion people live on Earth. Some scientists predict that by the year 2050 the population will grow to ten billion people. Think about how much additional food will be needed to feed the growing population. How will farmers be able to grow enough food?

Fortunately, both scientists and farmers are already hard at work trying to find answers to this question. **In laboratories, scientists are developing plants that are more resistant to insects, disease, and drought. They are also developing plants that produce more food per plant. On farms, new, efficient, "high-tech" farming practices are being used.**

Producing Better Plants

Wheat, corn, rice, and potatoes are the major sources of food for people on Earth today. To feed more people, then, the production, or yields, of these crops must be increased. This is not an easy task. One challenge facing farmers is that these crops grow only in certain climates. Another challenge is that the size and structure of these plants limit how much food they can produce.

Today scientists are using new technologies to address these challenges. Recall from Chapter 8 that scientists can manipulate the genetic material of certain bacteria to produce human insulin. The process that these scientists use is called genetic engineering. In **genetic engineering,** scientists alter an organism's genetic material to produce an organism with qualities that people find useful.

Scientists are using genetic engineering to produce plants that can grow in a wider range of climates. They are also engineering plants to be more resistant to damage from insects. For example, scientists have inserted genetic material from a bacterium into corn and tomato plants. The new genetic material enables the plants to produce substances that kill insects. Caterpillars or other insects that bite into the leaves of these plants are killed. Today, many kinds of genetically engineered plants are grown on experimental farms. Some of these plants may produce the crops of the future.

Figure 20 In this high-tech greenhouse, scientists control the environmental conditions as they develop new types of plants. *Applying Concepts How might new plant types lead to increased crop yields in the future?*

☑ *Checkpoint* *What are the four crops on which people depend?*

Improving the Efficiency of Farms

On the farms of the future, satellite images and computers will be just as important as tractors and harvesters. These new tools will allow farmers to practice "precision farming"—knowing just how much water and fertilizer different fields require. First, satellite images of the farmer's fields are taken. Then, a computer analyzes the images to determine the makeup of the soil in different fields on the farm. The computer uses the data to prepare a watering and fertilizing plan for each field. Precision farming benefits farmers because it saves time and money. It also increases crop yields by helping farmers maintain ideal conditions in all fields.

Figure 21 The map on the computer screen of this tractor shows the makeup of the soil in a farm's fields. The map was obtained by satellite imaging.

Precision farming also benefits the environment because farmers use only as much fertilizer as the soil needs. When less fertilizer is used, fewer nutrients wash off the land into lakes and rivers. As you read in Chapter 9, reducing the use of fertilizers is one way to prevent algal blooms from damaging bodies of water.

Hydroponics

In some areas of the world, poor soil does not support the growth of crops. For example, on some islands in the Pacific Ocean, the soil contains large amounts of salt from the surrounding ocean. Food crops will not grow in the salty soil.

On these islands, people can use hydroponics to grow food crops. **Hydroponics** (hy druh PAHN iks) is a method by which plants are grown in solutions of nutrients instead of in soil. Usually, the plants are grown in containers in which their roots are anchored in gravel or sand. The nutrient-rich water is pumped through the gravel or sand. Unfortunately, hydroponics is a costly method of growing food crops. But, the process allows people to grow crops in areas with poor farmland to help feed a growing population.

Section 5 Review

1. List three methods that farmers can use to increase crop yields.
2. Explain how genetic engineering may help farmers grow more food.
3. How does precision farming benefit farmers? How does it benefit the environment?
4. **Thinking Critically Applying Concepts** How are plants that are grown using hydroponics able to survive without soil?

Check Your Progress

CHAPTER PROJECT

Your plants should be near the end of their growth cycle. Continue to observe them. Harvest the seeds carefully, observe them, and compare them with the original seeds. If you have time, plant a few of these new seeds to begin the life cycle again.

SECTION 1 The Characteristics of Seed Plants

Key Ideas

◆ All seed plants have vascular tissue and produce seeds. All seed plants also have leaves, stems, and roots.

◆ A seed has three important parts: an embryo, stored food, and a seed coat.

◆ Photosynthesis occurs mainly in leaves. Stems support plants and transport materials between the roots and leaves. Roots anchor plants and absorb water and minerals.

Key Terms

phloem	cotyledon	transpiration
xylem	germination	cambium
seed	stomata	root cap
embryo		

SECTION 2 Gymnosperms

Key Ideas

◆ All gymnosperms produce naked seeds. Many gymnosperms also have needlelike or scalelike leaves, and grow deep root systems.

◆ To reproduce, gymnosperms produce pollen in male cones and egg cells in female cones. Pollen falls onto a female cone. In time, a sperm cell and an egg cell join. The zygote develops into the embryo of the seed.

Key Terms

gymnosperm	ovule
cone	pollination
pollen	

SECTION 3 Angiosperms

Key Ideas

◆ Two characteristics of angiosperms are that they produce flowers and fruits.

◆ To reproduce, the male parts of the flower produce pollen, while the female parts produce eggs. Pollen falls on the stigma. In time, the sperm cell and egg cell join in the ovule. The zygote develops into the seed's embryo.

Key Terms

angiosperm	sepal	fruit
ovary	stamen	monocot
flower	pistil	dicot
petal		

SECTION 4 Plant Responses and Growth

Key Ideas

◆ A tropism is a plant's growth response toward or away from a stimulus. Plants respond to touch, light, and gravity.

◆ Plant hormones control tropisms and many other plant functions.

Key Terms

tropism	hormone	auxin

SECTION 5 Feeding the World

INTEGRATING TECHNOLOGY

Key Ideas

◆ Genetic engineering, precision farming, and hydroponics can help farmers produce more crops to feed the world's growing population.

Key Terms

genetic engineering	hydroponics

USING THE INTERNET

ACTIVITY

www.science-explorer.phschool.com

C H A P T E R 11 R E V I E W

California Test Prep: Reviewing Content

Multiple Choice

Choose the letter of the best answer.

1. The process by which a seed sprouts is called
   a. pollination.　　b. fertilization.
   c. dispersal.　　d. germination.

2. In woody stems, new xylem cells are produced by
   a. bark.　　b. cambium.
   c. phloem.　　d. pith.

3. Which of the following is the male part of the flower?
   a. pistil　　b. ovule
   c. stamen　　d. petal

4. What kind of tropism do roots display when they grow into the soil?
   a. positive gravitropism
   b. negative gravitropism
   c. positive phototropism
   d. negative thigmotropism

5. The process of growing crops in a nutrient solution is called
   a. genetic engineering.
   b. hydroponics.
   c. precision farming.
   d. satellite imaging.

True or False

If the statement is true, write true. If it is false, change the underlined word or words to make the statement true.

6. <u>Stems</u> anchor plants and absorb water and minerals from the soil.

7. The needles of a pine tree are actually its <u>leaves</u>.

8. The seeds of <u>gymnosperms</u> are dispersed in fruits.

9. Plants that complete their life cycle in two years are called <u>perennials</u>.

10. The four basic food crops of the world are wheat, corn, rice, and <u>potatoes</u>.

Checking Concepts

11. Describe four different ways that seeds can be dispersed.

12. Explain the role that stomata play in leaves.

13. What are annual rings? Explain how they form.

14. Describe the structure of a female cone.

15. What is the difference between pollination and fertilization?

16. What role do plant hormones play in phototropism?

17. How can the use of hydroponics help increase the amount of food that can be grown on Earth?

18. **Writing to Learn** Imagine that you are a seed inside a plump purple fruit that is floating in a stream. Describe your experiences on the journey you take to the place where you germinate.

Thinking Visually

19. **Concept Map** Copy the concept map about seed plants onto a separate piece of paper. Then complete the map and add a title. (For more on concept maps, see the Skills Handbook.)

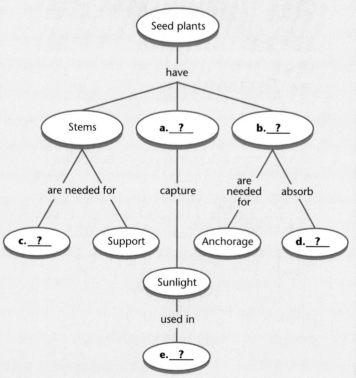

Test Prep: Skills

A scientist measured the rate of transpiration in an ash tree over an 18-hour period. She also measured how much water the tree's roots took up during the same period. Use the data in the graph below to answer Questions 20–22.

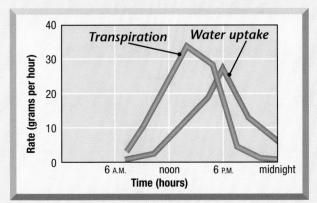

20. Interpreting Data At what time is transpiration at its highest? At what time is water uptake at its highest?

21. Inferring Why do you think the transpiration rate increases and decreases as it does during the 18-hour period?

22. Drawing Conclusions Based on the graph, what is one possible conclusion you can reach about the pattern of water loss and gain in the ash tree?

Thinking Critically

23. Relating Cause and Effect When a strip of bark is removed all the way around the trunk of a tree, the tree dies. Explain why.

24. Applying Concepts Explain why people who grow houseplants on windowsills should turn the plants every week or so.

25. Predicting Pesticides are designed to kill harmful insects. Sometimes, however, pesticides kill helpful insects as well. What effect could this have on angiosperms?

26. Making Judgments Suppose you were a scientist using genetic engineering to increase crop yields. What improvements would you try to introduce? How would they be beneficial?

Performance Assessment

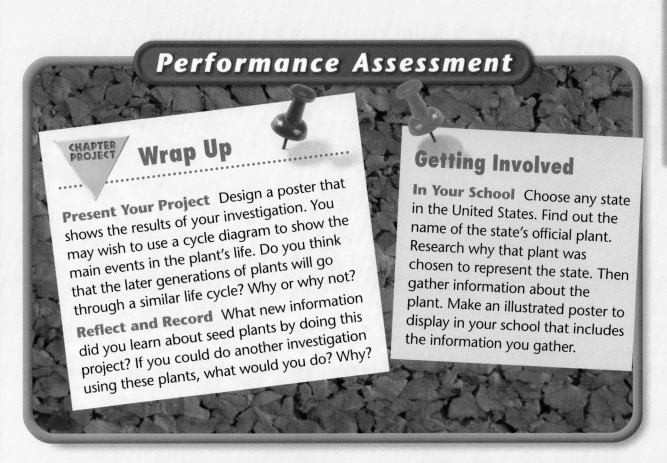

CHAPTER PROJECT **Wrap Up**

Present Your Project Design a poster that shows the results of your investigation. You may wish to use a cycle diagram to show the main events in the plant's life. Do you think that the later generations of plants will go through a similar life cycle? Why or why not?

Reflect and Record What new information did you learn about seed plants by doing this project? If you could do another investigation using these plants, what would you do? Why?

Getting Involved

In Your School Choose any state in the United States. Find out the name of the state's official plant. Research why that plant was chosen to represent the state. Then gather information about the plant. Make an illustrated poster to display in your school that includes the information you gather.

The graceful tentacles of this yellow cup coral help it to lure and catch food.

The following California Science Content Standards are addressed in this chapter:

1. All living organisms are composed of cells, from just one to many trillions, whose details usually are visible only through a microscope.

   f. As multicellular organisms develop, their cells differentiate.

2. A typical cell of any organism contains genetic instructions that specify its traits. Those traits may be modified by environmental influences.

   a. The differences between the life cycles and reproduction of sexual and asexual organisms.

3. Biological evolution accounts for the diversity of species developed through gradual processes over many generations.

   a. Both genetic variation and environmental factors are causes of evolution and diversity of organisms.

   d. How to construct a simple branching diagram to classify living groups of organisms by shared derived characteristics, and expand the diagram to include fossil organisms.

Alive and Well

When you hear the word *animal*, what picture comes to mind? You probably do not think of anything like this fingerlike yellow coral waving in the ocean current. But just like horses or sparrows, corals are animals, too.

Do animals such as corals really have anything in common with horses and sparrows? Keep this question in mind as you begin your study of animals. Instead of just reading about animals, though, you and your classmates will create a zoo in your classroom. Your zoo will feature crickets, earthworms, and other animals not usually found in zoos. In your role as zookeeper, you will select one animal to care for and study.

Your Goal To keep an animal safe and healthy for three weeks while you study its characteristics, needs, and behaviors.

To complete the project successfully, you must
- provide a healthy and safe environment for your animal
- keep the animal alive and well for the entire time of the project, and observe the animal's behavior
- prepare a report or illustrated booklet to show what you have learned about your animal
- follow the safety guidelines in Appendix A

Get Started After you have chosen an animal you want to care for, work with a partner to brainstorm questions you have about its survival needs. Then plan a way to find answers to your questions.

Check Your Progress You'll be working on this project as you study this chapter. To keep your project on track, look for Check Your Progress boxes at the following points.
Section 1 Review, page 372: Research your animal's needs and prepare its home.
Section 3 Review, page 383: Record your daily observations.
Section 4 Review, page 391: Analyze what you've learned and prepare your presentation.

Wrap Up At the end of the chapter (page 395), you will introduce your animal to your classmates and share your knowledge.

5. The anatomy and physiology of plants and animals illustrate the complementary nature of structure and function.
  a. Plants and animals have levels of organization for structure and function, including cells, tissues, organs, organ systems, and the whole organism.

  b. Organ systems function because of the contributions of individual organs, tissues, and cells. The failure of any part can affect the entire system.
7. Scientific progress is made by asking meaningful questions and conducting careful investigations.

  c. Communicate the logical connectio among hypothesis, science concepts tests conducted, data collected, and conclusions drawn from the scientif evidence.
  d. Construct scale models, maps and appropriately labeled diagrams to communicate scientific knowledge.

① What Is an Animal?

Is It an Animal?

1. Carefully examine each of the organisms that your teacher gives you.

2. Decide which ones are animals. Think about the reasons for your decision. Wash your hands after handling each of the organisms.

Think It Over
Forming Operational Definitions What characteristics did you use to decide whether each organism was an animal?

GUIDE FOR READING

◆ **What characteristics do all animals have in common?**

◆ **How are animals classified into groups?**

Reading Tip Before you begin to read, write your own definition of *animal*. Add to it or change it as you read.

In the waters off the north coast of Australia, a young box jellyfish floats along, looking more like a tiny transparent flower than an animal. After a time the young jellyfish will change form. As an adult, it will resemble a square bubble of clear jelly trailing bunches of long, wavy, armlike structures called tentacles.

To capture food, a box jellyfish's tentacles fire deadly venom at unlucky animals that happen to touch them. Humans are no exception. A swimmer who brushes the tentacles of a box jellyfish can die in only four minutes. In spite of their harmless appearance, adult box jellyfish have one of the strongest venoms on Earth.

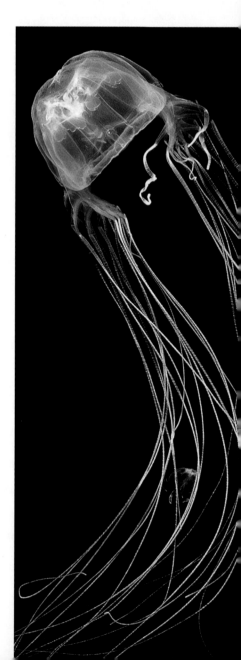

Figure 1 Don't be fooled by the delicate-looking tentacles of the Australian box jellyfish. Animals that brush against them can be killed by their venom—and become the jellyfish's next meal.

Characteristics of Animals

The box jellyfish may not look like most of the animals that you are familiar with, but it is indeed an animal. Biologists, scientists who study living organisms, have described over 1 million different animal species, and there are certainly many more. A **species** is a group of organisms that can mate with each other and produce offspring, who in turn can mate and reproduce.

All species of animals, including the beautiful but deadly box jellyfish, are similar in some important ways. **Animals are many-celled organisms that must obtain their food by eating other organisms.** In addition, most animals reproduce sexually and can move from place to place. Biologists look for these characteristics in deciding whether an organism is an animal.

How Animal Cells Are Organized All animals are multicellular; that is, their bodies are composed of many cells, the tiny working units that make up all living things. The cells of most animals are grouped together to form different kinds of tissue. A tissue is a group of similar cells that perform a specific job. For example, muscle tissue allows animals to move, while nerve tissue carries messages from one part of the body to another. Tissues may combine to form an organ, which is a group of different tissues that work together to perform a specific job that is more complex than the functions of each tissue by itself. Organs are made up of different types of tissue—your thigh bone, for example, is an organ that contains bone tissue, nerve tissue, and blood. In most animals, different organs combine to form an organ system, such as your skeletal system, shown in Figure 2.

How Animals Obtain Food Every animal is a **heterotroph** (HET ur oh trohf)—it cannot make food for itself, and must obtain food by eating other organisms. Contrast this with a green plant, which is an **autotroph** (AW toh trohf), an organism that makes its own food. Most animals take food into a cavity inside their bodies. Inside this cavity, the food is digested, or broken down into substances that the animal's body can absorb and use.

How Animals Reproduce Animals typically reproduce sexually. **Sexual reproduction** is the process by which a new organism forms from the joining of two sex cells—a tiny male sperm cell combines with a much larger female egg cell. The joining of egg and

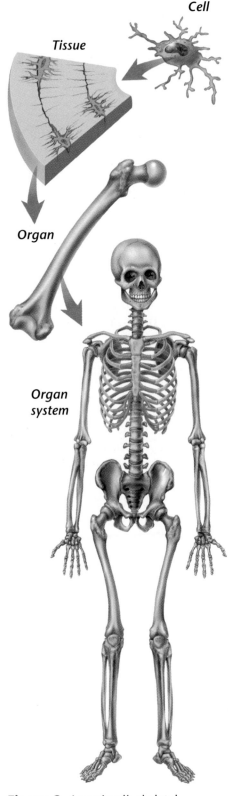

Cell

Tissue

Organ

Organ system

Figure 2 An animal's skeletal system has different levels of organization. Bone cells make up tissues, and tissues make up organs such as the thigh bone. *Classifying Is the skull best classified as an organ or as a tissue?*

ACTIVITY

Design an animal with a new and different way of moving. Your design should help your animal obtain food or get out of danger.

1. Make and label a drawing that shows how the animal would move.

2. Using clay, pipe cleaners, aluminum cans, construction paper, and whatever other materials are available, create a three-dimensional model of your animal.

3. Compare your animal to those of other classmates. What are some similarities? What are some differences?

Making Models What features of your design help your animal obtain food or escape danger?

sperm is called **fertilization.** Sperm and egg cells carry information about the characteristics of the parent that produced them— characteristics such as size and color. When sperm and egg unite, the resulting new individual has a combination of characteristics from both parents. It is something like each parent, but not exactly like either one.

Some animals can reproduce asexually as well as sexually. **Asexual reproduction** is the process by which a single organism produces a new organism identical to itself. Asexual reproduction does not involve a joining of sex cells from two individuals. Instead, the parent organism may divide to form two or more new organisms, or it may produce offspring from buds that grow on its body. A tiny animal called a hydra, for example, reproduces asexually by forming buds that eventually break off to form new hydras.

How Animals Move Animal movement can be fascinating to watch. Much of the movement is related to obtaining food, reproducing, and escaping danger. Barnacles, for example, wave feathery arms through the water to collect tiny food particles. Some geese must fly thousands of miles each spring to the place where they mate and lay eggs. And you've probably seen a cat claw its way up a tree trunk to get away from a snarling dog.

Some animals don't move from place to place. Adult oysters, sponges, and corals all stick firmly to underwater rocks and other solid surfaces. But most animals move freely at some point in their lives. For example, for its first few weeks of life, an oyster is a tiny swimmer—so tiny that you need a microscope to see it. Then the young oyster swims to a solid surface and attaches itself. It glues itself in place and undergoes changes in its form, eventually becoming an adult oyster within a shell.

✓ *Checkpoint* Contrast the ways in which heterotrophs and autotrophs obtain food.

Figure 3 Animals such as this Arabian stallion move with grace and power.

How Animals Meet Their Needs

If someone asked you to make a list of the things that you need to stay alive, you would probably write down *water, food,* and *oxygen.* Like all living things, animals need water because the chemical reactions that keep them alive, such as the breakdown of food, take place in water. Food provides animals with raw materials for growth and with energy for their bodies' activities, such as moving and breathing. To release that energy, the body's cells need oxygen. Some animals get oxygen from air; others absorb it from water.

Water, food, and oxygen must come from an animal's environment, or surroundings. An animal needs to be able to respond to its environment—for example, to find food and to run away from danger. Animals' bodies and behaviors are adapted for tasks such as these. An **adaptation** is a characteristic that helps an organism survive in its environment or reproduce.

Adaptations for Getting Food

Unlike plants that make their own food using sunlight, animals must obtain their food. Some animals eat plants, other animals eat animals, and still others eat both plants and animals.

Herbivores Animals that eat only plants are called **herbivores**. Grasshoppers, termites, and garden snails are some common smaller herbivores. Larger herbivores include cows, horses, and pandas. Herbivores have adaptations such as teeth with broad, flat surfaces that are good for grinding tough plants.

Carnivores Animals that eat only other animals are **carnivores**. Many carnivores are **predators** that hunt and kill other animals. Predators have adaptations that help them capture the animals

Figure 4 Animals have different adaptations for obtaining food. **A.** A carpet snake is a carnivore that feeds on lizards and other animals. **B.** A macaw is an herbivore that feeds on fruits and seeds. *Observing What feeding adaptations do you see in the photos?*

Sharpen your Skills

Inferring ACTIVITY

The pictures show the jawbones of two animals. Look at the pictures carefully, and decide what types of food each animal probably eats. List the observations on which you base your inferences.

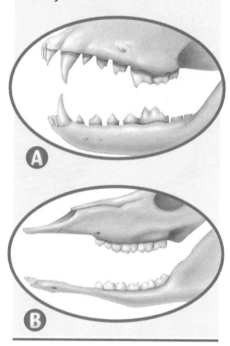

A

B

they feed upon, their **prey**. Wolves, for example, run down their prey. A wolf's adaptations include sharp claws, speed, and excellent hearing and eyesight. The teeth of most carnivores are sharp and pointed—they are adapted for cutting and stabbing.

Unlike wolves, sit-and-wait predators hide quietly and attack suddenly. Most of them blend in with their surroundings. Think of a frog sitting quietly by a pond. An insect flying by doesn't see the frog. Suddenly the frog flicks out its sticky tongue and catches the unsuspecting insect.

Omnivores Some animals eat both plants and animals; such an animal is an **omnivore**. A grizzly bear eats berries and roots, as well as insects, fish, and other small animals. Humans are also omnivores, as you know if you like hamburgers with tomato.

☑ *Checkpoint* *Describe some feeding adaptations of carnivores.*

Adaptations for Escaping Predators

In addition to feeding adaptations, animals have adaptations that help them avoid being eaten by predators. Some animals, such as box turtles and hedgehogs, have hard shells or spiny skins. Opossums and pill bugs "play dead" when they are attacked, so their predators lose interest. Stingers, claws, bitter-tasting flesh, or smelly sprays protect other animals. If you see a skunk, you stay far away from it. So do most predators.

Classification of Animals

Biologists classify animals in the animal kingdom into about 35 major groups, each of which is called a **phylum** (plural *phyla*). As you read this book, you will learn the characteristics of some of these phyla. Notice that in Figure 6, the phyla are arranged like the branches on a tree.

Figure 5 Hedgehogs, like this African pygmy hedgehog, roll up into spiny balls to protect themselves from possible predators.

Figure 6 labels (on the tree):
INSECTS, CENTIPEDES, SPIDERS, ARTHROPODS, CRUSTACEANS, SEGMENTED WORMS, BIRDS, REPTILES, MAMMALS, AMPHIBIANS, FISHES, MOLLUSKS, VERTEBRATES, ECHINODERMS, ROUNDWORMS, FLATWORMS, CNIDARIANS, SPONGES, UNICELLULAR ANCESTORS

The branching tree shows how biologists think the different phyla are related. For example, from their positions on the tree, you can see that segmented worms are more closely related to arthropods than to sponges.

The tree also shows the order in which biologists think animal life has evolved, or changed over time. This evolution process has resulted in all the different phyla that exist today. Biologists do not know the exact way in which evolution took place—they can only make inferences on the basis of the best evidence available. Notice that biologists think all animals arose from unicellular, or single-celled, ancestors, as shown at the base of the tree.

Figure 6 This branching tree shows how the major animal phyla are related to one another, and the approximate order in which they evolved. *Interpreting Diagrams To which group are flatworms more closely related—roundworms or mollusks?*

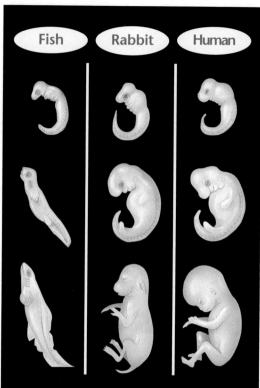

Fish　Rabbit　Human

Figure 7 Biologists often study embryo development when classifying animals. *Comparing and Contrasting Compare the embryos of three vertebrates—a fish, a rabbit, and a human. Which two animals show greater similarity in their development?*

Animals are classified, or put into groups, according to how they are related to other animals. **When biologists classify an animal, they look at the structure of its body and the way it develops as an embryo at the very beginning of its life. Biologists also examine the animal's DNA, which is a chemical in cells that controls an organism's inherited characteristics.** The more similar two animals are in those characteristics, the more closely they are probably related.

For example, look at the developing embryos shown in Figure 7. You can see that a rabbit embryo is more similar to a human embryo than it is to a fish embryo. This similarity provides one piece of evidence indicating that rabbits are more closely related to humans than they are to fishes. The structure of the animals' hearts provides another piece of evidence. The hearts of rabbits and humans are similar—but are quite different from the hearts of fishes.

One important structural characteristic used to classify animals is the presence or absence of a backbone, which is a series of bones that run down the center of the back. An animal that does not have a backbone is called an **invertebrate**. Jellyfishes, worms, snails, crabs, spiders, and insects are all invertebrates. Most animal species—about 95 percent—are invertebrates. In contrast, a **vertebrate** is an animal that has a backbone. Fishes, amphibians, reptiles, birds, and mammals are all vertebrates.

Aside from having—or not having—a backbone, animals also differ in the overall shape of their bodies. Although a few animals have lopsided bodies, most do not, as you will learn in the next section.

Section 1 Review

1. Describe two characteristics that all animals share.
2. List the major characteristics that are used to classify animals into groups.
3. List three needs that all animals must meet in order to survive.
4. **Thinking Critically Comparing and Contrasting** Contrast the ways in which wolves and frogs obtain their food, and identify one food-getting adaptation of each animal.

Check Your Progress
CHAPTER PROJECT

By now, you should have chosen your animal and learned from library research how to meet its needs. Discuss with your teacher your plans for obtaining, housing, and caring for your animal. After preparing your animal's home and obtaining some food for it, put the animal in its new home. (*Hint:* Be sure to consider how your animal will survive holidays and weekends.)

SECTION
②Symmetry

DISCOVER ● **ACTIVITY**

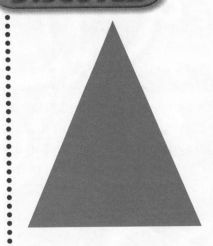

How Many Ways Can You Fold It?

1. Trace the triangle onto a sheet of paper and cut it out. Then draw a circle by tracing the rim of a glass or other round object. Cut out the circle.

2. Fold the triangle so that one half matches the other. Do the same with the circle.

3. See how many different ways you can fold each figure so that the two halves are identical.

Think It Over

Classifying Can you think of animals whose body shape could be folded in the same number of ways as the triangle? As the circle?

With its wings closed, a bright and colorful butterfly perches lightly on a flower, drinking nectar. Its delicate but strong wings are motionless as it drinks. Then, suddenly, those fragile-looking wings begin to move, and they lift the butterfly, seemingly effortlessly, into the air.

As you can see from the photo of the large copper butterfly in Figure 8, a butterfly's body has two halves, and each half looks almost like a reflection of the other. This balanced arrangement, called symmetry, is characteristic of many animals. A butterfly's symmetry contributes to its pleasing appearance. More importantly, the balanced wings help the butterfly to fly more easily.

> ### GUIDE FOR READING
>
> ◆ What types of symmetry do complex animals exhibit?
>
> *Reading Tip* Before you read, preview the illustrations in Figures 8 and 9. Predict how body shape is important to an animal.

Figure 8 If you could draw a line through this butterfly's body, it would divide the animal into two mirror-image halves. *Applying Concepts What is this balanced arrangement called?*

The Mathematics of Symmetry

In Figure 8, you can see that a line drawn down the middle of the butterfly produces two halves that are the same—they are mirror images. This dividing line is called a line of symmetry. An object has line symmetry, or **bilateral symmetry,** if there is a line that divides it into halves that are mirror images. A large copper butterfly has bilateral symmetry, as do an oak leaf, a spoon, and a pair of eyeglasses.

Contrast the butterfly's symmetry to that of a sea anemone. A sea anemone is circular if you look at it from the top, as in Figure 9. Any line drawn through its center will divide the sea anemone into two symmetrical halves. Like the sea anemone, many circular objects exhibit **radial symmetry**—they have many lines of symmetry that all go through a central point. Pie plates and bicycle wheels have radial symmetry.

✓ *Checkpoint* *How is radial symmetry different from bilateral symmetry?*

Symmetry in Animals

There are a few animals, such as most sponges, that exhibit no symmetry. These asymmetrical animals generally have very simple body plans. Sponges, for example, have no hearts, brains, kidneys, or nerve cells. **The bodies of complex animals all have either radial or bilateral symmetry.**

Animals with Radial Symmetry The external body parts of animals with radial symmetry are equally spaced around a central point, like spokes on a bicycle wheel. Because of the circular arrangement of their parts, radially symmetrical animals, such as jellyfishes, sea anemones, and sea urchins, do not have distinct front or back ends.

Animals with radial symmetry have several characteristics in common. All of them live in water. Most of them do not move very fast—they either stay in one spot, are moved along by water currents, or creep along the bottom. Few radially symmetrical animals are able to go out in search of prey. Instead, their watery environment carries food to them.

For a water animal that does not actively chase prey, the absence of a front end creates no disadvantage. Animals with radial symmetry learn about their environment primarily through senses of touch and taste, which function on the surfaces of their bodies. Because the animals are able to sense their environment in all directions, they can be ready to grab food coming from any direction.

Figure 9 Sea anemones have radial symmetry. A radially symmetrical object has many lines of symmetry that all go through a central point. *Observing How would you describe the shape of the sea anemone?*

Animals with Bilateral Symmetry Most animals you are familiar with have bilateral symmetry. For example, a fish has only one line of symmetry that divides it into mirror images. Each half of a fish has one eye, one nostril, half of a mouth, and one of each of the fish's pairs of fins. Your body also has bilateral symmetry.

In general, bilaterally symmetrical animals are larger and more complex than those with radial symmetry. Animals with bilateral symmetry have a front end that goes first as the animal moves along. These animals move more quickly and efficiently than most animals with radial symmetry. This is partly because bilateral symmetry allows for a streamlined, balanced body. In addition, most bilaterally symmetrical animals have sense organs in their front ends that pick up information about what is in front of them. Swift movement and sense organs help bilaterally symmetrical animals get food and avoid enemies.

Figure 10 Radially symmetrical animals, like the sea urchin at left, have no distinct front or back ends. In contrast, bilaterally symmetrical animals, like the tiger above, have a front end with sense organs that pick up information. Because of its balanced body plan, a tiger can also move quickly.

Section 2 Review

1. What two types of symmetry do complex animals exhibit? Describe each type.
2. How can bilateral symmetry be an advantage to a predator?
3. Draw a view of a bilaterally symmetrical animal to show its symmetry. Draw the line of symmetry.
4. **Thinking Critically** **Applying Concepts** Which capital letters of the alphabet have bilateral symmetry? Radial symmetry?

Science at Home

With a family member, observe as many different animals as possible in your yard or at a park. Look in lots of different places, such as in the grass, under rocks, and in the air. Explain to your family member the advantage to an animal of having a distinct front end. What is this type of body arrangement called?

A TALE TOLD BY TRACKS

Suppose that, on a chilly winter day, you hike through a park. You suspect that many animals live there, but you don't actually see any of them. Instead, you see signs that the animals have left behind, such as mysterious tracks in the snow. These tracks are evidence you can use to draw inferences about the animals, such as what size they are and what they were doing. Inferences are interpretations of observations that help you to explain what may have happened in a given situation.

Problem

What can you learn about animals by studying their tracks?

Skill Focus

observing, inferring

Procedure

1. Copy the data table into your notebook.
2. The illustration at the top of the next page shows the tracks, or footprints, left in the snow by animals living in a park. The illustration has been divided into three sections. Focus in on the tracks in Section 1.

3. Make two or more observations about the tracks and record them in your data table.
4. For each observation you listed, write one or more inferences that could be drawn from that observation.

DATA TABLE

Section	Observations	Inferences
Section 1		
Section 2		
Section 3		

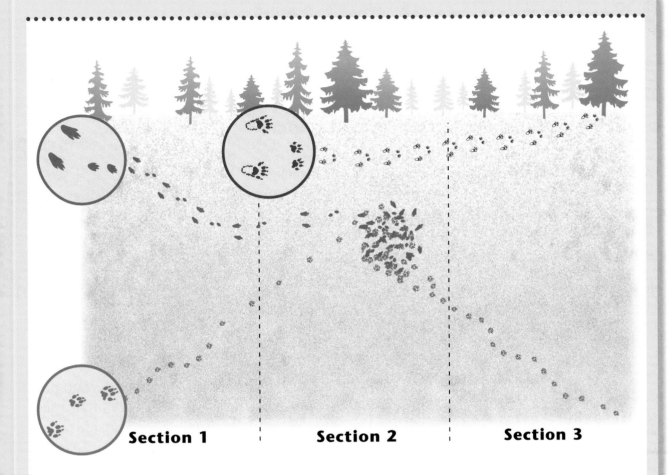

Section 1   **Section 2**   **Section 3**

5. Now look at the tracks in Section 2. Write two or more observations in the data table. For each observation, write one or more inferences.
6. Study the tracks in Section 3. Write two or more observations in the data table. Write at least one inference for each observation.

Analyze and Conclude

1. How many types of animals made the tracks shown in the illustration? Explain.
2. What inferences, if any, can you make about the relative sizes of the animals based on their tracks? Explain.
3. What can you infer about the speed of the animals' movements? Are they walking? Running? How can you tell?

4. In a paragraph, explain what you think happened to the animals and the order in which the events happened.
5. What inference do you feel most confident about and why? Which inference do you feel least confident about and why?
6. **Apply** How might making inferences be important in the work of a real detective? Explain.

More to Explore

Take a walk around your community looking for indirect evidence of animal life such as tracks, feathers, empty nests, and holes in the ground or in dead trees. For each discovery, record its location, at least two observations, and one or more inferences to explain each observation.

Eagerly but carefully, you and the others in your group put on scuba gear, preparing to dive into the ocean and see firsthand what lies beneath the surface. Over the side of the boat you go; the salty ocean water feels cool on your skin. As you slowly descend, you notice that you are surrounded by animals. You see many kinds of fishes, of course, but as you get to the ocean bottom, you notice other animals, too, some as strange as creatures from a science fiction movie. Some of these strange creatures may be sponges.

Sponges live all over the world—mostly in oceans, but also in freshwater rivers and lakes. Sponges are attached to hard surfaces underwater, and they are well adapted to their watery life. Moving currents carry food and oxygen to them, and these same currents take away their waste products. Water plays a role in their reproduction and helps their young find new places to live.

Sponges

Sponges don't look or act like most animals you know. In fact, they are so different that for a long time, people thought that sponges were plants. Like plants, adult sponges stay in one place. But unlike most plants, sponges take food into their bodies, which qualifies them for membership in the animal kingdom. These strange animals have been on Earth for about 540 million years.

◀ **Pink sponges on a Caribbean coral reef**

The bodies of most sponges have irregular shapes, with no symmetry. While some of their cells do specialized jobs, sponges lack the tissues and organs that most other animals have.

The Structure of a Sponge You might use a brightly colored, synthetic sponge to mop up a spill. That sponge is filled with holes, and so are the animals called sponges. **The body of a sponge is something like a bag that is pierced all over with openings called pores.** In fact, the name of the phylum to which sponges belong—phylum Porifera—means "having pores." Notice the many pores in the sponge in *Exploring a Sponge.*

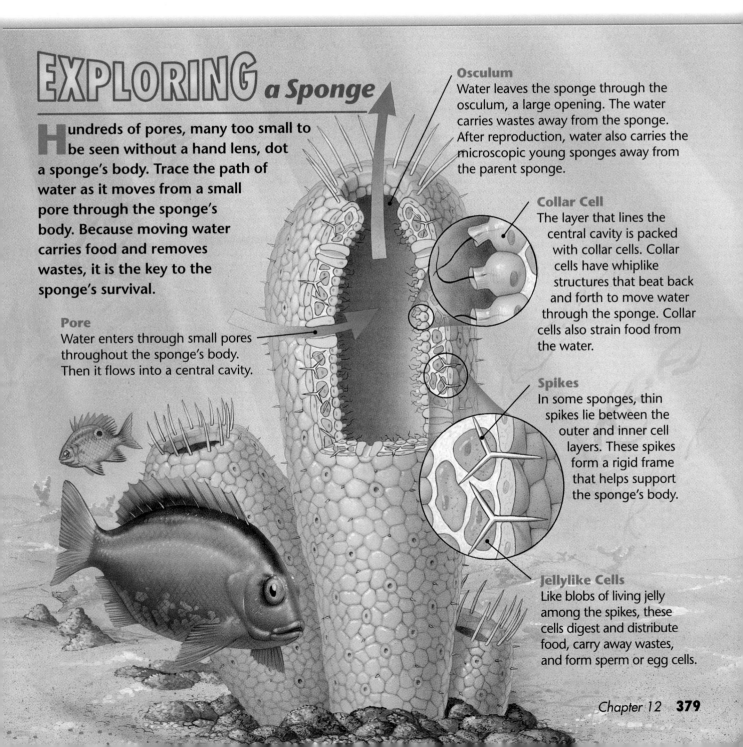

EXPLORING *a Sponge*

Hundreds of pores, many too small to be seen without a hand lens, dot a sponge's body. Trace the path of water as it moves from a small pore through the sponge's body. Because moving water carries food and removes wastes, it is the key to the sponge's survival.

Pore
Water enters through small pores throughout the sponge's body. Then it flows into a central cavity.

Osculum
Water leaves the sponge through the osculum, a large opening. The water carries wastes away from the sponge. After reproduction, water also carries the microscopic young sponges away from the parent sponge.

Collar Cell
The layer that lines the central cavity is packed with collar cells. Collar cells have whiplike structures that beat back and forth to move water through the sponge. Collar cells also strain food from the water.

Spikes
In some sponges, thin spikes lie between the outer and inner cell layers. These spikes form a rigid frame that helps support the sponge's body.

Jellylike Cells
Like blobs of living jelly among the spikes, these cells digest and distribute food, carry away wastes, and form sperm or egg cells.

Getting Food and Oxygen from Water Sponges feed by straining food particles from water. As water enters a sponge, it carries tiny organisms such as bacteria and protists. Collar cells on the inside of the central cavity trap these food particles and digest them. Sponges are very efficient at removing food particles from water. A sponge the size of a teacup is able to remove food from 5,000 liters of water per day. That's enough water to fill a truckload of two-liter soft-drink bottles!

INTEGRATING CHEMISTRY A sponge gets its oxygen from water too. The water contains oxygen, which moves from the water into the sponge's cells in a process known as diffusion. In diffusion, molecules of a substance move from an area in which they are highly concentrated to an area in which they are less concentrated. Oxygen is more highly concentrated in the water than it is in the sponge's cells. So the oxygen moves from the water into the sponge. Diffusion also carries waste products from the sponge's cells into the water.

Spikes The soft bodies of most sponges are supported by a network of spikes. Those spikes can be as sharp as needles, as anyone who has touched a live sponge knows. In addition, many sponges are tougher than wood, and some produce irritating substances. Even so, some fish eat sponges. A sponge dinner is probably like a sandwich made of thorns, sand, and cement, with a little awful-tasting goo mixed in.

Sponge Reproduction Sponges reproduce both asexually and sexually. Budding is one form of asexual reproduction in sponges. In budding, small new sponges grow from the sides of an adult sponge. Eventually these tiny sponges detach and begin life on their own. Sponges reproduce sexually too. Sponges do not have separate sexes—a single sponge forms eggs at one time of the year and sperm at a different time. At any one time of the year, some sponges are producing eggs and others are producing sperm. When a sponge produces sperm, the water currents that move through the sponge carry sperm from the sponge into the open water. The sperm may then enter the pores of another sponge and fertilize egg cells in that sponge.

After fertilization, a larva develops. A **larva** (plural *larvae*) is the immature form of an animal that looks very different from the adult. A sponge larva is a hollow ball of cells that swims through the water. Eventually the larva attaches to a surface and develops into a nonmoving adult sponge.

✓ *Checkpoint* As water flows through a sponge's body, what functions does it enable the sponge to perform?

Cnidarians

Some other organisms you might notice on an underwater dive are jellyfishes, sea anemones, and corals. At first glance, those animals look like they could be creatures from another planet. Most jellyfishes look like transparent bubbles that trail curtains of streamerlike tentacles. Sea anemones look like odd, underwater flowers. Some corals have branches that make them look like trees. Jellyfishes, sea anemones, and corals are **cnidarians** (nih DAIR ee uhnz), animals that have stinging cells and take their food into a hollow central cavity. **Members of the phylum Cnidaria are carnivores that use their stinging cells to capture their prey and defend themselves.** The stinging cells are located on the long, wavy tentacles.

Unlike sponges, cnidarians have specialized tissues. For example, because of muscle-like tissues, many cnidarians can move in interesting ways. Jellyfishes swim through the water, and hydras turn slow somersaults. Anemones stretch out, shrink down, and bend slowly from side to side. These movements are directed by nerve cells that are spread out like a spider web, or net. This nerve net helps the cnidarian respond quickly to danger or the presence of food.

Cnidarian Body Plans Cnidarians have two different body plans, both with radial symmetry. As you read about these two body plans, refer to Figure 12. A **polyp** (PAHL ip), such as a hydra, sea anemone, or coral, is shaped something like a vase, with the mouth opening at the top. Most polyps do not move around; they are adapted for a life attached to an underwater surface. In contrast, the bowl-shaped

Figure 11 All cnidarians live in watery environments. **A.** Hydras live in freshwater ponds and lakes, where they reproduce by budding. **B.** The Portuguese man-of-war is actually a colony of cnidarians living together. **C.** Sea anemones are large cnidarians that often live in groups in the ocean. *Comparing and Contrasting What characteristics do these three cnidarians share?*

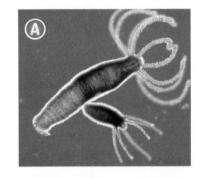

Hydra Doing?

In this activity, you will observe hydras in action. **ACTIVITY**

1. 🖱 Put a drop of water that contains hydras in a small unbreakable bowl or petri dish. Allow it to sit for about 15 minutes.

2. Use a hand lens to examine the hydras as they swim. Then gently touch the tentacles of a hydra with the end of a toothpick. Watch what happens.

3. Return the hydras to your teacher, and wash your hands.

Classifying Is a hydra a polyp or a medusa? Describe its method of movement.

medusa (muh DOO suh), such as a jellyfish, is adapted for a free-swimming life. Medusas, unlike polyps, have mouths that open downward. Some cnidarians go through both a polyp stage and a medusa stage during their lives. Others are polyps or medusas for their whole lives.

How Cnidarians Feed A cnidarian captures its prey by using its stinging cells to inject venom, a poisonous substance that paralyzes fish and other prey. Then the cnidarian's tentacles pull the prey animal to its mouth. From there the food passes into a body cavity where it is digested. Because cnidarians have a digestive system with only one opening, undigested food is expelled through the mouth.

Cnidarian Reproduction Cnidarians reproduce both asexually and sexually. For polyps, such as the hydra in Figure 11, budding is the most common form of asexual reproduction. Amazingly, in some polyps the entire animal splits into pieces. Each piece then forms a new polyp. Both kinds of asexual reproduction allow the numbers of cnidarians to increase rapidly in a short time.

Sexual reproduction in cnidarians occurs in a variety of ways. Some species of cnidarians have both sexes within one individual. In others, the sexes are in separate individuals, as in humans.

☑ *Checkpoint* How does a cnidarian obtain and digest food?

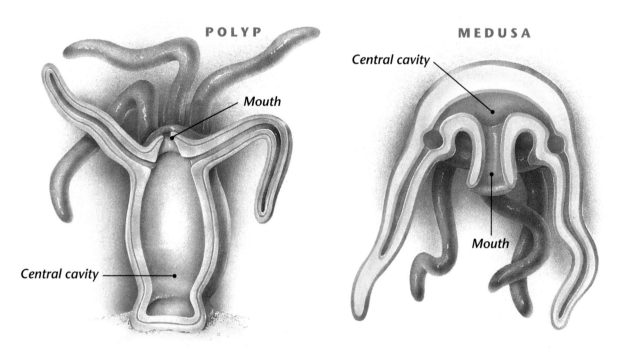

POLYP

MEDUSA

Mouth

Central cavity

Central cavity

Mouth

Figure 12 Cnidarians have two basic body forms, the vase-shaped polyp and the bowl-shaped medusa. *Comparing and Contrasting Contrast the location of the mouth in the polyp and the medusa.*

Life on a Coral Reef

In some warm, shallow ocean waters, just below the surface, you can find one of the most diverse ocean environments—a coral reef. Coral reefs seem to be made of stone. But in fact, coral reefs are built by cnidarians. At the beginning of its life, a free-swimming coral larva attaches to a solid surface. A broken shell, a sunken ship, or the skeleton of a once-living coral animal will do just fine.

The coral polyp reproduces asexually, and then its offspring reproduce asexually, too. The coral polyp then produces a hard, stony skeleton around its soft polyp body. Over time, that polyp may give rise to thousands of polyps, each with a hard skeleton. When the coral polyps die, their skeletons remain behind. Over thousands of years, as live corals add their skeletons to those that have died, rocklike masses called reefs grow up from the sea floor. Coral reefs can become enormous. The Great Barrier Reef off the coast of Australia is about 2,000 kilometers long.

Coral reefs, like the one in Figure 13, are home to more species of fishes and invertebrates than any other environment on Earth. Hundreds of sponge species live among the corals, constantly filtering water through their bodies. Worms burrow into the coral reef. Giant clams lie with their huge shells slightly open. Shrimp and crabs edge out of hiding places below the corals. At night, bright blue damsel fish settle into pockets in the coral. At dawn and dusk, sea turtles, sea snakes, and sharks all visit the reef, hunting for prey. These living things interact in complex ways,

Figure 13 Coral reefs provide homes and hunting grounds for a vast variety of sea animals. The bottom photo is a close-up of a group of individual coral polyps.

Section 3 Review

1. Describe the structure of a sponge's body.
2. Explain how cnidarians capture prey and defend themselves. In your explanation, refer to specific body structures.
3. Draw a diagram to show how water travels through a sponge. Show the path with an arrow.
4. **Thinking Critically** **Classifying** Why is a sponge classified as an animal?

Check Your Progress CHAPTER PROJECT
You should be observing your animal every day and writing your observations in your journal. Record how the animal looks, feeds, and behaves. Note any changes in the animal. Talk to your teacher before making any changes to your animal's home, feeding schedule, or other living conditions.

Coral Reefs in Danger

Coral reefs off the coasts of many nations are endangered, damaged, or threatened with destruction. Reefs house and protect many species of sea animals, including sponges, shrimp, sea turtles, and fishes. In addition, reefs protect coastlines from floods caused by ocean storms.

Although coral reefs are hard as rocks, the coral animals themselves are quite delicate. Recreational divers can damage the fragile reefs. Is it possible to protect the reefs while still allowing divers to explore them?

The Issues

What's the Harm in Diving? About 3.5 million recreational divers live in the United States. With so many divers it is hard to guarantee that no harm will occur to the coral reefs. In fact, divers can cause significant damage by standing on or even touching these fragile reefs. Carelessly dropping a boat anchor can crush part of a reef. Although most divers are careful, not all are, and accidents can always happen.

Harm to the reefs is even more likely to occur when divers collect coral for their own enjoyment or to sell for profit. You can see brightly colored coral from the sea in jewelry and in decorations.

Should Reefs Be Further Protected? The United States government has passed laws making it illegal, under most circumstances, to remove coral from the sea. Because a few divers break these laws, some people want to ban diving altogether. However, many divers say it's unfair to ban diving just because of a few lawbreakers.

Many divers consider coral reefs the most exciting and beautiful places in the ocean to explore. As recreational divers, photographers, scientists, and others visit and learn more about these delicate coral reefs, they increase their own and other's awareness of them. Public awareness may be the best way to ensure that these rich environments are protected.

More Than a Diving Issue Coral reefs in the Western Atlantic—such as those in Bermuda, the Bahamas, the Caribbean Islands, and Florida—are major tourist attractions that bring money and jobs to people in local communities. If diving were banned, local businesses would suffer significantly. Also, although divers can harm coral reefs, other human activities, such as ocean pollution, oil spills, and fishing nets, can also cause harm. In addition, natural events, such as tropical storms, changes in sea level, and changes in sea temperature, can also damage the fragile reefs.

You Decide

1. Identify the Problem

In your own words, explain the controversy surrounding diving near coral reefs.

2. Analyze the Options

List the arguments on each side of the issue. Note the pros and cons. How well would each position protect the reefs? Who might be harmed or inconvenienced?

3. Find a Solution

Write a newspaper editorial stating your position on whether diving should be allowed near coral reefs. State your position and reasons clearly.

SECTION
④ Worms

What Can You Learn About a Flatworm by Looking at It?

1. Your teacher will give you a planarian, a kind of flatworm. Pick the worm up with the tip of a small paintbrush. Place it carefully in a small, transparent container. Use a dropper to cover the planarian with spring water.

2. Observe the planarian with a hand lens for a few minutes. Look for a head and tail region. Look for two spots in the head region. Draw a picture of the planarian.

3. Observe and describe how the planarian moves.

4. Gently touch the planarian with a toothpick and observe how it behaves. Then return the planarian to your teacher, and wash your hands.

Think It Over
Observing What are some ways in which a planarian is different from a sponge?

You might think that all worms are small, slimy, and wriggly. But many worms do not fit that description. Some worms are almost three meters long and are as thick as your arm. Others look like glowing, furry blobs. Worms can flutter and glide or climb around with paddle-like bristles. Still others are very small and live in white tubes cemented to rocks.

What Worms Have in Common

It's hard to say exactly what worms are, because there are many kinds of worms, all with their own characteristics. **Biologists classify worms into several phyla—the three major ones are flatworms, roundworms, and segmented worms.** Flatworms belong to the phylum Platyhelminthes (plat ee HEL minth eez);

GUIDE FOR READING

◆ What are the three main groups of worms?

◆ What are the characteristics of each group of worms?

Reading Tip As you read, list the characteristics of flatworms, roundworms, and segmented worms.

Figure 14 The ocean flatworm, left, and the segmented Christmas tree worm, right, show some of the wide variety of ocean worms.

Figure 15 As you can tell from this spectacular spaghetti worm, not all worms are gray and tube shaped.

roundworms belong to the phylum Nematoda; segmented worms belong to the phylum Annelida.

All worms have some characteristics in common. All worms are invertebrates, and they all have long, narrow bodies without legs. In addition, all worms have tissues, organs, and organ systems. Also, all worms have bilateral symmetry. Unlike sponges or cnidarians, worms have head and tail ends.

Worms are the simplest organisms with a brain, which is a knot of nerve tissue located in the head end. Because a worm's brain and some of its sense organs are located in its head end, the worm can detect objects, food, mates, and predators quickly, and it can respond quickly, too. Sense organs, such as organs sensitive to light and touch, pick up information from the environment. The brain interprets that information and directs the animal's response. For example, if an earthworm on the surface of the ground senses a footstep, the worm will quickly return to its underground burrow.

Both sexual and asexual reproduction are found in the worm phyla. In many species of worms, there are separate male and female animals, as in humans. In other species each individual has both male and female sex organs. A worm with both sexes does not usually fertilize its own eggs. Instead, two worms mate and exchange sperm. Many worms reproduce asexually by methods such as breaking into pieces. In fact, if you cut some kinds of worms into several pieces, a whole new worm will grow from each piece. Earthworms cannot do this, but if you cut off the tail end of an earthworm, the front end will probably grow a new tail. This ability to regrow body parts is called **regeneration.**

✓ *Checkpoint* *What type of symmetry do worms exhibit?*

Flatworms

As you'd expect from their name, flatworms are flat. The bodies of flatworms, such as planarians, flukes, and tapeworms, are soft as jelly. Although tapeworms can grow to be 10 to 12 meters long, other flatworms are almost too small to be seen.

Most flatworms are parasites that obtain their food from their hosts. Instead of living on its own, a **parasite** is an organism that lives inside or on another organism. The parasite takes its food from the organism in or on which it lives, called the **host.** Parasites may rob their hosts of food and make them weak. They may injure the host's tissues or organs. Sometimes a parasite will kill its host, but usually the host survives.

Tapeworms Tapeworms are one kind of parasitic flatworm. A tapeworm's body is adapted to absorbing food from the host's digestive system. Some kinds of tapeworms can live in human hosts. Many tapeworms live in more than one host during their lifetime. Notice that in *Exploring the Life Cycle of a Dog Tapeworm*, the tapeworm has two different hosts—a rabbit and a dog.

EXPLORING the Life Cycle of a Dog Tapeworm

As an adult, the tapeworm lives in the digestive tract of a dog. The tapeworm has no mouth or digestive system; instead, it absorbs food directly through its body wall.

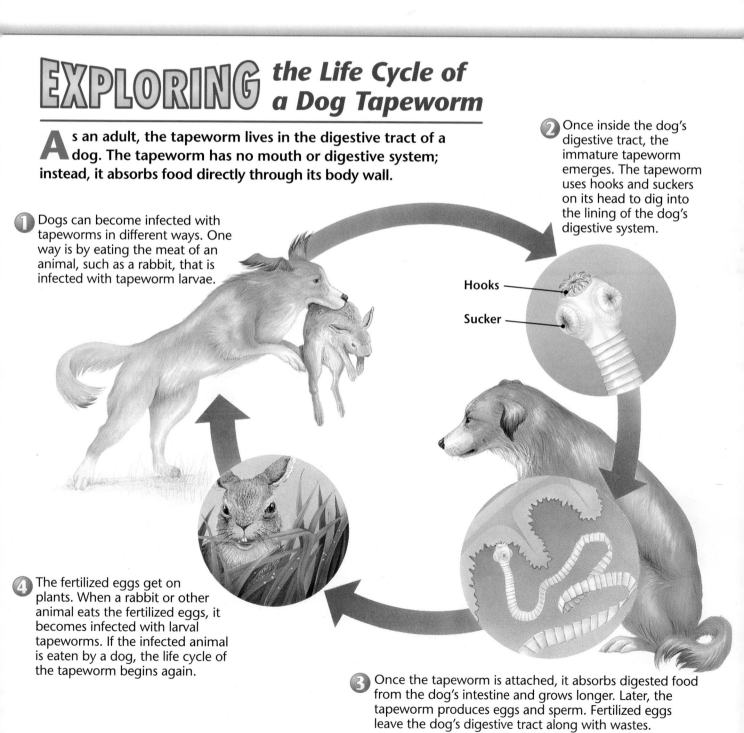

1 Dogs can become infected with tapeworms in different ways. One way is by eating the meat of an animal, such as a rabbit, that is infected with tapeworm larvae.

2 Once inside the dog's digestive tract, the immature tapeworm emerges. The tapeworm uses hooks and suckers on its head to dig into the lining of the dog's digestive system.

Hooks

Sucker

4 The fertilized eggs get on plants. When a rabbit or other animal eats the fertilized eggs, it becomes infected with larval tapeworms. If the infected animal is eaten by a dog, the life cycle of the tapeworm begins again.

3 Once the tapeworm is attached, it absorbs digested food from the dog's intestine and grows longer. Later, the tapeworm produces eggs and sperm. Fertilized eggs leave the dog's digestive tract along with wastes.

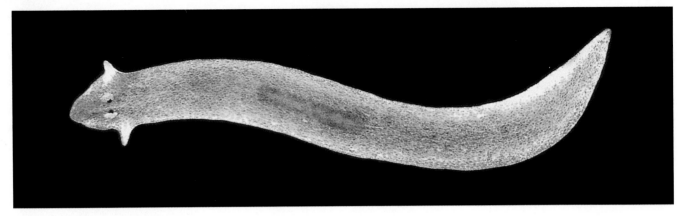

Figure 16 Planarians are flatworms that live in ponds, streams, and oceans. The eyespots on the planarian's head can distinguish between light and dark. *Inferring How is having a distinct head end an advantage to a planarian?*

Planarians Some flatworms are nonparasitic, or free-living. Unlike parasites, free-living organisms do not live in or on other organisms. Small free-living flatworms glide over the rocks in ponds, slide over damp soil, or swim slowly through the oceans like ruffled, brightly patterned leaves.

Planarians, such as the one in Figure 16, are scavengers—they feed on dead or decaying material. But they are also predators and will attack any animal smaller than they are.

If you look at a planarian's head, you can see two big dots that look like eyes. These dots are called eyespots, and they function something like eyes, although they cannot see a specific image like human eyes can. A planarian's head also has cells that pick up odors. Planarians rely mainly on smell to locate food. When a planarian smells food, it moves toward the food and glides onto it.

A planarian feeds like a vacuum cleaner. The planarian inserts a feeding tube into its food. Digestive juices flow out into the food, where they begin to break down the food while it is still outside the worm's body. Then the planarian sucks up the partly-digested bits of food. Digestion is then completed within a cavity inside the planarian. Food is distributed to body cells by diffusion. Like cnidarians, planarians have one opening in their digestive system. Undigested wastes exit through the feeding tube.

Roundworms

The next time you walk along a beach, consider that about a million roundworms live in each square meter of damp sand. Roundworms can live in nearly any moist environment—including forest soils, Antarctic sands, and even pools of super-hot water. Most are tiny and hard to see, but roundworms may be the most abundant animals on Earth.

Unlike flatworms, roundworms have cylindrical bodies. As you can see in Figure 17, they look like tiny strands of cooked spaghetti that are pointed at each end. If you look at roundworms under a microscope, you'd see their bodies thrashing from side to side.

Figure 17 The transparent bodies of these roundworms have been stained for better viewing under a microscope.

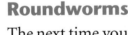

While many roundworms are carnivores or herbivores, others are parasites. Have you given worm medicine to a pet dog or cat? The medicine was probably meant to kill roundworm parasites, such as hookworms.

Unlike cnidarians or flatworms, roundworms have a digestive system that is like a tube, open at both ends. Food enters at the animal's mouth and wastes exit through an opening, called the **anus,** at the far end of the tube. Food travels in one direction through the roundworm's digestive system, as it does in most complex animals.

A one-way digestive system has certain advantages. It is something like an assembly line, with a different part of the digestive process happening at each place along the line. Digestion happens in orderly stages. First food is broken down by digestive juices.Then the digested food is absorbed into the animal's body. Finally wastes are eliminated. The advantage of this type of digestive process is that it enables the animal's body to use foods efficiently, by enabling it to absorb a large amount of the needed substances in foods.

☑ *Checkpoint You are using a microscope to look at a tiny worm. What would you look for to tell whether it is a roundworm?*

Segmented Worms

If you have ever dug in a garden in the spring, you have probably seen earthworms wriggling through the moist soil. Those familiar soil inhabitants are segmented worms. So are the exotic sea-floor worms that you see in Figure 18. Parasitic blood-sucking leeches are also segmented worms. Since their bodies are long and narrow, some segmented worms look a bit like flatworms and roundworms. But segmented worms may be more closely related to crabs and snails.

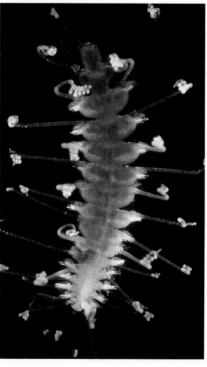

Figure 18 These segmented sea-floor worms belong to the same phylum as earthworms.

Segmented worms occupy nearly all environments, and most live in burrows or tubes. The burrow helps the worm hide both from possible predators and from possible prey. Many segmented worms that live in water are sit-and-wait predators. They leap out of their burrows to attack their prey.

Segmentation When you look at an earthworm, you notice that its body seems to consist of a series of rings separated by grooves, something like a vacuum-cleaner hose. **Earthworms and other segmented worms have bodies made up of many linked sections called segments.** An earthworm usually has more than 100 segments. On the outside, the segments look nearly identical. On the inside, some organs are repeated in most segments. For example, each segment has tubes that remove wastes. Other organs, however, such as the worm's reproductive organs, are found only in some segments. Nerve cords and a digestive tube run along the length of the worm's body. Like roundworms, earthworms have a one-way digestive system with two openings.

A Closed Circulatory System Segmented worms have a closed circulatory system. In a closed circulatory system, like your own, blood moves only within a connected network of tubes called blood vessels. In contrast, some animals, such as insects, have an open circulatory system in which blood leaves the blood vessels and sloshes around inside the body. A closed circulatory system can move blood around an animal's body much more quickly than an open circulatory system can. Blood quickly carries oxygen and food to cells. Because of this, an animal with a closed circulatory system can be larger and more active than one with an open circulatory system.

A long blood vessel runs along the top of the earthworm's body. That blood vessel pumps blood through five arches, as shown in Figure 19. From the arches, the blood passes into a blood vessel that runs along the lower part of the earthworm.

Figure 19 An earthworm's body is divided into over 100 segments. Some organs are repeated in most of those segments; others exist in only a few. *Interpreting Diagrams How does blood move through an earthworm's body?*

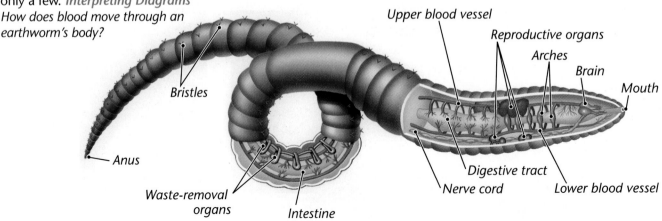

Upper blood vessel

Reproductive organs

Arches

Brain

Mouth

Bristles

Anus

Waste-removal organs

Intestine

Nerve cord

Digestive tract

Lower blood vessel

How Earthworms Live Earthworms tunnel for a living. They are scavengers that eat decayed plant and animal remains in the soil. On damp nights earthworms come up out of their burrows. They crawl on the surface of the ground, seeking leaves and soft fruits to drag underground and eat.

Night is a safe time for an earthworm to crawl on the surface, because many worm predators are asleep then. At night the air is damp, and this dampness helps keep the worm's skin moist. If a worm dries out, it will die, because it obtains oxygen through moisture on its skin.

Well-developed muscles let an earthworm move through its burrow. Stiff bristles stick out from each of the worm's segments. To crawl forward, an earthworm sticks its bristles in the ground and pulls itself along, much as a mountain climber uses an ice ax. Mountain climbers drive ice axes into a slippery slope and then pull themselves up.

Earthworms and Soil Earthworms are among the most **INTEGRATING EARTH SCIENCE** helpful inhabitants of garden and farm soil. They benefit people by improving the soil in which plants grow. Earthworm droppings make the soil more fertile. Earthworm tunnels loosen the soil and allow air, water, and plant roots to move through it. You have probably seen an earthworm tunnel entrance without realizing what it was—they are extremely common in lawns. To find one, look for a small, round hole in the ground with little lumps of soil next to it.

Section 4 Review

1. List the three major phyla of worms and give an example of each.
2. How does a dog tapeworm obtain its food?
3. Contrast a roundworm's digestive system to that of a planarian.
4. Describe the structure of an earthworm's body.
5. **Thinking Critically** Relating Cause and Effect If a dog is kept on a leash whenever it is outside, is it likely to get a tapeworm? Explain.

Check Your Progress
CHAPTER PROJECT
Begin to analyze what you have learned about your animal from your observations. Did you see a daily pattern to the animal's behavior? Think about what each kind of behavior accomplishes—whether it helps the animal obtain food or escape from danger, for example. Choose how you are going to present what you have learned—a written report, a talk, captioned illustrations, or some other method. Prepare charts or other visual aids.

Earthworm Responses

I n this lab, you will practice the skill of making hypotheses to learn more about earthworms.

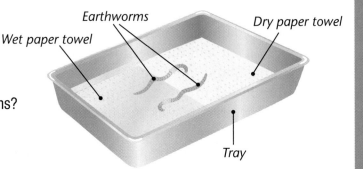

Earthworms

Wet paper towel

Dry paper towel

Tray

Problem

Do earthworms prefer dry or moist conditions? Do they prefer light or dark conditions?

Materials

plastic dropper	water	cardboard
clock or watch	paper towels	flashlight
2 earthworms	storage container	tray

Procedure

1. Which environment do you think earthworms prefer—dry or moist? Record your hypothesis in your notebook.
2. Use the dropper to sprinkle water on the worms. Keep the worms moist at all times.
3. Fold a dry paper towel and place it on the bottom of one side of your tray. Fold a moistened paper towel and place it on the other side.
4. Moisten your hands. Then place the earthworms in the center of the tray. Make sure that half of each earthworm's body rests on the moist paper towel and half rests on the dry towel. Handle the worms gently.
5. Cover the tray with the piece of cardboard. After five minutes, remove the cardboard and observe whether the worms are on the moist or dry surface. Record your observations.
6. Repeat Steps 4 and 5.
7. Return the earthworms to their storage container. Moisten the earthworms with water.
8. Which do you think earthworms prefer—strong light or darkness? Record your hypothesis in your notebook.

9. Cover the whole surface of the tray with a moistened paper towel.
10. Place the earthworms in the center of the tray. Cover half of the tray with cardboard. Shine a flashlight onto the other half.
11. After five minutes, note the locations of the worms. Record your observations.
12. Repeat Steps 10 and 11.
13. Moisten the earthworms and put them in the location designated by your teacher. Wash your hands after handling the worms.

Analyze and Conclude

1. Which environment did the worms prefer—moist or dry? Bright or dark? Did the worms' behavior support your hypotheses?
2. Use what you know about earthworms to explain how their responses to moisture and light help them survive.
3. **Think About It** What knowledge or experiences helped you make your hypotheses at the start of the experiments?

Design an Experiment

Do earthworms prefer a smooth or rough surface? Write your hypothesis. Then design an experiment to answer the question. Check with your teacher before carrying out your experiment.

SECTION 1 — What Is an Animal?

Key Ideas

- Animals are multicellular organisms that obtain food by eating other organisms. Animals can move. Most reproduce sexually.
- Animals need water, food, and oxygen to survive. Some animals are carnivores, or meat eaters. Others are herbivores, or plant eaters. Omnivores eat both plants and animals.
- When biologists classify an animal, they look at the structure of its body, its DNA, and the way its embryo develops. Some animals are vertebrates; most animal species are invertebrates.

Key Terms

species	heterotroph
autotroph	sexual reproduction
fertilization	asexual reproduction
adaptation	herbivore
carnivore	predator
prey	omnivore
phylum	invertebrate
vertebrate	

SECTION 2 — Symmetry

INTEGRATING **MATHEMATICS**

Key Ideas

- The bodies of complex animals all have either radial or bilateral symmetry.
- Animals with radial symmetry have body parts arranged around a central point. They do not have distinct front ends.
- Animals with bilateral symmetry have one line that divides them into two mirror images. These animals, which usually have a distinct front end, are generally more complex than radially symmetrical animals.

Key Terms
bilateral symmetry
radial symmetry

SECTION 3 — Sponges and Cnidarians

Key Ideas

- A sponge obtains food by straining water taken in through its pores. Sponges have no tissues or organs.
- Cnidarians, which include jellyfishes and hydras, are carnivores with stinging cells that help capture prey. Cnidarians have two body plans—polyp and medusa.
- Corals are cnidarians with hard skeletons around their soft bodies. Over time, the skeletons of corals form coral reefs.

Key Terms
larva
cnidarian
polyp
medusa

SECTION 4 — Worms

Key Ideas

- The three major worm phyla are flatworms, roundworms, and segmented worms.
- Most flatworms are parasites that obtain food from their hosts. Planarians are nonparasitic flatworms.
- Roundworms have a digestive system that is a tube open at both ends.
- Segmented worms have bodies made up of many segments. Segmented worms have a closed circulatory system in which blood is contained in blood vessels.
- Earthworms help farmers and gardeners by loosening and fertilizing the soil.

Key Terms

regeneration	parasite	host
anus		

USING THE INTERNET ACTIVITY

www.science-explorer.phschool.com

California Test Prep: Reviewing Content

Multiple Choice

Choose the letter of the best answer.

1. Organisms that make their own food are called
   a. omnivores.
   b. autotrophs.
   c. heterotrophs.
   d. carnivores.

2. Which of the following is *not* one of the major characteristics that biologists use to classify an animal?
   a. the structure of its body
   b. its height or length
   c. the development of its embryo
   d. its DNA

3. An animal with many lines of symmetry
   a. is bilaterally symmetrical.
   b. is radially symmetrical.
   c. has no symmetry.
   d. has line symmetry.

4. Which animal is a medusa?
   a. coral
   b. jellyfish
   c. planarian
   d. sea anemone

5. Which animal has a one-way digestive system?
   a. earthworm
   b. planarian
   c. sponge
   d. jellyfish

True or False

If the statement is true, write true. If it is false, change the underlined word or words to make the statement true.

6. <u>All</u> animals are made up of many cells.

7. <u>Sexual</u> reproduction produces offspring that are not exactly like either parent.

8. Fish have <u>radial symmetry</u>.

9. The bodies of <u>cnidarians</u> contain many pores.

10. The bodies of <u>roundworms</u> are segmented.

Checking Concepts

11. Explain the relationship among cells, tissues, and organs.

12. An oxygen molecule has just passed into a sponge's cell. Describe how it got there.

13. Compare a medusa and a polyp.

14. Are humans parasitic or free-living animals? Explain.

15. You dig up a handful of damp soil from the forest and examine it with a microscope. What kind of animal would probably be there in the greatest numbers? Explain.

16. **Writing to Learn** You are a small fish visiting a coral reef for the first time. What interesting sights would you see? Are there dangers to watch out for? In a paragraph, describe your adventures at the coral reef.

Thinking Visually

17. **Flowchart** The partially completed flowchart below shows how water travels through a sponge. Copy the flowchart onto a separate sheet of paper. Then complete it and add a title. (For more on flowcharts, see the Skills Handbook.)

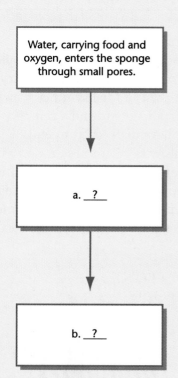

Water, carrying food and oxygen, enters the sponge through small pores.

↓

a. ___?___

↓

b. ___?___

Test Prep: Skills

A scientist used a pesticide on one field and left a nearby field untreated. Next, she marked off five plots of equal size in each field. Then she dug up a cubic meter of soil beneath each plot, and counted the earthworms in the soil. The table below shows her data. Use the table to answer Questions 18–20.

Field with Pesticide		Untreated Field	
Plot	Worms per cubic meter	Plot	Worms per cubic meter
A	730	F	901
B	254	G	620
C	319	H	811
D	428	I	576
E	451	J	704

18. **Controlling Variables** Identify the manipulated and responding variables in this experiment.

19. **Calculating** Calculate the average number of worms per cubic meter in the treated field. Then do the same for the untreated field.

20. **Drawing Conclusions** How did this pesticide affect the population of worms in the soil?

Thinking Critically

21. **Comparing and Contrasting** Compare the ways in which a sponge, a planarian, and a roundworm digest their food.

22. **Predicting** The sand in a desert is bright orange. What color would sit-and-wait predators in that desert probably be? Explain.

23. **Relating Cause and Effect** If a pesticide killed off many of the earthworms in a garden, how might that affect the plants growing in that soil?

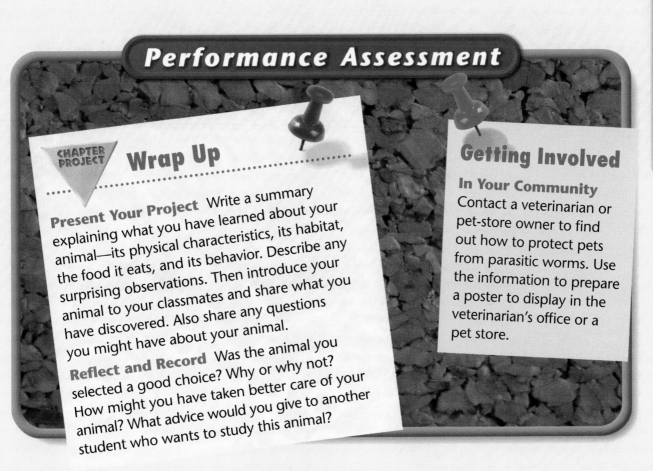

Performance Assessment

CHAPTER PROJECT Wrap Up

Present Your Project Write a summary explaining what you have learned about your animal—its physical characteristics, its habitat, the food it eats, and its behavior. Describe any surprising observations. Then introduce your animal to your classmates and share what you have discovered. Also share any questions you might have about your animal.

Reflect and Record Was the animal you selected a good choice? Why or why not? How might you have taken better care of your animal? What advice would you give to another student who wants to study this animal?

Getting Involved

In Your Community
Contact a veterinarian or pet-store owner to find out how to protect pets from parasitic worms. Use the information to prepare a poster to display in the veterinarian's office or a pet store.

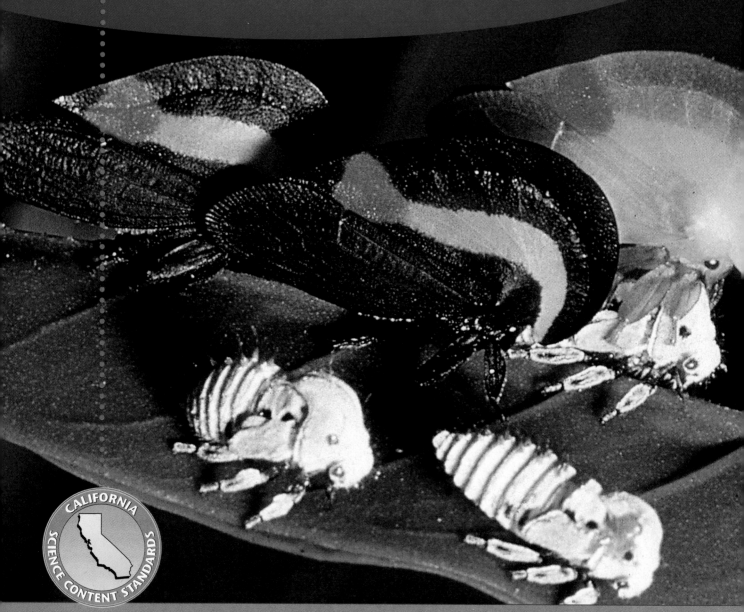

The following California Science Content Standards are addressed in this chapter:

1. All living organisms are composed of cells, from just one to many trillions, whose details usually are visible only through a microscope.

   f. As multicellular organisms develop, their cells differentiate.

2. A typical cell of any organism contains genetic instructions that specify its traits. Those traits may be modified by environmental influences.

   a. The differences between the life cycles and reproduction of sexual and asexual organisms.

3. Biological evolution accounts for the diversity of species developed through gradual processes over many generations.

   a. Both genetic variation and environmental factors are causes of evolution and diversity of organisms.

Going Through Changes

Look at the changes a treehopper insect goes through in its lifetime! In its white nymph stage, it doesn't look anything like an adult treehopper. Most of the animals you will read about in this chapter also change their form during their life cycles. In this project, you will view these kinds of changes firsthand as you observe mealworm development.

Your Goal To observe how different conditions affect mealworm development.

To complete this project successfully, you must

◆ compare mealworm development under two different conditions

◆ record your mealworm observations daily for several weeks

◆ draw conclusions about the effects of those conditions on development

◆ follow the safety guidelines in Appendix A

Get Started Find two containers, such as clean margarine tubs with lids, in which to keep the mealworms. Get some mealworm food, such as cornflakes, and a plastic spoon to transfer the food and count the mealworms. Choose two conditions, such as two different temperatures or food sources, and plan how to test the two conditions.

Check Your Progress You'll be working on this project as you study this chapter. To keep your project on track, look for Check Your Progress boxes at the following points.

Section 2 Review, page 411: Record your daily observations.
Section 3 Review, page 417: Sketch the stages of development.
Section 5 Review, page 426: Draw conclusions about mealworm development under each of the conditions.

Wrap Up At the end of the chapter (page 429), you will report on your results.

Treehoppers undergo dramatic changes in form during their lives. The whitish nymphs gradually turn into light green young adults. The young adults gradually change into dark green mature adults.

4. Evidence from rocks allows us to understand the evolution of life on Earth.

   e. Fossils provide evidence of how life and environmental conditions have changed.

5. The anatomy and physiology of plants and animals illustrate the complementary nature of structure and function.

a. Plants and animals have levels of organization for structure and function, including cells, tissues, organs, organ systems, and the whole organism.

b. Organ systems function because of the contributions of individual organs, tissues, and cells. The failure of any part can affect the entire system.

7. Scientific progress is made by asking meaningful questions and conducting careful investigations.

c. Communicate the logical connectio among hypothesis, science concepts tests conducted, data collected, and conclusions drawn from the scientif evidence.

DISCOVER
ACTIVITY

How Can You Classify Shells?

1. Obtain an assortment of shells from your teacher. Examine each one carefully. Look at the shells and feel their surfaces.

2. Compare the outer surface of each shell to the inner surface.

3. Classify the shells into two or more groups based on the characteristics you observe.

Think It Over
Inferring How might it help an animal to have a shell?

GUIDE FOR READING

◆ What are the main characteristics of mollusks?

◆ What are the major groups of mollusks?

Reading Tip As you read, make a compare/contrast table to distinguish among the different mollusk groups.

From the shells of clams, Native Americans in the North-east carved purple and white beads called wampum. They wove these beads into belts with complex designs that often had special, solemn significance. A wampum belt might record a group's history. When warring groups made peace, they exchanged weavings made of wampum. Iroquois women would honor a new chief with gifts of wampum strings.

The hard shells of clams provided the material for wampum, and the soft bodies within the shells were a major source of food for Native Americans who lived along the seacoast. Today, clams and similar animals, such as scallops and oysters, are still valuable sources of food for people in many parts of the world.

What Are Mollusks?

Clams, oysters, and scallops are all mollusks (phylum Mollusca). So are snails and octopuses. **Mollusks** are invertebrates with soft, unsegmented bodies that are often protected by hard outer shells. **In addition to soft bodies often covered with shells, mollusks have a thin layer of tissue called a mantle that covers their internal organs.** The mantle also produces the mollusk's shell. Most mollusks move with a muscular structure called a foot. The feet of different kinds of mollusks are adapted for various uses, such as crawling, digging, or catching prey.

Mollusks live nearly everywhere on Earth. Most live in water, from mountain streams to the deep ocean, but some live on land, usually in damp places.

▼ Wampum string and clamshell

Figure 1 Some mollusks, like the chambered nautilus, left, are protected by shells. Other mollusks, like the nudibranch, right, do not have shells. *Classifying What characteristics do these two organisms share?*

Like segmented worms, mollusks have bilateral symmetry. However, unlike segmented worms, the body parts of mollusks are not repeated. Instead, their internal organs, such as the stomach and reproductive organs, are all located together in one area. A mollusk's internal organs include a pair of **kidneys**, organs that remove the wastes produced by an animal's cells.

Most water-dwelling mollusks have **gills**, organs that remove oxygen from water. The gills are attached to the mantle and have a rich supply of blood vessels. Within these thin-walled blood vessels, oxygen from the surrounding water diffuses into the blood, while carbon dioxide diffuses out. The gills of most mollusks are covered by tiny, hairlike structures called cilia. The beating movement of these cilia makes water flow over the gills.

Many mollusks have an organ called a **radula** (RAJ oo luh) (plural *radulae*), which is a flexible ribbon of tiny teeth. Acting like sandpaper, the tiny teeth scrape food from a surface such as a leaf. A radula may have as many as 250,000 teeth. Biologists use the arrangement of teeth in the radula to help classify mollusks.

 Checkpoint How is the body structure of a mollusk different from that of a segmented worm?

Evidence of Early Mollusks

INTEGRATING EARTH SCIENCE Mollusks were living in Earth's oceans about 540 million years ago. Much evidence for this comes from fossil shells in limestone rocks. Some kinds of limestone are partially made from the shells of ancient, ocean-dwelling mollusks. After the mollusks died, their shells were broken into tiny pieces by waves and water currents. These shell pieces, along with the hard remains of other organisms, piled up on the ocean floor. These hard materials then underwent a chemical change in which they became cemented together to form limestone. During this process, some shells—or parts of shells—remained unbroken and eventually became fossils.

Snails and Their Relatives

Biologists classify mollusks into groups based on physical characteristics such as the presence of a shell, the type of shell, the type of foot, the arrangement of teeth in the radula, and the complexity of the nervous system. **The three major groups of mollusks are gastropods, bivalves, and cephalopods.**

The most numerous mollusks are the gastropods. **Gastropods**, which include snails and slugs, are mollusks that have a single shell or no shell at all. Most snails have a single, coiled shell, while many slugs have no shell. Gastropods usually creep along on a broad foot. Gastropods get their name, which means "stomach foot," from the fact that most of them have their foot on the same side of their body as their stomach. To learn more about the body of a gastropod, look at *Exploring a Snail.*

You can find gastropods nearly everywhere on Earth. They live in oceans, on rocky shores, in fresh water, and on dry land, too. Some snails even live in treetops.

Some gastropods are herbivores, while others are scavengers that feed on decaying material. Still others are carnivores. For example, the oyster drill is a snail that makes a hole in an oyster's shell by releasing acid and then boring a hole with its radula. The oyster drill then scrapes away the oyster's soft body.

Many snails have a tight-fitting plate or trapdoor on their foot that fits securely into the opening of their shell. When this kind of snail is threatened by a predator, it withdraws into its shell and tightly closes its trapdoor. Snails also pull back into their shells when conditions are dry and then come out when conditions are moist again. When they are sealed up in this way, gastropods can survive incredibly long times. In one museum the shells of two land snails, presumed to be dead, were glued to a piece of cardboard. Four years later, when someone put the cardboard in water, one of the snails crawled away!

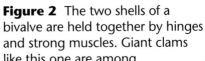 *Checkpoint* *How did gastropods get their name?*

Figure 2 The two shells of a bivalve are held together by hinges and strong muscles. Giant clams like this one are among the largest bivalves in the world.

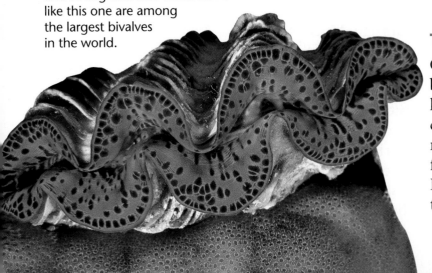

Two-Shelled Mollusks

Clams, oysters, scallops, and mussels are **bivalves**, mollusks that have two shells held together by hinges and strong muscles. Unlike other mollusks, bivalves do not have radulae. Instead, most are filter feeders; they strain their food from water. Bivalves use their gills to capture food as they breathe. Food particles stick to mucus

EXPLORING *a Snail*

Like other gastropods, a snail has a head with sense organs, and it has a wide, muscular foot. The snails shown here live in a pond.

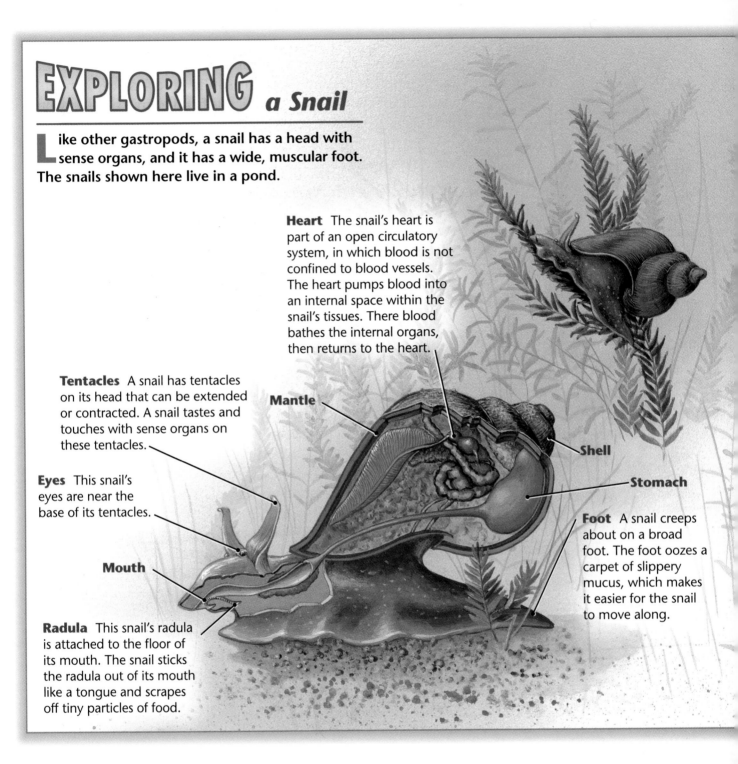

Heart The snail's heart is part of an open circulatory system, in which blood is not confined to blood vessels. The heart pumps blood into an internal space within the snail's tissues. There blood bathes the internal organs, then returns to the heart.

Tentacles A snail has tentacles on its head that can be extended or contracted. A snail tastes and touches with sense organs on these tentacles.

Eyes This snail's eyes are near the base of its tentacles.

Mouth

Radula This snail's radula is attached to the floor of its mouth. The snail sticks the radula out of its mouth like a tongue and scrapes off tiny particles of food.

Mantle

Shell

Stomach

Foot A snail creeps about on a broad foot. The foot oozes a carpet of slippery mucus, which makes it easier for the snail to move along.

that covers the gills. The cilia on the gills then move the food particles into the bivalve's mouth.

Bivalves are found in all kinds of watery environments. As adults, most bivalves stay in one place or move slowly. After their larval stage, for example, oysters and mussels attach themselves to an underwater surface. Clams, in contrast, are active; they use a thin foot to burrow down into the sand or mud. Scallops can also move from place to place. In fact, when startled, scallops clap their shells together and leap rapidly in the water over the sand.

Sometimes sand or grit becomes lodged between a bivalve's mantle and its shell, irritating the soft mantle. Just as you might put smooth tape around rough bicycle handlebars to protect your hands, the bivalve's mantle produces a smooth, pearly coat to cover the irritating object. Eventually a pearl forms around the grit. Some oysters make pearls so beautiful that they are used in jewelry.

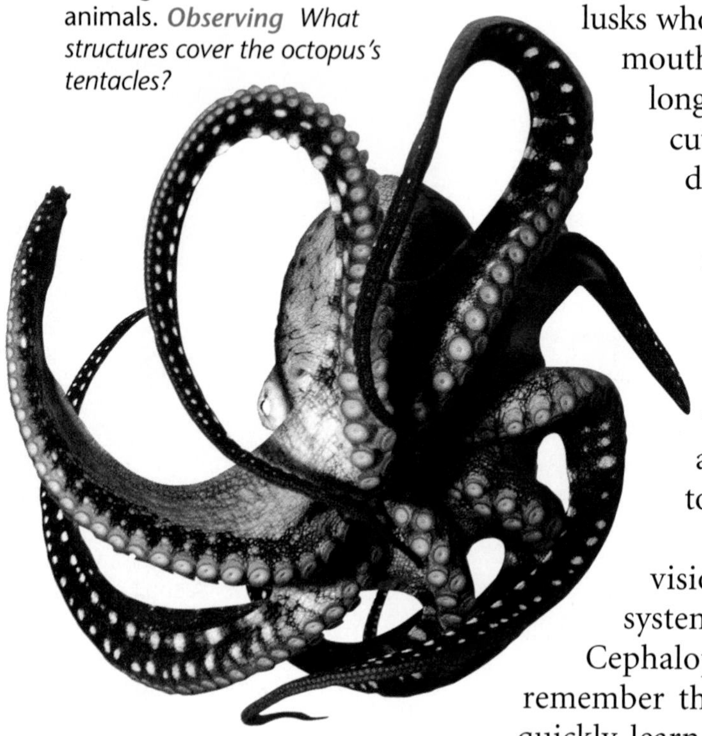

Mollusks with Tentacles

Octopuses, cuttlefish, nautiluses, and squids are **cephalopods**, mollusks whose feet are adapted to form tentacles around their mouths. Some octopuses have tentacles almost 5 meters long! While nautiluses have an external shell, squids and cuttlefish have a small shell within the body. Octopuses do not have shells.

Cephalopods capture food with their flexible, muscular tentacles. Sensitive suckers on the tentacles receive sensations of taste as well as touch. A cephalopod doesn't have to touch something to taste it; the suckers respond to chemicals in the water. For example, when an octopus feels beneath a rock, its tentacle may find a crab by taste before it touches it.

Cephalopods have large eyes and excellent vision. They also have the most complex nervous system, including a large brain, of any invertebrate. Cephalopods are highly intelligent animals that can remember things they have learned. In captivity, octopuses quickly learn when to expect deliveries of food and how to escape from their tanks.

INTEGRATING PHYSICS All cephalopods live in the ocean, where they swim by jet propulsion. They squeeze a current of water out of the mantle cavity through a tube, and like rockets, shoot off in the opposite direction. By turning the tube around, they can steer in any direction.

Figure 3 Octopuses live in coral reefs where they hide in holes when they are not hunting crabs and other small animals. *Observing What structures cover the octopus's tentacles?*

Section 1 Review

1. What characteristics do most mollusks have in common?
2. List the three main groups of mollusks. Describe the main characteristics of each group.
3. Explain how bivalves obtain food.
4. **Thinking Critically** **Predicting** Would gills function well if they had few blood vessels? Explain.

Science at Home

Visit a local supermarket with a family member and identify any mollusks that are being sold as food. Be sure to look in places other than the fish counter, such as the canned-foods section. Discuss the parts of the mollusks that are used for food and the parts that are not edible.

402

A Snail's Pace

In this lab, you will use the skill of measuring to investigate how fast a snail moves in different water temperatures.

Problem

How do changes in environmental temperature affect the activity level of a snail?

Materials

freshwater snail	thermometer	ruler
plastic petri dish	graph paper	timer

spring water at three temperatures:
   cool (9–13°C); medium (18–22°C);
   warm (27–31°C)

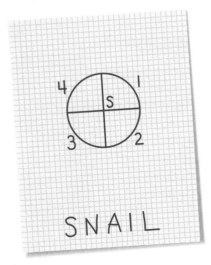

Procedure

1. Create a data table for recording the water temperatures and the distance the snail travels at each temperature.

2. On one sheet of graph paper labeled *Snail,* trace a circle using the base of an empty petri dish. Divide and label the circle as shown in the illustration. On a second sheet of graph paper labeled *Data,* draw three more circles like the one in the illustration.

3. Place the petri dish over the circle on the Snail page, fill it with cool water, and record the water temperature. Then place the snail in the water just above the "S" in the circle. Be sure to handle the snail gently.

4. For five minutes, observe the snail. Record its movements by drawing a line that shows its path in the first circle on the Data page.

5. Find the distance the snail moved by measuring the line you drew. You may need to measure all the parts of the line and add them together. Record the distance in your data table.

6. Repeat Steps 3 through 5, first with medium-temperature water and then with warm water. Record the snail's paths in the second circle and third circle on the Data page.

7. Return the snail to your teacher when you are done. Wash your hands thoroughly.

8. For each temperature, compute the class average for distance traveled.

Analyze and Conclude

1. Make a bar graph showing the class average for each temperature. How does a snail's activity level change as temperature increases?

2. Do you think the pattern you found would continue at higher temperatures? Explain.

3. **Think About It** What factors in this lab were difficult to measure? How could you change the procedure to obtain more accurate measurements? Explain.

Design an Experiment

Design an experiment to measure the rate at which a snail moves in an aquarium with gravel on the bottom. Obtain your teacher's permission before trying your experiment.

② Arthropods

Will It Bend and Move?

1. Have a partner roll a piece of cardboard around your arm to form a tube that covers your elbow. Your partner should put three pieces of tape around the tube to hold it closed— one at each end and one in the middle.

2. With the tube in place, try to write your name on a piece of paper. Then try to scratch your head.

3. Keep the tube on your arm for 10 minutes. Observe how the tube affects your ability to do things.

Think It Over
Inferring Insects and many other animals have rigid skeletons on the outside of their bodies. Why do their skeletons need joints?

GUIDE FOR READING

◆ What are the major characteristics of arthropods?

◆ What are the main groups of arthropods?

Reading Tip Before you read, rewrite the headings in this section as questions. Answer the questions as you read.

O n a moonless night at the edge of a wooded area, a moth flits from flower to flower, drinking nectar. Nearby, a hungry spider waits in its web that stretches, nearly invisible, between bushes. Suddenly, the moth gets caught by the spider web. The sticky threads of the web trap one of the moth's wings. As the trapped moth struggles to free itself, the spider rushes toward it. At the last second, the moth gives a strong flap, breaks free, and flutters away—safe! Next time, the moth may not be so lucky.

The hungry spider and lucky moth are both arthropods. Insects and spiders are probably the arthropods you are most familiar with, but the phylum also includes animals such as crabs, lobsters, centipedes, and scorpions. Scientists have identified about 875,000 different species of arthropods, and there are probably many more that have not yet been discovered. Earth has more species of arthropods than of all other animals combined.

◀ Spider awaiting prey

Figure 4 Some arthropods, like the Sally lightfoot crab at left, have a hard exoskeleton. Others, like the Promethea moth caterpillar below, have a leathery exoskeleton. *Making Generalizations What role does an exoskeleton play?*

Characteristics of Arthropods

Members of the **arthropod** phylum (phylum Arthropoda) share certain important characteristics. **An arthropod is an invertebrate that has an external skeleton, a segmented body, and jointed attachments called appendages.** Wings, mouthparts, and legs are all appendages. Jointed legs are such a distinctive characteristic that the arthropod phylum is named for it. *Arthros* means "joint" in Greek, and *podos* means "foot" or "leg."

Arthropods have additional characteristics in common, too. Arthropods have open circulatory systems—the blood leaves the blood vessels and bathes the internal organs. Most arthropods reproduce sexually. Unlike an earthworm, which has both male and female organs in its body, most arthropods are either male or female. Most arthropods have internal fertilization—sperm and egg unite inside the body of the female. This contrasts to external fertilization, which takes place outside an animal's body.

A Skeleton on the Outside If you were an arthropod, you would be completely covered by a waterproof shell. This waxy **exoskeleton,** or outer skeleton, protects the animal and helps prevent evaporation of water. Water animals are surrounded by water, but land animals need a way to keep from drying out. Arthropods were the first animals to move out of water and onto land, and their exoskeletons probably enabled them to do this.

INTEGRATING CHEMISTRY Arthropod exoskeletons are made of a material called **chitin** (KY tin). Chitin is made of long molecules that are built from many smaller building blocks, like links in a chain. Long-chain molecules like chitin are called polymers. Cotton fibers and rubber are polymers, too. For any

Figure 5 This rainforest cicada has just molted. You can see its old exoskeleton still hanging on the leaf just below it. *Applying Concepts Why must arthropods molt?*

Figure 6 Arthropod groups differ in the numbers of body sections, legs, and antennae, and in where they are found. *Interpreting Charts Which group of arthropods has no antennae?*

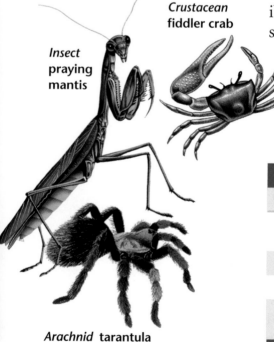

Crustacean fiddler crab

Insect praying mantis

Arachnid tarantula

polymer, the kinds, numbers, and the arrangement of its small building blocks determine its characteristics. Chitin's building blocks make it tough and flexible.

As an arthropod grows larger, its exoskeleton cannot expand. The growing arthropod is trapped within its exoskeleton, like a knight in armor that is too small for him. Arthropods solve this problem by occasionally shedding their exoskeletons and growing new ones that are larger. The process of shedding an outgrown exoskeleton is called **molting**. After an arthropod has molted, its new skeleton is soft for a time. During that time, the arthropod has less protection from danger than it does after its new skeleton has hardened.

Segmented Bodies Arthropods' bodies are segmented, something like an earthworm's. The segmented body plan is easiest to see in centipedes and millipedes, which have bodies made up of many identical-looking segments. You can also see segments on the tails of shrimp and lobsters.

In some groups of arthropods, several body segments become joined into distinct sections, with each section specialized to perform specific functions. Figure 6 shows the number of body sections and other physical characteristics that are typical of the three largest groups of arthropods.

Appendages Just as your fingers are appendages attached to your palms, many arthropods have jointed appendages attached to their bodies. The joints in the appendages give the animal flexibility and enable it to move. If you did the Discover activity, you saw how important joints are for allowing movement.

Arthropod appendages tend to be highly specialized tools. For example, the appendages attached to the head of a crayfish include mouthparts that it uses for crushing food. A crayfish also has two pairs of antennae. An

Comparisons of the Largest Arthropod Groups

Characteristic	Crustaceans	Arachnids	Insects
Number of body sections	2 or 3	2	3
Number of legs	5 or more pairs	4 pairs	3 pairs
Number of antennae	2 pairs	none	1 pair
Where found?	in water or damp places	mostly on land	mostly on land

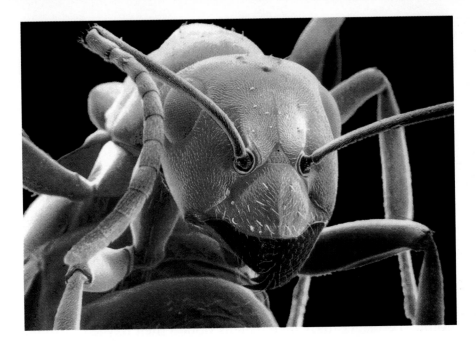

Figure 7 This wood ant's appendages include its antennae, legs, and mouthparts. It uses its mouthparts first to saw its food into small pieces and then to chew it.

antenna (plural *antennae*) is an appendage on the head that contains sense organs. A crayfish's antennae have organs for smelling, tasting, touching, and keeping balance. Legs are also appendages. Most of the crayfish's legs are adapted for walking, but the crayfish uses its first pair of legs, which have claws, for catching prey and defending against predators. The wings that most insects have are also appendages.

☑ *Checkpoint* *How do exoskeletons enable many arthropods to live on land?*

Origin of Arthropods

Since segmented worms and arthropods both have segmented bodies with appendages attached to some segments, many biologists have inferred that these two groups of animals have a common ancestor. However, DNA evidence indicates that arthropods and segmented worms may not be as closely related as previously thought.

Arthropods have been on Earth for about 540 million years. Like most other animal groups, arthropods first arose in the oceans. Today, however, they live almost everywhere. Some kinds of arthropods, like crayfish and crabs, are adapted to live in fresh or salt water. Very few insects, in contrast, live in salt water, but they live just about everywhere else.

Crustaceans

The major groups of arthropods are crustaceans, arachnids, centipedes, millipedes, and insects. If you've ever eaten shrimp cocktail or crab cakes, you've dined on crustaceans. A **crustacean** is an arthropod that has two or three body sections and usually

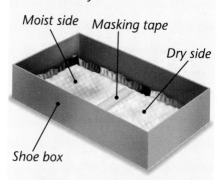
has three pairs of appendages for chewing. In addition, crustaceans always have five or more pairs of legs; each body segment has a pair of legs or modified legs attached to it. Crustaceans are the only arthropods that have two pairs of antennae. *Exploring a Crayfish* shows a typical crustacean.

Life Cycle   Most crustaceans, such as crabs, barnacles, and shrimp, begin their lives as microscopic, swimming larvae. The bodies of these larvae do not resemble those of adults. Crustacean larvae develop into adults by **metamorphosis** (met uh MAWR fuh sis), a process in which an animal's body undergoes dramatic changes in form during its life cycle.

Environments   Nearly every kind of watery environment is home to crustaceans, which usually obtain their oxygen through gills. Crustaceans thrive in freshwater lakes and rivers, and even in puddles that last a long time. You can find crustaceans in the deepest parts of oceans, floating in ocean currents, and crawling along coastlines. A few crustaceans live in damp areas on land, too. Some huge crabs even live in the tops of palm trees!

Feeding   Crustaceans obtain food in many ways. Many eat dead plants and animals. Others are predators, eating animals they have killed. The pistol shrimp is a predator with an appendage that moves with such force that it stuns its prey. Krill, which are shrimplike crustaceans found in huge swarms in cold ocean waters, are herbivores that eat plantlike microorganisms. In turn, krill are eaten by predators such as fishes, penguins, seals, sea birds, and even by great blue whales, the world's largest animals.

☑ *Checkpoint* *An animal has an exoskeleton, two body sections, and eight legs. Is it a crustacean? Why or why not?*

Spiders and Their Relatives

Spiders, mites, and ticks are the arachnids that people most often encounter. To qualify as an **arachnid** (uh RAK nid), an arthropod must have only two body sections. The first section is a combined head and chest. The hind section, called the **abdomen**, contains the arachnid's reproductive organs and part of its digestive tract. Arachnids have eight legs, but no antennae. They breathe with organs called book lungs or with a network of tiny tubes that lead to openings on the exoskeleton.

Spiders   Spiders are the most familiar, most feared, and most fascinating kind of arachnid. All spiders are predators, and most of them eat insects. Some spiders, such as tarantulas and wolf spiders, run down their prey, while others, such as golden garden spiders, spin webs and wait for their prey to become entangled.

EXPLORING *a Crayfish*

Crayfish are crustaceans that live in ponds, streams, or rivers, where they hide beneath rocks and burrow in the mud. Some build a tall mud "chimney" around their burrow entrance. Crayfish will eat nearly any animal or plant, dead or alive, including other crayfish.

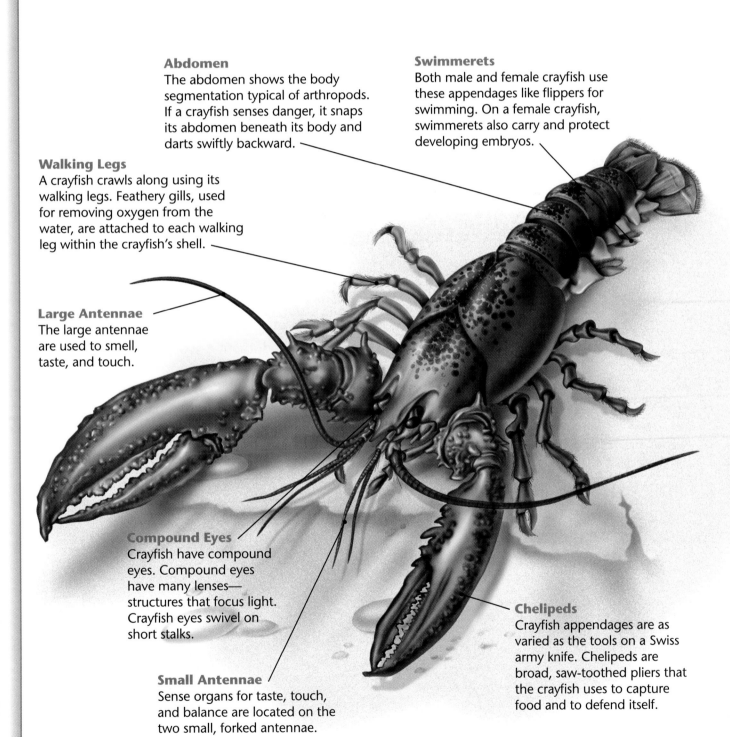

Abdomen
The abdomen shows the body segmentation typical of arthropods. If a crayfish senses danger, it snaps its abdomen beneath its body and darts swiftly backward.

Swimmerets
Both male and female crayfish use these appendages like flippers for swimming. On a female crayfish, swimmerets also carry and protect developing embryos.

Walking Legs
A crayfish crawls along using its walking legs. Feathery gills, used for removing oxygen from the water, are attached to each walking leg within the crayfish's shell.

Large Antennae
The large antennae are used to smell, taste, and touch.

Compound Eyes
Crayfish have compound eyes. Compound eyes have many lenses—structures that focus light. Crayfish eyes swivel on short stalks.

Small Antennae
Sense organs for taste, touch, and balance are located on the two small, forked antennae.

Chelipeds
Crayfish appendages are as varied as the tools on a Swiss army knife. Chelipeds are broad, saw-toothed pliers that the crayfish uses to capture food and to defend itself.

Spiders have hollow fangs, which are organs that inject venom into prey. Spider venom turns the tissues of the prey into mush. Later the spider uses its fangs like drinking straws, sucking in the mush. In spite of what some people might think, spiders rarely bite people. When they do, most spider bites are painful but not life-threatening. However, the bites of the brown recluse or the black widow may require hospital care.

Mites If chiggers have ever given you an itchy rash, you've had an unpleasant encounter with tiny arachnids called mites. Chiggers and many other mites are parasites. Ear mites, for example, give dogs and cats itchy ears. Mites are everywhere. Even the cleanest houses have microscopic dust mites. If you are allergic to dust, you may actually be allergic to the exoskeletons of dust mites. Mites also live in fresh water and in the ocean.

Ticks Ticks are parasites that live on the outside of a host animal's body. Nearly every kind of land animal has a species of tick that sucks its blood. Some ticks that attack humans can carry diseases. Lyme disease, for example, is spread by the bite of an infected deer tick.

Scorpions Scorpions, which live mainly in hot climates, are also arachnids. Usually active at night, scorpions hide in cool places during the day—under rocks and logs, or in holes in the ground, for example.

At the end of its abdomen, a scorpion has a spinelike stinger. The scorpion uses the stinger to inject venom into its prey, which is usually a spider or insect. Sometimes scorpions sting people. These stings, while painful, usually do not cause serious harm.

☑ *Checkpoint* *How do spiders obtain and digest their food?*

Figure 8 Arachnids are arthropods with two body sections, eight legs, and no antennae. **A.** A tick is a parasite that attaches itself to its prey to feed upon its blood. **B.** A scorpion is a carnivore that injects venom from a stinger at the end of its abdomen. **C.** The Honduran tarantula, a spider, uses its fangs to inject venom into a racer snake.

Centipedes and Millipedes

Centipedes and millipedes have highly segmented bodies, as you can see in Figure 9. Centipedes have one pair of legs attached to each segment, and some centipedes have over 100 segments. In fact, the word *centipede* means "hundred feet." Centipedes are swift predators with sharp jaws. They inject venom into the smaller animals that they catch for food.

Millipedes, which may have more than 80 segments, have two pairs of legs on each segment—more legs than any other arthropod. Though *millipede* means "thousand feet," they don't have quite that many legs. Most millipedes are herbivores that graze on partly decayed leaves. When they are disturbed, millipedes can curl up into an armored ball and squirt an awful-smelling liquid at a potential predator.

Figure 9 Centipedes and millipedes are arthropods with many body segments. Centipedes, left, are carnivores, while millipedes, right, are herbivores. *Comparing and Contrasting How can you tell the difference between these two organisms?*

Section 2 Review

1. Identify four characteristics that all arthropods share.
2. List the major groups of arthropods.
3. What characteristic distinguishes crustaceans from all other arthropods?
4. What are the main characteristics of arachnids?
5. **Thinking Critically** **Applying Concepts** Some seafood restaurants serve a dish called soft-shelled crab. What do you think happened to the crab just before it was caught? Why is that process important?

Check Your Progress

CHAPTER PROJECT

Construct a data table in your notebook. Each day, observe both groups of mealworms. Record how many mealworms in each group are still wormlike larvae, how many have formed motionless pupae, and how many, if any, have become adult insects. (*Hint:* You will learn about the stages of insect metamorphosis in Section 3. You may find it helpful to refer to *Exploring Insect Metamorphosis* on page 415 as you fill in your data table.)

DISCOVER .... ACTIVITY

What Kinds of Appendages Do Insects Have?

1. Your teacher will give you a collection of insects. Examine the insects carefully.

2. Note the physical characteristics of each insect's body covering.

3. Count the legs, wings, body sections, and antennae on each insect.

4. Carefully observe the appendages—antennae, mouthparts, wings, and legs. Contrast the appendages on different insects. Then return the insects to your teacher and wash your hands.

Think It Over

Observing Compare the legs and wings of two different species of insect. What kind of movements is each insect adapted to perform?

GUIDE FOR READING

◆ What are the characteristics of insects?

◆ What is the overall impact of insects on humans?

Reading Tip As you read, make an outline of this section using the headings as the main topics.

Monarch butterflies, with their beautiful orange and black wings, may seem delicate, but they are champion travelers. Every autumn, about 100 million of these butterflies fly south from southeastern Canada and the eastern United States, heading for the mountains of central Mexico. Some monarch butterflies fly thousands of kilometers before they reach their destination.

The monarch butterflies who make this long journey have never been to Mexico before. But somehow they find their way to the same trees where their ancestors, now dead, spent the previous winter. No one is certain how they are able to do this.

In the spring, the butterflies fly northward. After flying a few hundred miles, they stop, mate, lay eggs, and die. But their children—and later, their grandchildren and great-grandchildren—continue the northward journey. Eventually, monarch butterflies reach the area their ancestors left the previous fall.

Wintering monarch butterflies ▼

The Insect Body

The monarch butterfly is an **insect**, as is a dragonfly, cockroach, or bee. You can identify insects, like other arthropods, by counting their body sections and legs. **Insects are arthropods with three body sections, six legs, one pair of antennae, and usually one or two pairs of wings.** The three body regions are the head, thorax, and abdomen. An insect's **thorax,** or mid-section, is the section to which wings and legs are attached. Sense organs, such as the eyes and antennae, are located on an insect's head. The abdomen contains many of the insect's internal organs. You can see all three body sections on the grasshopper in Figure 11.

Like most crustaceans, insects usually have two large compound eyes, which contain many lenses. Compound eyes are especially keen at seeing movement. Most insects also have small simple eyes, which can distinguish between light and darkness.

Insects obtain oxygen through a system of tubes. These tubes lead to openings on the insect's exoskeleton. Air, which contains oxygen, enters the insect's body through these tubes and travels directly to the insect's body cells.

☑ Checkpoint *How are an insect's compound eyes different from its simple eyes?*

From Egg to Adult

Insects begin life as tiny, hard-shelled, fertilized eggs. After they hatch, insects begin a process of metamorphosis that eventually produces an adult insect. Each insect species undergoes one of two different types of metamorphosis.

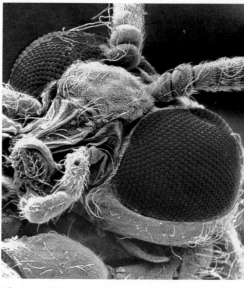

Figure 10 Most insects, like this black fly, have compound eyes with many lenses. Because compound eyes are very effective at seeing movement, insects can quickly escape from potential predators.

Figure 11 A grasshopper's body, like that of every insect, consists of three sections. *Interpreting Diagrams To which section are the grasshopper's legs attached?*

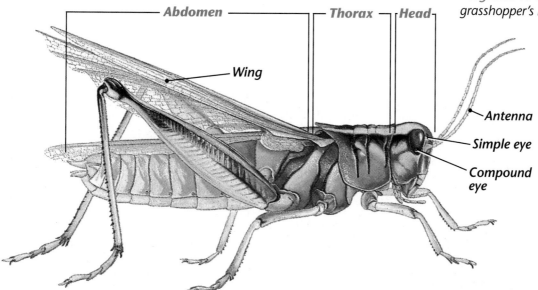

The two types of insect metamorphosis are shown in *Exploring Insect Metamorphosis.* The first type, which is called **complete metamorphosis**, has four dramatically different stages: egg, larva, pupa, and adult. As you learned in Chapter 12, a larva is an immature form of an animal that looks significantly different from the adult. Insect larvae, such as the caterpillars of butterflies and moths, usually look something like worms. Larvae are specialized for eating and growing. After a time, the larva goes into the second stage of complete metamorphosis and becomes a **pupa** (plural *pupae*). During the pupal stage, the insect is enclosed in a protective covering and gradually changes from a larva to an adult. A butterfly in a chrysalis and a moth in a cocoon are examples of insect pupae. When it has completed its development, an adult insect emerges from the protective pupa. Beetles, butterflies, houseflies, and ants all undergo complete metamorphosis.

In contrast, the second type of metamorphosis, called **gradual metamorphosis**, has no distinctly different larval stage—an egg hatches into a stage called a **nymph**, which often resembles the adult insect. A nymph may molt several times before becoming an adult. Grasshoppers, termites, cockroaches, and dragonflies go through gradual metamorphosis.

☑ *Checkpoint* **List the stages of complete metamorphosis.**

How Insects Feed

The rule seems to be this: If it is living, or if it once was living, some kind of insect will eat it. Everyone knows that insects eat plants and parts of plants, such as leaves and nectar. But insects also eat products that are made from plants, such as paper. The next time you open a very old book, watch for book lice. These very small insects live in old books, chewing tiny crooked tunnels through the pages.

Insects feed on animals, too. Some, like fleas and mosquitoes, feed on the blood of living animals. Others, like dung beetles, feed on animal droppings. Still others, like burying beetles, feed on the decaying bodies of dead animals.

Insect mouthparts are adapted for a highly specific way of getting food. For example, a bee has a bristly tongue that laps nectar from flowers, and a mosquito has sharp mouthparts for jabbing and sucking blood.

Figure 12 This caterpillar feeds almost continuously. As a larva, it must store all the energy it will need for its pupal stage.

EXPLORING *Insect Metamorphosis*

Depending on the species, an insect develops into an adult through one of the two processes shown here. Fireflies undergo complete metamorphosis, while grasshoppers undergo gradual metamorphosis.

Adult male firefly

COMPLETE METAMORPHOSIS

1 Egg Female fireflies lay their eggs in moist places. The eggs of fireflies glow in the dark.

2 Larva The eggs hatch into larvae that feed on snails and slugs. Firefly larvae are called glowworms because they give off light.

3 Pupa After a time, the firefly larva becomes a pupa. Inside the protective pupal case, wings, legs, and antennae form.

4 Adult When its development is complete, an adult firefly crawls out of its pupal case and unfurls its crumpled wings. After its exoskeleton hardens, the adult begins a life centered around feeding, flying into new areas, and mating. Adult fireflies flash their light to attract mates.

GRADUAL METAMORPHOSIS

Adult male grasshopper

1 Egg A female grasshopper uses the tip of her abdomen to jab holes in the soil where she lays her eggs.

2 Nymph Eggs hatch into nymphs that look much like miniature adults, except that they have no wings, or only small ones.

3 Larger Nymph A nymph feeds until its exoskeleton becomes too tight, and then it molts. The nymph molts four or five times before becoming an adult.

4 Adult Most insects undergoing gradual metamorphosis emerge from the final molt equipped with full-sized wings. Once its wings have hardened, the adult flies off to mate and begin the cycle again.

Figure 13 The well-camouflaged thorn insect, left, and leaf insect, right, have very effective built-in defenses against predators. *Observing Why do you think the insect on the left is called a thorn insect?*

Defending Themselves

Insects have many defenses against predators, including a hard exoskeleton that helps protect them. Many insects can run quickly or fly away from danger, as you know if you've ever tried to swat a fly. Some insects, such as stinkbugs, smell or taste bad to predators. Other insects, such as bees and wasps, defend themselves with painful stings.

One of the most common defenses is **camouflage,** or protective coloration, in which the insect blends with its surroundings so perfectly that it is nearly invisible to a predator. Test yourself by trying to find the camouflaged insects in Figure 13. Walking sticks, many caterpillars, and grasshoppers are just a few insects that use camouflage as a defense.

Other insects are protected by their resemblance to different animals. The spots on the wings of certain moths, for example, resemble large eyes; predators who see these spots often avoid the moths, mistaking them for much larger animals.

☑ *Checkpoint* *What are four ways in which insects protect themselves?*

Insects and Humans

For every person alive today, scientists estimate that there are at least 200 million living insects. Many of those insects have an impact on people's lives. Some species of insects do major damage to crops. In addition, insects such as flies, fleas, and mosquitoes can carry microorganisms that cause diseases in humans. For example, when they bite humans, some mosquito species can transmit the microorganism that causes malaria.

The vast majority of insects, however, are harmless or beneficial to humans. Bees make honey, and the larvae of the silkworm moth spin the fibers used to make silk cloth. Some insects prey on harmful insects, helping to reduce those insect populations. And while some insects destroy food crops, many more insects, such as butterflies and flies, enable food crops and other plants to reproduce by carrying pollen from one plant to another. If insects were to disappear from Earth, you would never get a mosquito bite. But you wouldn't have much food to eat, either.

Controlling Insect Pests

INTEGRATING ENVIRONMENTAL SCIENCE People have tried to eliminate harmful insects by applying chemicals, called pesticides, to plants. However, pesticides also kill helpful insects, such as bees, and can harm other animals, including some birds. And after a time, insect populations become resistant to the pesticides—the pesticides no longer kill the insects.

Scientists are searching for other ways to deal with harmful insects. One method is the use of biological controls. Biological controls introduce natural predators or diseases into insect populations. For example, ladybug beetles can be added to fields where crops are grown. Ladybugs prey on aphids, which are insects that destroy peaches, potatoes, and other crop plants. Soil also can be treated with bacteria that are harmless to humans but cause diseases in the larvae of pest insects such as Japanese beetles. These biological controls kill only one or a few pest species. Because biological controls kill only specific pests, they are less damaging to the environment than insecticides.

Figure 14 Bees and other pollinators are among the most beneficial of all insects. As a bee drinks nectar from a flower, pollen sticks to its body. When the insect carries that pollen to the next plant it eats from, it helps that plant to reproduce.

Section 3 Review

1. List the characteristics that insects share.
2. Identify two ways in which insects benefit humans.
3. Compare and contrast complete and gradual metamorphosis.
4. **Thinking Critically Inferring** Honeybees sting predators that try to attack them. Hover flies, which do not sting, resemble honeybees. How might this resemblance be an advantage to the hover fly?

Check Your Progress CHAPTER PROJECT
Continue observing the mealworms every day. Update the data table with your observations. As you observe the mealworms at different stages of development, make a sketch of a larva, a pupa, and an adult.

What's Living in the Soil?

The soil beneath a tree, in a garden, or under a rock is home to many organisms, including a variety of arthropods. Each of these patches of soil can be thought of as a miniature environment with its own group of living residents. In this lab, you will examine one specific soil environment.

Problem

What kinds of animals live in soil and leaf litter?

Skills Focus

observing, classifying, inferring

Materials

2-liter plastic bottle	large scissors
coarse steel wool	trowel
cheesecloth	large rubber band
gooseneck lamp	hand lens
large, wide-mouthed jar	small jar
fresh sample of soil and leaf litter	

Procedure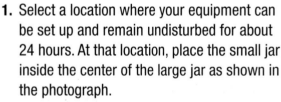

1. Select a location where your equipment can be set up and remain undisturbed for about 24 hours. At that location, place the small jar inside the center of the large jar as shown in the photograph.

2. Use scissors to cut a large plastic bottle in half. **CAUTION:** *Cut in a direction away from yourself and others.* Turn the top half of the bottle upside down to serve as a funnel.

3. Insert a small amount of coarse steel wool into the mouth of the funnel to keep the soil from falling out. Do not pack the steel wool too tightly. Leave spaces for small organisms to crawl through. Place the funnel into the large jar as shown in the photograph.

4. Using the trowel, fill the funnel with soil and surface leaf litter. When you finish handling the leaves and soil, wash your hands thoroughly.

5. Look closely to see whether the soil and litter are dry or wet. Record your observation.

6. Make a cover for your sample by placing a piece of cheesecloth over the top of the funnel. Hold the cheesecloth in place with a large rubber band. Immediately position a lamp about 15 cm above the funnel, and turn on the light. Allow this set-up to remain undisturbed for about 24 hours. **CAUTION:** *Hot light bulbs can cause burns. Do not touch the bulb.*

7. When you are ready to make your observations, turn off the lamp. Leave the funnel and jar in place while making your observations. Use a hand lens to examine each organism in the jar. **CAUTION:** *Do not touch any of the organisms.*

8. Use a data table like the one on the next page to sketch each type of organism and to record other observations. Be sure to include evidence that will help you classify the organisms. (*Hint:* Remember that some animals may be at different stages of metamorphosis.)

DATA TABLE

Sketch of Organism	Number Found	Size	Important Characteristics	Probable Phylum

9. Examine the soil and leaf litter, and record whether this material is dry or wet.

10. When you are finished, follow your teacher's directions about returning the organisms to the soil.

Analyze and Conclude

1. Describe the conditions of the soil environment at the beginning and end of the lab. What caused the change?

2. What types of animals did you collect in the small jar? What characteristics did you use to identify each type of animal? Which types of animals were the most common?

3. Why do you think the animals moved down the funnel away from the soil?

4. **Apply** Using what you have learned about arthropods and other animals, make an inference about the role that each animal you collected plays in the environment.

More to Explore

What kinds of organisms might live in other soil types—for example, soil at the edge of a pond, dry sandy soil, or commercially prepared potting soil? Propose one or more ways to answer this question.

SECTION 4 The Sounds of Insects

DISCOVER

What Causes Sound?

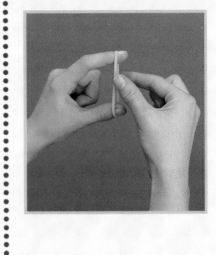

1. Form a letter C with the index finger and thumb of one hand. Stretch a rubber band over the tips of your finger and thumb, as shown in the picture. Predict what will happen when you pluck the rubber band.

2. Pluck the rubber band so that it makes a sound. Observe the rubber band as it is making a sound. Note how the rubber band moves.

3. Repeat Step 2, but as soon as you pluck the rubber band, touch it so that it stops moving. Note what happens to the sound.

Think It Over

Inferring What is the relationship between sound and vibration?

GUIDE FOR READING

◆ How is sound produced?

◆ What function does sound serve for many insects?

Reading Tip As you read about the way in which sound is produced, refer to Figure 16.

Somewhere in your neighborhood, on this warm spring evening, a cricket is singing. With a flashlight in your hand, you quietly move toward the chirpy sound. When you're right on top of the sound, you turn on your light and see a black insect on the ground. Its wings are slightly raised, and are scraping against one another so fast that they look blurry. You have found a male cricket who is using sound to attract a mate. A female cricket may soon respond to his call.

How is Sound Produced?

The wings of the cricket vibrate—they move back and forth, faster than the eye can follow. When the cricket's wings stop moving, the chirping stops and all becomes quiet. Why is this so?

Figure 15 This male Borneo cricket can rub his wings together very quickly to make a chirping sound. He uses this chirping sound to call potential mates.

Figure 16 The vibration of a guitar string produces waves that consist of alternate areas in which air molecules are compressed and spread out. *Applying Concepts How does the sound of the guitar reach your ear?*

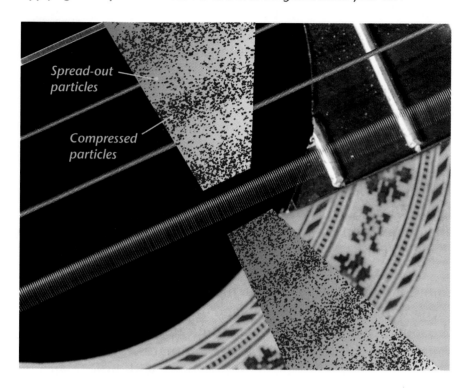

Spread-out particles

Compressed particles

All sound is produced by vibrations that create waves that move outward from the source. Figure 16 shows how the vibrations of a guitar string create sound. After you pull the string to the left and release it, the moving string bumps into air particles in its path. It shoves these particles together, compressing them, and pushes the compressed particles outward. This compressed area is followed by an area in which the air particles are spread out.

Since the guitar string keeps moving back and forth, over and over, it creates many alternating regions of compressed particles and spread-out particles. Together, the compressions and spread-out areas move outward in waves from the guitar string, as Figure 16 shows. The rapidly moving wings of a cricket produce sound in much the same way as a vibrating guitar string.

Sound waves must travel through a medium—a solid, a liquid, or a gas. The sound waves made by both the guitar strings and cricket wings travel through air, which is a gas. Sound can also travel through liquids, such as water, and through solids, such as wood. If you tap on your desk and lower your ear to the desk at the same time, you can hear sound vibrations traveling through solid material.

☑ *Checkpoint* *Through what medium does the sound of thunder travel?*

Communicating by Sound

Insects make sound in a variety of ways. Many insects make sounds in the same way that guitars and other stringed instruments do. They rub a roughened part of their body against a sharp-edged part. The rough part is something like a guitar pick, and the sharp part is like the instrument's strings. Crickets chirp and katydids make their sandpapery songs with a rough patch on each wing.

Different species of insects use different parts of their bodies to produce sound. Large black beetles rub their hind wings against rough patches on their abdomen, making a faint screeching sound. Deathwatch beetles tap on the ground with their heads. Cicadas have thin sheets of tissue called tymbals on their abdomens. Tymbals produce sound by vibrating like the covering of a drum.

Hissing cockroaches are among the few insects that make sounds by forcing air out of their bodies. This is the same method that is used by humans and other vertebrates to produce the sounds with which they communicate.

Many insects use sound to attract mates. Usually it is the male that does the singing; that is the case with insects such as crickets, grasshoppers, and katydids. However, in some species the female makes the sound. For example, female mosquitoes attract males by using their wings to make distinctive, high-pitched vibrations.

Section 4 Review

1. Explain how beating a drum produces a sound.
2. What is communicated by the song of a grasshopper or cicada?
3. Describe two different ways in which insects produce sounds.
4. **Thinking Critically Applying Concepts**
   You are traveling in a spaceship in outer space, where there is no air. Another spaceship speeds past you. Does the spaceship make a sound? Why or why not?

Science at Home

You can use a spring toy like the one above to show your family how sound waves travel. Have a family member hold one end of the spring. Hold the other end in your hand. Gently stretch the spring so that it is fully extended and parallel to the floor. Start a wave moving by pushing on one end. Point out how the wave of compressed coils travels along the spring. Explain to your family how the wave is similar to a sound wave traveling through the air.

SECTION
5 Echinoderms

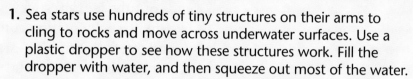

DISCOVER ··· ACTIVITY

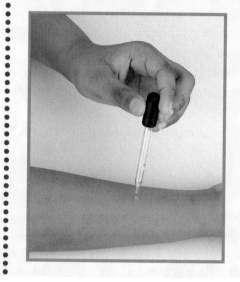

How Do Sea Stars Hold On?

1. Sea stars use hundreds of tiny structures on their arms to cling to rocks and move across underwater surfaces. Use a plastic dropper to see how these structures work. Fill the dropper with water, and then squeeze out most of the water.

2. Squeeze one last drop of water onto the inside of your arm. Then, while squeezing the bulb, touch the tip of the dropper into the water drop. With the dropper tip against your skin, release the bulb.

3. Hold the dropper by the tube and lift it slowly, paying attention to what happens to your skin.

Think It Over
Predicting Besides moving and clinging to surfaces, what might sea stars use their suction structures for?

They look like stars, pincushions, coins, and cucumbers— are these creatures really animals? Sea stars, brittle stars, and basket stars have star-shaped bodies. Sea urchins look like living pincushions, while sand dollars are flat, round discs. Sea cucumbers, with green algae growing within their tissues, look like dill pickles—until they slowly start to crawl along the sand. All of these odd little animals belong to the same phylum.

The "Spiny Skinned" Animals

Biologists classify sea stars, sea urchins, sand dollars, and sea cucumbers as echinoderms (phylum Echinodermata). An **echinoderm** (ee KY noh durm) is a radially symmetrical invertebrate that lives on the ocean floor. *Echinoderm* means "spiny skinned." This name is appropriate because the skin of most of these animals is supported by a spiny internal skeleton, or **endoskeleton**, made of plates that contain calcium.

Adult echinoderms have a unique kind of radial symmetry in which body parts, usually in multiples of five, are arranged like spokes on a wheel. If you count the legs on a sea star or the body sections of a sea urchin, you will almost always get five or a multiple of five.

GUIDE FOR READING

◆ What characteristics are typical of echinoderms?

Reading Tip Before you read, look at *Exploring a Sea Star* on page 425 to note some echinoderm characteristics.

▼ Magnificent sea urchin

In addition to five-part radial symmetry and an endoskeleton, echinoderms also have an internal fluid system called a **water vascular system.** The **water vascular system** consists of fluid-filled tubes within the echinoderm's body. Portions of the tubes can contract, squeezing water into structures called tube feet, which are external parts of the water vascular system. The ends of tube feet are sticky and, when filled with water, they act like small, sticky suction cups. The stickiness and suction enable the tube feet to grip the surface beneath the echinoderm. Most echinoderms also use their tube feet to move along slowly and to capture food. If you turn a sea star upside down, you will see rows of moving tube feet.

Echinoderms crawl about on the bottom of the ocean, seeking food, shelter, and mates. Like other radially symmetrical animals, echinoderms do not have a head end where sense organs and nerve tissue are found. Instead, they are adapted to respond to food, mates, or predators coming from any direction.

Most echinoderms are either male or female. Eggs are usually fertilized right in the seawater, after the female releases her eggs and the male releases his sperm. The fertilized eggs develop into tiny, swimming larvae that eventually undergo metamorphosis and become adult echinoderms.

✓ *Checkpoint* *What is the function of an echinoderm's tube feet?*

Figure 17 This red sea star is in the process of regenerating two of its arms, possibly lost in a struggle with a predator.

Sea Stars

Sea stars are predators that eat mollusks, crabs, and even other echinoderms. A sea star uses its arms and tube feet, shown in *Exploring a Sea Star,* to capture prey. The sea star grasps a clam with all five arms. Then it pulls on the tightly closed shells with its tube feet. When the shells open, the sea star forces its stomach out through its mouth and into the opening between the clam's shells. Digestive chemicals break down the clam's tissues, and the sea star sucks in the partially digested body of its prey. Sea star behavior is quite impressive for an animal that doesn't have a brain.

If a sea star loses an arm, it can grow a replacement. The process by which an animal grows a new part to replace a lost one is called regeneration. Figure 17 shows a sea star with two partially regenerated arms. A few species of sea stars can even grow a whole animal from a single arm. Some sea stars reproduce by splitting into many parts. The arms pull the sea star apart in five different directions and five new sea stars regenerate!

EXPLORING *a Sea Star*

Sea stars, which are also called starfishes, usually have five arms. However, some have as many as fifty arms.

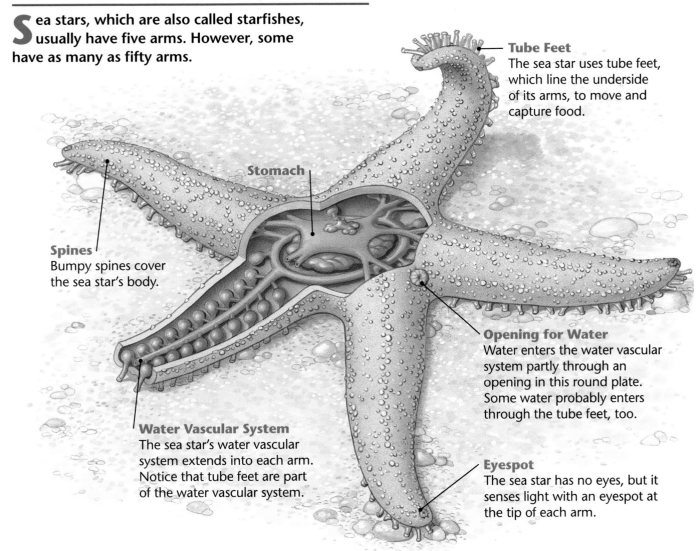

Tube Feet
The sea star uses tube feet, which line the underside of its arms, to move and capture food.

Stomach

Spines
Bumpy spines cover the sea star's body.

Water Vascular System
The sea star's water vascular system extends into each arm. Notice that tube feet are part of the water vascular system.

Opening for Water
Water enters the water vascular system partly through an opening in this round plate. Some water probably enters through the tube feet, too.

Eyespot
The sea star has no eyes, but it senses light with an eyespot at the tip of each arm.

Other Echinoderms

Brittle stars are close relatives of sea stars. Like sea stars, brittle stars have five arms, but their arms are long and slender, with flexible joints. Like sea stars, brittle stars can regenerate lost arms. Brittle stars' tube feet, which have no suction cups, are used for catching food but not for moving. Instead, brittle stars propel themselves along the ocean bottom by moving their giant arms against the ground. They are among the most mobile of all the echinoderms.

Unlike sea stars and brittle stars, sand dollars and sea urchins have no arms. Sand dollars look like large coins. Their flat bodies are covered with very short spines that help them burrow into sand.

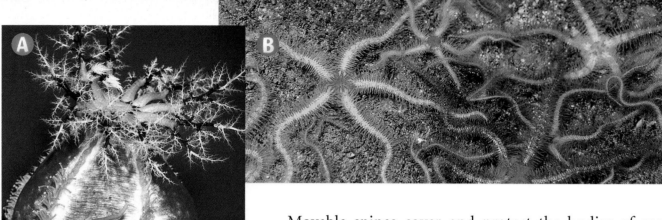

Movable spines cover and protect the bodies of sea urchins, making them look like pincushions or round brushes. The spines cover a central shell that is made of plates joined together. Sea urchins move by using bands of tube feet that extend out between the spines. With the five strong teeth that can be projected from their mouths, sea urchins can scrape algae, chew seaweed, and crush pieces of coral and the shells of small mollusks. Some sea urchins use their teeth and spines to dig themselves into rock crevices to hide from predators.

As you might expect from their name, sea cucumbers look a little bit like leathery-skinned cucumbers—but you won't see one in a tossed salad. These strange animals, which live on the sandy or rocky ocean floor, can be red, brown, blue, or green. Their bodies are soft, flexible, and muscular. Sea cucumbers have rows of tube feet on their underside, enabling them to crawl slowly along the ocean bottom. At one end of a sea cucumber is a mouth surrounded by tentacles. The sea cucumber, which is a filter feeder, can lengthen its tentacles to sweep food toward its mouth, and then pull the tentacles back into its tough skin.

Figure 18 The blue-and-red sea cucumber **(A)**, spiny brittle stars **(B)**, and sand dollar **(C)** are all echinoderms. *Observing What type of symmetry do these organisms exhibit?*

Section 5 Review

1. Identify the main characteristics of echinoderms.
2. Define *regeneration* and explain how it applies to sea stars.
3. Compare and contrast sea urchins and sea stars.
4. **Thinking Critically Inferring** How are tube feet adapted to slow, rather than rapid, movement?

Check Your Progress
CHAPTER PROJECT

Continue to examine the mealworm containers every day and record your data. In your notebook, record any differences between the two groups of mealworms. Begin to draw conclusions about how the different conditions affected metamorphosis. When you have finished working with the insects, return them to your teacher.

SECTION 1 Mollusks

Key Ideas

◆ Most mollusks have shells, soft bodies, a mantle covering internal organs, and a muscular foot.

◆ Mollusks are classified based on the presence of a shell, the type of shell, the type of foot, the arrangement of teeth in the radula, and the complexity of the nervous system.

◆ Major groups of mollusks include gastropods, bivalves, and cephalopods.

Key Terms

mollusk   kidney
gill   radula
gastropod   bivalve
cephalopod

SECTION 2 Arthropods

Key Ideas

◆ Arthropods have an exoskeleton, jointed appendages, and a segmented body.

◆ Major groups of arthropods include crustaceans, arachnids, centipedes, millipedes, and insects.

◆ Crustaceans are the only arthropods with two pairs of antennae.

◆ Arachnids have two body sections, eight legs, and no antennae.

Key Terms

arthropod   exoskeleton   chitin
molting   antenna   crustacean
metamorphosis   arachnid   abdomen

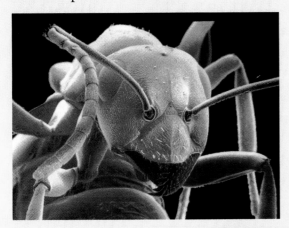

SECTION 3 Insects

Key Ideas

◆ Insects are arthropods with three body sections, six legs, one pair of antennae, and usually one or two pairs of wings.

◆ An insect undergoing complete metamorphosis goes through four distinct stages—egg, larva, pupa, and adult. An insect undergoing gradual metamorphosis hatches from an egg to a nymph; the nymph may molt several times before becoming an adult.

◆ While some insects are harmful to humans, the vast majority are harmless or beneficial.

Key Terms

insect   thorax
complete metamorphosis   pupa
gradual metamorphosis   nymph
camouflage

SECTION 4 The Sounds of Insects

INTEGRATING PHYSICS

Key Ideas

◆ Sound is generated by something that vibrates. Sound travels in waves through solids, liquids, and gases.

◆ Many insects use sound to attract mates.

SECTION 5 Echinoderms

Key Ideas

◆ Echinoderms are characterized by an endoskeleton, five-part radial symmetry, and a water vascular system.

◆ Echinoderms include sea stars, sea urchins, brittle stars, and sea cucumbers.

Key Terms

echinoderm   endoskeleton
water vascular system

USING THE INTERNET

www.science-explorer.phschool.com

California Test Prep: Reviewing Content

Multiple Choice

Choose the letter of the best answer.

1. Mollusks with tentacles are known as
   a. cephalopods.
   b. gastropods.
   c. bivalves.
   d. sea stars.
2. Which of these is true of the legs of arthropods?
   a. They always number six.
   b. They are always attached to the abdomen.
   c. They are rigid.
   d. They are jointed.
3. At which stage of its development is a moth enclosed in a cocoon?
   a. egg
   b. larva
   c. pupa
   d. adult
4. Sound can travel through
   a. solids only.
   b. liquids only.
   c. gases only.
   d. solids, liquids, and gases.
5. A sea star is a(n)
   a. mollusk.
   b. arthropod.
   c. echinoderm.
   d. sponge.

True or False

If the statement is true, write true. If it is false, change the underlined word or words to make the statement true.

6. All <u>arthropods</u> have an exoskeleton.
7. All <u>sea urchins</u> have two pairs of antennae.
8. An insect's midsection is called an <u>abdomen</u>.
9. Many insects use <u>sound</u> to attract mates.
10. All echinoderms have an <u>endoskeleton</u>.

Checking Concepts

11. Explain how a snail uses its radula.
12. How is a cephalopod's way of moving different from that of most mollusks?
13. Describe five things that a crayfish can do with its appendages.
14. How is the process by which a spider digests its food similar to that of a sea star?
15. How are centipedes different from millipedes?
16. Identify some ways in which insects harm people.
17. How are insects different from other arthropods?
18. How does sound travel from its source?
19. How is an echinoderm's radial symmetry different from that of a jellyfish?
20. **Writing to Learn** Imagine that you are a lobster that has just molted. Using vivid, precise words, describe a dangerous situation that you might encounter before your new exoskeleton has hardened.

Thinking Visually

21. **Concept Map** The concept map below shows the classification of arthropods. Copy the map and complete it. (For more on concept maps, see the Skills Handbook.)

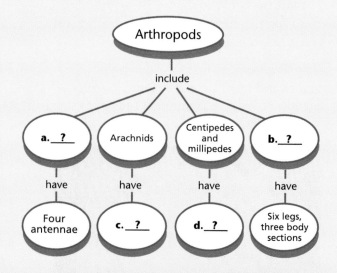

Test Prep: Skills

The following information appeared in a book on insects. Use it to answer Questions 22–25.

"A hummingbird moth beats its wings an average of 85 times per second, and it flies at a speed of about 17.8 kilometers per hour (kph). A bumblebee's wings beat about 250 times per second, and it flies about 10.3 kph. A housefly's wings beat about 190 times per second, and it flies about 7.1 kph."

22. **Creating Data Tables** Make a data table to organize the wing-beat rate and flight speed information above.

23. **Graphing** Construct two bar graphs: one showing the three insect wing-beat rates and another showing the flight speeds.

24. **Interpreting Data** Which of the three insects has the highest wing-beat rate? Which insect flies the fastest?

25. **Drawing Conclusions** On the basis of the data, do you see any relationship between the rate at which an insect beats its wings and the speed at which it flies? Explain. What factors besides wing-beat rate might affect an insect's flight speed?

Thinking Critically

26. **Applying Concepts** Explain why the development of a lion, which grows larger as it changes from a tiny cub to a 200-pound adult, is not metamorphosis.

27. **Comparing and Contrasting** Compare and contrast bivalves and cephalopods.

28. **Making Judgments** Do you think that pesticides should be used to kill harmful insects? Support your ideas with facts.

29. **Relating Cause and Effect** Sea stars sometimes get caught in fishing nets. At one time, in an attempt to protect clams from their natural predators, workers on fishing boats cut the sea stars into pieces and threw the pieces back in the water. What do you think happened to the sea star population? Explain.

30. **Classifying** Your friend said he found a dead insect that had two pairs of antennae and eight legs. Is this possible? Why or why not?

Performance Assessment

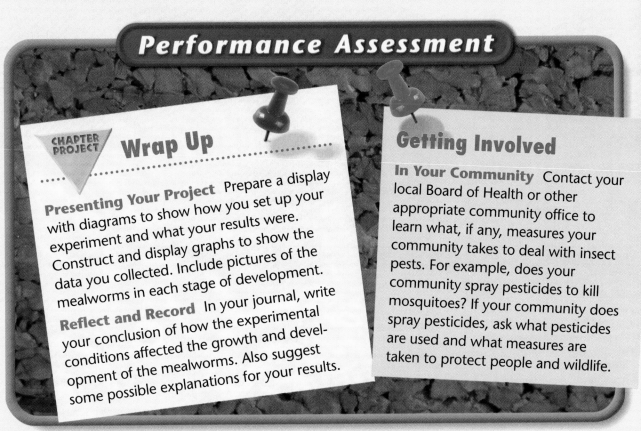

CHAPTER PROJECT **Wrap Up**

Presenting Your Project Prepare a display with diagrams to show how you set up your experiment and what your results were. Construct and display graphs to show the data you collected. Include pictures of the mealworms in each stage of development.

Reflect and Record In your journal, write your conclusion of how the experimental conditions affected the growth and development of the mealworms. Also suggest some possible explanations for your results.

Getting Involved

In Your Community Contact your local Board of Health or other appropriate community office to learn what, if any, measures your community takes to deal with insect pests. For example, does your community spray pesticides to kill mosquitoes? If your community does spray pesticides, ask what pesticides are used and what measures are taken to protect people and wildlife.

This three-horned chameleon has just invited a cricket to lunch.

The following California Science Content Standards are addressed in this chapter:

2. A typical cell of any organism contains genetic instructions that specify its traits. Those traits may be modified by environmental influences.

   a. The differences between the life cycles and reproduction of sexual and asexual organisms.

3. Biological evolution accounts for the diversity of species developed through gradual processes over many generations.

   a. Both genetic variation and environmental factors are causes of evolution and diversity of organisms.

   c. How independent lines of evidence from geology, fossils, and comparative

anatomy provide a basis for the theory of evolution.

   d. How to construct a simple branching diagram to classify living groups of organisms by shared derived characteristics, and expand the diagram to include fossil organisms.

   e. Extinction of a species occurs when the environment changes and the

Animal Adaptations

The chameleon sits still on a twig, as if frozen. Only its eyes move as it sights a cricket resting nearby. Suddenly, the chameleon's long tongue shoots out and captures the unsuspecting cricket, pulling the insect into its mouth. Watch any animal for a few minutes and you will see many ways in which it is adapted for life in its environment. How does the animal capture food, escape from predators, or obtain oxygen? To help answer these questions, you will create models of three different animals—a fish, an amphibian, and a reptile—and show how each is adapted to the environment in which it lives.

Your Goal To construct three-dimensional models of a fish, an amphibian, and a reptile that show how each is adapted to carry out an essential life function in its environment.

To complete the project successfully, you must
- ◆ select one important adaptation to show
- ◆ build a three-dimensional model of each animal, showing how it carries out the function you selected
- ◆ include a poster that explains how each animal's adaptation is suited to its environment
- ◆ follow the safety guidelines in Appendix A

Get Started Pair up with a classmate and share what you already know about fishes, amphibians, and reptiles. Discuss the following questions: Where do these organisms live? How do they move around? How do they protect themselves? Begin thinking about the characteristics that you would like to model.

Check Your Progress You'll be working on this project as you study this chapter. To keep your project on track, look for Check Your Progress boxes at the following points:
Section 2 Review, page 443: Select a fish to model.
Section 3 Review, page 450: Make a model of an amphibian.
Section 4 Review, page 460: Model a reptile. Begin your poster.

Wrap Up At the end of the chapter (page 467), you will display your models and poster.

---

adaptive characteristics of a species are insufficient for its survival.

4. Evidence from rocks allows us to understand the evolution of life on Earth.

c. The rock cycle includes the formation of new sediment and rocks. Rocks are often found in layers with the oldest generally on the bottom.

e. Fossils provide evidence of how life and environmental conditions have changed.

g. How to explain significant developments and extinctions of plant and animal life on the geologic time scale.

5. The anatomy and physiology of plants and animals illustrate the complementary nature of structure and function.

a. Plants and animals have levels of organization for structure and function, including cells, tissues, organs, organ systems, and the whole organism.

c. How bones and muscles work together to provide a structural framework for movement.

What Is a Vertebrate?

How Is an Umbrella Like a Skeleton?

1. Open an umbrella. Turn it upside down and examine how it is made.

2. Now fold the umbrella, and watch how the braces and ribs collapse against the central pole.

3. Think of what would happen if you removed the ribs from the umbrella and then tried to use it during a rainstorm.

Think It Over

Inferring What is the function of the ribs of an umbrella? How are the ribs of the umbrella similar to the bones in your skeleton? How are they different?

GUIDE FOR READING

◆ What main characteristic is shared by all vertebrates?

◆ How do vertebrates differ in the way in which they control body temperature?

Reading Tip As you read, write a definition, in your own words, of each boldfaced science term.

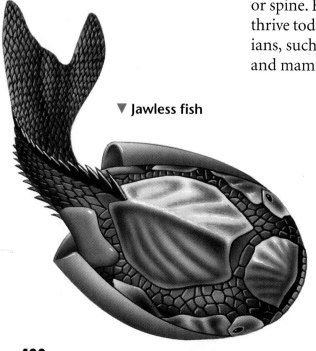

▼ Jawless fish

Look backward in time, into an ocean 530 million years ago. There you see a strange-looking creature, about as long as your middle finger. The creature is swimming with a side-to-side motion, like a flag flapping in an invisible wind. Its tail-fin is broad and flat. Tiny armorlike plates cover its small body. Its eyes are set wide apart. If you could see inside the animal, you would notice that it has a backbone. You are looking at one of the earliest vertebrates, at home in an ancient sea.

Recall from Chapter 12 that vertebrates are animals with a backbone, which is also called a vertebral column, spinal column, or spine. Fishes were the first vertebrates to appear, and they still thrive today in Earth's waters. Other vertebrates include amphibians, such as frogs, and reptiles, such as snakes, as well as birds and mammals.

The Chordate Phylum

Vertebrates are a subgroup in the phylum Chordata. Members of this phylum, called **chordates** (KAWR daytz), share these characteristics: at some point in their lives, they have a notochord, a nerve cord, and slits in their throat area. The phylum name comes from the **notochord,** a flexible rod that supports the animal's back. Some chordates, like the lancelet in Figure 1, keep the notochord all their lives. Others, such as tunicates, have a notochord as larvae, but not as adults. In vertebrates, part or all of the notochord is replaced by a backbone. A few vertebrates have backbones made of **cartilage,** a connective tissue that is softer than bone, but flexible and strong. Most vertebrates have backbones made of hard bone.

Besides a notochord, all chordates have a nerve cord that runs down their back—your spinal cord is such a nerve cord. The nerve cord is the connection between the brain and the nerves, on which messages travel back and forth. Many other groups of animals—crustaceans and worms, for example—have nerve cords, but their nerve cords do not run down their backs.

In addition, chordates have slits in their throat area called pharyngeal (fayr uhn JEE uhl) slits. Fishes keep these slits as part of their gills for their entire lives, but in many vertebrates, including humans, pharyngeal slits disappear before birth.

Figure 1 This lancelet exhibits all the typical characteristics of a chordate. It has a notochord that helps support its body, pharyngeal slits that help it to breathe, and a nerve cord.

✓ *Checkpoint* *What characteristics do all chordates share?*

The Backbone and Endoskeleton

A vertebrate's backbone runs down the center of its back. The backbone is formed by many similar bones, called **vertebrae** (singular *vertebra*), lined up in a row, like beads on a string. Joints between the vertebrae give the vertebral column flexibility. You are able to bend over and tie your sneakers partly because your backbone is flexible. Each vertebra has a hole in it that allows the spinal cord to pass through it. The spinal cord fits into the vertebrae like fingers fit into rings.

A vertebrate's backbone is part of an endoskeleton, or internal skeleton. The endoskeleton supports and protects the body, helps give it shape, and gives muscles a place to attach. In addition to the backbone, the vertebrate's endoskeleton includes

Figure 2 The bodies of all vertebrates are supported by an endoskeleton with a backbone. *Comparing and Contrasting What are two ways in which the cow and chicken skeletons are similar? What are two ways in which they are different?*

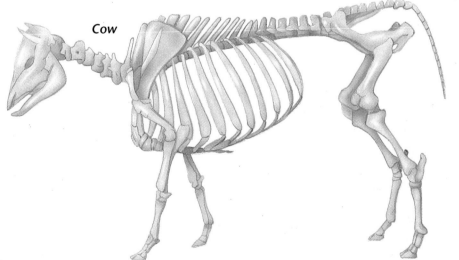

Cow

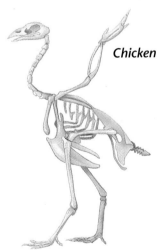

Chicken

Bead-y Bones

You can use a string and beads to model the structure of a vertebrate's backbone.

1. Tie a large knot at one end of a piece of string.

2. Slide beads onto the string one by one. Stop when there is just enough string left to tie another large knot.

3. Tie a large knot in the unknotted end of the string.

4. Try to bend the string of beads at different places.

Making Models What does the string represent in your model? What do the beads represent?

the skull and ribs. The skull protects the brain and sense organs. The ribs attach to the vertebrae and protect the heart, lungs, and other internal organs. Many vertebrates also have arm and leg bones adapted for a variety of movements.

A vertebrate's endoskeleton has several important characteristics. For one thing, unlike an arthropod's exoskeleton, it grows as the animal grows. It also forms an internal frame that supports the body against the downward pull of gravity, while allowing easy movement. Because of these endoskeleton characteristics, vertebrates can grow bigger than animals with exoskeletons or no skeletons at all.

☑ *Checkpoint* *What functions does a vertebrate's skeleton perform?*

Maintaining Body Temperature

One characteristic that distinguishes the major groups of vertebrates from each other is the way in which they control their body temperature. **Most fishes, amphibians, and reptiles have a body temperature that is close to the temperature of their environment. In contrast, birds and mammals have a stable body temperature that is typically much warmer than their environment.** Fishes, amphibians, and reptiles are ectotherms. An **ectotherm** is an animal whose body does not produce much internal heat—its body temperature changes depending on the temperature of its environment. For example, when a turtle is lying in the sun on a riverbank, it has a higher body temperature than when it is swimming in a cool river. Ectotherms are sometimes called "coldblooded," but this term is misleading because the blood of ectotherms is often quite warm.

Figure 3 Like other ectotherms, this woma python's body temperature changes depending on the temperature of its environment. When ectotherms live in hot places, like this Australian desert, they retreat to cooler spots during the hottest part of the day.

In contrast to a turtle, a beaver would have the same body temperature whether it was in cool water or on warm land. The beaver is a mammal, and mammals and birds are endotherms. An **endotherm** is an animal whose body controls and regulates its temperature by controlling the internal heat it produces. An endotherm's body temperature usually does not change much, even when the temperature of its environment changes.

Endotherms also have other adaptations, such as fur or feathers and sweat glands, for maintaining their body temperature. Fur and feathers keep endotherms warm on cool days. On hot days, on the other hand, some endotherms sweat. As the sweat evaporates, the animal is cooled. Because endotherms can keep their body temperatures stable, they can live in a greater variety of environments than ectotherms can.

Evolution of Vertebrates

The first tiny chordates swam in Earth's waters long before vertebrates appeared. If you look at Figure 5 on the next page, you will see that the pattern of vertebrate evolution looks something like a branching tree. Fossil evidence indicates that the earliest vertebrates were fishes, which first appeared about 530 million years ago. Amphibians, which appeared on Earth about 380 million years ago, are descended from fishes. Then, about 320 million years ago, amphibians gave rise to reptiles. Both mammals and birds, which you will learn about in Chapter 15, are descended from reptiles. Mammals appeared about 220 million years ago. Birds, which were the latest group of vertebrates to arise, appeared about 150 million years ago.

Figure 4 Though Antarctic winter temperatures can fall to −50°C, a dense coat keeps adult emperor penguins warm. A thick, fluffy baby coat keeps a penguin chick warm until it gets its adult coat.
Inferring Do you think the emperor penguin is an ectotherm or an endotherm?

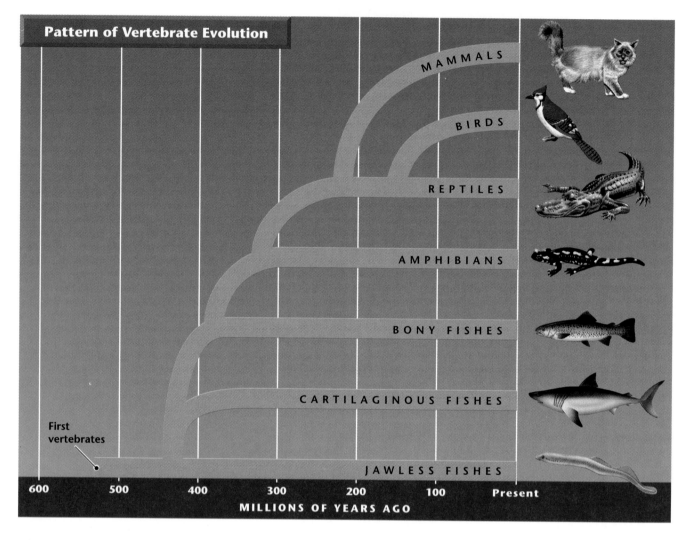

Pattern of Vertebrate Evolution

MAMMALS

BIRDS

REPTILES

AMPHIBIANS

BONY FISHES

CARTILAGINOUS FISHES

First vertebrates

JAWLESS FISHES

| 600 | 500 | 400 | 300 | 200 | 100 | Present |

MILLIONS OF YEARS AGO

Figure 5 The diagram shows the branching pattern of vertebrate evolution. The first vertebrates, the jawless fishes, arose about 530 million years ago. *Interpreting Diagrams About how much time passed between the time when fishes first appeared and the time that birds arose?*

Section 1 Review

1. What are three functions of a backbone?
2. Explain how ectotherms and endotherms differ in the way they control their body temperature. Give two examples of each.
3. What two groups of present-day vertebrates are the descendants of reptiles?
4. **Thinking Critically** **Making Generalizations** Would you expect ectotherms or endotherms to be more active at night? Explain your answer.

Science at Home

Have members of your family feel the tops of the vertebrae running down the center of their backs. Then have them feel the hard skull beneath the skin on their foreheads. In addition, if you have fish with bones for dinner, examine the fish skeleton with your family after dinner, pointing out the backbone. Show where the spinal cord runs through the vertebrae. Discuss the functions of the backbone and skull.

SECTION

2 Fishes

How Does Water Flow Over a Fish's Gills?

1. Closely observe a fish in an aquarium for a few minutes. Note how frequently the fish opens its mouth. Water moves through the fish's mouth across its gills.

2. Notice the flaps on each side of the fish's head behind its eyes. Observe how the flaps open and close.

3. Observe the movements of the mouth and the flaps at the same time. Note any relationship between the movements of these two structures.

Think It Over

Observing What do the flaps on the sides of the fish do when the fish opens its mouth? What role do you think these two structures play in a fish's life?

In the warm waters of a coral reef, a fish called a moray eel hovers in the water, barely moving. A smaller fish, a wrasse, swims up to the moray and begins to eat tiny parasites that are attached to the moray's skin. Like a vacuum cleaner on a rug, the wrasse moves slowly over the moray eel, eating dead skin and bacteria as well as parasites. The wrasse even cleans inside the moray's mouth and gills. Both fishes benefit from this cleaning. The moray gets rid of parasites and other unwanted materials, and the wrasse gets a meal.

Both the wrasse and the moray it cleans belong to the vertebrate group known as fishes. A **fish** is a vertebrate that lives in the water and has fins, which are structures used for moving. In addition, most fishes are ectotherms, obtain oxygen through gills, and have scales. Scales are thin, overlapping plates that cover the skin of a fish. They are made of a hard substance similar to that of your fingernails.

Fishes make up the largest group of vertebrates—nearly half of all vertebrate species are fishes. In addition, fishes have been swimming in Earth's waters for more than 500 million years—longer than any other kind of vertebrate.

GUIDE FOR READING

◆ How do fish use their gills?

◆ What are the three groups of fishes?

Reading Tip As you read about the different groups of fishes, make a table that compares and contrasts the characteristics of the groups.

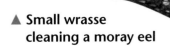

▲ Small wrasse cleaning a moray eel

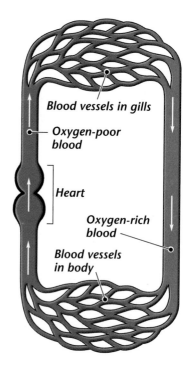

Figure 6 Trace the path of blood through a fish's one-loop circulatory system. *Interpreting Diagrams Where does the blood pick up oxygen?*

Labels on figure:
Blood vessels in gills
Oxygen-poor blood
Heart
Oxygen-rich blood
Blood vessels in body

Obtaining Oxygen

Fishes get their oxygen from water. As a fish cruises along, it automatically opens its mouth, as you observed in the Discover activity, and takes a gulp of water. The water, which contains oxygen, moves through openings in the fish's throat region that lead to the gills. Gills, which look like tiny feathers, are red because of the many blood vessels within them. **As water flows over the gills, oxygen moves from the water into the fish's blood, while carbon dioxide, a waste product, moves out of the blood and into the water.** After flowing over the gills, water leaves the fish by flowing out through slits beneath the gill covers.

From the gills, the blood travels throughout the fish's body, supplying the body cells with oxygen. Like all vertebrates, fishes have a closed circulatory system, in which blood flows through blood vessels to all regions of the body. The heart of a fish pumps blood in one continuous loop—from the heart to the gills, from the gills to the rest of the body, and back to the heart. Trace this path in Figure 6.

Moving and Feeding

Fins help fish swim. A typical fin, such as those on the angelfish in Figure 7, consists of a thin membrane stretched across bony supports. Like a wide canoe paddle, a fin provides a large surface to push against the water. If you've ever swum wearing a pair of swim fins and noticed how much faster you move through the water, you understand the great advantage of the large surface of a fin.

Because fishes spend most of their time hunting for food or feeding, most of their movements are related to eating. The bodies of most fishes are adapted for efficient feeding. Some carnivores, such as barracuda, have sharp and pointed teeth—good for stabbing smaller fishes. Insect-eating fish, such as trout, have short, blunt teeth with which they grip and crush their prey. Filter feeders, such as basking sharks, use comblike structures on their gills to filter tiny animals and plants from the water.

A fish's highly developed nervous system and sense organs help it find food and avoid predators. Fishes can see much better in water than you can. Keen senses of touch, smell, and taste also help fishes capture food. A shark can smell and taste even a tiny amount of blood—as little as one drop in 115 liters of water! Some fishes have taste organs in unusual places; a catfish, for example, tastes with its whiskers.

Checkpoint How does having fins help a fish?

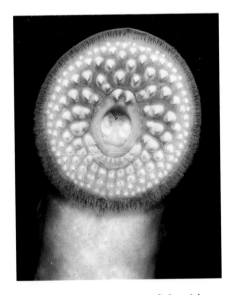

Figure 7 A fish's fins act as paddles to propel it through the water. You can clearly see the bone structure of a fin on the skeleton of an angelfish.

How Fishes Reproduce

Most fishes have external fertilization. Recall from Chapter 13 that in external fertilization, the eggs are fertilized outside of the female's body. The male hovers close to the female and spreads a cloud of sperm over the eggs as she releases them. Sharks and guppies, in contrast, have internal fertilization, in which the eggs are fertilized inside the female's body. The young fish then develop inside her body. When they are mature enough to live on their own, she gives birth to them.

Fishes Without Jaws

Biologists classify fishes into three major groups: jawless fishes, cartilaginous fishes, and bony fishes. They are distinguished from one another by the structure of their mouths and the types of skeletons they have. Jawless fishes were the earliest vertebrates. Today there are only about 60 species. Modern jawless fishes are unlike other fishes in that they have no scales. Their skeletons are made of cartilage, and they do not have pairs of fins. Most remarkably, they cannot bite like other fishes because their mouths do not have jaws! How can a fish without a jaw eat? The mouths of jawless fishes have structures for scraping, stabbing, and sucking.

Hagfishes and lampreys are the only kinds of jawless fishes. Hagfishes look like large, slimy worms. They crawl into the bodies of dead or dying fishes and use their sandpapery tongue to consume their decaying tissues. Many lampreys are parasites of other fishes. They attach their mouths to healthy fishes and then suck in the tissues and blood of their victims. If you look at the lamprey's mouth in Figure 8, you can probably imagine the damage it can do.

Figure 8 Lampreys are fish with eel-shaped bodies. They use their sharp teeth and suction-cup mouth to feed on other fish. *Classifying To what group of fishes do lampreys belong?*

Cartilaginous Fishes

Sharks, rays, and skates are cartilaginous (cahrt uhl AJ uh nuhs) fishes. As the group's name suggests, the skeletons of these fishes are made of cartilage, just like the skeletons of jawless fishes. However, unlike lampreys and hagfishes, cartilaginous fishes have jaws and pairs of fins. Pointed, toothlike scales cover their bodies, giving them a texture that is rougher than sandpaper. Cartilaginous fishes are all carnivores. Rays and skates live on the ocean floor, where they filter feed or hunt mollusks, crustaceans, and small fishes.

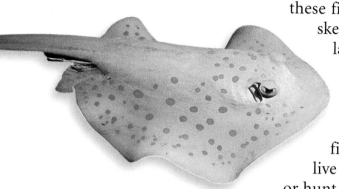

Figure 9 This blue-spotted ray is a cartilaginous fish that lives on the ocean floor. *Comparing and Contrasting* How do cartilaginous fishes differ from jawless fishes?

A Shark's Body Most shark bodies are streamlined so they can move quickly through the water. A shark's mouth is usually on the bottom part of its head. It contains jagged teeth arranged in rows. Most sharks use only the first couple of rows for feeding—the remaining rows are replacements. If a shark loses a front-row tooth, a tooth behind it moves up to replace it.

Always on the Move Most sharks cannot pump water over their gills. Instead they rely on swimming or currents to keep water moving across their gills. When sharks sleep, they position themselves in currents that send water over their gills.

Sharks spend most of their time hunting for food. They will attack and eat nearly anything that smells like food. Because they see poorly, sometimes they swallow strange objects. For example, one shark was found to have a raincoat, three overcoats, and an automobile license plate in its stomach.

☑ *Checkpoint* *Why must sharks always keep water moving over their gills?*

Figure 10 This sand tiger shark exhibits a very familiar shark trait—many sharp teeth. Despite this shark's ferocious appearance, however, sand tiger sharks do not typically attack humans.

Bony Fishes

Most familiar kinds of fishes, such as trout, tuna, and goldfish, have skeletons made of hard bone. Their bodies are covered with scales, and a pocket on each side of the head holds the fish's gills. Each gill pocket is covered by a flexible flap that opens to release water. To learn more about the major characteristics of bony fishes, look closely at the perch in *Exploring a Bony Fish*.

Swim Bladders and Buoyancy If you drop a brick into water, **INTEGRATING PHYSICS** it sinks to the bottom. A wooden block, in contrast, floats on the surface. Unlike the brick or the block, fishes neither sink nor float on the surface.

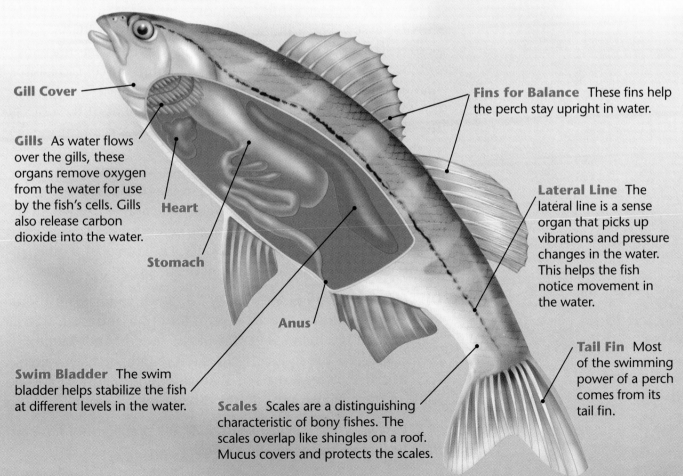

EXPLORING a Bony Fish

In a quiet, shady area near the bank of a stream or pond, you might find some yellow perch swimming along. These freshwater fish, which like slow-moving water, travel in groups called schools.

Gill Cover

Gills As water flows over the gills, these organs remove oxygen from the water for use by the fish's cells. Gills also release carbon dioxide into the water.

Heart

Stomach

Anus

Swim Bladder The swim bladder helps stabilize the fish at different levels in the water.

Scales Scales are a distinguishing characteristic of bony fishes. The scales overlap like shingles on a roof. Mucus covers and protects the scales.

Fins for Balance These fins help the perch stay upright in water.

Lateral Line The lateral line is a sense organ that picks up vibrations and pressure changes in the water. This helps the fish notice movement in the water.

Tail Fin Most of the swimming power of a perch comes from its tail fin.

441

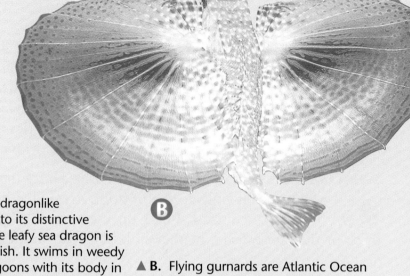

Figure 11 The photographs show just a few species of bony fishes. *Making Generalizations What characteristics do all of these fish have in common?*

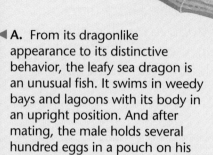

◄ **A.** From its dragonlike appearance to its distinctive behavior, the leafy sea dragon is an unusual fish. It swims in weedy bays and lagoons with its body in an upright position. And after mating, the male holds several hundred eggs in a pouch on his belly until they are ready to hatch.

▲ **B.** Flying gurnards are Atlantic Ocean fish that have winglike pectoral fins. Though flying gurnards do not really fly, they do use their "wings" for underwater gliding and for attracting mates.

Instead, they swim at different depths in the water. Most bony fishes have an organ called a **swim bladder**, an internal gas-filled sac that helps the fish stabilize its body at different depths.

A swim bladder is filled with oxygen, nitrogen, and carbon dioxide gases. The volume of gases in the swim bladder can become larger or smaller. This change in volume affects the buoyant force on the fish. **Buoyant force** (BOI uhnt force) is the force that water exerts upward on any underwater object. If the buoyant force on an object is greater than the weight of the object, then the object floats. If the buoyant force is less than the weight of the object, the object sinks. A brick sinks because it weighs more than the buoyant force pushing upward against it; a wooden block floats because it weighs less than the buoyant force.

A fish has greater buoyancy when the volume of gases in its swim bladder is large than when the gas volume is small. By adjusting its buoyancy as it moves in the water, a fish can float at different depths without using a large amount of energy.

Diversity of Bony Fishes Bony fishes, which make up about 95 percent of all fish species, live in both salt and fresh water. Some live in the lightless depths of the oceans, and seldom, if ever, come near the surface. Others thrive in light-filled waters, such as those of coral reefs or shallow ponds. Figure 11 shows some of the great variety of bony fishes.

✓ *Checkpoint If a pencil floats, how does the buoyant force on the pencil compare to the pencil's weight?*

442

D. Balloonfish are spiny puffer fish that live in warm waters all over the world. When a balloonfish is threatened, it swallows large amounts of water or air to make itself into a spiny ball. Few predators would dare take a bite! ▼

▲ **C.** These brightly colored anemone fish swim safely through the tentacles of a sea anemone. The sea anemone's tentacles can be fatal to other fishes, but they don't harm the anemone fish. Each type of anemone fish prefers to live in one specific type of anemone.

Food for People

INTEGRATING ENVIRONMENTAL SCIENCE People used to think of oceans and rivers as having a limitless supply of fish. Recently, though, overfishing has drastically reduced populations of the Atlantic codfish, Pacific salmon, and many other fish species. Some countries are trying to stop overfishing. The United States, Canada, and other countries have recently set limits on the amounts of certain kinds of fish that can be caught. In addition, some fishes, such as catfish, are being raised in "fish farms." This practice reduces the demand for fish caught in rivers and oceans.

Section 2 Review

1. Could a fish obtain oxygen if it could not open its mouth? In explaining your answer, describe the role of the fish's gills.
2. How is a shark's skeleton different from a perch's?
3. Describe the ways in which two different fishes are adapted to obtain food.
4. **Thinking Critically** **Predicting** How might a shark's hunting be affected if it were unable to smell?

Check Your Progress

CHAPTER PROJECT

By now you should have decided on the adaptation that you want to model. Select a specific fish in which to model this adaptation. Reference books, software, and magazine articles can help you make this choice. Then assemble your materials and build your model. *(Hint:* You might want to go to a pet store to observe how fish and other vertebrates move.)

Home Sweet Home

For an artificial environment to work, it must meet the needs of the organisms that live in it. In this lab, you will build an aquarium for guppies, whose natural environment is warm, fresh water.

Problem

How does an aquarium enable fish to survive?

Skills Focus

making models, posing questions

Materials

gravel	metric ruler	guppies
snails	guppy food	dip net
tap water	thermometer	water plants
aquarium filter	aquarium heater	

rectangular aquarium tank (15 to 20 liters) with cover

Procedure

1. Wash the aquarium tank with lukewarm water—do not use soap. Then place it on a flat surface in indirect sunlight.
2. Rinse the gravel and spread it over the bottom of the tank to a depth of about 3 cm.
3. Fill the tank about two-thirds full with tap water. Position several water plants in the tank by gently pushing their roots into the gravel. Wash your hands after handling the plants.
4. Add more water until the level is about 5 cm from the top.

5. Place the filter in the water and turn it on. Insert an aquarium heater into the tank, and turn it on. Set the temperature to 25°C. **CAUTION:** *Do not touch electrical equipment with wet hands.*
6. Allow the water to "age" by letting it stand for 2 days. Aging allows the chlorine to evaporate.
7. When the water has aged and is at the proper temperature, add guppies and snails to the tank. Include one guppy and one snail for each 4 liters of water. Cover the aquarium. Wash your hands after handling the animals.
8. Observe the aquarium every day for 2 weeks. Feed the guppies a small amount of food daily. Look for evidence that the fish and snails have adapted to their new environment. Also look for the ways they carry out their life activities, such as feeding and respiration. Record your observations.
9. Use a dip net to keep the gravel layer clean and to remove any dead plants or animals.

Analyze and Conclude

1. How does the aquarium meet the following needs of the organisms living in it: (a) oxygen supply, (b) proper temperature, and (c) food?
2. What happens to the oxygen that the fish take in from the water in this aquarium? How is that oxygen replaced?
3. **Apply** How is an aquarium like a guppy's natural environment? How is it different?

More to Explore

Write a plan for adding a different kind of fish to the aquarium. Include a list of questions that you would need to have answered before you could carry out your plan. Get the approval of your teacher before going ahead with your plan.

SECTION 3 Amphibians

DISCOVER .... ACTIVITY

What's the Advantage of Being Green?

1. Count out 20 dried yellow peas and 20 green ones. Mix them up in a paper cup.

2. Cover your eyes. Have your partner gently scatter the peas onto a large sheet of green paper.

3. Uncover your eyes. Have your partner keep time while you pick up as many peas, one at a time, as you can find in 15 seconds.

4. When 15 seconds are up, count how many peas of each color you picked up.

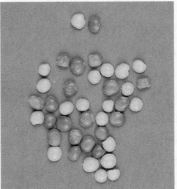

5. Repeat Steps 2 through 4, but this time you scatter the peas and keep time while your partner picks up the peas.

6. Compare your results with those of your partner and your classmates.

Think It Over

Inferring Many frogs are green, and the environment in which they live is mostly green. What advantage does a frog have in being green?

If you walk through a damp, wooded area in the Northeast, you may be surrounded by them. But chances are good that you'll never see one. During the day, they hide in holes in the ground and cracks in rocks. At night they scramble over the decaying leaves on the forest floor, searching for food. Some climb to the tops of bushes and rocks to find their prey. What are these creatures that roam by night? They are red-backed salamanders.

Most of these slender, long-tailed animals are only as long as your longest finger. They may be small, but there are a lot of them. Some northeastern woodlands probably have more red-backed salamanders than all birds and mammals combined.

GUIDE FOR READING

◆ What is the life cycle of an amphibian like?

◆ How are amphibians adapted for movement on land?

Reading Tip Before you begin to read, write two or three things you already know about amphibians. After you have read this section, add three things you have learned.

Figure 12 Red-backed salamanders are the most common amphibians in some damp northeastern woodlands.

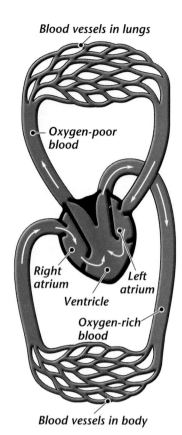

Blood vessels in lungs

Oxygen-poor blood

Right atrium

Left atrium

Ventricle

Oxygen-rich blood

Blood vessels in body

Figure 13 An adult amphibian's circulatory system has two loops. One loop runs from the heart to the lungs and back, and the second runs from the heart to the body and back.

Gills to Lungs

The red-backed salamander is one kind of amphibian; frogs and toads are others. An **amphibian** is an ectothermic vertebrate that spends its early life in water. The word *amphibian* means "double life," and amphibians have exactly that. **After beginning their lives in the water, most amphibians spend their adulthood on land, returning to water to reproduce.**

Most amphibians lay their eggs in water. Amphibian eggs hatch into larvae that swim and have gills for obtaining oxygen. As they undergo metamorphosis and become adults, most amphibians lose their gills and acquire lungs. Adult amphibians also obtain oxygen and get rid of carbon dioxide through their thin, moist skin.

Amphibian Circulation

The circulatory system of a tadpole—the larval form of a frog or toad—has a single loop, like that of a fish. In contrast, the circulatory system of many adult amphibians has two loops. In the first loop, blood flows from the heart to the lungs and skin, and picks up oxygen. This oxygen-rich blood then returns to the heart. In the second loop, the blood flows to the rest of the body, delivering oxygen-rich blood to the cells.

As you read about the heart, trace the path of blood through the amphibian's circulatory system shown in Figure 13. The hearts of most amphibians have three inner spaces, or chambers. The two upper chambers of the heart, called **atria** (singular *atrium*), receive blood. One atrium receives oxygen-rich blood from the lungs, and the other receives oxygen-poor blood from the rest of the body. From the atria, blood moves into the lower chamber, the **ventricle**, which pumps blood out to the lungs and body. Oxygen-rich and oxygen-poor blood mix in the ventricle.

✓ *Checkpoint* *Compare the functions of the atria and ventricle.*

Reproduction and Development

On spring evenings near a lake or pond, you can usually hear a loud chorus of "peepers," male frogs calling to attract mates. Most frogs and toads have external fertilization—a female frog releases eggs that are then fertilized by the male's sperm. In contrast, most salamanders have internal fertilization—the eggs are fertilized before they are laid.

Figure 14 The throat of this "peeper" inflates as he calls out to potential mates.

Amphibian eggs are coated with clear jelly that keeps moisture in and helps protect them from infection. Inside each fertilized egg, a tiny embryo develops. In a few days, larvae wriggle out of the jelly and begin a free-swimming, fishlike life.

Most amphibian parents don't take care of their eggs after fertilization, but some do. For example, in one species of South American river toad, the male presses the fertilized eggs into the skin of the female's back. Skin grows over the eggs, and the young go through the tadpole stage beneath their mother's skin, safe from predators. Tiny frogs eventually hatch out of her skin.

Most amphibians undergo metamorphosis. Trace the process of frog metamorphosis in Figure 15. Hind legs appear first, accompanied by changes in the skeleton, circulatory system, and digestive system. Later the front legs appear. At about the same time, the tadpole loses its gills and starts to breathe with its lungs.

Unlike the tadpoles of frogs and toads, the larvae of salamanders resemble the adults. Most salamander larvae undergo a metamorphosis in which they lose their gills. However, the changes are not as dramatic as those that happen during frog and toad metamorphosis.

Figure 15 During its metamorphosis from tadpole to adult, a frog's body undergoes a series of dramatic changes. *Applying Concepts How do these changes prepare a frog for living on land?*

Language Arts
CONNECTION

When a tadpole becomes an adult frog, it moves to an unfamiliar location—a land environment that is very different from the watery one in which it has been living. While real tadpoles need no instructions for how to accomplish this move, you are about to write an imaginary guidebook for tadpoles that prepares them for their move onto land.

In Your Journal

First, brainstorm what types of information might be useful to the tadpole, such as how solid ground is different from water and where a frog might find food. Then choose four or five of your ideas and write a brief suggestion for each. Write in a lively way, using descriptive language.

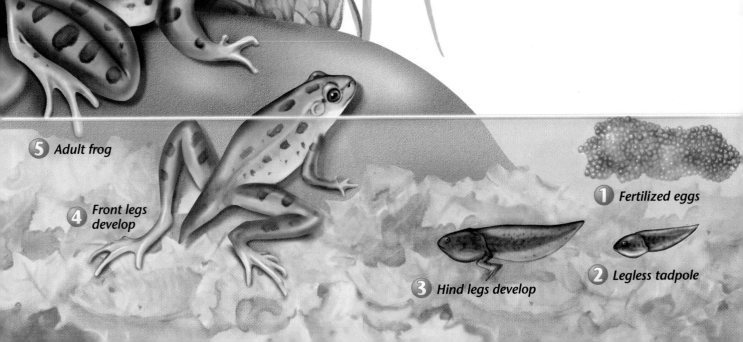

5 **Adult frog**

4 **Front legs develop**

3 **Hind legs develop**

2 **Legless tadpole**

1 **Fertilized eggs**

Getting Around on Land

Because it is not supported by water's buoyancy, a land animal needs a strong skeleton to support its body against the pull of gravity. In addition, a land animal needs some way of moving. Fins work in water, but they don't work on land. **Most adult amphibians have strong skeletons and muscular limbs adapted for movement on land.** Amphibians were the first vertebrates to have legs.

The eyes of amphibians are adapted to life on land. A transparent membrane helps keep them from drying out. Amphibians also have eyelids. Unlike fishes and tadpoles, whose wide-open eyes are always bathed in water, adult amphibians can close their eyes.

Frogs and Toads

When most people hear the word *amphibian*, they first think of frogs and toads—amphibians that are adapted for hopping and leaping. This kind of movement requires powerful hind-leg muscles and a skeleton that can absorb the shock of landing. The feet of frogs and toads have other adaptations, too. The webbed feet and long toes of bullfrogs form swim fins that help the frogs dart through the water. Tree frogs have toe pads with adhesive suckers that provide secure holds as the frogs leap from twig to twig.

It is usually easy to distinguish a frog from a toad. The skin of a frog is smooth and very moist, while that of a toad is drier and bumpy. Many toads have large lumps behind their eyes. These are actually skin glands that ooze a poisonous liquid when the toad is attacked by a predator such as a raccoon.

Although most tadpoles are herbivores, most adult frogs and toads are predators that feed on insects or other small animals. Insects don't usually see the frogs and toads that prey on them, because many frogs and toads are colored in such a way that they blend in with their environment. Green frogs, such as the one shown in *Exploring a Frog,* are brownish-green, making them hard to see in the ponds and meadows where they live. If you did the Discover activity, you learned that it is hard to see something green against a green background. Besides concealing frogs and toads from prey, their coloring also helps protect them from enemies.

✓ *Checkpoint* *How can you tell a frog from a toad?*

Salamanders

Salamanders are amphibians that keep their tails as adults. Their bodies are long and usually slender. Unlike frogs and toads, the

EXPLORING *a Frog*

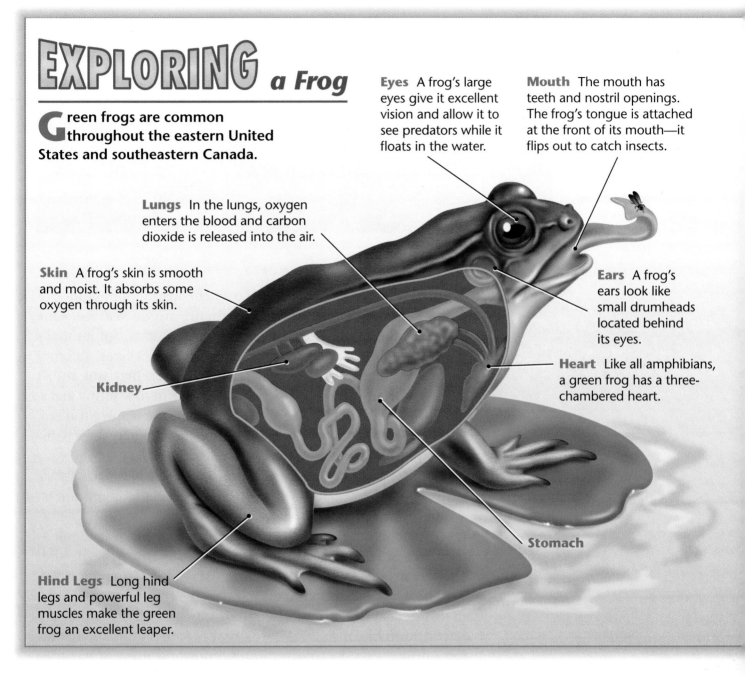

Green frogs are common throughout the eastern United States and southeastern Canada.

Eyes A frog's large eyes give it excellent vision and allow it to see predators while it floats in the water.

Mouth The mouth has teeth and nostril openings. The frog's tongue is attached at the front of its mouth—it flips out to catch insects.

Lungs In the lungs, oxygen enters the blood and carbon dioxide is released into the air.

Skin A frog's skin is smooth and moist. It absorbs some oxygen through its skin.

Ears A frog's ears look like small drumheads located behind its eyes.

Kidney

Heart Like all amphibians, a green frog has a three-chambered heart.

Stomach

Hind Legs Long hind legs and powerful leg muscles make the green frog an excellent leaper.

legs of salamanders are not adapted for jumping. Rather, salamanders stalk and ambush the small invertebrates that they eat. Most salamanders return to water each year to breed and lay their eggs. The eggs hatch into larvae that swim, feed, and soon grow into adults.

Some kinds of salamanders live in water all of their lives, while many other kinds live almost entirely on land. Some salamanders that live only on land do not have lungs. They rely on their thin, moist skins to obtain oxygen from air and to remove carbon dioxide from their blood. These lungless salamanders do not even return to water to reproduce. They lay their eggs in moist places on land, and they look like miniature adults when they hatch, not like larvae with gills.

Figure 16 This young red-spotted newt is among the many amphibians in danger from poisons in its environment.

Amphibians in Danger

INTEGRATING ENVIRONMENTAL SCIENCE All over the world, populations of amphibians are decreasing. One reason is the destruction of amphibian habitats. An animal's **habitat** is the specific environment in which it lives. When a swamp is filled in or a forest is cut, an area that was moist becomes drier. Few amphibians can survive in dry, sunny areas. But habitat destruction does not account for the whole problem, because amphibians are declining even in areas where their habitats have not been damaged.

Because their skins are very thin and their eggs lack shells, amphibians are especially sensitive to changes in the environment. Poisons in the environment, such as insecticides and other chemicals, can pollute the waters that are essential to the life of an amphibian. Even small amounts of these chemicals can weaken adult amphibians, kill amphibian eggs, or cause tadpoles to be deformed.

The decline in amphibians may be a warning that other animals are also in danger. The environmental changes that are hurting amphibians may eventually affect other animals, including humans. To try to save amphibians and prevent harm to other animals, scientists are working to understand what is causing amphibian numbers to decline.

Section 3 Review

1. Why is it said that amphibians have a double life?
2. Compare an adult amphibian's skeleton and method of moving to those of a fish.
3. How has forest destruction affected amphibians? Why has it had this effect?
4. **Thinking Critically Relating Cause and Effect** A lungless salamander cannot survive if its skin dries out. Explain why.

Check Your Progress CHAPTER PROJECT

At this point, you should have chosen an amphibian to model. Make sure that you are modeling the same type of adaptation that you did for the fish. (*Hint:* Before you begin constructing your model, make a sketch of what it will look like.)

4 Reptiles

DISCOVER • ACTIVITY • • •

How Do Snakes Feed?

1. To model how a snake feeds, stretch a sock cuff over a grapefruit "prey" by first pulling on one side and then on the other. Work the grapefruit down into the "stomach." A snake's jawbones can spread apart like the sock cuff.

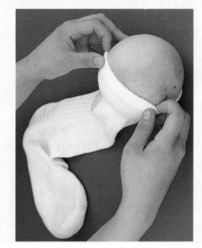

2. Remove the grapefruit and put a rubber band around the sock about 8 cm below the opening. The rubber band represents the firmly joined jawbones of a lizard. Now try to repeat Step 1.

Think It Over

Inferring What is the advantage of having jawbones like a snake's?

The king cobra of Southeast Asia, which can grow to more than 4 meters, is the world's longest venomous snake. When it encounters a predator, a king cobra flattens its neck and rears up. Its ropelike body sways back and forth, and its tongue flicks in and out.

A king cobra's fearsome behavior in response to a predator contrasts with the gentle way it treats its eggs. King cobras are one of the only snakes that build nests. The female builds a nest of grass and leaves on the forest floor. She lays her eggs inside the nest and guards them until they hatch.

Protection from Drying Out

Like other reptiles, king cobras lay their eggs on land rather than in water. A **reptile** is an ectothermic vertebrate that has lungs and scaly skin. In addition to snakes, lizards, turtles, and alligators are also reptiles.

GUIDE FOR READING

◆ What are some adaptations that allow reptiles to live on dry land?

◆ How is a reptile's egg different from an amphibian's egg?

Reading Tip As you read, write brief summaries of the information under each heading.

◀ King cobra

Unlike amphibians, reptiles can spend their entire lives on dry land. Reptiles were the first vertebrates that were well adapted to live on land, and they were the dominant land animals for about 160 million years. About 7,000 kinds of reptiles are alive today, but they are only a tiny fraction of a group that once dominated the land.

You can think of a land animal as a pocket of water held within a bag of skin. To thrive on land, an animal must have adaptations that keep the water within the "bag" from evaporating in the dry air. **The eggs, skin, and kidneys of reptiles are adapted to conserve water.**

An Egg With a Shell The eggs of reptiles are fertilized internally. While they are still inside the body of the female, fertilized eggs are covered with membranes and a shell. **Unlike an amphibian's egg, a reptile's egg has a shell and membranes that protect the developing embryo and help keep it from drying out.** Reptile eggs look much like bird eggs, except that their shells are soft and leathery, instead of rigid. Tiny holes, or pores, in the shell let oxygen in and carbon dioxide out. Since their eggs conserve water, reptiles—unlike amphibians—can lay their eggs on dry land.

Look carefully at Figure 17 to see how the membranes of a reptile's egg are arranged. One membrane holds the liquid that surrounds the embryo. Like bubble wrap that cushions breakable objects, the liquid keeps the embryo from getting crushed. The liquid also keeps the embryo moist. A second membrane holds the yolk, which provides the embryo with the food its cells must have to grow. A third membrane holds the embryo's wastes.

Figure 17 The egg from which this turtle is hatching provided it with food, moisture, and protection when it was an embryo. *Relating Cause and Effect List the parts of the egg that help keep the embryo from drying out.*

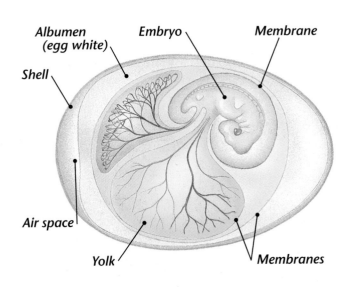

Albumen (egg white) Embryo Membrane

Shell

Air space

Yolk Membranes

Skin and Kidneys Unlike amphibians, which have thin, moist skin, reptiles have dry, tough skins covered with scales. This scaly skin protects reptiles and helps keep water in their bodies. Another adaptation that helps keep water inside a reptile's body is its kidneys, which are organs that filter wastes from the blood. The wastes are then excreted in a watery fluid called **urine**. The kidneys of reptiles concentrate the urine so that they lose very little water.

☑ *Checkpoint* *List two functions of a reptile's skin.*

Obtaining Oxygen from the Air

Reptiles get their oxygen from the air. Like you, most reptiles breathe entirely with lungs. Like adult amphibians, reptiles have two loops in which their blood circulates through their bodies. In the first loop, the blood travels from the heart to the lungs and back to the heart. In the thin, moist surfaces of lung tissue, the oxygen moves into the blood and carbon dioxide moves out. In the second loop, blood travels from the heart to the tissues of the body. In the tissues, oxygen moves out of the blood and carbon dioxide moves into it. Then the blood returns to the heart. Like amphibians, the hearts of most reptiles have three chambers—two atria and one ventricle—and some mixing of oxygen-rich and oxygen-poor blood occurs.

Lizards

Most reptiles alive today are either lizards or snakes. These two groups of reptiles are closely related and share some important characteristics. Both have skin covered with overlapping scales. As lizards and snakes grow, they shed their skins, replacing the worn scales with a new coat. Most lizards and snakes live in warm areas.

Figure 18 The skin color of this chameleon can change in response to factors in its environment, such as changes in temperature.

EXPLORING a Lizard

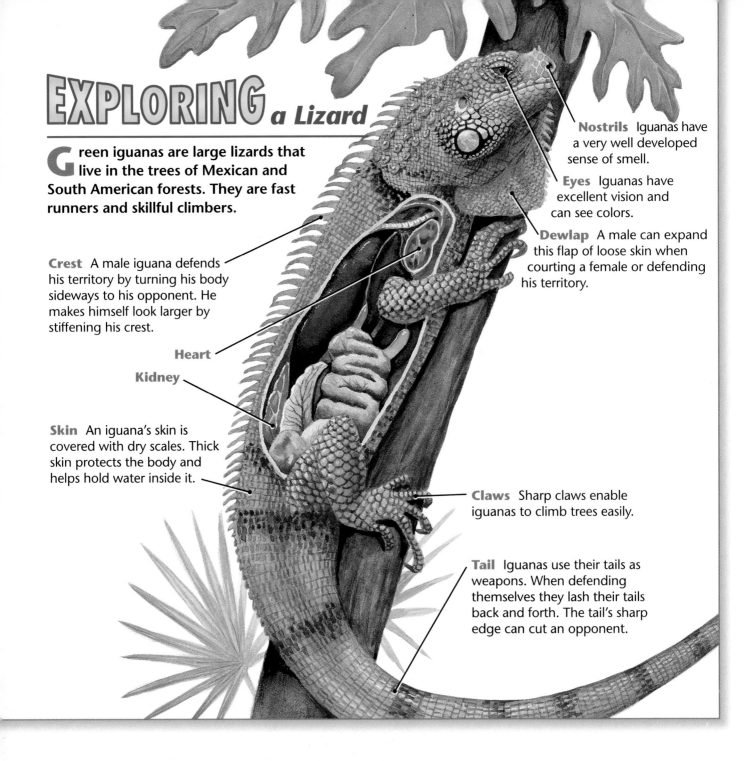

Green iguanas are large lizards that live in the trees of Mexican and South American forests. They are fast runners and skillful climbers.

Crest A male iguana defends his territory by turning his body sideways to his opponent. He makes himself look larger by stiffening his crest.

Heart

Kidney

Skin An iguana's skin is covered with dry scales. Thick skin protects the body and helps hold water inside it.

Nostrils Iguanas have a very well developed sense of smell.

Eyes Iguanas have excellent vision and can see colors.

Dewlap A male can expand this flap of loose skin when courting a female or defending his territory.

Claws Sharp claws enable iguanas to climb trees easily.

Tail Iguanas use their tails as weapons. When defending themselves they lash their tails back and forth. The tail's sharp edge can cut an opponent.

Lizards differ from snakes in one obvious way. Lizards have four legs, usually with claws on the toes. Many lizards have long tails, slender bodies, movable eyelids, and external ears.

A few lizards, including the iguana shown in *Exploring a Lizard,* are herbivores that eat leaves. Most lizards, however, are carnivores that capture food by jumping at it. While large lizards will eat large prey such as frogs and ground-dwelling birds, most small lizards are insect-hunters. Chameleons, which are found in Africa and India, have a sticky tongue adapted for snaring insects. This elastic tongue shoots out rapidly, extending as long as the chameleon's head and body put together!

Snakes

Snakes are able to live in almost every sort of habitat, from deserts to swamps. They are similar to lizards, but streamlined, both externally and internally. Snakes have no legs, eyelids, or external ears, and most snakes have only one lung.

Snakes on the Move If you've ever seen a snake slither across the ground, you know that when it moves, its long, thin body bends into curves. Snakes move by contracting, or shortening, bands of muscles that are connected to their ribs and backbones. Alternate contractions of muscles on the right and left sides produce a slithering side-to-side motion.

How Snakes Feed All snakes are carnivores, and some eat large prey. If you did the Discover activity, you learned that a snake's jawbones can spread widely apart. In addition, the bones of a snake's skull can move to let the snake swallow an animal much larger in diameter than itself. Most snakes, however, feed on small rodents, such as mice.

Snakes capture their prey in different ways. The sharp-tailed snakes of western North America, which eat only slugs, have long, curved front teeth for hooking their slippery prey. Some West Indian boas are bat hunters that wait in ambush at the entrances to caves where bats live. At twilight, when the bats fly out of the cave to feed, the snakes snatch them out of the air.

Some snakes, such as rattlesnakes and copperheads, have venom glands attached to hollow teeth called fangs. When these snakes bite a prey animal, venom flows down inside the fangs. The venom enters the flesh of the prey and kills it quickly.

☑ *Checkpoint* **How do snakes move?**

Figure 19 A wide variety of snakes live on Earth, some adapted to almost every habitat. **A.** The temple viper from Thailand has one of the strongest venoms of any snake. **B.** Although the kingsnake is not venomous, it is quite aggressive—a kingsnake will even attack and eat a rattlesnake. *Making Generalizations How are snakes different from lizards?*

A

B

Soaking Up Those Rays

In this lab, you will examine and interpret data associated with an ectotherm.

Problem

How do some lizards control their body temperatures in the extreme heat of a desert environment?

Materials

paper   pencil

Procedure

1. The data in the diagram below were collected by scientists studying how lizards control their body temperature. Examine the data.
2. Copy the data table on the next page into your notebook.
3. Organize the data in the diagram by filling in the table, putting the appropriate information in each column. Begin by writing a brief description of each type of lizard behavior.
4. Complete the data table using the information in the diagram.

Analyze and Conclude

1. How did the lizard's body temperature vary from 6 A.M. until 8 P.M.?
2. What are the three sources of heat that caused the lizard's body temperature to rise during the day?
3. During the hottest part of the day, what were the air and ground temperatures? Why do you think the lizard's temperature remained below 40°C?
4. Predict what the lizard's body temperature would have been from 8 P.M. to 6 A.M. Explain your prediction.

6 A.M.–7 A.M.
Emerging from burrow
Air temperature **20°C**
Ground temperature **28°C**
Body temperature **25°C**

7 A.M.–9 A.M.
Basking (lying on ground in sun)
Air temperature **27°C**
Ground temperature **29°C**
Body temperature **32.6°C**

9 A.M.–12 noon
Active (moving about)
Air temperature **27°C**
Ground temperature **30.8°C**
Body temperature **36.6°C**

DATA TABLE

Activity	Description of Activity	Time of Day	Air Temperature (°C)	Ground Temperature (°C)	Body Temperature (°C)
1. Emerging					
2. Basking					
3. Active					
4. Retreat					
5. Stilting					
6. Retreat					

5. Based on what you learned from the data, explain why it is misleading to say that an ectotherm is a "coldblooded" animal.

6. Predict what would happen to your own body temperature if you spent a brief period outdoors in the desert at noon. Predict what your temperature would be if you spent time in a burrow at 7 P.M. Explain your predictions.

7. Think About It Why is it helpful to organize data in a data table before you try to interpret the data?

More to Explore

Make one or more bar graphs of the temperature data. Explain what the graphs show you. How do these graphs help you interpret the data?

12 noon–2:30 P.M.
Retreat to burrow
Air temperature **40.3°C**
Ground temperature **53.8°C**
Body temperature **39.5°C**

2:30 P.M.–6 P.M.
Stilting (belly off ground)
Air temperature **34.2°C**
Ground temperature **47.4°C**
Body temperature **39.5°C**

6 P.M.–9 P.M.
Retreat to burrow
Air temperature **25°C**
Ground temperature **26°C**
Body temperature **25°C**

Figure 20 Turtles vary greatly in their feeding habits. **A.** The green sea turtle lives entirely at sea and is a carnivore. **B.** The Galapagos tortoise lives on land, where it eats mainly cacti.

Turtles

A turtle is a reptile whose body is covered by a protective shell, which is made from the turtle's ribs and backbone. As you can see in Figure 20, the bony plates of the shell are covered by large scales made from the same material as the skin's scales. Some turtle shells can cover the whole body—a box turtle can draw its head, legs, and tail inside its shell for protection. Turtles like the snapping turtle have much smaller shells. Soft-shelled turtles, as their name suggests, have shells that are as soft as pancakes. Soft-shelled turtles lie in stream beds, concealed from predators, with only their nostrils and eyes above the sand.

The feeding habits of turtles are quite diverse. The largest turtles, the leatherbacks, are carnivores. Leatherbacks, which can weigh over 500 kilograms, are sea turtles that feed mainly on venomous jellyfishes. The stinging cells of the jellyfish can kill other animals, but the leatherback's tough skin seems to be unharmed by them. The giant Galapagos tortoises, on the other hand, are herbivores that feed mainly on cacti. They carefully scrape the prickly spines off before swallowing the cactus. Turtles have sharp-edged beaks instead of teeth. The razor-sharp beaks of soft-shelled turtles can chop fishes in two.

Figure 21 Alligators, left, and crocodiles, right, are the largest reptiles still living on Earth. They are similar in many ways, including appearance. *Comparing and Contrasting How can you tell the difference between an alligator and a crocodile?*

Alligators and Crocodiles

If you walk along a lake in Florida, you just might see an alligator swimming silently in the water. Most of its body lies beneath the surface, but you can see its large, bulging eyes above the surface. Alligators, crocodiles, and their relatives are the largest living reptiles. The American alligator can grow to be more than 5 meters long.

How do you tell an alligator from a crocodile? Look for teeth—but use binoculars and stay far away! Alligators have broad, rounded snouts, with only a few teeth visible when their mouths are shut. In comparison, crocodiles have pointed snouts, and you can see most of their teeth. Both alligators and crocodiles spend much of their days resting in the sun or the water.

Alligators and crocodiles are carnivores that hunt mostly at night. They have several adaptations to help them capture prey. They use their strong, muscular tails to swim rapidly through the water. Their jaws are equipped with many large, sharp, and pointed teeth. Their jaw muscles are extremely strong when biting down. Although alligators will eat dogs, raccoons, and deer, they usually do not attack humans.

Unlike most other reptiles, crocodiles and alligators care for their eggs and newly hatched young. After laying eggs in a nest of rotting plants, the female stays near the nest. From time to time she comes out of the water and crawls over the nest to keep it moist. After the tiny alligators or crocodiles hatch, the female scoops them up in her huge mouth. She carries them from the nest to a nursery area in the water where they will be safer. For as long as a year, she will stay near her young, which make gulping quacks when they're alarmed. When their mother hears her young quack, she rushes toward them.

☑ *Checkpoint* *How are alligators and crocodiles adapted for catching prey?*

Sharpen your Skills

Drawing Conclusions

ACTIVITY

Scientists incubated, or raised, eggs of one alligator species at four different temperatures. When the alligators hatched, the scientists counted the numbers of males and females. The table below shows the results.

Incubation Temperature	Number of Females	Number of Males
29.4°C	80	0
30.6°C	19	13
31.7°C	13	38
32.8°C	0	106

Use the data to answer these questions.
1. What effect does incubation temperature have on the sex of the alligators?
2. Suppose a scientist incubated 50 eggs at 31°C. About how many of the alligators that hatched would be males? Explain.

Extinct Reptiles—The Dinosaurs

Millions of years ago, huge turtles and fish-eating reptiles swam in the oceans. Flying reptiles soared through the skies. And from about 225 million years ago until 65 million years ago, reptiles were the major form of vertebrate life on land. Snakes and lizards basked on warm rocks. And there were dinosaurs of every description. Unlike today's reptiles, dinosaurs may have been endothermic. Some dinosaurs, such as the *Brachiosaurus* in Figure 22, were the largest land animals that have ever lived.

Dinosaurs were the earliest vertebrates that had legs positioned directly beneath their bodies. This adaptation allowed them to move more easily than animals, such as salamanders, whose legs stick out to the sides of their bodies. Most herbivorous dinosaurs, such as *Brachiosaurus,* walked on four legs; most carnivores, such as the huge *Tyrannosaurus rex,* ran on two legs.

Dinosaurs became extinct about 65 million years ago, long before humans appeared on Earth. Several theories try to explain their disappearance, but no one is sure why they became extinct. A change in climate from warm to cool probably played a role. One leading theory suggests that a huge meteorite, a chunk of rock sailing through space, crashed into Earth. The impact sent up thick clouds of dust that blocked out the sun. The decrease in sunlight not only made Earth cooler, it also decreased plant growth, thus limiting food supplies. Dust from massive volcanic eruptions may also have blocked out sunlight. The dinosaurs were unable to survive in these changed conditions and died out.

Today, it's only in movies that dinosaurs shake the ground with their footsteps. But in a way, dinosaurs still exist. Birds may be descended from certain small dinosaurs. Some biologists think that birds are dinosaurs with feathers.

Figure 22 *Brachiosaurus* grew to be over 22.5 meters long—longer than two school buses put together. *Observing What adaptation is demonstrated by the legs of* Brachiosaurus *and many other dinosaurs?*

Section 4 Review

1. Describe three adaptations that enabled reptiles to live on land.
2. Explain how the structure of a reptile's egg protects the developing embryo.
3. Explain how snakes are able to eat large prey.
4. **Thinking Critically Making Generalizations** If some dinosaurs had been endotherms, what advantage might they have had over other reptiles?

Check Your Progress

CHAPTER PROJECT

Assemble the materials you need in order to build your reptile model. Make sure that your model clearly shows how the animal is adapted for the same function as your fish and amphibian. Begin preparing a written explanation of the adaptations that your three models demonstrate. Your written explanation should include labeled diagrams.

SECTION 5 Vertebrate History in Rocks

DISCOVER ·······································**ACTIVITY**···

What Can You Tell From an Imprint?

1. Flatten some modeling clay into a thin sheet on a piece of paper.

2. Firmly but gently press two or three small objects into different sections of the clay. The objects might include such things as a key, a leaf, a feather, a pencil, a postage stamp, a flower, or a raisin. Don't let anyone see the objects you are using.

3. Carefully remove the objects from the clay, leaving only the objects' imprints.

4. Exchange your sheet of imprints with a partner. Try to identify the objects that made the imprints.

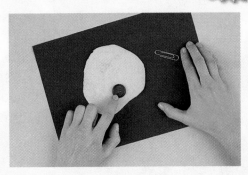

Think It Over

Observing In general, what types of objects made the clearest imprints? If those imprints were fossils, what could you learn about the objects by looking at their "fossils"? What couldn't you learn?

Millions of years ago, in an ancient pond, some fish died and their bodies settled into the mud on the bottom. Soon heavy rains fell, and more mud washed into the pond, covering the fish. The fish's soft tissues decayed, but their bones remained. After many thousands of years, the mud hardened into rock, and the fish bones became the fossils shown here.

GUIDE FOR READING

◆ What can scientists learn from studying fossils?

Reading Tip Predict what you will learn in this section. Then read to see whether your prediction is correct.

◀ Fossilized fish

Fossils in Sedimentary Rock

A **fossil** is the hardened remains or other evidence of a living thing that existed a long time in the past. Sometimes a fossil is an imprint in rock, such as an animal's footprint or the outline of a leaf. Other fossils are the remains of bones or other parts of living things—a chemical process has taken place in which the organism's tissues have become replaced by hard minerals. Because most living tissues decay rapidly, only a very few organisms become preserved as fossils.

Fossils occur most frequently in the type of rock known as sedimentary rock. **Sedimentary rock** is made of hardened layers of sediments—particles of clay, sand, mud, or silt. Have you ever

Discovering Vertebrate Fossils

People have been discovering fossils since ancient times. However, it is only within the last few centuries that people have understood that fossils are the remains of extinct organisms. Here are some especially important fossil discoveries.

1822
Dinosaur Tooth

In a quarry near Lewes, England, Mary Ann Mantell discovered a strange-looking tooth embedded in stone. Her husband Gideon drew the picture of the tooth shown here. The tooth belonged to the dinosaur *Iguanodon*.

| 1675 | 1725 | 1775 | 1825 |

1677
Dinosaur-Bone Illustration

Robert Plot, the head of a museum in England, published a book that had an illustration of a huge fossilized thighbone. Plot thought that the bone belonged to a giant human, but it probably was the thighbone of a dinosaur.

1811
Sea Reptile

Along the cliffs near Lyme Regis, England, 12-year-old Mary Anning discovered the fossilized remains of the giant sea reptile now called *Ichthyosaurus*. Mary became one of England's first professional fossil collectors.

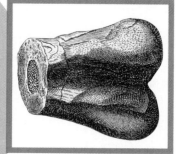

washed a dirty soccer ball and seen sand and mud settle on the bottom of the sink? If you washed a dozen soccer balls, the sink bottom would be covered with a layer of sediment. Sediments build up in many ways. For example, wind can blow a thick layer of sand onto dunes. Sediments can also form when muddy water stands in an area for a long time. Muddy sediment in the water will eventually settle to the bottom and build up.

Over a very long time, layers of sediments can be pressed and cemented together to form rock. As sedimentary rock forms, traces of living things that have been trapped in the sediments are sometimes preserved as fossils.

☑ *Checkpoint* **What are two ways in which fossils form?**

In Your Journal

If you could interview the discoverer of one of these fossils, what questions would you ask about the fossil and how it was found? Write a list of those questions in your journal. Then use reference materials to try to find the answers to some of them.

1902

Tyrannosaurus

A tip from a local rancher sent Barnum Brown, a fossil hunter, to a barren, rocky area near Jordan, Montana. There Brown found the first relatively complete *Tyrannosaurus rex* skeleton.

1991

Dinosaur Eggs in China

Digging beneath the ground, a farmer on Green Dragon Mountain in China uncovered what may be the largest nest of fossil dinosaur eggs ever found. A paleontologist chips carefully to remove one of the eggs from the rock.

1875	1925	1975	2025

1861

Bird Bones

A worker in a stone quarry in Germany discovered *Archaeopteryx*, a feathered, birdlike animal that also had many reptile characteristics.

1964

Deinonychus

In Montana, paleontologist John Ostrom discovered the remains of a small dinosaur, *Deinonychus*. This dinosaur was probably a predator who could move rapidly. This fossil led scientists to hypothesize that dinosaurs may have been endotherms.

Chapter 14 **463**

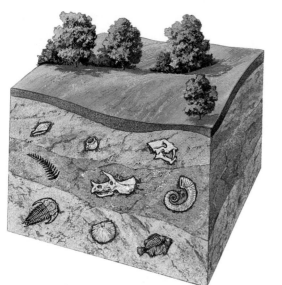

Figure 23 The diagram shows fossils in layers of sedimentary rocks. *Interpreting Diagrams Which rock layer probably contains the oldest fossils? Explain.*

Interpretation of Fossils

What information can scientists learn from fossils? **Paleontologists** (pay lee uhn TAHL uh jihsts), the scientists who study extinct organisms, examine fossil structure and make comparisons to present-day organisms. **By studying fossils, paleontologists can infer how a species changed over time.** One important piece of information that paleontologists can learn from a fossil is its approximate age.

One method for estimating a fossil's age takes advantage of the process in which sediments form. Think about sediments settling out of water—the lowest layers are deposited first, and newer sediments settle on top of the older layers. Therefore, fossils in higher layers of rock are often younger than fossils in lower layers.

However, rock layers can become tilted or even turned upside down. Natural events such as earthquakes and human events such as construction can change the position of rock layers. Therefore, a fossil's position in rock is not always a reliable indication of its age. Scientists must usually rely on other methods to help determine a fossil's age. For example, fossils—and the rocks in which they are found—contain some radioactive chemical elements. These radioactive elements decay, or change into other chemical elements, over a known period of time. The more there is of the decayed form of the element, the older the fossil.

Paleontologists have used fossil evidence to piece together the history of the major groups of vertebrates. As new fossils are found, paleontologists will reinterpret the fossil evidence and possibly revise their ideas about when different animal groups first appeared and how the groups may be related to one another.

Section 5 Review

1. How can paleontologists use fossils to determine how a species changed over time?
2. Describe how sedimentary rock forms.
3. Describe the process by which a leaf becomes fossilized.
4. **Thinking Critically Inferring** Fossil A is found in a rock layer 200 meters below the surface of the ground. Fossil B is found in the same rock formation, but at a depth of 150 meters. Which fossil is probably older? What additional evidence would help verify the fossils' ages?

Science at Home

Does your family store newspapers or magazines in a stack? With someone in your family, check the dates of the newspapers in the stack. Going from the top of the pile to the bottom, are the newspapers in any particular order? If the oldest newspapers are on the bottom and the newest on top, you can relate this to the way in which sediments are laid down. Ask family members to imagine that two fossils were trapped in different newspapers. Explain which fossil would probably be older, and why.

SECTION 1 — What Is a Vertebrate?

Key Ideas

◆ Vertebrates have a backbone that is part of an endoskeleton. The endoskeleton supports, protects, and gives shape to the body.

◆ Most fishes, amphibians, and reptiles are ectotherms. Mammals and birds are endotherms.

Key Terms

chordate   notochord   cartilage
vertebra   ectotherm   endotherm

SECTION 2 — Fishes

Key Ideas

◆ A fish is a vertebrate that lives in the water and has fins. Most fishes are ectotherms, obtain oxygen through gills, and have scales.

◆ Major groups of fishes include jawless fishes, cartilaginous fishes, and bony fishes.

Key Terms

fish
swim bladder
buoyant force

SECTION 3 — Amphibians

Key Ideas

◆ An amphibian is a moist-skinned, ectothermic vertebrate. Most amphibians spend their early lives in water and adulthood on land, returning to water to reproduce.

◆ Major groups of amphibians include frogs, toads, and salamanders.

◆ Adult amphibians have strong skeletons and muscular limbs adapted for moving on land.

Key Terms

amphibian   atrium   ventricle
habitat

SECTION 4 — Reptiles

Key Ideas

◆ A reptile is an ectothermic vertebrate that has lungs and scaly skin. Reptiles can spend their entire lives on dry land.

◆ The leathery eggs, scaly skin, and the kidneys of reptiles are adapted to conserving water.

◆ Major groups of reptiles include lizards, snakes, turtles, and alligators and crocodiles.

Key Terms

reptile
urine

SECTION 5 — Vertebrate History in Rocks

INTEGRATING EARTH SCIENCE

Key Ideas

◆ Sedimentary rock forms from hardened layers of sediments such as clay, mud, or sand.

◆ Fossils are found primarily in sedimentary rock.

◆ Paleontologists study fossils to infer how organisms, including vertebrates, have changed over time. Scientists are always reinterpreting fossil evidence.

Key Terms

fossil   sedimentary rock   paleontologist

USING THE INTERNET   *ACTIVITY*

www.science-explorer.phschool.com

California Test Prep: Reviewing Content

Multiple Choice
Choose the letter of the best answer.

1. Which fishes do not have jaws, scales, or paired fins?
   a. sharks
   b. lampreys and hagfishes
   c. sturgeons
   d. ocean sunfish

2. A bony fish uses a swim bladder to
   a. propel itself through water.
   b. regulate its buoyancy.
   c. remove wastes.
   d. pump water over its gills.

3. Adult frogs must return to the water to
   a. catch flies.
   b. obtain all their food.
   c. reproduce.
   d. moisten their gills.

4. Which of the following animals breathes with lungs?
   a. shark   b. lamprey
   c. larval salamander   d. lizard

5. Fossils are rare because
   a. there were few living things in ancient times.
   b. scientists have only searched for fossils in Africa and the United States.
   c. most fossils have sunk to the ocean floor.
   d. the bodies of dead organisms decay rapidly.

True or False
If the statement is true, write true. If it is false, change the underlined word or words to make the statement true.

6. Birds and mammals are <u>endotherms</u>.
7. If a shark loses a <u>fin</u>, another one will move into its place.
8. <u>Buoyant force</u> is the force that pushes upward against an underwater object.
9. Amphibians usually begin their lives <u>on land</u>.
10. Paleontologists are scientists who study <u>fishes</u>.

Checking Concepts

11. Describe the main characteristics of chordates.
12. How do fish reproduce?
13. Describe the life cycle of a frog.
14. How is an amphibian's circulatory system different from that of a fish?
15. Explain how the structure of a reptile's egg protects the embryo inside.
16. Compare and contrast lizards and snakes.
17. Why does a snake move in a wavelike pattern rather than in a straight line?
18. What may have caused the dinosaurs to become extinct?
19. Describe two methods that scientists use to determine the age of a fossil.
20. **Writing to Learn** Write a description of an hour in the life of a shark. Before you begin to write, list the events you want to include, and arrange those events in the sequence in which you want them to occur. As you write, use words such a *then* and *a moment later* to let your readers know that the shark is progressing from one activity to another.

Thinking Visually

21. **Compare/Contrast Table** Copy the table comparing fish groups onto a separate sheet of paper. Then complete the table and add a title. (For more on compare/contrast tables, see the Skills Handbook.)

Kind of Fish	Kind of Skeleton	Jaws?	Scales	Example
Jawless Fishes	a. ?	no	b. ?	c. ?
d. ?	e. ?	f. ?	toothlike scales	shark
Bony Fishes	bone	g. ?	h. ?	i. ?

Test Prep: Skills

A scientist performed an experiment on five goldfish to test the effect of water temperature on "breathing rate"—the rate at which the fish open and close their gill covers. The graph shows the data that the scientist obtained at four different temperatures. Use the graph to answer Questions 22–24.

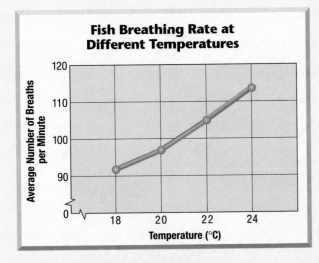

Fish Breathing Rate at Different Temperatures

Average Number of Breaths per Minute (y-axis: 90, 100, 110, 120)
Temperature (°C) (x-axis: 18, 20, 22, 24)

22. **Controlling Variables** Identify the manipulated variable and the responding variable in this experiment.
23. **Interpreting Data** How does the breathing rate at 18°C compare to the breathing rate at 22°C?
24. **Drawing Conclusions** Based on the data shown in the graph, what is the relationship between water temperature and goldfish breathing rate?

Thinking Critically

25. **Comparing and Contrasting** Compare the ways a tadpole and an adult frog obtain oxygen.
26. **Applying Concepts** Imagine that you are in the hot desert sun with a wet paper towel. You must keep the towel from drying out. What strategy can you copy from reptiles to keep the towel wet?

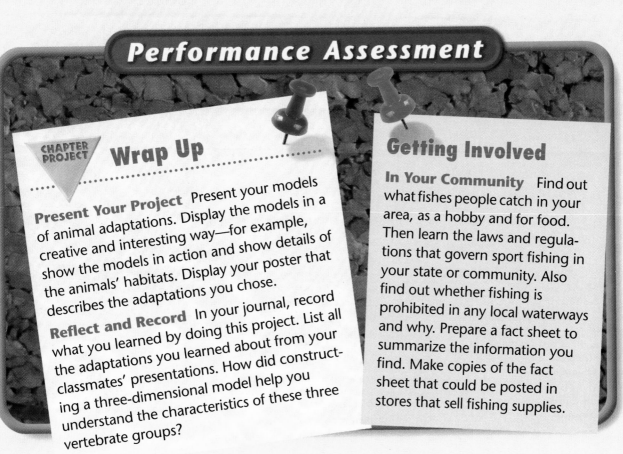

Performance Assessment

CHAPTER PROJECT **Wrap Up**

Present Your Project Present your models of animal adaptations. Display the models in a creative and interesting way—for example, show the models in action and show details of the animals' habitats. Display your poster that describes the adaptations you chose.

Reflect and Record In your journal, record what you learned by doing this project. List all the adaptations you learned about from your classmates' presentations. How did constructing a three-dimensional model help you understand the characteristics of these three vertebrate groups?

Getting Involved

In Your Community Find out what fishes people catch in your area, as a hobby and for food. Then learn the laws and regulations that govern sport fishing in your state or community. Also find out whether fishing is prohibited in any local waterways and why. Prepare a fact sheet to summarize the information you find. Make copies of the fact sheet that could be posted in stores that sell fishing supplies.

CALIFORNIA SCIENCE CONTENT STANDARDS

The following California Science Content Standards are addressed in this chapter:

2. A typical cell of any organism contains genetic instructions that specify its traits. Those traits may be modified by environmental influences.

  a. The differences between the life cycles and reproduction of sexual and asexual organisms.

3. Biological evolution accounts for the diversity of species developed through gradual processes over many generations.

  a. Both genetic variation and environmental factors are causes of evolution and diversity of organisms.

  c. How independent lines of evidence from geology, fossils, and comparative anatomy provide a basis for the theory of evolution.

4. Evidence from rocks allows us to understand the evolution of life on Earth.

  e. Fossils provide evidence of how life and environmental conditions have changed.

  g. How to explain significant developments and extinctions of plant and animal life on the geologic time scale.

Bird Watch

One of the best ways to learn about animals is to watch them in action. In this project, you'll watch birds and other animals that visit a bird feeder. You may be surprised at how much you will discover. How do birds eat? Which ones eat first? How do different birds interact? What happens if a squirrel arrives on the scene? Careful observation and record keeping will reveal answers to these questions. They may also raise new questions for you to answer.

Your Goal To make detailed observations of the birds that appear at a bird feeder.

To complete this project successfully, you must
◆ observe the feeder regularly for at least two weeks, and identify the kinds of birds that visit the feeder
◆ make detailed observations of how the birds at your feeder eat
◆ describe the most common kinds of bird behavior
◆ follow the safety guidelines in Appendix A

Get Started Begin by meeting with some classmates to share your knowledge about the birds in your area. What kinds of birds can you expect to see? What types of foods do birds eat? Brainstorm how you could find out more about the birds that live in your area.

Check Your Progress You'll be working on this project as you study this chapter. To keep your project on track, look for Check Your Progress boxes at the following points.
Section 1 Review, page 479: Identify birds (and mammals) that come to the feeder. Observe how the animals interact.
Section 2 Review, page 482: Observe how birds feed.
Section 4 Review, page 496: Interpret your bird-feeding data, and prepare your graphs.

Wrap Up At the end of this chapter (page 499), you will share what you have learned about birds and their behavior.

This broad-tailed hummingbird enjoys a sip of nectar from a beardtongue flower.

---

5. The anatomy and physiology of plants and animals illustrate the complementary nature of structure and function.

   b. Organ systems function because of the contributions of individual organs, tissues, and cells.

   c. How bones and muscles work together to provide a structural framework for movement.

e. The function of the umbilicus and placenta during pregnancy.

6. Physical principles underlie biological structures and functions.

   j. Contractions of the heart generate blood pressure, and heart valves prevent backflow of blood in the circulatory system.

7. Scientific progress is made by asking meaningful questions and conducting careful investigations.

   c. Communicate the logical connection among hypothesis, science concepts, tests conducted, data collected, and conclusions drawn from the scientific evidence.

SECTION
1 Birds

What Are Feathers Like?

1. Examine a feather. Observe its overall shape and structure. Use a hand lens to examine the many hairlike barbs that project out from the feather's central shaft.

2. With your fingertip, gently stroke the feather from bottom to top. Observe whether the barbs stick together or separate.

3. Gently separate two barbs in the middle of the feather. Rub the separated edges with your fingertip.

4. Use a hand lens to examine the feather, including the edges of the two separated barbs. Draw a diagram of what you observe.

5. Now rejoin the two separated barbs by gently pulling outward from the shaft. Then wash your hands.

Think It Over

Observing Once barbs have been separated, is it easy to rejoin them? How might this be an advantage to the bird?

GUIDE FOR READING

◆ What characteristics do birds have in common?

◆ How are birds adapted to their environments?

Reading Tip Before you read, look at *Exploring a Bird* on page 473 and make a list of unfamiliar terms. As you read, write definitions for the terms.

One day in 1861, in a limestone quarry in what is now Germany, Hermann von Meyer was inspecting rocks. Meyer, who was a fossil hunter, spotted something dark in one of the rocks. It was the blackened fossil imprint of a feather! Excited, Meyer began searching for a fossil of an entire bird. Though it took a month, he eventually found what he was looking for—a skeleton surrounded by the clear imprint of many feathers. The fossil was given the scientific name *Archaeopteryx* (ahr kee AHP tur iks), meaning "ancient, winged thing."

Paleontologists estimate that *Archaeopteryx* lived about 145 million years ago. *Archaeopteryx* didn't look much like the birds you know. It looked more like a reptile with wings. While no modern bird has any teeth, *Archaeopteryx* had a mouthful of them. No modern bird has a long, bony tail, either, but *Archaeopteryx* did. However, unlike any reptile, extinct or modern, *Archaeopteryx* had feathers— its wings and tail were covered with them. Paleontologists think that *Archaeopteryx* and today's birds descended from some kind of reptile, possibly from a dinosaur.

Figure 1 The extinct bird *Archaeopteryx* may have looked like this.

Figure 2 John James Audubon painted this little blue heron in 1832.
(© Collection of the New York Historical Society)

What Is a Bird?

Modern **birds** all share certain characteristics. **A bird is an endothermic vertebrate that has feathers and a four-chambered heart, and lays eggs.** Birds have scales on their feet and legs, evidence of their descent from reptiles. In addition, most birds can fly.

The flight of birds is an amazing feat that people watch with delight and envy. All modern birds—including ostriches, penguins, and other flightless birds—evolved from ancestors that could fly.

The bodies of birds are adapted for flight. For example, the bones of a bird's forelimbs form wings. In addition, many of a bird's bones are nearly hollow, making the bird's body extremely lightweight. Flying birds have large chest muscles that move the wings. Finally, feathers are a major adaptation that help birds fly.

☑ *Checkpoint* *List four ways in which birds are adapted for flight.*

Feathers

The rule is this: If it has feathers, it's a bird. Feathers probably evolved from reptiles' scales. Both feathers and reptile scales are made of the same tough material as your fingernails.

Birds have different types of feathers. If you've ever picked up a feather from the ground, chances are good that it was a contour feather. A **contour feather** is one of the large feathers that give shape to a bird's body. The long contour feathers that extend beyond the body on the wings and tail are called flight feathers. When a bird flies, these feathers help it balance and steer.

In Figure 3, you can see that a contour feather consists of a central shaft and many hairlike projections, called barbs, that are arranged parallel to each other. If you examined a contour feather in the Discover activity, you know that you can "unzip" its flat surface by pulling apart the barbs. When birds fly, their feathers sometimes become "unzipped." To keep their flight feathers in good condition, birds often pull the feathers through their bills in an action called preening. Preening "zips" the barbs back together again, smoothing the ruffled feathers.

INTEGRATING PHYSICS In addition to contour feathers, birds have short, fluffy **down feathers** that are specialized to trap heat and keep the bird warm. Down feathers are found right next to a bird's skin, at the base of contour feathers. Down feathers are soft and flexible, unlike contour feathers. Down feathers mingle and overlap, trapping air. Air is a good **insulator**—a material that does not conduct heat well and therefore helps prevent it from escaping. By trapping a blanket of warm air next to the bird's skin, down feathers slow the rate at which the skin loses heat. In effect, down feathers cover a bird in lightweight long underwear.

☑ *Checkpoint* *Why do you think quilts and jackets are often stuffed with down feathers?*

Food and Body Temperature

Birds have no teeth. To capture, grip, and handle food, birds primarily use their bills. Each species of bird has a bill shaped to help it feed quickly and efficiently. For example, the pointy, curved bill of a hawk acts like a meathook. A hawk holds its prey with its claws and uses its sharp bill to pull off bits of flesh. In contrast, the straight, sharp bill of a woodpecker is a tool for chipping into wood. When a woodpecker chisels a hole in a tree and finds a tasty insect, the woodpecker spears the insect with its long, barbed tongue.

After a bird eats its food, digestion begins. Each organ in a bird's digestive system is adapted to process food. Many birds have an internal storage tank, or **crop,** that allows them to store food inside the body after swallowing it. Find the crop in *Exploring a Bird,* and notice that it is connected to the stomach.

Figure 3 Birds are the only animals that have feathers. **A.** Down feathers act as insulation to trap warmth next to a bird's body. **B.** Contour feathers, like this one from a Steller's jay, give a bird its shape and help it to fly. *Observing Where do you see down feathers and contour feathers on the family of Emperor geese above?*

The first part of the stomach is long and has thin walls. Here food is bathed in chemicals that begin to break it down. Then the partially digested food moves to a thick-walled, muscular part of the stomach called the **gizzard,** which squeezes and grinds the partially digested food. Remember that birds do not have teeth—their gizzard performs the grinding function of teeth. The gizzard may contain small stones that the bird has swallowed. These stones help with the grinding by rubbing against the food and crushing it.

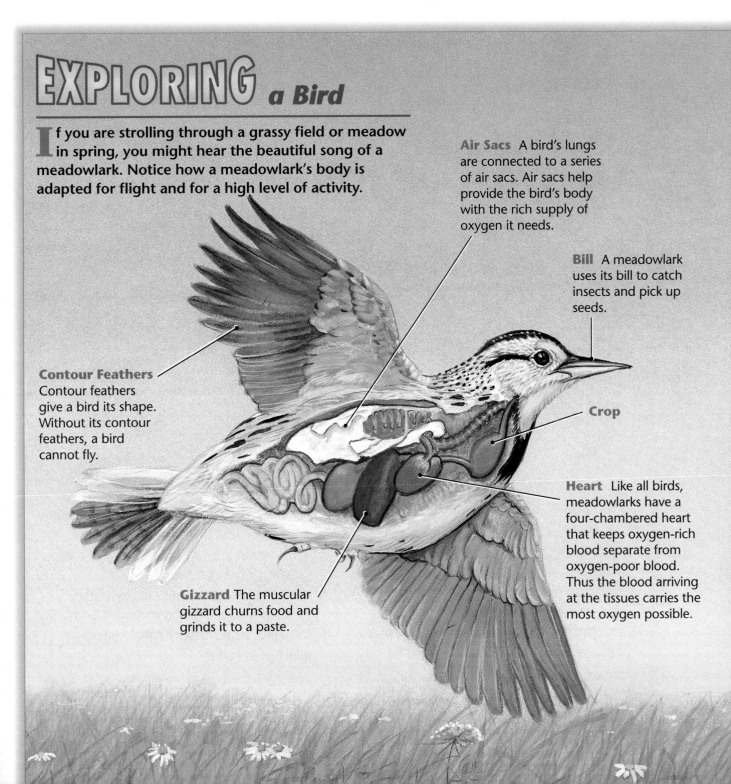

EXPLORING *a Bird*

If you are strolling through a grassy field or meadow in spring, you might hear the beautiful song of a meadowlark. Notice how a meadowlark's body is adapted for flight and for a high level of activity.

Air Sacs A bird's lungs are connected to a series of air sacs. Air sacs help provide the bird's body with the rich supply of oxygen it needs.

Bill A meadowlark uses its bill to catch insects and pick up seeds.

Contour Feathers Contour feathers give a bird its shape. Without its contour feathers, a bird cannot fly.

Crop

Gizzard The muscular gizzard churns food and grinds it to a paste.

Heart Like all birds, meadowlarks have a four-chambered heart that keeps oxygen-rich blood separate from oxygen-poor blood. Thus the blood arriving at the tissues carries the most oxygen possible.

Like all animals, birds use the food they eat for energy. Because birds are endotherms, they need a lot of energy to maintain their body temperature. It also takes an enormous amount of energy to power the muscles used in flight. Each day an average bird eats food equal to about a quarter of its body weight. When people say, "You're eating like a bird," they usually mean that you're eating very little. But if you were actually eating as a bird does, you would be eating huge meals. You might eat 100 hamburger patties in one day!

Drawing Conclusions

LOOKING AT AN OWL'S LEFTOVERS

In this lab, you will gather evidence and draw conclusions about an owl's diet.

Problem

What can you learn about owls' diets from studying the pellets that they cough up?

Materials

owl pellet   hand lens   dissecting needle
metric ruler   forceps

Procedure

1. An owl pellet is a collection of undigested materials that an owl coughs up after a meal. Write a prediction describing what items you expect an owl pellet to contain. List the reasons for your prediction.
2. Use a hand lens to observe the outside of an owl pellet. Record your observations.

3. Use one hand to grasp the owl pellet with forceps. Hold a dissecting needle in your other hand, and use it to gently separate the pellet into pieces. **CAUTION:** *Dissecting needles are sharp. Never cut material toward you; always cut away from your body.*
4. Using the forceps and dissecting needle, carefully separate the bones from the rest of the pellet. Remove any fur that might be attached to bones.

Delivering Oxygen to Cells

Cells must receive plenty of oxygen to release the energy contained in food. Flying requires much energy. Therefore, birds need a highly efficient way to get oxygen into their body and to their cells. Birds have a system of air sacs in their body that connects to the lungs. The air sacs enable birds to extract much more oxygen from each breath of air than other animals can.

The circulatory system of a bird is also efficient at getting oxygen to the cells. Unlike amphibians and most reptiles,

Shrew	House mouse	Meadow vole	Mole	Rat
				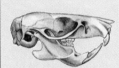
Upper jaw has at least 18 teeth; tips of the teeth are brown. Skull length is 23 mm or less.	Upper jaw has 2 biting teeth and extends past lower jaw. Skull length is 22 mm or less.	Upper jaw has 2 biting teeth that are smooth, not grooved. Skull length is more than 23 mm.	Upper jaw has at least 18 teeth. Skull length is 23 mm or more.	Upper jaw has 2 biting teeth. Upper jaw extends past lower jaw. Skull length is 22 mm or more.

5. Group similar bones together in separate piles. Observe the skulls, and draw them. Record the number of skulls, their length, and the number, shape, and color of the teeth.

6. Use the chart on this page to determine what kinds of skulls you found. If any skulls do not match the chart exactly, record which animal the skulls resemble most.

7. Try to fit together any of the remaining bones to form complete or partial skeletons. Sketch your results.

8. Wash your hands thoroughly with soap when you are finished.

Analyze and Conclude

1. How many animals' remains were in the pellet? What data led you to that conclusion?

2. Combine your results with those of your classmates. Which three animals were eaten most frequently?

3. Owls cough up about two pellets a day. Based on your class's data, what can you conclude about the number of animals an owl might eat in one month?

4. **Think About It** In this lab, you were able to examine only the part of the owl's diet that it did not digest. How might this fact affect your confidence in the conclusions you reached?

More to Explore

Design a study that might tell you how an owl's diet varies at different times of the year. Give an example of a conclusion you might expect to draw from such a study.

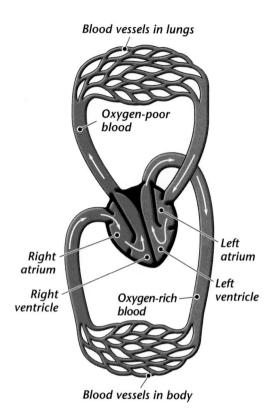

Figure 4 Birds have hearts with four chambers. Notice how the left side of the heart is completely separate from the right side. This separation prevents oxygen-rich blood from mixing with oxygen-poor blood. *Comparing and Contrasting Contrast a bird's circulatory system with that of an amphibian, as shown on page 446, Figure 13. How do the circulatory systems differ?*

whose hearts have three chambers, birds have hearts with four chambers—two atria and two ventricles. Trace the path of blood through a bird's two-loop circulatory system in Figure 4. The right side of a bird's heart pumps blood to the lungs, where the blood picks up oxygen. Oxygen-rich blood then returns to the left side of the heart, which pumps it to the rest of the body. The advantage of a four-chambered heart is that there is no mixing of oxygen-rich and oxygen-poor blood. Therefore, blood that arrives in the body's tissues has plenty of oxygen.

Nervous System and Senses

In order to fly, birds must have very quick reactions. To appreciate why, imagine how quickly you would have to react if you were a sparrow trying to land safely on a tree branch. You approach the tree headfirst, diving into a maze of tree branches. As you approach, you only have an instant to find a place where you can land safely and avoid crashing into those branches. If birds had slow reactions, they would not live very long.

A bird can react so quickly because of its well-developed brain and finely-tuned senses of sight and hearing. The brain of a bird controls such complex activities as flying, singing, and finding food. Most birds have keener eyesight than humans. A flying vulture, for example, can spot food on the ground from a height of more than one and a half kilometers. Some birds have excellent hearing, too. How could keen hearing help an owl search for prey in a dark forest?

Reproducing and Caring for Young

Like reptiles, birds have internal fertilization and lay eggs. Bird eggs are similar to reptile eggs, except that their shells are harder. In most bird species, the female lays the eggs in a nest that has been prepared by one or both parents.

Bird eggs will only develop at a temperature close to the body temperature of the parent bird. A parent bird usually incubates the eggs by sitting on them to keep them warm. In some species, incubating the eggs is the job of one parent. Female robins, for example, incubate their delicate blue eggs. In other species, such as pigeons, the parents take turns incubating the eggs.

Birds differ in the length of time that it takes for their chicks to develop until hatching. Sparrow eggs take only about 12 days. Chicken eggs take about 21 days, and albatross eggs take about 80 days. In general, the larger the bird species, the longer its incubation time.

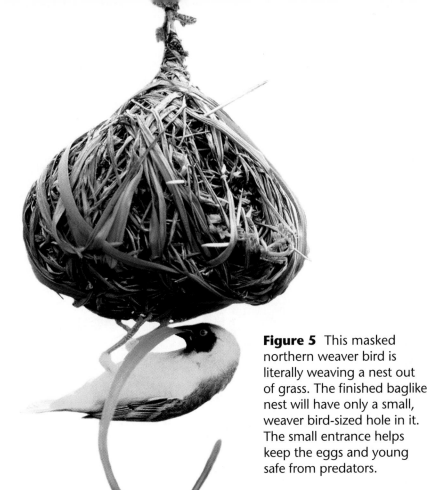

Figure 5 This masked northern weaver bird is literally weaving a nest out of grass. The finished baglike nest will have only a small, weaver bird-sized hole in it. The small entrance helps keep the eggs and young safe from predators.

When it is ready to hatch, a chick pecks its way out of the eggshell. Some newly hatched chicks, such as bluebirds and robins, are featherless, blind, and so weak they can barely lift their heads to beg for food. Other chicks, such as ducks, chickens, and pheasants, are covered with down and can run about soon after they have hatched. Most parent birds feed and protect their young at least until they are able to fly.

✓ *Checkpoint* How do bird eggs differ from reptile eggs?

Diversity of Birds

With almost 10,000 species, birds are the most diverse land-dwelling vertebrates. **In addition to adaptations for flight, birds have adaptations—such as the shapes of their legs, claws, and bills—for living in widely diverse environments.** For example, the long legs and toes of wading birds, such as herons and cranes, make wading easy, while the toes of perching birds, such as goldfinches and mockingbirds, can automatically lock onto a branch or other perch. The bills of ducks enable them to filter tiny plants and animals from water. Birds also have adaptations for flying, finding mates, and caring for their young. You can see a variety of bird adaptations in *Exploring Birds* on the next page.

EXPLORING Birds

Every bird has adaptations that help it live in its environment. Note how the bill and feet of each of these birds are adapted to help the bird survive.

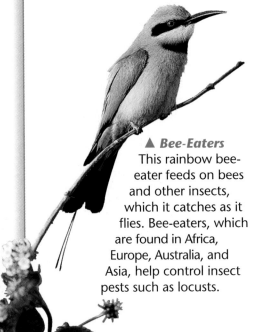

▲ **Bee-Eaters**
This rainbow bee-eater feeds on bees and other insects, which it catches as it flies. Bee-eaters, which are found in Africa, Europe, Australia, and Asia, help control insect pests such as locusts.

▲ **Long-Legged Waders**
The roseate spoonbill is found in the southern United States and throughout much of South America. The spoonbill catches small animals by sweeping its long, flattened bill back and forth underwater.

▲ **Woodpeckers**
The pileated woodpecker is the largest woodpecker in North America—adults average about 44 centimeters in length. This woodpecker feeds on insects it finds in holes it has chiseled into trees.

Ostriches
The ostrich, found in Africa, is the largest living bird. It cannot fly, but it can run at speeds greater than 60 kilometers per hour. Its speed helps it escape from predators. ▼

Birds of Prey
The American kestrel, a small falcon, catches its food by hovering in the air and scanning the ground. When it sees prey, such as an insect, the kestrel swoops down and grabs it. Kestrels are found worldwide.
▼

◀ Owls
Owls are predators that hunt mostly at night. Sharp vision and keen hearing help owls find prey in the darkness. Razor-sharp claws and great strength allow larger owls, like this eagle owl, to prey on animals as large as deer.

Why Birds Are Important

A walk through the woods or a park would be dull without birds. You wouldn't hear their musical songs, and you wouldn't see them flitting gracefully from tree to tree. But people benefit from birds in practical ways, too. Birds and their eggs provide food, while feathers are used to stuff pillows and clothing.

 INTEGRATING ENVIRONMENTAL SCIENCE Birds also play an important role in the environment. Nectar-eating birds, like hummingbirds, carry pollen from one flower to another, thus enabling some flowers to reproduce. Seed-eating birds, like painted buntings, carry the seeds of plants to new places. This happens when the birds eat the fruits or seeds of a plant, fly to a new location, and then eliminate some of the seeds in digestive wastes. In addition, birds are some of the chief predators of pest animals. Hawks and owls eat many rats and mice, while many perching birds feed on insect pests.

▲ Perching Birds
There are over 5,000 species of perching birds. They represent more than half of all the bird species in the world. The painted bunting, a seed-eating bird, lives in the southern United States and northern Mexico.

Section 1 Review

1. What characteristics do modern birds share with reptiles? How are birds different from reptiles?
2. Choose two different bird species and describe how they are adapted to obtain food in their environment.
3. Predict how the size of crop harvests might be affected if all birds disappeared from Earth.
4. **Thinking Critically Comparing and Contrasting** Compare contour feathers with down feathers, noting both similarities and differences.

Check Your Progress

CHAPTER PROJECT

By now you should have set up your bird feeder. As you begin making observations, use a field guide to identify the species of birds. Count and record the number of each species that appears. Also observe the birds' behaviors. How long do birds stay at the feeder? How do birds respond to other birds and mammals? Look for signs that some birds are trying to dominate others.

SECTION 2 The Physics of Bird Flight

DISCOVER ·· ACTIVITY

What Lifts Airplanes and Birds Into the Air?

1. Cut a strip of notebook paper 5 centimeters wide and 28 centimeters long. Insert about 5 centimeters of the paper strip into the middle of a book. The rest of the paper strip should hang over the edge.

2. Hold the book up so that the paper is below your mouth.

3. Blow gently across the top of the paper and watch what happens to the paper. Then blow harder.

Think It Over
Predicting If a strong current of air flowed across the top of a bird's outstretched wing, what might happen to the bird?

GUIDE FOR READING

◆ How is a bird able to fly?

Reading Tip Before you read, look at Figure 6 on page 481. Then predict how a bird's wing is similar to that of an airplane.

From ancient times, people have dreamed of soaring into the air like birds. When people first started experimenting with flying machines, they tried to glue feathers to their arms or to strap on feathered wings. Many failures, crash-landings, and broken bones later, these people had learned that feathers by themselves weren't the secret of flight. If an object is to fly, it must be lightweight. Another key to flying—for birds and insects as well as for airplanes—lies in the shape of wings and the way in which air moves across them.

How Air Moves Across a Wing

All objects on land are surrounded by an invisible ocean of air. Air is a mixture of gas molecules that exert pressure on the objects they surround. You see the results of air pressure when

▼ Owl in flight

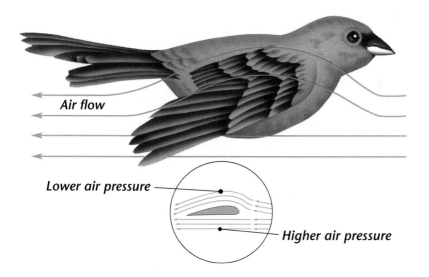

Air flow

Lower air pressure

Higher air pressure

Figure 6 Air moves faster across a wing's upper surface than across its lower surface. The fast-moving air exerts less pressure than the slow-moving air. *Relating Cause and Effect* How does this difference in pressure help a bird to fly?

you blow up a balloon. The pressure of the air molecules pushing on the sides of the balloon makes the balloon expand.

Moving air exerts less pressure than air that is not moving. The faster air moves, the less pressure it exerts. In the Discover activity, the air blowing across the top of the paper was in motion. The moving air above the paper exerted less pressure than the air beneath it, so the paper rose.

Like the paper, a wing is surrounded by air molecules that exert pressure on the wing's surfaces. The lower surface of a wing—whether it belongs to a bird, an insect, or an airplane—is flatter than the upper surface. This difference between the shapes of the upper and lower surfaces of a wing helps birds, insects, and airplanes to fly. In Figure 6, you can see that the curved upper surface of a wing is a little longer than the flatter lower surface. When the wing moves forward, air travels the longer distance over the upper wing in the same amount of time as it takes to travel the shorter distance beneath the wing. Therefore, the air moves faster over the upper surface.

Because fast-moving air exerts less pressure than air that is moving slowly, the air above the wing exerts less pressure than the air beneath the wing. **The difference in pressure above and below the bird's wing produces an upward force that causes the wing to rise.** That upward force is called **lift.**

☑ *Checkpoint* How is the air pressure above a moving wing different from the air pressure below the wing?

Birds in Flight

Wing shape alone does not enable a bird to fly—it must have some way of getting off the ground. To do this, a bird pushes off with its legs. The bird must also move forward, since lift depends

It's Plane to See

Use this activity to discover how wing shape is important for flight.

1. Work with a partner to design a paper airplane with wings shaped like those of a bird. You can use any of these materials: paper, tape, glue, paper clips, string, rubber bands, and staples. Draw a sketch of your design.

2. Construct your "birdplane" and make one or two trial flights. If necessary, modify your design and try again.

3. Compare your design with those of other groups. Which designs were most successful?

Making Models In what ways was the flight of your airplane like the flight of a bird? In what ways was it different?

Figure 7 As it glides above the ocean's surface, this gannet searches for a school of mackerel or herring. When its search is successful, it will dive into the water to claim its catch.

on air moving over its wings. So, at the same time that the bird pushes off from the ground, it sharply pulls its wings down. This downstroke provides the power that pushes the bird forward and upward.

Once they are in the air, birds fly in a variety of ways. All birds flap their wings at least part of the time. Flapping requires a lot of energy. Most small birds, such as sparrows, depend heavily on flapping flight. Canada geese and many other birds that travel long distances also use flapping flight.

Unlike flapping flight, soaring and gliding flight involve little wing movement. Birds soar and glide with their wings extended, as shown in Figure 7. When soaring, birds rise up into the sky on currents of warm air. In contrast, when gliding, birds coast downward through the air. Because they require less wing movement, soaring and gliding use less energy than flapping.

Sometimes birds fly with a combination of soaring and gliding. They "take the elevator up" by flying into a current of warm, rising air. The birds stretch their wings out and circle round and round within the column of rising air. High in the atmosphere the column of warm air grows cooler and ceases to rise. At this point the soaring bird "gets off the elevator" and begins gliding downward until it reaches the next "up elevator" of rising air. Predatory birds that spot their food from the air, such as hawks, often soar and glide.

The peregrine falcon, a predatory bird, is one of the fastest fliers. It catches its prey—often other birds such as pigeons—in flight. When it is pursuing prey, a peregrine's speed may reach 300 kilometers per hour. But it is not always useful for birds to fly fast. Birds that are migrating, or traveling long distances, take it slow but steady, usually flying 30 to 70 kilometers per hour.

 Section 2 Review

1. How is lift related to air pressure?
2. Explain how a bird takes off from the ground and begins to fly.
3. Compare and contrast flapping flight, soaring, and gliding.
4. **Thinking Critically Relating Cause and Effect** If a bird loses too many contour feathers, it can no longer fly. Relate this to the feathers' role in giving shape to a bird's wing.

Check Your Progress

CHAPTER PROJECT

As you continue your bird-feeder observations, pay careful attention to the way in which two or three different kinds of birds feed. Note the shapes of their beaks and how they use their beaks to pick up and crack seeds. Note how each bird's head moves during feeding. Also note whether certain birds prefer particular kinds of seeds. Write your detailed observations in your notebook.

What Is a Mammal?

What Are Mammals' Teeth Like?

1. Wash your hands before you begin. Then, with a small mirror, examine the shapes of your teeth. Observe the incisors (the front teeth); the pointed canine teeth; the premolars that follow the canine teeth; and the molars, which are the large teeth in the rear of your jaws.

2. Compare and contrast the structures of the different kinds of teeth.

3. Use your tongue to feel the cutting surfaces of the different kinds of teeth in your mouth.

4. Bite off a piece of cracker and chew it. Observe the teeth that you use to bite and chew. Wash your hands when you are finished.

Think It Over

Inferring What is the advantage of having teeth with different shapes?

---

igh in the Himalaya Mountains of Tibet, several yaks inch their way, single file, along a narrow cliff path. The cliff plunges thousands of meters to the valley below, so one false step can mean disaster. But the sure-footed yaks, carrying heavy loads of grain, slowly but steadily cross the cliff and make their way through the mountains.

Yaks, which are related to cows, have large lungs and a complex system of chest muscles that enables them to breathe deeply and rapidly. These structures allow yaks to obtain the oxygen necessary to survive at high altitudes. People who live in the mountains of central Asia have depended on yaks for thousands of years. Not only do yaks carry materials for trade, they also pull plows and provide milk. Mountain villagers weave blankets from yak hair and make shoes and ropes from yak hides.

The yak is a member of the group of vertebrates called **mammals,** a diverse group that share many characteristics. **All mammals are endothermic vertebrates with a four-chambered heart, and skin covered with fur or hair. The young of most mammals are born alive, and every young mammal is fed with milk produced in its mother's body.** In addition, mammals have teeth of different shapes that are adapted to their diets.

GUIDE FOR READING

◆ What characteristics do all mammals share?

Reading Tip As you read this section, write one or two sentences summarizing the information under each heading.

▼ Himalayan yak

Today there are about 6,000 different species of mammals. There are mammals that you may never have seen, such as kangaroos and wildebeests, as well as familiar mammals such as dogs, cats, bats, and mice.

Mammals First Appear

Two hundred and seventy million years ago, before dinosaurs appeared, and long before birds appeared, there was a group of animals that had a blend of reptilian and mammalian characteristics. They were more like reptiles than mammals, but they resembled mammals in some ways, such as in the shapes of their teeth. These mammal-like reptiles, which became extinct about 160 million years ago, were the ancestors of the true mammals.

The earliest mammals were small, mouse-sized animals that lived in habitats dominated by dinosaurs. These early mammals may have been nocturnal, or active mainly at night, presumably the time when the dinosaurs were inactive or asleep. It was only after the dinosaurs disappeared, about 65 million years ago, that large mammals first evolved.

Most mammals, such as kangaroos and giraffes, became specialized to live on land. Other mammals, such as dolphins, became adapted to life in Earth's waters, while still others, the bats, became adapted to flight.

Fur and Hair

All mammals have fur or hair at some point in their lives. Like a bird's down feathers, thick fur provides lightweight insulation

Figure 8 The amount of fur or hair covering a mammal's body varies greatly. **A.** Hippopotamuses live in hot regions such as Africa year-round and have little hair. **B.** Gray wolves live in the northern half of North America and have thick fur coats during the cold winter months. During the summer, however, their coats are thinner.
Comparing and Contrasting Compare the function of a mammal's fur or hair to that of down feathers.

that prevents body heat from escaping. Fur and hair help mammals maintain a stable body temperature in cold weather. Each strand of hair or fur is composed of dead cells strengthened with the same tough material that strengthens feathers. Hair grows from living cells located below the surface of the skin.

The amount of hair that covers the skin of a mammal varies a great deal from group to group. Some mammals, such as whales and manatees, have only a few bristles. Others, including dogs and weasels, have thick, short fur. The fur of sea otters is thickest of all—on some areas of its body, a sea otter can have 150,000 hairs per square centimeter! Human bodies are covered with hair, but in places the hairs are spaced widely apart.

In general, animals that live in cold regions have thicker coats of fur than animals in warmer environments, as you can see by contrasting the hippopotamus and wolf in Figure 8. Mammals such as wolves and rabbits that live in places where cold and warm seasons alternate usually grow thicker coats in winter than in summer.

Fur is not the only adaptation that allows mammals to live in cold climates. Mammals also have a layer of fat beneath their skins. Fat, like fur and feathers, is an insulating material that keeps heat in the body. Recall that mammals are endotherms, which means that their bodies produce enough heat to maintain a stable body temperature regardless of the temperature of their environment.

☑ *Checkpoint* *What is the major function of fur or hair?*

Insulated Mammals
In this activity, **ACTIVITY** you will discover whether or not fat is an effective insulator.

1. Put on a pair of rubber gloves.
2. Spread a thick coating of solid white shortening on the outside of one of the gloves. Leave the other glove uncoated.
3. Put both hands in a bucket or sink filled with cold water.

Inferring Which hand got cold faster? Explain how this activity relates to mammalian adaptations.

Teeth

Endotherms need a lot of energy to maintain their body temperature, and that energy comes from food. Mammals' teeth are adapted to chew their food, breaking it into small bits that make digestion easier. Unlike reptiles and fishes, whose teeth usually all have the same shape, most mammals have teeth with four different shapes. **Incisors** are flat-edged teeth used to bite off and cut parts of food. **Canines** are sharply pointed teeth that stab food and tear into it. **Premolars** and **molars** grind and shred food into tiny bits.

The size, shape, and hardness of a mammal's teeth reflect its diet. For example, the canines of carnivores are especially large and sharp. Large carnivores, such as lions and tigers, use their canines as meat hooks that securely hold the prey while the carnivore kills it. The molars of herbivores, such as deer and woodchucks, have upper surfaces that are broad and flat—ideal for grinding and mashing plants.

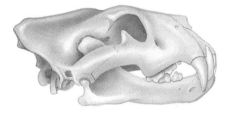

Figure 9 Lions have sharp, pointed teeth. Note the especially long canine teeth. *Inferring What kind of diet do lions eat?*

Getting Oxygen to Cells

To release energy, food molecules must combine with oxygen inside cells. Therefore, a mammal needs an efficient way to get oxygen into the body and to the cells that need it.

Like reptiles and birds, all mammals breathe with lungs—even mammals such as whales that live in the ocean. Mammals breathe in and out because of the combined action of rib muscles and a large muscle called the **diaphragm** located at the bottom of the chest. The lungs have a huge, moist surface area where oxygen can dissolve and then move into the bloodstream.

Like birds, mammals have a four-chambered heart and a two-loop circulation. One loop pumps oxygen-poor blood from the heart to the lungs and then back to the heart. The second loop pumps oxygen-rich blood from the heart to the tissues of the mammal's body, and then back to the heart.

✓ *Checkpoint How do mammals take air into their bodies?*

Nervous System and Senses

The nervous system and senses of an animal receive information about its environment and coordinate the animal's movements. The brains of mammals enable them to learn, remember, and behave in complex ways. Squirrels, for example, feed on

nuts. In order to do this, they must crack the nutshell to get to the meat inside. Squirrels learn to use different methods to crack different kinds of nuts, depending on where the weak points in each kind of shell are located.

The senses of mammals are highly developed and adapted for the ways that individual species live. Tarsiers, which are active at night, have huge eyes that enable them to see in the dark. Humans, monkeys, gorillas, and chimpanzees are able to see objects in color. This ability is extremely useful because these mammals are most active during the day when colors are visible.

Most mammals hear well. Bats even use their sense of hearing to navigate. Bats make high-pitched squeaks that bounce off objects. The echoes give bats information about the shapes of objects around them and about how far away the objects are. Bats use their hearing to fly at night and to capture flying insects.

Most mammals have highly developed senses of smell. Many mammals, including dogs and cats, use smell to track their prey. By detecting the scent of an approaching predator, antelopes use their sense of smell to protect themselves.

Movement

One function of a mammal's nervous system is to direct and coordinate complex movement. No other group of vertebrates can move in as many different ways as mammals can. Like most mammals, camels and leopards have four limbs and can walk and run. Other four-limbed mammals have specialized ways of moving. For example, kangaroos hop, gibbons swing by their arms from branch to branch, and flying squirrels glide down from high perches. Moles use their powerful front limbs to burrow through the soil. Bats, in contrast, are adapted to fly through the air—their front limbs are wings. Whales, dolphins, and other sea mammals have no hind limbs—their front limbs are flippers adapted for swimming in water.

Classifying

Unlike humans, birds and bats both fly. Does this mean that bats are more closely related to birds than to humans? Use the diagrams below to find out. The diagrams show the front-limb bones of a bird, a bat, and a human. Examine them carefully, noting similarities and differences. Then decide which two animals are more closely related. Give evidence to support your classification.

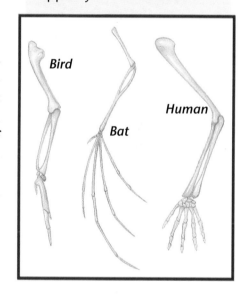

Bird

Human

Bat

Figure 10 Mammals, like these springboks, have large brains. A springbok's brain processes complex information about its environment and then quickly decides on an appropriate action.

Figure 11 This young giraffe is feeding on milk produced by its mother, as do all young mammals.

Reproducing and Caring for Young

Like reptiles and birds, mammals have internal fertilization. Although a few kinds of mammals lay shelled eggs, the young of most mammals develop within their mothers' bodies and are never enclosed in an eggshell. All mammals, even those that lay eggs, feed their young with milk produced in **mammary glands**. In fact, the word *mammal* comes from the term *mammary*.

Young mammals are usually quite helpless for a long time after being born. Many are born without a coat of insulating fur. Their eyes are often sealed and may not open for weeks. For example, black bear cubs are surprisingly tiny when they are born. The blind, nearly hairless cubs have a mass of only 240 to 330 grams—about as small as a grapefruit. The mass of an adult black bear, in contrast, ranges from about 120 to 150 kilograms—about 500 times as large as a newborn cub!

Young mammals usually stay with their mother or both parents for an extended time. After black bear cubs learn to walk, they follow their mother about for the next year, learning how to be a bear. They learn things that are important to their survival, such as which mushrooms and berries are good to eat and how to rip apart a rotten log and find good-tasting grubs within it. During the winter, when black bears go through a period of inactivity, the young bears stay with their mother. The following spring, she will usually force them to live independently.

Section 3 Review

1. List five characteristics that all mammals share.
2. Name three ways in which mammals are similar to birds. Then list three ways in which they are different.
3. Relate the shape of any mammal's teeth to its diet.
4. Explain how a keen sense of hearing is an advantage to a bat.
5. **Thinking Critically Making Generalizations** What characteristics enable mammals to live in colder environments than reptiles can?

Science at Home

With a family member, examine the nutrition facts listed on a container of whole milk. What types of nutrients does whole milk contain? Discuss why milk is an ideal source of food for young, growing mammals.

KEEPING WARM

Any time you wear a sweater or socks made of wool, you are using a mammalian adaptation to keep yourself warm. Suppose a manufacturer claims that its wool socks keep your feet as warm when the socks are wet as when they are dry. In this investigation, you will test that claim.

Problem

Do wool products provide insulation from the cold? How well does wool insulate when it is wet?

Skills Focus

controlling variables, interpreting data

Materials

tap water, hot
beaker, 1 L
clock or watch
a pair of wool socks
tap water, room temperature
3 containers, 250 mL, with lids

scissors
3 thermometers
graph paper

Procedure

1. Put one container into a dry woolen sock. Soak a second sock with water at room temperature, wring it out so it's not dripping, and then slide the second container into the wet sock. Both containers should stand upright. Leave the third container uncovered.

2. Create a data table in your notebook, listing the containers in the first column. Provide four more columns in which to record the water temperatures during the experiment.

3. Use scissors to carefully cut a small "X" in the center of each lid. Make the X just large enough for a thermometer to pass through.

4. Fill a beaker with about 800 mL of hot tap water. Then pour hot water nearly to the top of each of the three containers. **CAUTION:** *Avoid spilling hot water on yourself or others.*

5. Place a lid on each of the containers, and insert a thermometer into the water through the hole in each lid. Gather the socks around the thermometers above the first two containers so that the containers are completely covered.

6. Immediately measure the temperature of the water in each container, and record it in your data table. Take temperature readings every 5 minutes for at least 15 minutes.

Analyze and Conclude

1. Graph your results using a different color to represent each container. Graph time in minutes on the horizontal axis and temperature on the vertical axis.

2. Compare the temperature changes in the three containers. Relate your findings to the insulation characteristics of mammal skin coverings.

3. **Apply** Suppose an ad for wool gloves claims that the gloves keep you warm even if they get wet. Do your findings support this claim? Why or why not?

Design an Experiment

Design an experiment to compare how wool's insulating properties compare with those of other natural materials (such as cotton) or manufactured materials (such as acrylic). Obtain your teacher's approval before conducting your experiment.

Animals and Medical Research

In laboratories around the world, scientists search for cures for cancer, AIDS, and other diseases. Scientists use millions of animals each year in research—mostly to test drugs and surgical procedures. Finding treatments could save millions of human lives. However, these experiments can hurt and even kill animals.

The Issues

Why Is Animal Testing Done? If you have ever used an antibiotic or other medicine, animal testing has helped you. The United States Food and Drug Administration requires that new medicines be tested on research animals before they can be used by humans. Through testing, researchers can learn whether a drug works and what doses are safe. Because of animal research, many serious diseases can now be treated or prevented. New treatments for AIDS, cancer, and Alzheimer's disease will also depend on animal testing.

Which Animals Are Used for Testing? Most often mice, rats, and other small mammals are used. These animals reproduce rapidly, so scientists can study many generations in a year. Since apes and monkeys are similar to humans in many ways, they are often used to test new treatments for serious diseases. In other cases, researchers use animals that naturally get diseases common to humans. Cocker spaniels, for example, often develop glaucoma, an eye disease that can cause blindness. Surgeons may test new surgical treatments for the disease on cocker spaniels.

What Happens to Research Animals? In a typical laboratory experiment, a group of animals will first be infected with a disease. Then they will be given a drug to see if it can fight off the disease. In many cases, the animals suffer, and some die. Some people are concerned that laboratory animals do not receive proper care.

What Are the Alternatives? Other testing methods do exist. For example, in some cases, scientists can use computer models to test drugs or surgical treatments. Another testing method is to mix drugs with animal cells grown in petri dishes. Unfortunately, neither computer models nor cell experiments are as useful as tests on living animals.

You Decide

1. Identify the Problem
In a sentence, describe the controversy over using animals in medical research.

2. Analyze the Options
Review the different positions. Is animal testing acceptable? Is it acceptable for some animals but not for others? Is animal research never acceptable? List the benefits and drawbacks of each option.

3. Find a Solution
Suppose you are a scientist who has found a possible cure for a type of cancer. The drug needs to be tested on research animals first, but you know that testing could harm the animals. What would you do? Support your opinion with sound reasons.

Diversity of Mammals

DISCOVER

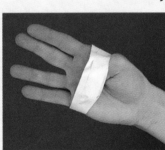

How Is a Thumb Useful?

1. Tape the thumb of your writing hand to your palm so that you cannot move your thumb. The tape should keep your thumb from moving but allow your other fingers to move freely.

2. Pick up a pencil with the taped hand and try to write your name.

3. Keep the tape on for 5 minutes. During that time, try to use your taped hand to do such everyday activities as lifting a book, turning the pages, and untying and retying your shoes.

4. Remove the tape and repeat all the activities you tried to do when your thumb was taped. Observe the position and action of your thumb and other fingers as you perform each activity.

Think It Over

Inferring Humans, chimpanzees, and gorillas all have thumbs that can touch the other four fingers. What advantage does that kind of thumb give to the animal?

How is a koala similar to a panda? Both are furry, cuddly-looking mammals that eat leaves. How is a koala different from a panda? Surprisingly, koalas and pandas belong to very different groups of mammals—koalas are marsupials, and pandas are placental mammals. **Members of the three groups of mammals—monotremes, marsupials, and placental mammals—are classified on the basis of how their young develop.**

GUIDE FOR READING

◆ What characteristic is used to classify mammals into three groups?

Reading Tip As you read this section, write a definition in your own words for each new science term.

Giant panda (left) and koala (right)

Figure 12 The spiny anteater, left, and the duck-billed platypus, right, could share the "Weirdest Mammal" award. Both are monotremes, the only mammals whose young hatch from eggs.

Monotremes

If you held a "Weirdest Mammal in the World" contest, two main contenders would be spiny anteaters and duck-billed platypuses. There are two species of spiny anteaters and only one species of duck-billed platypus, all living in Australia and New Guinea. These are the only species of monotremes that are alive today. **Monotremes** are mammals that lay eggs.

Spiny Anteaters These monotremes look like pincushions with long noses. They have sharp spines scattered throughout their brown hair. As their name implies, spiny anteaters eat ants, which they dig up with their powerful claws.

A female spiny anteater lays one to three leathery-shelled eggs directly into the pouch on her belly. After the young hatch, still in the pouch, they drink milk that seeps out of pores on the mother's skin. They stay in the pouch until they are six to eight weeks old, when their spines start to irritate the mother anteater, and she scratches them out of her pouch.

Duck-billed Platypuses The duck-billed platypus has webbed feet and a bill, but it also has fur and feeds its young with milk. Platypuses, which live in the water, construct a maze of tunnels in muddy banks. The female lays her eggs in an underground nest. The eggs hatch about two weeks later. After they hatch, the tiny offspring feed by lapping at the milk that oozes onto the fur of their mother's belly.

Marsupials

Koalas, kangaroos, bandicoots, wallabies, and opossums are some of the better known marsupials. **Marsupials** are mammals whose young are born alive, but at an early stage of development, and they usually continue to develop in a pouch on their mother's body. Marsupials were once widespread, but today they are found mostly in South America, Australia, and New Guinea. Opossums are the only marsupials found in North America.

Marsupials have a very short **gestation period,** the length of time between fertilization and birth. Opossums, for example, have a gestation period of only about 13 days. Newborn marsupials are tiny—the newborns of one opossum species are only about 10 millimeters long! When they are born, marsupials are blind, hairless, and pink. They crawl along the wet fur of their mother's belly until they reach her pouch. Once inside, they find one of her nipples and attach to it. They remain in the pouch at least until they have grown enough to peer out of the pouch opening.

Kangaroos The largest marsupials are kangaroos, which are found in Australia and nearby islands. Some male kangaroos are over 2 meters tall—taller than most humans. Kangaroos have powerful hind legs for jumping and long tails that help them keep their balance. A female kangaroo gives birth to only one baby, called a joey, at a time. Kangaroos are herbivores, so they eat foods such as leaves and grasses.

Opossums The common opossum is an omnivore that comes out of its nest at dusk to search for fruits, plants, insects, or other small animals to eat. Opossums are good climbers. They can grasp branches with their long tails. If a predator attacks it, an opossum will often "play dead"—its body becomes limp, its mouth gapes open, and its tongue lolls out of its mouth. Female opossums may give birth to 21 young at a time, but most female opossums have only 13 nipples. The first 13 young opossums that get into the pouch and attach to nipples are the only ones that survive.

☑ *Checkpoint* **What do the young of marsupials do immediately after they are born?**

Figure 13 Gray kangaroos, above, and opossums, below, are marsupials, mammals whose young live for a time in the mother's pouch. *Classifying How do marsupials differ from monotremes?*

Placental Mammals

Unlike a monotreme or a marsupial, a **placental mammal** develops inside its mother's body until its body systems can function independently. In *Exploring Placental Mammals* on the next page, you can see some members of this group.

EXPLORING Placental Mammals

From tiny moles to huge elephants, placental mammals exhibit a great variety of size and body form. Note how each group is adapted for obtaining food or for living in a particular environment.

▲ Insect-eaters
Star-nosed moles and their relatives have sharp cutting surfaces on all of their teeth. Star-nosed moles spend much of their time in water searching for prey with their sensitive, tentacled snouts.

Flying Mammals ▲
Bats fly, but they are mammals, not birds. The wings of bats are made of a thin skin that stretches from their wrists to the tips of their long finger bones.

▲ Rabbits and Hares
Leaping mammals like this black-tailed jack rabbit have long hind legs specialized for spectacular jumps. Rabbits and hares have long, curved incisors for gnawing.

Rodents ▲
Rodents are gnawing mammals such as rats, beavers, squirrels, mice, and the North American porcupine shown here. Their teeth are adapted to grind down their food. The four incisors of most rodents keep growing throughout their lives but are constantly worn down by gnawing.

▲ Primates
This group of mammals with large brains includes humans, monkeys, and apes such as this chimpanzee. Many primates have opposable thumbs—thumbs that can touch the other four fingers. An opposable thumb makes the hand capable of complex movements, such as grasping and throwing.

▲ Hoofed Mammals
Mammals with hooves are divided into two groups—those with an even number of toes and those with an odd number of toes. Cows, deer, and pigs all have an even number of toes, while horses and zebras belong to the odd-numbered group.

▲ Toothless Mammals
Sloths, such as the one shown here, are toothless mammals, as are armadillos. Although a few members of this group have small teeth, most have none.

Carnivores ▶
This river otter belongs to the group known as carnivores, or meat eaters. Other mammals in this group include dogs, cats, raccoons, bears, weasels, and seals. Large canine teeth and toes with claws help carnivores catch and eat their prey.

Marine Mammals
Whales, manatees, and these Atlantic spotted dolphins are ocean-dwelling mammals that evolved from cowlike, land-dwelling ancestors. The bodies of marine mammals show no external trace of hind limbs, although hind limbs have been found in their fossilized ancestors. ▼

Mammals With Trunks ▲
Elephants' noses are long trunks that they use for collecting food and water.

Figure 14 Young mammals usually require much parental care. On a rocky slope in Alaska, this Dall's sheep, a placental mammal, keeps a close watch on her lamb.

The name of this group comes from the **placenta,** an organ in pregnant female mammals that passes materials between the mother and the developing embryo. Food and oxygen pass from the mother to her young through the placenta. Wastes pass from the young through the placenta to the mother, where they are eliminated by her body. The umbilical cord connects the young to the placenta. Most mammals, including humans, are placental mammals.

Placental mammals are classified into groups on the basis of characteristics such as how they eat and how their bodies are adapted for moving. For example, whales, dolphins, and porpoises all form one group of mammals that have adaptations for swimming. The mammals in the carnivore group, which includes cats, dogs, otters, and seals, are all predators that have enlarged canine teeth. Primates, which include monkeys, apes, and humans, all have large brains and eyes that face forward. In addition, the forelimbs of many primates have adaptations for grasping. For example, the human thumb can touch all four other fingers. As you learned if you did the Discover activity, it is difficult to grasp objects if you cannot use your thumb.

Placental mammals vary in the length of their gestation periods. Generally, the larger the placental mammal, the longer its gestation period. For example, African elephants are the largest land-dwelling placental mammals. The gestation period for an elephant averages about 21 months. A house mouse, on the other hand, gives birth after a gestation period of only about 20 days.

Section 4 Review

1. Explain the difference in the development of the young of monotremes, marsupials, and placental mammals.
2. What is the function of the placenta?
3. Describe the feeding adaptations of three groups of placental mammals.
4. **Thinking Critically Inferring** Many hoofed mammals feed in large groups, or herds. What advantage could this behavior have?

Check Your Progress

CHAPTER PROJECT

Continue to observe bird behavior at your bird feeder and record your observations in your notebook. Now is the time to plan your presentation. You may want to include the following information in your presentation: drawings of the different birds you observed, detailed descriptions of bird behaviors, and other interesting observations you made. (Hint: Prepare bar graphs to present numerical data, such as the number of times that different species visited the feeder.)

SECTION 1 Birds

Key Ideas

◆ Birds are endothermic vertebrates that have feathers and a four-chambered heart and lay eggs. Most birds can fly.

◆ Contour feathers give shape to a bird's body and aid in flight. Down feathers provide insulation.

◆ Birds care for their young by keeping the eggs warm until hatching and by protecting the young at least until they can fly.

◆ Birds have adaptations, such as the shapes of their toes and bills, for living and obtaining food in different environments.

Key Terms
bird
contour feather
down feather
insulator
crop
gizzard

SECTION 2 The Physics of Bird Flight

INTEGRATING PHYSICS

Key Ideas

◆ Air flowing over the curved upper surface of a moving wing exerts less downward pressure than the upward pressure from the air flowing beneath the wing. The difference in pressure produces lift that causes the wing to rise.

◆ Birds fly in three basic ways—flapping flight, soaring, and gliding. Flapping flight requires more energy than soaring or gliding.

Key Term
lift

SECTION 3 What Is a Mammal?

Key Ideas

◆ Mammals are vertebrates that are endothermic, have skin covered with hair or fur, feed their young with milk from the mother's mammary glands, and have teeth of different shapes adapted to their diets.

◆ A mammal's fur or hair provides insulation that helps reduce the loss of body heat.

◆ Mammals use a large muscle called the diaphragm to breathe in and out. Mammals have a four-chambered heart and a two-loop circulation.

Key Terms
mammal   incisors   canines
premolars   molars   diaphragm
mammary gland

SECTION 4 Diversity of Mammals

Key Ideas

◆ Mammals are classified into three groups on the basis of how their young develop. Monotremes lay eggs. Marsupials give birth to live young who continue to develop in the mother's pouch. The young of placental mammals develop more fully before birth than do the young of marsupials.

◆ Placental mammals are divided into groups on the basis of adaptations, such as those for feeding and moving.

Key Terms
monotreme
marsupial
gestation period
placental mammal
placenta

USING THE INTERNET
ACTIVITY
www.science-explorer.phschool.com

California Test Prep: Reviewing Content

Multiple Choice

Choose the letter of the best answer.

1. Which of these characteristics is found only in birds?
   a. scales
   b. wings
   c. feathers
   d. four-chambered heart

2. A four-chambered heart is an advantage because
   a. it keeps oxygen-rich and oxygen-poor blood separate.
   b. it allows oxygen-rich and oxygen-poor blood to mix.
   c. blood can move through it quickly.
   d. it slows the flow of blood.

3. What causes the lift that allows a bird's wing to rise?
   a. reduced air pressure beneath the wing
   b. reduced air pressure above the wing
   c. air that is not moving
   d. jet propulsion

4. Which muscle helps mammals move air into and out of their lungs?
   a. air muscle   b. diaphragm
   c. placenta   d. gestation

5. Kangaroos, koalas, and opossums are all
   a. monotremes.
   b. primates.
   c. marsupials.
   d. placental mammals.

True or False

If the statement is true, write true. If it is false, change the underlined word or words to make the statement true.

6. *Archaeopteryx* shows the link between birds and reptiles.

7. A bird's gizzard grinds food.

8. The slower air moves, the less pressure it exerts.

9. Fur and down feathers have a similar function.

10. Marsupials are mammals that lay eggs.

Checking Concepts

11. Explain how the skeleton of a bird is adapted for flight.

12. How is a bird's ability to fly related to the shape of its wings?

13. Explain how soaring birds like vultures use rising air currents in their flight.

14. Contrast the structure and function of incisors and molars.

15. Identify and explain two ways in which mammals are adapted to live in cold climates.

16. How is a mammal's ability to move a function of its nervous system?

17. What is one way in which the bodies of dolphins are different from those of land mammals?

18. **Writing to Learn** You are a documentary filmmaker preparing to make a short film about spiny anteaters. First, think of a title for the film. Then plan two scenes that you would include in the film and write the narrator's script. Your scenes should show what the animals look like and what they do.

Thinking Visually

19. **Compare/Contrast Table** The table below compares three groups of mammals. Copy the table onto a separate sheet of paper. Then complete it and add a title. (For more on compare/contrast tables, see the Skills Handbook.)

Characteristic	Monotremes	Marsupials	Placental Mammals
How Young Begin Life	a. __?__	b. __?__	c. __?__
How Young Are Fed	milk from pores or slits on mother's skin	d. __?__	e. __?__
Example	f. __?__	g. __?__	h. __?__

Test Prep: Skills

The data table below shows the approximate gestation period of several mammals and the approximate length of time that those mammals care for their young after birth. Use the information in the table to answer Questions 20–22.

Mammal	Gestation Period	Time Spent Caring for Young After Birth
Deer mouse	0.75 month	1 month
Chimpanzee	8 months	24 months
Harp seal	11 months	0.75 month
Elephant	21 months	24 months
Bobcat	2 months	8 months

20. **Graphing** Decide which kind of graph would be best for showing the data in the table. Then construct two graphs—one for gestation period and the other for time spent caring for young.

21. **Interpreting Data** Which mammals in the table care for their young for the longest time? The shortest time?

22. **Drawing Conclusions** What seems to be the general relationship between the size of the mammal and the length of time for which it cares for its young? Which animal is the exception to this pattern?

Thinking Critically

23. **Predicting** If a rodent were fed a diet consisting only of soft food that it did not need to gnaw, what might its front teeth look like after several months?

24. **Making Generalizations** What is the general relationship between whether an animal is an endotherm and whether it has a four-chambered heart? Relate this to the animal's need for energy.

25. **Comparing and Contrasting** Why might monotremes be considered a link between reptiles and mammals?

Performance Assessment

CHAPTER PROJECT Wrap Up

Presenting Your Project When you present your project to your classmates, display the graphs, charts, and pictures you constructed. Be sure to include a description of the ways in which birds eat and interesting examples of bird behavior that you observed.

Reflect and Record In your journal, analyze how successful the project was. Was the bird feeder located in a good place for attracting birds and observing them? Did many birds come to the feeder—if not, why might this have happened? What are the advantages and limitations of using field guides for identifying birds? What did you learn from completing the project?

Getting Involved

In Your Community Many communities have animal shelters that try to find homes for stray animals. Find a shelter in or near your community. Find out how the shelter finds homes for animals and how the animals at the shelter are cared for. What requirements must a family fulfill before adopting an animal? Make up an information sheet about the shelter. With your teacher's permission, post it or distribute it in your school.

The Secret of Silk

What animal—

was a secret for thousands of years?

was smuggled across mountains in a hollow cane?

is good to eat, especially stir-fried with garlic and ginger?

is not really what its name says it is?

If you guessed that this amazing animal is the silkworm, you are right. The silk thread that this caterpillar spins is woven into silk cloth. For at least 4,000 years people have treasured silk.

Chinese legends say that in 2640 B.C., a Chinese empress accidentally dropped a silkworm cocoon in warm water and watched the thread unravel. She had discovered silk. But for thousands of years, the Chinese people kept the work of silkworms a secret. Death was the penalty for telling the secret.

Then, it is said, in A.D. 552, two travelers from Persia visited China and returned to the West carrying silkworm eggs hidden in their hollow canes. Ever since then, the world has enjoyed the beauty of silk—its warmth, strength, softness, and shimmer.

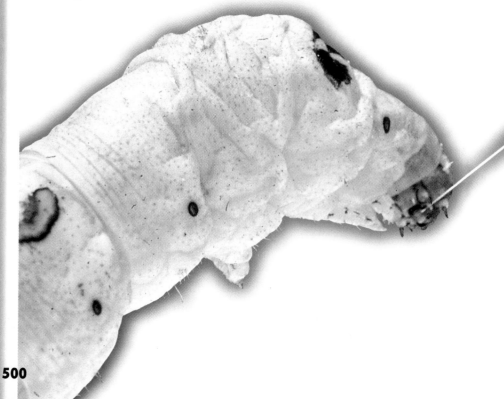

Metamorphosis of the Silkworm

The silkworm is not really a worm; it's the larva of an insect—a moth named *Bombyx mori*. In its entire feeding period, this larva consumes about 20 times its own weight in mulberry leaves. The silkworm undergoes complete metamorphosis during its life.

1 The adult female moth lays 300 to 500 eggs, each the size of a pinhead. After about ten days at 27°C, the larvae—which people call silkworms—hatch from the eggs and begin to eat. Mulberry leaves are the insects' source of food.

2 For the next 40 to 45 days, the larvae consume great quantities of mulberry leaves. The silkworms molt each time their exoskeletons become too tight. After the last molting and feeding stage, the silkworms begin to build their cocoons.

3 To spin its cocoon, each silkworm produces two single strands from its two silk glands. Another pair of glands produces a sticky substance that binds the two strands together. The silkworm pushes this single strand out through a small tube in its head. Once in the air, the strand hardens and the silkworm winds the strand around itself in many layers to make a thick cocoon. The single silk strand may be as long as 900 meters—more than two laps around an Olympic track.

4 After 14 to 18 days, the adult moths emerge from the cocoons. The new moth does not eat or fly. It mates, the female lays eggs, and 2 to 3 days later both the male and female die.

Science Activity

Examine a silkworm cocoon. After softening the cocoon in water, find the end of the strand of silk. Pull this strand, wind it onto an index card, and measure its length.

With a partner, design an experiment to compare the strength of the silk thread you just collected to that of cotton and/or nylon thread of the same weight or thickness.

◆ Develop a hypothesis about the strength of the threads.

◆ Decide on the setup you will use to test the threads.

◆ Check your safety plan with your teacher.

The Silk Road

Long before the rest of the world learned how silk was made, the Chinese were trading this treasured fabric with people west of China. Merchants who bought and sold silk traveled along a system of hazardous routes that came to be known as the Silk Road. The Silk Road stretched 6,400 kilometers from Ch'ang-an in China to the Mediterranean Sea. Silk, furs, and spices traveled west toward Rome along the road. Gold, wool, glass, grapes, garlic, and walnuts moved east toward China.

Travel along the Silk Road was treacherous and difficult. For safety, traders traveled in caravans of many people and animals. Some kinds of pack animals were better equipped to handle certain parts of the journey than others. Camels, for instance, were well suited to the desert; they could store large amounts of water and withstand most sandstorms. Yaks were often used in the high mountains.

The entire journey along the Silk Road could take years. Many people and animals died along the way. Very few individuals or caravans traveled the length of the Silk Road.

Silk fabric became highly prized in Rome. In fact, it was said that the first silk products to reach Rome after 50 B.C. were worth their weight in gold. The Chinese, of course, kept the secret of the silkworm and controlled silk production. They were pleased that the Romans thought that silk grew on trees. It was not until about A.D. 550 that the Roman Empire learned the secret of silk.

In time, silk production spread around the world. The Silk Road, though, opened forever the exchange of goods and ideas between China and the West.

EUROPE

Rome

Black Sea

ASIA MINO

7 Antioch

The Silk Road
200 B.C. to A.D. 200

1 Ch'ang-an
From Ch'ang-an in northern China, the Silk Road headed west along a corridor between the Nan Shan Mountains and the Gobi Desert.

2 Dunhuang
At Dunhuang, in an oasis, or fertile green area, of the Gobi Desert, caravans took on rested pack animals. Beyond Dunhuang, the silk route split.

3 Takla Makan Desert
The desert is well named—Takla Makan means "Go in and you won't come out!" Most travelers avoided the scorching heat of the desert and journeyed along the edges of this great wasteland of sand.

Social Studies Activity

Suppose you are a merchant traveling from Dunhuang to Kashgar. You will be carrying silk, furs, and cinnamon to Kashgar where you'll trade for gold, garlic, and glass, which you will carry back to Dunhuang. Plan your route and hire a guide.

◆ Look at the map to find the distances and the physical features you will see on your journey.

◆ Explain why you chose the route you did.

◆ List the animals and supplies that you will take.

◆ Write a help-wanted ad for a guide to lead your caravan.

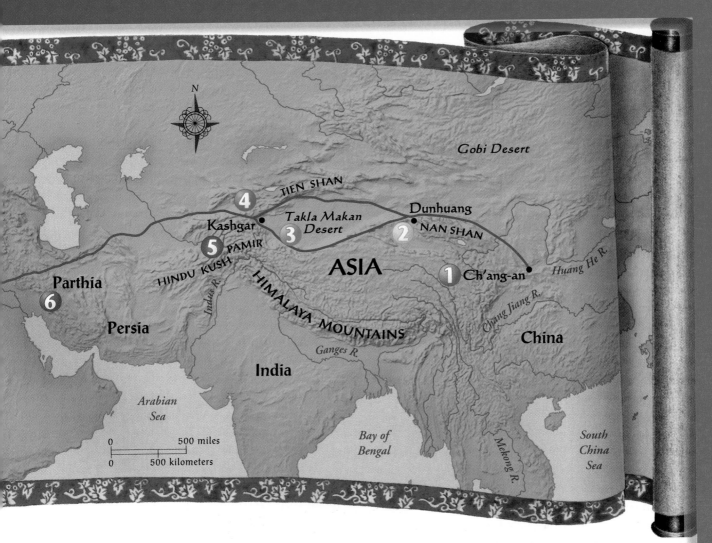

4 Kashgar

The silk routes along the northern and southern edges of the Takla Makan Desert came together at Kashgar. The perilous part of the Silk Road was still ahead.

5 Pamir Mountains

Traveling west from Kashgar, caravans faced some of the highest mountains in the world. The towering Pamir Mountains are more than 6,000 meters high. Once traders crossed the mountains, though, travel on the Silk Road was less difficult. Traders journeyed west through Persia to cities on the Mediterranean Sea.

6 Parthia

For a while, Parthian traders controlled part of the Silk Road. In 53 B.C., Rome was a mighty power around the Mediterranean Sea. That year when the Roman and Parthian armies were at battle, the Parthians suddenly turned to face their enemy and attacked with deadly arrows. Then, in the bright light of noon, the Parthians unrolled huge banners of gold-embroidered silk. The Romans were so dazzled by the brilliance that they surrendered.

7 Antioch

Trade flourished in Antioch, where silk was traded for gold. Ships carried silk and spices on the Mediterranean Sea from Antioch to Rome, Egypt, and Greece.

503

The Gift of Silk

A myth is a story handed down from past cultures—often to explain an event or natural phenomenon. Myths may be about gods and goddesses or about heroes.

The Yellow Emperor, Huang Di, who is mentioned in this Chinese myth, was a real person. Some stories say that he was the founder of the Chinese nation. He was thought to be a god who came to rule on Earth. Here the silkworm goddess appears to him at a victory celebration.

The Goddess of the Silkworm

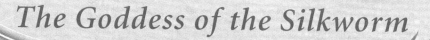

A GODDESS descended from the heavens with a gift for the Yellow Emperor. Her body was covered with a horse's hide, and she presented two shining rolls of silk to the god. She was the "goddess of the silkworm", sometimes called the "lady with a horse's head". Long, long ago she had been a beautiful girl, but now a horse's skin grew over her body. If she pulled the two sides of the skin close to her body she became a silkworm with a horse's head, spinning a long, glittering thread of silk from her mouth. It is said she lived in a mulberry tree, producing silk day and night in the wild northern plain. This is her story.

Once in ancient times there lived a man, his daughter and their horse. Often the man had to travel, leaving his daughter alone at home to take care of the beast. And often the girl was lonely. One day, because she missed her father she teased the horse: "Dear long-nosed one, if you could bring my father home right how, I'd marry you and be your wife." At that the horse broke out of his harness. He galloped away and came quickly to the place where the master was doing business. The master, surprised to see his beast, grasped his mane and jumped up on his back. The horse stood mournfully staring in the direction he had come from, so the man decided there must be something amiss at home and hurried back.

When they arrived home, the daughter explained that she had only remarked that she missed her father and the horse had dashed off wildly. The man said nothing but was secretly pleased to own such a remarkable animal and fed him special sweet hay. But the horse would not touch it and whinnied and reared each time he saw the girl.

The man began to worry about the horse's strange behavior, and one day he said to the girl,

Luxurious hand-embroidered silk fabric has been made in China for thousands of years.

"Why is it that our horse behaves so strangely whenever you are about?"

So the young girl confessed the teasing remark she had made.

When he heard this the father was enraged, "For shame to say such a thing to an animal! No one must know of this! You will stay locked in the house!"

Now the man had always liked this horse, but he would not hear of its becoming his son-in-law. That night, to prevent any more trouble, he crept quietly into the stable with his bow and arrow and shot the horse through the heart. Then he skinned it and hung up the hide in the courtyard.

Next day, when the father was away, the girl ran out of the house to join some other children playing in the courtyard near the horse hide. When she saw it she kicked it angrily and said, "Dirty horse hide! What made you think such an ugly long-snouted creature as you could become my. . . ."

But before she could finish, the hide suddenly flew up and wrapped itself around her, swift as the wind, and carried her away out of sight. The other children watched dumbfounded; there was nothing they could do but wait to tell the old man when he arrived home.

Her father set out immediately in search of his daughter, but in vain. Some days later a neighbouring family found the girl wrapped up in the hide in the branches of a mulberry tree. She had turned into a wormlike creature spinning a long thread of shining silk from her horse-shaped head, spinning it round and round her in a soft cocoon.

Such is the story of the goddess of the silkworm. The Yellow Emperor was delighted to receive her exquisite gift of silk . . . . He ordered his official tailor, Bo Yu, to create new ceremonial robes and hats. And Lei Zu, the revered queen mother of gods and people, wife of the Emperor, began then to collect silkworms and grow them. And so it was that the Chinese people learned of silk.

—Yuan Ke, *Dragons and Dynasties,* translated by Kim Echlin and Nie Zhixiong

Language Arts Activity

What two details in the myth tell you that silkworms were important to the Chinese people?

The girl in the myth gets into trouble because she breaks her promise. Write a story of your own using the idea of a broken promise.

◆ Decide on the place, time, and main characters.
◆ Think about the events that will happen and how your story will conclude.

Counting on Caterpillars

Lai opened the door to the silkworm room. She was greeted by the loud sound of thousands of silkworms crunching on fresh leaves from mulberry trees. Lai enjoyed raising silkworms, but it was hard work. Over its lifetime, each silkworm eats about twenty times its own weight.

Lai had a chance to care for more silkworms. But first she had to figure out how many more she could raise. She now had 6,000 silkworms that ate the leaves from 125 mulberry trees. Should she have her parents buy another piece of land with another 100 mulberry trees? If she had 100 more trees, how many more silkworms could she feed?

Analyze. 125 trees can feed 6,000 silkworms. You want to know the number of silkworms 100 trees will feed. Write a proportion, using n to represent the number of silkworms.

▲ Silkworms are fed fresh mulberry leaves every four hours, around the clock.

Write the proportion.

$$\frac{\text{trees}}{\text{silkworms}} \rightarrow \frac{125}{6{,}000} = \frac{100}{n} \leftarrow \frac{\text{trees}}{\text{silkworms}}$$

Cross multiply. $125 \times n = 6{,}000 \times 100$

Simplify. $125n = 600{,}000$

Solve. $n = \dfrac{600{,}000}{125}$ $n = 4{,}800$

Think about it. "Yes," she decided. She could raise 4,800 more silkworms!

Math Activity

Solve the following problems.

1. Lai's friend Cheng also raises silkworms. He buys mulberry leaves. If 20 sacks of leaves feed 12,000 silkworms a day, how many sacks of leaves will 9,600 silkworms eat per day?

2. When Lai's silkworms are ready to spin, she places them in trays. If 3 trays can hold 150 silkworms, how many trays does Lai use for her 6,000 silkworms?

3. A silkworm spins silk at a rate of about 30.4 centimeters per minute. (a) How many centimeters can it spin in an hour? (b) It takes a silkworm 60 hours to spin the entire cocoon. How many centimeters is that?

4. Lai's silk thread contributes to the creation of beautiful silk clothes. It takes the thread of 630 cocoons to make a blouse and the thread of 110 cocoons to make a tie. (a) If each of Lai's 6,000 silkworms produces a cocoon, how many blouses can be made from the thread? (b) How many ties can be made?

Tie It Together

Plan a Silk Festival

People use silk in many ways other than just to make fine clothing. Did you know that silk was used for parachutes during World War II? Or that some bicycle racers choose tires containing silk because they provide good traction? Today, silk is used for a variety of purposes, including:

- recreation: fishing lines and nets, bicycle tires;
- business: electrical insulations, typewriter and computer ribbons, surgical sutures;
- decoration: some silkscreen printing, artificial flowers

Work in small groups to learn about one of the ways that people have used silk in the past or are using it today. Devise an interesting way to share your project with the class, such as

- a booth to display or advertise a silk product;
- a skit in which you wear silk;
- a historical presentation on the uses of silk in other countries;
- a presentation about a process, such as silkscreen painting or silk flowers.

Ask volunteers to bring pictures or silk products to class. After rehearsing or reviewing your presentation, work with other groups to decide how to organize your Silk Festival.

▼ **Racers at the Tour de France often use tires containing silk on their bicycles.**

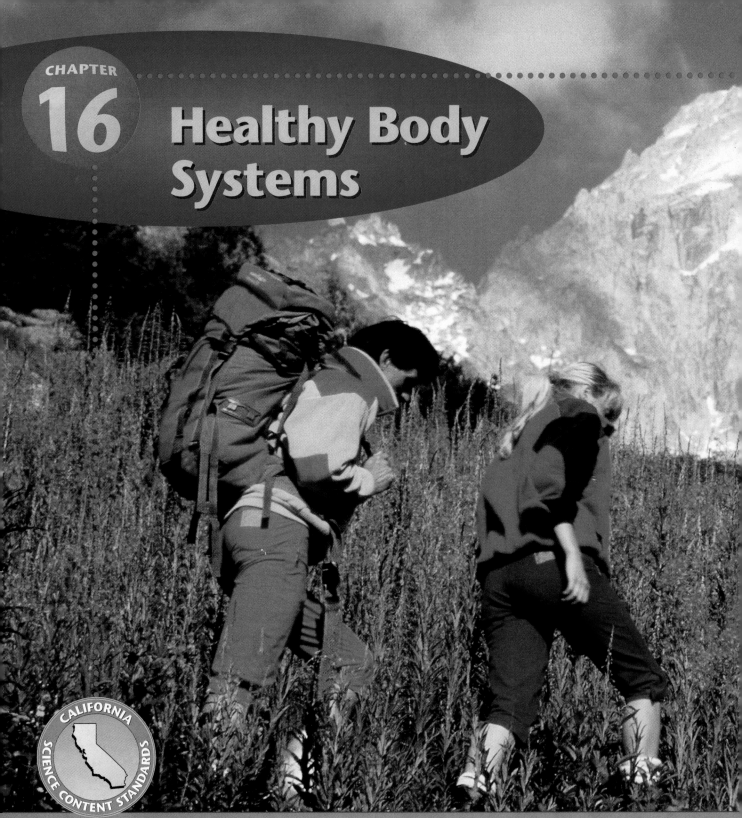

CALIFORNIA SCIENCE CONTENT STANDARDS

The following California Science Content Standards are addressed in this chapter:

1. All living organisms are composed of cells, from just one to many trillions, whose details usually are visible only through a microscope.

   a. Cells function similarly in all living organisms.

   c. The nucleus is the repository for genetic information in plant and animal cells.

5. The anatomy and physiology of plants and animals illustrate the complementary nature of structure and function.

   a. Plants and animals have levels of organization for structure and function, including cells, tissues, organs, organ systems, and the whole organism.

   b. Organ systems function because of the contributions of individual organs, tissues, and cells. The failure of any part can affect the entire system.

7. Scientific progress is made by asking meaningful questions and conducting careful investigations.

Time for a Change

Surrounded by spectacular scenery, the hikers slowly climb to the top of the mountain. Hiking is good exercise—it helps keep your heart, lungs, bones, and muscles in good shape. Other healthful behaviors include eating a balanced diet and getting about eight hours of sleep each night. Behaviors such as these, if performed over and over, become good health habits.

Unfortunately, some habits can harm your health. But bad habits can be changed. One way to change a bad health habit is to replace it with a healthful behavior. For example, if you sit and watch television every day after school, try going for a bike ride with a friend instead.

Your Goal To identify a health habit you want to change, and to carry out a plan to change that habit.

To complete this project successfully, you must
- ◆ choose an unhealthy habit you want to change
- ◆ design a plan to change the unwanted habit—a plan that is realistic and has step-by-step goals
- ◆ keep a daily log to record your progress
- ◆ follow the safety guidelines in Appendix A

Get Started Preview the chapter to identify some habits that can harm your health. Choose one and identify a positive health behavior you could substitute. Begin to think about an overall goal and a realistic plan to achieve your goal.

Check Your Progress You'll be working on this project as you study this chapter. To keep your project on track, look for Check Your Progress boxes at the following points.
Section 1 Review, page 515: Choose the behavior that you want to change, and make a plan.
Section 2 Review, page 521: Keep a log of your progress.

Wrap Up At the end of the chapter (page 529), you will reflect on your successes and setbacks, and identify your next steps.

b. Utilize a variety of print and electronic resources (including the World Wide Web) to collect information as evidence as part of a research project.

d. Construct scale models, maps and appropriately labeled diagrams to communicate scientific knowledge.

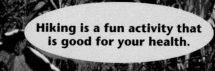

Hiking is a fun activity that is good for your health.

How the Body Is Organized

How Do You Lift Books?

1. Stack one book on top of another one.

2. Lift the two stacked books in front of you so the lowest book is about level with your shoulders. Hold the books in this position for 30 seconds. While you are performing this activity, note how your body responds. For example, how do your arms feel at the beginning and toward the end of the 30 seconds?

3. Balance one book on the top of your head. Walk a few steps with the book on your head.

Think It Over

Inferring List all the parts of your body that worked together as you performed the activities in Steps 1 through 3.

GUIDE FOR READING

◆ What are the levels of organization in the body?

◆ What are the four basic types of tissue in the human body?

Reading Tip Before you read, preview *Exploring Levels of Organization in the Body.* Write down any unfamiliar words. Then, as you read, write their definitions.

The bell rings—lunchtime at last! You hurry down the noisy halls toward the cafeteria. The unmistakable aroma of hot pizza makes your mouth water. At last, after waiting in line, you pick up a plate with a slice of pizza and some salad. When you get to the cashier, you dig in your pocket for lunch money. Then, carefully balancing your tray, you scan the crowded cafeteria for your friends. You spot them, walk to their table, sit down, and begin to eat.

Think for a minute about how many parts of your body were involved in the simple act of getting and eating your lunch. You heard the bell with your ears and smelled the pizza with your nose. Bones and muscles worked together as you walked to the cafeteria, picked up your food, and sat down at the table. Without your brain, you couldn't have remembered where you put your lunch money. Once you began to eat, your teeth chewed the food and your throat muscles swallowed it. Then other parts of your digestive system, such as your stomach, began to process the food for your body to use.

Levels of Organization

Every minute of the day, whether you are eating, studying, playing basketball, or even sleeping, your body is busily at work. Each part of the body has a specific job to do, and all the different parts work together. This smooth functioning is due partly to the way in which the human body is organized. **The levels of organization in the human body consist of cells, tissues, organs, and organ systems.** The smallest unit is the cell, and the largest is the organ system. As you read about each level of organization, refer to *Exploring Levels of Organization in the Body,* which shows how your skeletal system is organized.

☑ *Checkpoint* *What is the largest level of organization in the human body?*

EXPLORING *Levels of Organization in the Body*

The skeletal system supports your body and gives it shape. Like all other organ systems in your body, it consists of organs made up of tissues and tissues made up of cells.

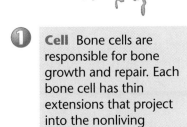

1 **Cell** Bone cells are responsible for bone growth and repair. Each bone cell has thin extensions that project into the nonliving material around it, which the cells produce.

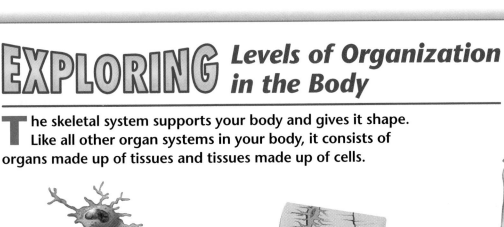

2 **Tissue** Bone tissue consists of living cells that are widely separated from one another by hard, nonliving material. This hard material gives bones their strength.

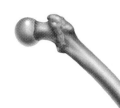

3 **Organ** The thigh bone, or femur, is an organ that consists of different kinds of tissues. Besides tissue made of bone cells, a bone contains blood and nerve tissue.

4 **Organ System** The skeletal system is made up of over 200 bones. In addition, it includes cartilage, the tough tissue that gives shape to your nose and ears. The ligaments that hold bones together are also part of the skeletal system.

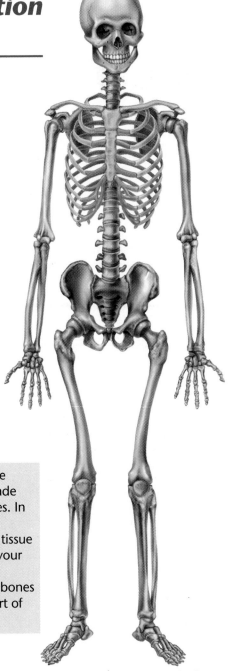

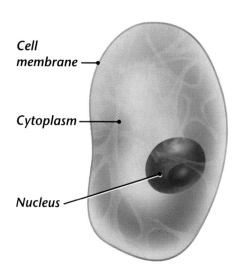

Figure 1 The cells in your body are surrounded by a cell membrane, and most have a nucleus. The cytoplasm is the area between the cell membrane and the nucleus.

Cell membrane

Cytoplasm

Nucleus

How Is a Book Organized?

ACTIVITY

In this activity, you will analyze the levels of organization in a book.

1. Examine this textbook to see how it is subdivided— into chapters, sections, and so on.

2. Make a concept map that shows this pattern of organization. Place the largest subdivision at the top of the map and the smallest at the bottom.

3. Compare the levels of organization in this book to those in the human body.

Making Models Which level of organization in the book represents cells? Which represent tissues, organs, and organ systems?

Cells

A **cell** is the basic unit of structure and function in a living thing. Complex organisms are composed of many cells in the same way a building is composed of many bricks. The human body contains about 100 trillion cells. Cells are quite tiny, and most cannot be seen without a microscope.

Most animal cells, including those in the human body, have a structure similar to the cell in Figure 1. The **cell membrane** forms the outside boundary of the cell. Inside the cell membrane is a large structure called the **nucleus.** The nucleus is the control center that directs the cell's activities and contains information that determines the cell's characteristics. When the cell divides, or reproduces, this information is passed onto the newly formed cells. The area between the cell membrane and the nucleus is called the **cytoplasm.** The cytoplasm contains a clear, jellylike substance in which many important cell structures are found.

Cells carry on the processes that keep organisms alive. Inside cells, for example, molecules from digested food undergo chemical reactions that provide energy for the body's activities.

☑ *Checkpoint* *What is the function of the nucleus?*

Tissues

The cell is the smallest unit of organization in your body; the next level is a tissue. A **tissue** is a group of similar cells that perform the same function. **The human body contains four basic types of tissue: muscle tissue, nerve tissue, connective tissue, and epithelial tissue.** To see examples of each of these tissues, look at Figure 2.

Like the muscle cells that form it, **muscle tissue** can contract, or shorten. By doing this, muscle tissue makes parts of your body move. When you turn the pages of this book or focus your eyes on this page, you are using muscle tissue.

While muscle tissue carries out movement, nerve tissue directs and controls it. **Nerve tissue** carries messages back and forth between the brain and every other part of the body. Your brain is made up mostly of nerve tissue.

Connective tissue provides support for your body and connects all its parts. Bone is one kind of connective tissue; its strength and hardness support your body and protect its delicate structures. Fat, which pads parts of your body, provides insulation from cold, and stores energy, is also a connective tissue. So is blood, which travels to all parts of your body.

Epithelial tissue (ep uh THEE lee ul) covers the surfaces of your body, inside and out. Some epithelial tissue, such as the outermost layer of your skin, protects the delicate structures that lie

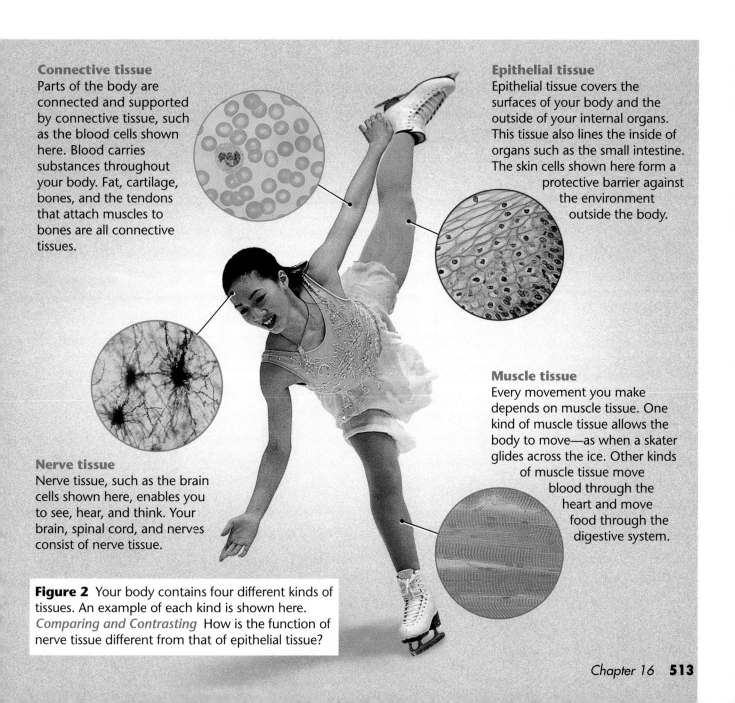

Connective tissue
Parts of the body are connected and supported by connective tissue, such as the blood cells shown here. Blood carries substances throughout your body. Fat, cartilage, bones, and the tendons that attach muscles to bones are all connective tissues.

Epithelial tissue
Epithelial tissue covers the surfaces of your body and the outside of your internal organs. This tissue also lines the inside of organs such as the small intestine. The skin cells shown here form a protective barrier against the environment outside the body.

Nerve tissue
Nerve tissue, such as the brain cells shown here, enables you to see, hear, and think. Your brain, spinal cord, and nerves consist of nerve tissue.

Muscle tissue
Every movement you make depends on muscle tissue. One kind of muscle tissue allows the body to move—as when a skater glides across the ice. Other kinds of muscle tissue move blood through the heart and move food through the digestive system.

Figure 2 Your body contains four different kinds of tissues. An example of each kind is shown here. *Comparing and Contrasting* How is the function of nerve tissue different from that of epithelial tissue?

beneath it. Other kinds of epithelial tissue absorb or release substances. The lining of your digestive system consists of epithelial tissue. Some of the cells in this tissue release chemicals used in digestion, while others absorb digested food.

Organs and Organ Systems

Your stomach, heart, brain, and lungs are all organs. An **organ** is a structure that is composed of different kinds of tissue. Like a tissue, an organ performs a specific job. The job of an organ, however, is generally more complex than that of a tissue. The heart, for example, pumps blood throughout your body, over and over again. The heart contains all four kinds of tissue—muscle, nerve, connective, and epithelial. Each tissue type contributes to the overall job of pumping blood.

Each organ in your body is part of an **organ system,** a group of organs that work together to perform a major function. Your heart is part of your circulatory system, which carries oxygen and other materials throughout the body. Besides the heart, blood vessels are organs in the circulatory system. Figure 4 describes the major organ systems in the human body.

The different organ systems work together and depend on one another. You can compare the functioning of the human body to the work it takes to put on a school play. A play needs actors, of course, but it also needs a director, someone to make the costumes, and people to sell tickets. Similarly, when you ride a bike, you use your muscular and skeletal systems to steer and push the pedals. But you also need your nervous system to direct your arms and legs to move. Your respiratory, digestive, and circulatory systems work together to fuel your muscles with the energy they need. And your excretory system removes the wastes produced while your muscles are hard at work.

Figure 3 Each musician in the band contributes to the overall sound of the music. In the same way, each organ system in your body works with the other organ systems to keep you alive and healthy.

Organ Systems in the Human Body

Endocrine Controls many body processes—such as intake of sugar by cells—by means of chemicals.

Excretory Removes wastes.

Immune Fights disease.

Muscular Enables the body to move; moves food through the digestive system; keeps the heart beating.

Nervous Detects and interprets information from the environment outside the body and from within the body; controls most body functions.

Reproductive Produces sex cells that can unite with other sex cells to create offspring; controls male and female characteristics.

Respiratory Takes oxygen into ▶ the body and eliminates carbon dioxide.

Skeletal Supports the body, protects it, and works with muscles to allow movement; makes blood cells and stores some materials.

Skin Protects the body, keeps water inside the body, and helps regulate body temperature.

▲ **Circulatory** Carries needed materials to the body cells; carries wastes away from body cells; helps fight disease.

Digestive Takes food into the body, breaks food down, and absorbs the digested materials.

Figure 4 The human body is made up of eleven organ systems. *Interpreting Charts* Which two systems work together to get oxygen to your cells?

Section 1 Review

1. List the four levels of organization in the human body. Give an example of each level.
2. What are the four types of tissue found in the human body? What is the general function of each type?
3. Describe the structure of an animal cell.
4. **Thinking Critically Applying Concepts** What systems of the body are involved when you prepare a sandwich and then eat it?

Check Your Progress
CHAPTER PROJECT

Once you have chosen a behavior that you want to change, make a day-by-day plan. Get your teacher's approval for the plan. Then set up a log in which you will record your progress. Start now to work toward your first goal. *(Hint:* Your plan will be more successful if you set realistic intermediate goals along the way. For example, if you want to get more exercise, begin by exercising three times a week for a short period. Over time, you can gradually increase your exercise time and frequency.)

A Body of Knowledge

In this lab, you will discover how much you already know about the human body.

Problem

Where are some important organs in the human body located?

Skills Focus

observing, inferring, posing questions

Materials

outline of the human body   colored pencils

Procedure

1. Obtain an outline of the human body and five colored pencils. Notice that the outline shows a front view of the body, and that the right and left sides of the body are labeled.
2. Use one color to draw in the heart at the size and shape that you think it is. Draw the heart in the approximate place in the body where you think it is located. Label the heart on your drawing.
3. Select three different colors to represent the brain, lungs, and stomach. Draw each of these organs, showing its general size and shape and where you think it is located. Label each organ.

4. Choose one of the organs you just drew, and think of other organs that may be part of the same organ system. Draw those organs and label them. If the organs are part of a pathway, draw arrows to show the path.

Analyze and Conclude

1. Create a chart that lists the brain, heart, lungs, and stomach in the first column. In the second column, describe your understanding of the function of each of those organs.
2. Describe the role of the organ system you drew. How does it function in the body?
3. **Apply** For each organ in your chart, write one question you would like to have answered. Then write one question about the organ system you drew.

More to Explore

Find illustrations in this book that show the correct location of the organs you drew. Use a new body outline to make more accurate drawings of the organs and organ system.

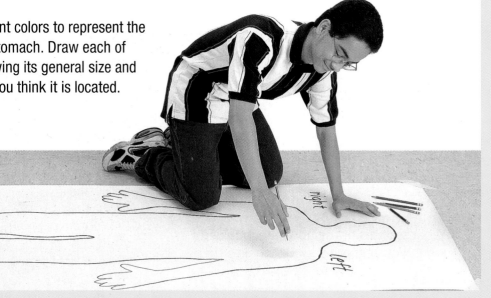

2 Keeping the Body in Balance

DISCOVER

What Happens When You Are Startled?

1. Read this activity, and then close your eyes.

2. Your teacher is behind you and will pop a balloon at any moment.

3. Pay attention to how your body reacts when you hear the balloon pop. Observe whether you jump and whether your heartbeat rate and breathing rate change.

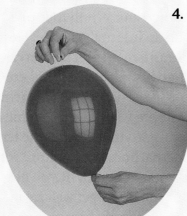

4. Observe how your body returns to normal after it responds to the sound.

Think It Over

Predicting How might your body respond if you suddenly saw a huge, threatening animal rushing toward you? How might your response be an advantage to you?

Imagine that you are trapped in a damp, dark dungeon. Somewhere near you is a deep, water-filled pit into which you could fall. Overhead swings a pendulum with a razor-sharp edge. With each swing, the pendulum lowers closer and closer to your body.

The main character in Edgar Allan Poe's story "The Pit and the Pendulum" finds himself in that very situation. Here's his reaction: "A fearful idea now suddenly drove the blood in torrents upon my heart. . . . I at once started to my feet, trembling convulsively in every fibre. . . . Perspiration burst from every pore, and stood in cold, big beads upon my forehead."

GUIDE FOR READING

◆ What is homeostasis?

◆ What happens during the alarm stage of stress?

Reading Tip Before you read, write the headings in this section on a piece of paper, leaving a space after each. As you read, write a summary of the information under each heading.

Sharpen your Skills

Interpreting Data

ACTIVITY

A scientist fed a strong sugar solution to an animal. The scientist then checked the concentration of sugar in the animal's blood during the next three hours. The table below shows the results of the experiment.

Time After Eating Sugar (minutes)	Sugar Concentration (milligrams/ 100 milliliters)
0	75
30	125
60	110
90	90
120	75
150	75
180	75

Explain how the data show homeostasis at work. *(Hint: Think about what happened to the blood-sugar level during the first hour and then during the next two hours.)*

Homeostasis

Poe's character is reacting to danger. Your body, too, responds to threatening or startling events in specific ways. For example, your heart and breathing rates increase. Once you are no longer in danger or startled, your heart slows down. As the saying goes, you "breathe more easily."

The body's return to normal after a scare is one example of **homeostasis** (hoh mee oh STAY sis), the body's tendency to maintain an internal balance. **Homeostasis is the process by which an organism's internal environment is kept stable in spite of changes in the external environment.**

To see homeostasis in action, all you have to do is take your temperature when the air is chilly. Then take it again in an overheated room. No matter what the temperature of the air around you, your internal body temperature will be close to 37 degrees Celsius, as long as you are healthy. If you get sick, your body temperature may rise. But when you get well again, it returns to 37 degrees.

Your body has various ways of maintaining homeostasis. For example, you need food and water to stay alive. When your body is low on either of these substances, your brain sends signals that result in your feeling hungry or thirsty. When you eat or drink, you maintain homeostasis by providing your body with substances that it needs.

Figure 5 The wind is icy and the ground is covered with snow. In spite of the chill, the body temperatures of these sledders remain fairly constant at about 37° Celsius.
Applying Concepts What is the term for the body's tendency to maintain a stable internal environment?

518

INTEGRATING CHEMISTRY When you perspire on a hot day, your body is maintaining its internal balance. When perspiration evaporates, the liquid water becomes water vapor, which is a gas. In order for a liquid to become a gas, heat must be added to it. As the water in perspiration evaporates, it absorbs heat from your body and carries it away. This removal of heat helps cool you down and enables your body to maintain a constant temperature on a hot day.

☑ *Checkpoint* *How do feelings of thirst help your body maintain homeostasis?*

Stress and Homeostasis

The rapid heartbeat and trembling of the character in "The Pit and the Pendulum" are both signs of stress. **Stress** is the reaction of your body and mind to threatening, challenging, or disturbing events. Many things can act as stressors, or events that cause stress. A snarling dog, an argument with a friend, or an upcoming oral report can all be stressors. Stress upsets homeostasis, and your body reacts in specific ways.

Physical Responses to Stress Figure 6 shows what happens in your body within seconds after you experience stress. During this stage, which is called the alarm stage, your body releases a

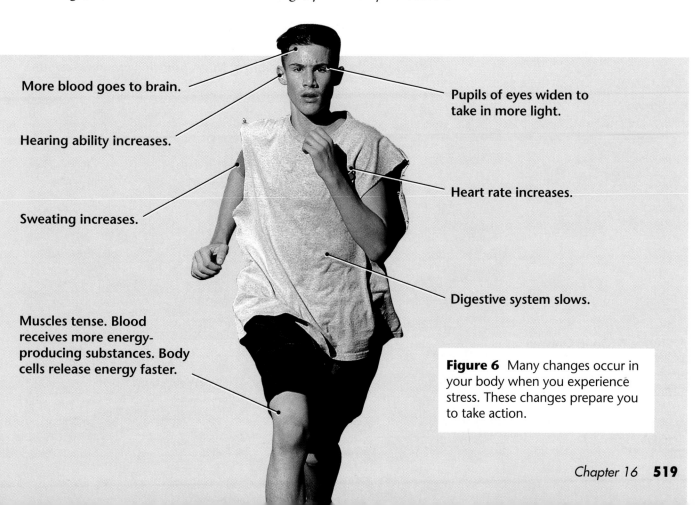

More blood goes to brain.

Hearing ability increases.

Sweating increases.

Muscles tense. Blood receives more energy-producing substances. Body cells release energy faster.

Pupils of eyes widen to take in more light.

Heart rate increases.

Digestive system slows.

Figure 6 Many changes occur in your body when you experience stress. These changes prepare you to take action.

The quotation from "The Pit and the Pendulum" that you read at the beginning of this section (page 517) describes a character's reaction to extreme stress. Notice how the author, Edgar Allan Poe, uses detailed descriptions of the character's physical reactions, such as his rapid heartbeat and sweating, to convey the character's fear.

In Your Journal

Create a situation in which a character faces an extremely stressful situation. Describe the character's physical reactions and feelings. Make sure to use vivid and precise descriptive words that clearly convey the character's reactions.

chemical called **adrenaline** into your bloodstream. **Adrenaline gives you a burst of energy and causes many other changes in your body. These changes prepare you to take quick action.**

The effects of adrenaline, which take only a few seconds, are dramatic. Your breathing quickens, sending more oxygen to your body cells to provide energy for your muscles. That extra oxygen gets to your cells rapidly because your heart begins to beat faster. The faster heartbeat increases the flow of blood to your muscles and some other organs. In contrast, less blood flows to your skin and digestive system, so that more is available for your arms and legs. The pupils of your eyes become wider, allowing you to see better.

Fight or Flight The reactions caused by adrenaline are sometimes called the "fight-or-flight" response, because they prepare you either to fight the stressor or to take flight and escape. Scientists think that the fight-or-flight response was important for primitive people who faced wild-animal attacks and similar dangers. Today, the same reactions still occur with any stressor, whether it is a snarling dog or a social studies test.

During the fight-or-flight response, your body systems work together to respond to the stressor. For example, your respiratory system provides you with extra oxygen, which your circulatory system delivers to the parts of your body that need it. Your muscular system, in turn, works with your skeletal system to help you move—fast.

☑ *Checkpoint During the alarm stage, how do your eyes respond?*

Figure 7 Oops! One sure way to cause stress is to do too many things at once. *Relating Cause and Effect How does stress affect a person's heartbeat and breathing rates?*

Long-Term Stress

The alarm stage of stress only lasts for a short time. If the stress is over quickly, your body soon returns to its normal state. Some kinds of stressors, however, continue for a long time. Suppose, for example, you are stressed because you are moving to a new community. You cannot fight the stressor, and you cannot run away from it either. When a stressful situation does not go away quickly, your body cannot restore homeostasis. If you do not deal with the stress, you may become tired, irritable, and have trouble getting along with others. In addition, you may be more likely to become ill.

Dealing With Stress

Stress is a normal part of life. No one can avoid stress entirely. When you are in a stressful situation, it is important that you recognize it and take action to deal with it, rather than pretending that the stressor doesn't exist. For example, suppose you aren't doing well in math class. If you accept the problem and deal with it—perhaps by asking your teacher for help—your stress will probably decrease.

In addition, when you are experiencing long-term stress, physical activity can help you feel better. Riding a bike, skating, or even raking leaves can take your mind off the stress. It is also important to talk about the situation and your feelings with friends and family members.

Figure 8 When you are under stress, it is important to find ways to relax.

Section 2 Review

1. What is homeostasis?
2. Describe what happens during the alarm stage of stress.
3. Explain how your body temperature is an example of homeostasis.
4. What problems may result if a stressful situation does not go away quickly?
5. **Thinking Critically Making Judgments** What are three helpful ways of dealing with stress?

Check Your Progress
CHAPTER PROJECT

By now you should be carrying out your behavior-change plan. Keep a daily log to monitor your successes and setbacks. Don't be discouraged if things do not go exactly as you planned—just make adjustments to get yourself back on track. (*Hint:* Enlist your family and friends to support your effort. In addition, give yourself rewards, such as a trip to the movies, for reaching each intermediate goal you set.)

SECTION 3 Wellness

How Well Do You Take Care of Your Health?

Answer *yes* or *no* to each question.

1. Do you engage in vigorous exercise, such as sports or brisk walking, several times a week?

2. Do you eat at least three servings of vegetables, two servings of fruit, and six servings of grain foods, such as bread, rice, and pasta, every day?

3. Do you get about eight hours of sleep each night?

4. Do you face and deal with stressful situations rather than ignore them?

5. Are you happy with yourself most of the time?

6. Do you have friends and family members you can turn to for help with a problem?

Think It Over

Making Judgments Add up the number of *yes* answers you gave. The more *yes* answers, the healthier the lifestyle you lead.

GUIDE FOR READING

◆ What are the three components of wellness?

◆ How can you think through a decision to make sure it is good for your health?

Reading Tip As you read, write a definition, in your own words, of each boldfaced term.

Tension is high as the soccer ball whizzes toward you. You aim your kick, and the ball soars into the net. You have scored the winning goal!

Playing soccer can be a great experience. The exercise is good for your body. But soccer does more than just keep your body healthy. It's fun to be part of a team and to share the thrill of competition. When your team plays well, you feel good about yourself and gain confidence in your abilities.

Components of Wellness

Everything you do, from playing soccer to going to the movies with friends, affects your overall level of health. **Wellness** is being at your best possible level of health—in your body, in your mind, and in your relationships with others. **Wellness has three components—physical health, mental health, and social health.**

Physical Health Your **physical health** consists of how well your body functions. When you are physically healthy, you have energy to carry out your daily tasks. To ensure your physical health, you need to eat healthy foods, exercise regularly, get enough sleep, and wear protective gear when you play sports. You also need to avoid harmful activities, such as smoking.

Mental Health Your **mental health** involves your feelings, or emotions—how you feel about yourself and how you handle the day-to-day demands of your life. When you are mentally healthy, you recognize your achievements and learn from your mistakes. Mentally healthy people handle stress well—by changing the stressful situation when they can, and by engaging in stress-relieving activities. In addition, people who are mentally healthy generally feel good about themselves.

Social Health **Social health** refers to how well you get along with others. When you are socially healthy, you have loving relationships, respect the rights of others, and give and accept help. Building healthy relationships with family members, making and keeping friends, and communicating your needs to others are all important for social health.

For teenagers especially, peer pressure can have an impact on social health. **Peer pressure** consists of pressure from your friends and classmates to behave in certain ways. Peer pressure can be good, if your friends encourage you to work hard in school and participate in sports and other healthy activities. Sometimes, however, you may experience peer pressure to do harmful things, such as drinking alcohol. Socially healthy people understand that it is okay to say no when they are asked to do things that can harm themselves or others.

Figure 9 Wellness means being at your best possible level of health. Having fun with friends (top) is part of social health. Physical health (middle) is important for demanding sports such as soccer. The feeling of accomplishment that comes from playing an instrument (bottom) helps develop mental health.

Wellness in the Balance

In this activity, you will make a mobile showing the three aspects of wellness.

1. Cut out a cardboard triangle about 20 cm on each side. Label the sides of the triangle "Physical Health," "Mental Health," and "Social Health." Tape a string to the center of the triangle.

2. Cut pictures from magazines showing activities that contribute to each of the three components of wellness.

3. Glue each picture onto a separate piece of cardboard. Tape one end of a string to each picture. Tape the other end to the appropriate side of the triangle. Hang the mobile from the center string.

Making Models How does your mobile show that all three components of wellness are important?

Overall Wellness Like three pieces in a jigsaw puzzle, your physical health, mental health, and social health are linked together. You can understand this if you think about what happens when a soccer team wins a game. To make the kick to score a goal, your body needs to be in good physical health. If you play well, you feel good about yourself—excited, happy, and proud. When you celebrate with your teammates, you enjoy good social relationships.

☑ *Checkpoint* How is social health different from mental health? How are they related?

Evaluating Your Wellness

Think for a minute about your overall level of health—physical, mental, and social. How healthy are you? You could think of your overall level of health as a point on a **continuum,** which is a gradual progression through many stages between one extreme and another. The illness-wellness continuum is shown in Figure 10. The far right end of the continuum represents perfect wellness, and the far left end represents very poor health, or even early death. The point in the middle is neutral—neither ill nor well. Your level of wellness is represented by a point somewhere between the two ends. For the most part, it is the behaviors that you choose that determine where on the continuum your level of health falls.

Figure 10 A person's level of health can be represented by a point on the illness-wellness continuum.
Making Judgments How can you improve your health and move closer to the wellness end of the continuum?

Loss of health   **Improving health**

Very poor health   *Neither sick nor well*   *Excellent health*

Figure 11 Snowboarding can affect your health in positive or negative ways. By taking proper precautions and being careful, snowboarding can be a positive experience.

Improving Your Health

Your health doesn't have to stay in the same place on the illness-wellness continuum. Working on wellness is a lot like keeping your room clean. You can't clean your room just once. After a few days, dirty clothes pile up, your trash basket overflows, and dust settles on everything. Like keeping your room tidy, you must work to improve your wellness every day.

Factors You Cannot Change Before you plan how to improve your wellness, you need to recognize that there are some health-related factors that you cannot change. Some of these may be traits that you inherited from your parents, such as skin that sunburns easily. However, you can still work toward wellness. You can use a sunscreen and limit your exposure to sunlight.

INTEGRATING ENVIRONMENTAL SCIENCE You probably cannot change the environment in which you live, even though it affects your health. Polluted air can damage the lungs and make the circulatory system struggle to get oxygen to the cells. Polluted water can carry chemicals and microorganisms that harm the body. Although you by yourself may not be able to change your environment, you can avoid some environmental risks. You can, for example, refuse to swim or fish in polluted water.

Making Wise Decisions Every day you make many decisions that affect your health. Some of these decisions, such as whether to wear a jacket on a cold day, are fairly simple. Others, such as how to deal with a friend who is pressuring you to use tobacco, may be a lot more complicated. For help with very important decisions, talk to a parent, teacher, or other trusted adult.

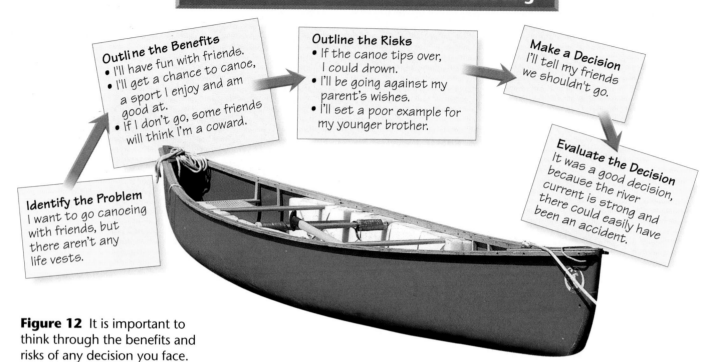

Decision: Whether or Not to Go Canoeing

Outline the Benefits
- I'll have fun with friends.
- I'll get a chance to canoe, a sport I enjoy and am good at.
- If I don't go, some friends will think I'm a coward.

Outline the Risks
- If the canoe tips over, I could drown.
- I'll be going against my parent's wishes.
- I'll set a poor example for my younger brother.

Make a Decision
I'll tell my friends we shouldn't go.

Evaluate the Decision
It was a good decision, because the river current is strong and there could easily have been an accident.

Identify the Problem
I want to go canoeing with friends, but there aren't any life vests.

Figure 12 It is important to think through the benefits and risks of any decision you face. *Problem Solving What decision would you reach if you were faced with this problem?*

To make a healthy decision, it is important to think through the benefits and risks of an action you might take. You increase the likelihood of making a healthy decision if you think about it carefully beforehand. Evaluate the advantages and disadvantages of each choice you might make. Figure 12 shows how decision making can work in a real situation.

In this textbook, you will learn many ways to improve your health. You will discover that this textbook is something like an owner's manual. It will explain how your body works, and give you some suggestions for keeping your body healthy. The decision to do that is up to you.

Section 3 Review

1. Identify the three components of wellness. Briefly explain each one.
2. Explain the process involved in making a healthy decision.
3. Give an example of something that might change a person's position on the illness-wellness continuum. In which direction would the person move?
4. **Thinking Critically** **Inferring** How might having a friend who is very wellness-conscious affect your own level of wellness? Explain.

Science at Home

Explain to your family what the concept of wellness means. Then work with family members to identify four or five changes that you, as a family, could make to improve family wellness. Make sure to include changes that would improve mental and social health as well as physical health.

SECTION 1 How the Body Is Organized

Key Ideas

◆ The levels of organization in the human body consist of cells, tissues, organs, and organ systems.

◆ The cell is the basic unit of structure and function in living things. The human body contains about 100 trillion cells.

◆ A tissue is a group of cells that perform the same function. The human body contains four basic types of tissue—muscle, nerve, connective, and epithelial.

◆ Organs, which are composed of different kinds of tissue, perform complex functions. An organ system is a group of organs that work together to perform a major function.

Key Terms

cell
cell membrane
nucleus
cytoplasm
tissue
muscle tissue

nerve tissue
connective tissue
epithelial tissue
organ
organ system

SECTION 2 Keeping the Body in Balance

Key Ideas

◆ Homeostasis is the process by which an organism's internal environment is kept stable in spite of changes in the external environment.

◆ Stress disturbs homeostasis. When under stress, the body releases adrenaline, which causes many changes in the body. The changes prepare the body to take quick action.

◆ Exercise and relaxing activities can help relieve stress.

Key Terms

homeostasis   stress   adrenaline

SECTION 3 Wellness

INTEGRATING **HEALTH**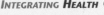

Key Ideas

◆ Wellness is being at the best possible level of health. The three components of wellness are physical health, mental health, and social health.

◆ Physical health consists of how well the body functions. Mental health consists of how you feel about yourself and how well you handle the demands of your life. Social health is how well you get along with other people.

◆ A person's overall level of wellness can range from very poor health to excellent health. Most people fall somewhere between those two points. Behavior can affect wellness, either by harming it or improving it.

◆ To make a health-related decision, you should consider both the benefits and the risks of any action.

Key Terms

wellness
physical health
mental health

social health
peer pressure
continuum

USING THE INTERNET ACTIVITY

www.science-explorer.phschool.com

California Test Prep: Reviewing Content

Multiple Choice

Choose the letter of the best answer.

1. A group of similar cells that perform a similar function is called a(n)
   a. cell.
   b. organ.
   c. tissue.
   d. organ system.

2. The control center of the cell is the
   a. cell membrane.
   b. cell fluid.
   c. cytoplasm.
   d. nucleus.

3. Which type of tissue is blood?
   a. muscle tissue
   b. epithelial tissue
   c. connective tissue
   d. nerve tissue

4. The term most closely associated with homeostasis is
   a. growth.
   b. stability.
   c. temperature.
   d. energy.

5. Which of the following is *not* a way to protect your social health?
   a. getting enough sleep
   b. making friends
   c. respecting the rights of others
   d. accepting help

True or False

If the statement is true, write true. If it is false, change the underlined word or words to make the statement true.

6. <u>Epithelial</u> tissue makes parts of your body move.

7. The <u>circulatory</u> system carries needed materials to the body cells.

8. The brain is an example of <u>an organ</u>.

9. The fight-or-flight response is part of the body's reaction to <u>peer pressure</u>.

10. Feeling good about yourself is one aspect of <u>social</u> health.

Checking Concepts

11. Explain the relationship between cells, tissues, organs, and organ systems.

12. What is the function of the respiratory system?

13. How does hunger help your body maintain homeostasis?

14. Think of a situation that might cause long-term stress. Identify some ways in which a person might deal with that stress.

15. List two possible health hazards in the environment, and explain how you might protect yourself from them.

16. **Writing to Learn** Imagine that you write a newspaper advice column called Ask Dr. Wellness. You receive the following letter:
   Dear Dr. Wellness: I am under a great deal of stress because I will soon be trying out for a major part in the school play. I want the part badly. How can I deal with this stress?
   　　　　Aspiring Actor
   Write an answer to this letter that gives Aspiring Actor some specific suggestions.

Thinking Visually

17. **Concept Map** The concept map below diagrams the three components of wellness. Copy the map and complete it. (For more on concept maps, see the Skills Handbook.)

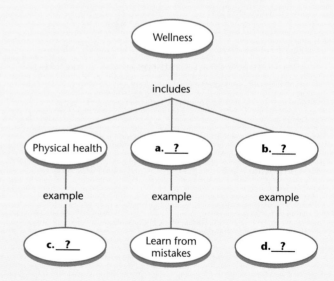

Test Prep: Skills

The graph below shows the effects of the temperature of the environment on a girl's skin temperature and on the temperature inside her body. Use the graph to answer Questions 18–21.

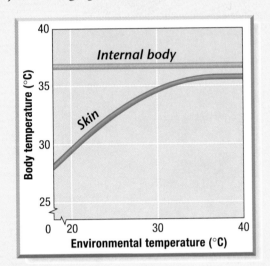

18. **Interpreting Data** As the temperature of the environment rises, what happens to the girl's internal temperature? How does this demonstrate homeostasis?

19. **Developing Hypotheses** What happens to the temperature of the girl's skin? Hypothesize why this pattern differs from the pattern shown by the girl's internal temperature.

20. **Predicting** Suppose the girl went outdoors on a chilly fall morning. Predict what would happen to her internal body temperature and skin temperature.

21. **Designing Experiments** Design an experiment to test your prediction from Question 20.

Thinking Critically

22. **Making Judgments** Suppose some friends were pressuring you to go skateboarding on a road with heavy traffic. Identify the benefits and risks of the choices you have. Then make a decision and explain your reasons.

23. **Inferring** Why do you think scientists classify blood as a connective tissue?

24. **Making Generalizations** How is homeostasis important to the survival of living things?

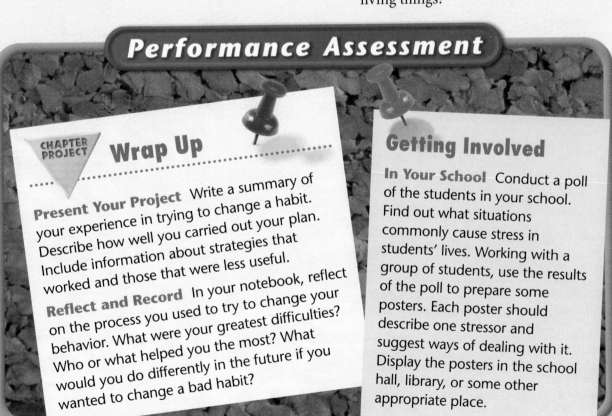

Performance Assessment

Wrap Up

CHAPTER PROJECT

Present Your Project Write a summary of your experience in trying to change a habit. Describe how well you carried out your plan. Include information about strategies that worked and those that were less useful.

Reflect and Record In your notebook, reflect on the process you used to try to change your behavior. What were your greatest difficulties? Who or what helped you the most? What would you do differently in the future if you wanted to change a bad habit?

Getting Involved

In Your School Conduct a poll of the students in your school. Find out what situations commonly cause stress in students' lives. Working with a group of students, use the results of the poll to prepare some posters. Each poster should describe one stressor and suggest ways of dealing with it. Display the posters in the school hall, library, or some other appropriate place.

CALIFORNIA
SCIENCE CONTENT STANDARDS

The following California Science Content Standards are addressed in this chapter:

1. All living organisms are composed of cells, from just one to many trillions, whose details usually are visible only through a microscope.

   f. As multicellular organisms develop, their cells differentiate.

5. The anatomy and physiology of plants and animals illustrate the complementary nature of structure and function.

   a. Plants and animals have levels of organization for structure and function, including cells, tissues, organs, organ systems, and the whole organism.

   b. Organ systems function because of the contributions of individual organs, tissues, and cells. The failure of any part can affect the entire system.

   c. How bones and muscles work together to provide a structural framework for movement.

6. Physical principles underlie biological structures and functions.

   f. Light interacts with matter by transmission (including refraction), absorption, or scattering (including reflection).

On the Move

People are able to perform an amazing variety of movements. For example, a baseball player can swing a bat, a chef can twirl pizza dough, and an artist can mold clay into a sculpture. Behind every human movement, there's a complex interaction of bones, muscles, and other parts of the body.

In this chapter, you'll find out how bones and muscles work. And in this project, you'll take a close look at a simple movement, such as stretching a leg, bending an arm at the elbow, or another movement you choose.

Your Goal To make a working model that shows how bones and muscles interact to move the body in a specific way.

To complete this project you will
◆ select a specific movement, and identify all of the major bones, joints, and muscles that are involved
◆ design an accurate physical model of the movement
◆ explain how the bones and muscles make the movement possible
◆ follow the safety guidelines in Appendix A

Get Started Let all group members name a motion from a sport or other familiar activity that they'd like to investigate. If the motion is long or complicated, discuss how to simplify it for the project. Also consider what kind of model you'll make, such as a wood or cardboard cutout, clay structure, or computer animation. Then write up a plan for your teacher's approval.

Check Your Progress You'll be working on this project as you study this chapter. To keep your project on track, look for Check Your Progress boxes at the following points.
Section 1 Review, page 539: Choose a simple motion to analyze and sketch.
Section 3 Review, page 549: Create your working model.

Wrap Up At the end of the chapter (page 559), you'll demonstrate your working model.

For this baseball player to hit the ball, his bones and muscles must work together in a coordinated manner.

h. How to compare joints in the body (wrist, shoulder, thigh) with structures used in machines and simple devices (hinge, ball-and-socket, and sliding joints).

i. How levers confer mechanical advantage and how the application of this principle applies to the musculoskeletal system.

7. Scientific progress is made by asking meaningful questions and conducting careful investigations.

a. Select and use appropriate tools and technology to perform tests, collect data, and display data.

b. Utilize a variety of print and electronic resources (including the World Wide Web) to collect information as evidence

as part of a research project.

c. Communicate the logical connection among hypothesis, science concepts, tests conducted, data collected, and conclusions drawn from the scientific evidence.

d. Construct scale models, maps and appropriately labeled diagrams to communicate scientific knowledge.

CHAPTER 17 ASSESSMENT

California Test Prep: Reviewing Content

Multiple Choice
Choose the letter of the best answer.

1. Blood cells are produced in
   a. compact bone.
   b. marrow.
   c. cartilage.
   d. ligaments.
2. Joints that allow only forward or backward movement are
   a. pivot joints.
   b. ball and socket joints.
   c. hinge joints.
   d. gliding joints.
3. Muscles that help the skeleton move are
   a. cardiac muscles.
   b. smooth muscles.
   c. skeletal muscles.
   d. involuntary muscles.
4. A fixed point around which a lever rotates is called the
   a. fulcrum.
   b. input.
   c. output.
   d. mechanical advantage.
5. Which structures help to maintain body temperature?
   a. oil glands   b. follicles
   c. sweat glands   d. ligaments

True or False
If the statement is true, write true. If it is false, change the underlined word or words to make the statement true.

6. Spongy bone is filled with <u>cartilage</u>.
7. The connective tissue that connects the bones in a movable joint is called a <u>tendon</u>.
8. <u>Skeletal</u> muscle is sometimes called striated muscle.
9. The force exerted on an object that causes the object to move is called <u>work</u>.
10. The <u>epidermis</u> contains nerve endings and blood vessels.

Checking Concepts

11. Describe the structure of a bone.
12. List the four kinds of movable joints. Describe how each kind of joint functions.
13. How does the appearance of smooth muscle differ from that of skeletal muscle when viewed with a microscope?
14. Explain how skeletal muscles work in pairs to move a body part.
15. Why are smooth muscles called involuntary muscles?
16. Describe each of the three classes of levers and give an example of each in the human body.
17. Describe the life cycle of an epidermal cell.
18. Why is it important to limit your exposure to the sun?
19. **Writing to Learn** Write an article for your school newspaper about preventing skeletal and muscular injuries. The article should focus on ways in which athletes can decrease the risk of injuries during sports.

Thinking Visually

20. **Concept Map** Copy the concept map about muscles onto a separate sheet of paper. Then complete it and add a title. (For more information on concept maps, see the Skills Handbook.)

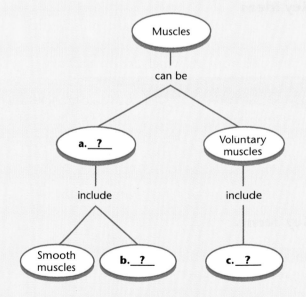

Test Prep: Skills

The table below rates different activities as to how well they improve muscular strength and flexibility. Use the table to answer Questions 21–23.

Fitness Ratings of Physical Activities

Activity	Builds Muscular Strength	Improves Flexibility
Baseball/Softball	Low	Moderate
Gymnastics	Very High	Very High
Karate	Moderate	High
Soccer	Moderate	Moderate
Weight Training	Very High	Moderate

21. **Interpreting Data** Which activities rate highest for strength? For flexibility?
22. **Inferring** Would ballet improve muscular strength or flexibility? Why?
23. **Designing Experiments** Design an experiment to determine if an activity that you do increases muscular strength. How would you measure improvements in your strength?

Thinking Critically

24. **Inferring** Disks of rubbery cartilage are found between the vertebrae. What function do you think these disks serve?
25. **Applying Concepts** At birth, the joints in an infant's skull are flexible and not yet fixed. As the child develops, the bones become more rigid and grow together. Why is it important that the bones of an infant's skull not grow together too rapidly?
26. **Comparing and Contrasting** How are ligaments and tendons similar? How are they different?
27. **Predicting** If smooth muscle had to be consciously controlled, what problems could you foresee in day-to-day living?
28. **Relating Cause and Effect** A person who is exposed to excessive heat may suffer from a condition known as heat stroke. The first sign of heat stroke is that the person stops sweating. Why is this condition a life-threatening emergency?

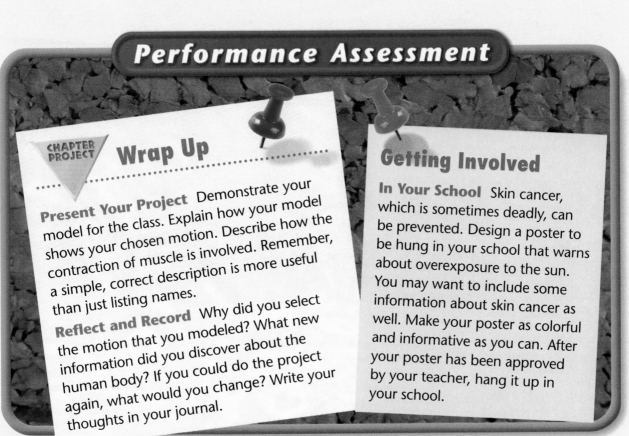

Performance Assessment

CHAPTER PROJECT Wrap Up

Present Your Project Demonstrate your model for the class. Explain how your model shows your chosen motion. Describe how the contraction of muscle is involved. Remember, a simple, correct description is more useful than just listing names.

Reflect and Record Why did you select the motion that you modeled? What new information did you discover about the human body? If you could do the project again, what would you change? Write your thoughts in your journal.

Getting Involved

In Your School Skin cancer, which is sometimes deadly, can be prevented. Design a poster to be hung in your school that warns about overexposure to the sun. You may want to include some information about skin cancer as well. Make your poster as colorful and informative as you can. After your poster has been approved by your teacher, hang it up in your school.

CALIFORNIA SCIENCE CONTENT STANDARDS

The following California Science Content Standards are addressed in this chapter:

5. The anatomy and physiology of plants and animals illustrate the complementary nature of structure and function.

   a. Plants and animals have levels of organization for structure and function, including cells, tissues, organs, organ systems, and the whole organism.

   b. Organ systems function because of the contributions of individual organs, tissues, and cells. The failure of any part can affect the entire system.

7. Scientific progress is made by asking meaningful questions and conducting careful investigations.

   a. Select and use appropriate tools and technology to perform tests, collect data, and display data.

   b. Utilize a variety of print and electronic resources (including the World Wide Web) to collect information as evidence as part of a research project.

   d. Construct scale models, maps and appropriately labeled diagrams to communicate scientific knowledge.

PROJECT 18

What's for Lunch?

When you see fresh vegetables in a market, which kinds appeal to you? In the school cafeteria at lunch time, which foods do you select? When you're hungry and grab a snack, what do you choose? This chapter looks at foods and the process of digestion that goes on in your body. It also explains how your food choices affect your health. In this project, you'll take a close look at the foods you select each day.

Your Goal To compare your eating pattern to the recommendations in the Food Guide Pyramid.

To complete this project successfully, you must
- ◆ keep an accurate record of everything you eat and drink for three days
- ◆ create graphs to compare your eating pattern with the recommendations in the Food Guide Pyramid
- ◆ make changes, if needed, during another three-day period to bring your diet closer to the recommendations in the Food Guide Pyramid

Get Started Begin by deciding how to best keep an accurate, complete food log. How will you make sure you record everything you eat, including snacks and drinks? How will you decide which category each food falls into? How will you determine serving sizes? Prepare a plan for keeping a food log, and give it to your teacher for approval.

Take your pick! Local markets offer a wide choice of tasty fruits and vegetables.

Check Your Progress You'll be working on this project as you study this chapter. To keep your project on track, look for Check Your Progress boxes at the following points.

Section 1 Review, page 569: Keep a food log for three days.
Section 2 Review, page 575: Create graphs to compare your food choices to the recommended number of servings.
Section 4 Review, page 587: Make changes to improve your diet.

Wrap Up At the end of the chapter (page 591), you'll prepare a written summary of what you've learned.

SECTION 1 Food and Energy

DISCOVER

Food Claims—Fact or Fiction?

1. Examine the list of statements at the right. Copy the list onto a separate sheet of paper.

2. Next to each statement, write *agree* or *disagree*. Give a reason for your response.

3. Discuss your responses with a small group of classmates. Compare the reasons you gave for agreeing or disagreeing with each statement.

Think It Over

Posing Questions List some other statements about nutrition that you have heard. How could you find out whether the statements are true?

Fact or Fiction?

a. Athletes need more protein in their diets than other people do.

b. The only salt that a food contains is the salt that you have added to it.

c. As part of a healthy diet, everyone should take vitamin supplements.

d. You can go without water for longer than you can go without food.

GUIDE FOR READING

◆ What are the six nutrients needed by the body?

◆ What is the function of water in the body?

Reading Tip As you read, create a table that includes the function and sources of each nutrient group.

Imagine a Thanksgiving dinner—roast turkey on a platter, delicious stuffing, and lots of vegetables—an abundance of colors and aromas. Food is an important part of many happy occasions, of times shared with friends and family. Food is also essential. Every living thing needs food to stay alive.

Why You Need Food

Foods provide your body with materials for growing and for repairing tissues. Food also provides energy for everything you do—running, playing a musical instrument, reading, and even sleeping. By filling those needs, food enables your body to maintain homeostasis. Recall that homeostasis is the body's ability to keep a steady internal state in spite of changing external conditions. Suppose, for example, that you cut your finger. Food provides both the raw materials necessary to grow new skin and the energy that powers this growth.

Your body converts the foods you eat into nutrients. **Nutrients** (NOO tre unts) are the substances in food that provide the raw materials and energy the body needs to carry out all the essential processes. **There are six kinds of nutrients necessary for human health— carbohydrates, fats, proteins, vitamins, minerals, and water.**

562

INTEGRATING PHYSICS Carbohydrates, fats, and proteins all provide the body with energy. When nutrients are used by the body for energy, the amount of energy they release can be measured in units called calories. One **calorie** is the amount of energy needed to raise the temperature of one gram of water by one Celsius degree. Most foods contain many thousands of calories of energy. Scientists usually use the term *Calorie,* with a capital *C,* to measure the energy in foods. One Calorie is the same as 1,000 calories. For example, one serving of popcorn may contain 60 Calories, or 60,000 calories, of energy. The more Calories a food has, the more energy it contains.

You need to eat a certain number of Calories each day to meet your body's energy needs. This daily energy requirement depends on a person's level of physical activity. It also changes as a person grows and ages. Infants and small children grow very rapidly, so they generally have the highest energy needs. Your current growth and level of physical activity affect the number of Calories you need. The more active you are, the higher your energy needs are.

Carbohydrates

The nutrients called **carbohydrates** (kar boh HY drayts), which are nutrients composed of carbon, oxygen, and hydrogen, are a major source of energy. One gram of carbohydrate provides your body with four Calories of energy. Carbohydrates also provide the raw materials to make parts of cells. Based on their chemical structure, carbohydrates are divided into two groups, simple carbohydrates and complex carbohydrates.

Figure 1 Your body obtains energy from carbohydrates. The sugars in fruits are simple carbohydrates. Starch is a complex carbohydrate found in grains and other plant products.

Sharpen your Skills

Predicting

ACTIVITY

Obtain food samples from your teacher. Write a prediction stating whether each food contains starch. Then test your predictions. First, put on your apron. Then use a plastic dropper to add three drops of iodine to each food sample. **CAUTION:** *Iodine can stain skin and clothing. Handle it carefully.* If the iodine turns blue-black, starch is present. Which foods contain starch?

Simple Carbohydrates Simple carbohydrates are also known as sugars. There are many types of sugars. They are found naturally in fruits, milk, and some vegetables. Sugars are also added to foods such as cookies, candies, and soft drinks. One sugar, **glucose** (GLOO kohs), is the major source of energy for your body's cells. However, most foods do not contain large amounts of glucose. The body converts other types of sugars into glucose, the form of sugar the body can use.

Complex Carbohydrates Complex carbohydrates are made up of many sugar molecules linked together in a chain. Starch is a complex carbohydrate found in plant foods such as potatoes, rice, corn, and grain products, such as pasta, cereals, and bread. To use starch as an energy source, your body first breaks it down into smaller, individual sugar molecules. Only then can your body release the molecules' energy.

Like starch, **fiber** is a complex carbohydrate found in plant foods. However, unlike starch, fiber cannot be broken down into sugar molecules by your body. Instead, the fiber passes through the body and is eliminated. Because your body cannot digest it, fiber is not considered a nutrient. Fiber is an important part of the diet, however, because it helps keep the digestive system functioning properly. Fruits, vegetables, and nuts contain fiber. So do products made with whole grains, such as some breads and cereals.

Nutritionists recommend that 50 to 60 percent of the Calories in a diet come from carbohydrates. When choosing foods containing carbohydrates, it is better to eat more complex carbohydrates than simple carbohydrates. Sugars can give a quick burst of energy, but starches provide a more even, long-term energy source. In addition, foods that are high in starch usually contain a variety of other nutrients. Foods made with a lot of sugar, such as candy, cookies, and soft drinks, usually have few valuable nutrients.

☑ *Checkpoint* ***What are the two types of carbohydrates? Give an example of each.***

Figure 2 Fiber is found in fruits, whole-grain foods, and the other foods shown here. *Applying Concepts Why is fiber important in the diet?*

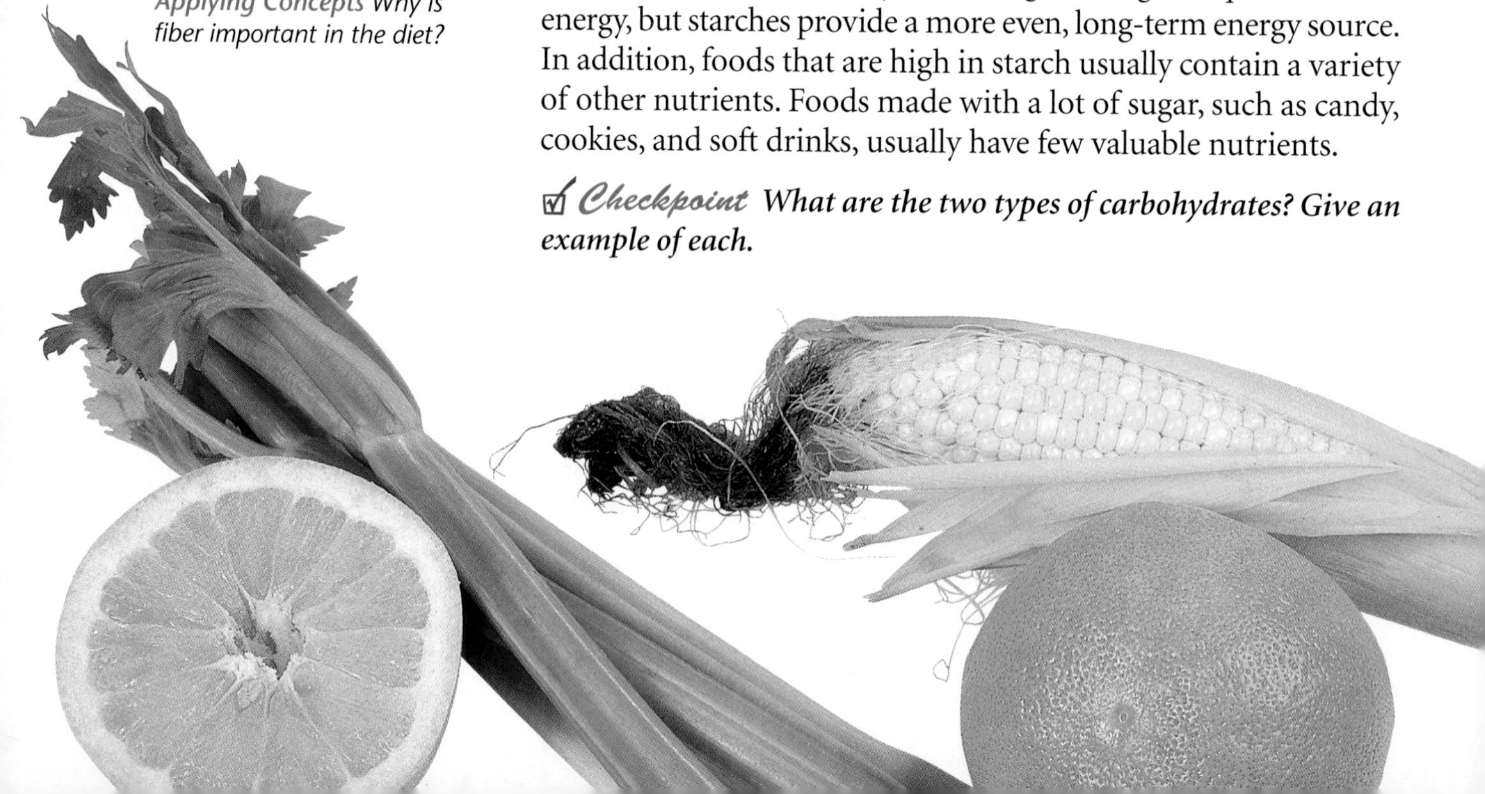

Figure 3 You obtain fats from foods such as steak, ice cream, and cooking oils. *Classifying Which of these foods contain saturated fats?*

Fats

Like carbohydrates, **fats** are high-energy nutrients that are composed of carbon, oxygen, and hydrogen. However, fats contain more than twice as much energy as an equal amount of carbohydrates. In addition, fats perform other important functions. For example, they form part of the structure of cells. Fatty tissue also protects and supports your internal organs and acts as insulation to keep heat inside your body.

Fats are classified as either unsaturated fats or saturated fats, based on their chemical structure. **Unsaturated fats** are usually liquid at room temperature. Most oils, such as olive oil and canola oil, are unsaturated fats. Unsaturated fat is also found in some types of seafood, such as salmon. **Saturated fats** are usually solid at room temperature. Animal products, such as meat, dairy products, and egg yolks, contain relatively large amounts of saturated fat. Some oils, such as palm oil and coconut oil, are also high in saturated fat.

Foods that contain saturated fat often contain cholesterol as well. **Cholesterol** (kuh LES tur awl) is a waxy, fatlike substance found only in animal products. Like fats, cholesterol is an important part of your body's cells. But your liver makes all of the cholesterol your body needs. Therefore, cholesterol is not a necessary part of the diet.

Although people need some fats in their diet, they only need a small amount. Nutritionists recommend that no more than 30 percent of the Calories eaten each day come from fats. In particular, people should limit their intake of saturated fats and cholesterol. Extra fats and cholesterol in the diet can lead to a buildup of a fatty material in the blood vessels. This fatty buildup can cause heart disease. You will learn about the connections among fats, cholesterol, and heart disease in Chapter 19.

Math TOOLBOX

Calculating Percent

A percent (%) is a number compared to 100. For example, 30% means 30 out of 100.

Here is how to calculate the percent of Calories from fat in a person's diet. Suppose that a person eats a total of 2,000 Calories in one day. Of those Calories, 500 come from fats.

1. Write the comparison as a fraction:

$$\frac{500}{2,000}$$

2. Multiply the fraction by 100% to express it as a percent:

$$\frac{500}{2,000} \times \frac{100\%}{1} = 25\%$$

Calories from fat made up 25% of the person's diet that day.

Figure 4 Meats and these other foods are sources of protein.

Proteins

Proteins are nutrients that contain nitrogen as well as carbon, hydrogen, and oxygen. Proteins are needed for tissue growth and repair. They also play a part in chemical reactions within cells. Proteins can serve as a source of energy, but they are a less important source of energy than carbohydrates or fats. Foods that contain high amounts of protein include meat, poultry, fish, dairy products, nuts, beans, and lentils. About 12 percent of your daily Calorie intake should come from proteins.

Amino Acids Proteins are made up of small units called **INTEGRATING CHEMISTRY** **amino acids** (uh MEE noh), which are linked together chemically to form large protein molecules. Thousands of different proteins are built from only about 20 different amino acids. Your body can make about half of the amino acids it needs. The others, called essential amino acids, must come from the foods you eat.

Complete and Incomplete Proteins Proteins from animal sources, such as meat and eggs, are called complete proteins because they contain all the essential amino acids. Proteins from plant sources, such as beans, grains, and nuts, are called incomplete proteins because they are missing one or more essential amino acids. Different plant foods lack different amino acids. Therefore, to obtain all the essential amino acids from plant sources alone, people need to eat a variety of plant foods.

✓ *Checkpoint* *What is meant by the term* incomplete protein?

Vitamins

The life of a sailor in the 1700s could be difficult indeed. For one thing, sailors on long voyages ate hard, dry biscuits, salted meat, and not much else. In addition, many sailors developed a serious disease called scurvy. People with scurvy suffer from bleeding gums, stiff joints, and sores that do not heal.

A Scottish doctor, James Lind, hypothesized that scurvy was the result of the sailors' poor diet. Lind divided sailors with scurvy into groups and fed different foods to each group. The sailors who were fed citrus fruits—oranges and lemons—quickly recovered from the disease. In 1754, Lind recommended that all sailors eat citrus fruits. When Lind's recommendations were finally carried out by the British Navy in 1795, scurvy disappeared from the navy.

Scurvy is caused by the lack of a nutrient called vitamin C. **Vitamins** act as helper molecules in a variety of chemical reactions within the body. The body needs only small amounts of vitamins. Figure 5 lists the vitamins necessary for health. The body can make a few of these vitamins. For example, bacteria that live in your intestines make small amounts of vitamin K.

Figure 5 Both fat-soluble vitamins and water-soluble vitamins are necessary to maintain health. *Interpreting Charts What foods provide a supply of both vitamins A and B_6?*

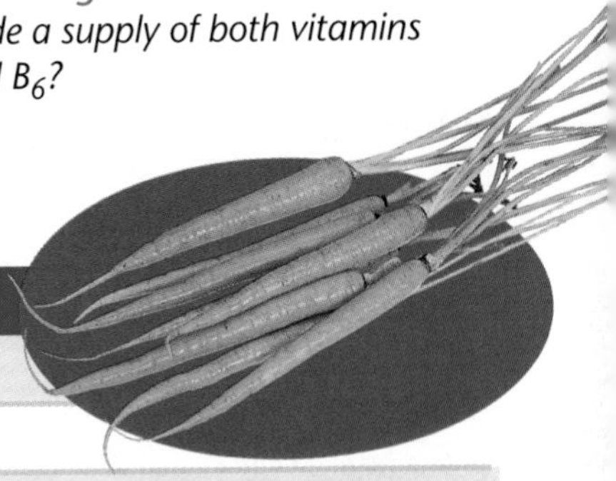

Essential Vitamins		
Vitamin	**Sources**	**Function**
Fat-soluble		
A	Dairy products; eggs; liver; yellow, orange, and dark green vegetables; fruits	Maintains healthy skin, bones, teeth, and hair; aids vision in dim light
D	Fortified dairy products; fish; eggs; liver; made by skin cells in presence of sunlight	Maintains bones and teeth; helps in the use of calcium and phosphorus
E	Vegetable oils; margarine; green, leafy vegetables; whole-grain foods; seeds; nuts	Aids in maintenance of red blood cells
K	Green, leafy vegetables; milk; liver; made by bacteria in the intestines	Aids in blood clotting
Water-soluble		
B_1 (thiamin)	Pork; liver; whole-grain foods; legumes; nuts	Needed for breakdown of carbohydrates
B_2 (riboflavin)	Dairy products; eggs; leafy, green vegetables; whole-grain breads and cereals	Needed for normal growth
B_3 (niacin)	Many protein-rich foods; milk; eggs; meat; fish; whole-grain foods; nuts; peanut butter	Needed for release of energy
B_6 (pyridoxine)	Green and leafy vegetables; meats; fish; legumes; fruits; whole-grain foods	Helps in the breakdown of proteins, fats, and carbohydrates
B_{12}	Meats; fish; poultry; dairy products; eggs	Maintains healthy nervous system; needed for red blood cell formation
Biotin	Liver; meat; fish; eggs; legumes; bananas; melons	Aids in the release of energy
Folic acid	Leafy, green vegetables; legumes; seeds; liver	Needed for red blood cell formation
Pantothenic acid	Liver; meats; fish; eggs; whole-grain foods	Needed for the release of energy
C	Citrus fruits; tomatoes; potatoes; dark green vegetables; mangoes	Needed to form connective tissue and fight infection

However, people must obtain most vitamins from foods. If people eat a wide variety of foods, they will probably get enough of each vitamin. Most people do not need to take vitamin supplements.

Vitamins are classified as either fat-soluble or water-soluble. Fat-soluble vitamins dissolve in fat, and they are stored in fatty tissues in the body. Vitamins A, D, E, and K are all fat-soluble vitamins. Water-soluble vitamins dissolve in water and are not stored in the body. This fact makes it especially important to include sources of water-soluble vitamins—vitamin C and all the B vitamins—in your diet every day.

☑ *Checkpoint* *List the fat-soluble vitamins.*

Minerals

Like vitamins, minerals are needed by your body in small amounts. **Minerals** are nutrients that are not made by living things. They are present in soil and are absorbed by plants through their roots. You obtain minerals by eating plant foods or animals that have eaten plants. Figure 6 lists some minerals you

Figure 6 Eating a variety of foods each day provides your body with the minerals it needs.
Interpreting Charts Which minerals play a role in regulating water levels in the body?

◀ **Source of calcium**

▼ **Source of potassium**

Essential Minerals		
Mineral	**Sources**	**Function**
Calcium	Milk; cheese; dark green, leafy vegetables; tofu; legumes	Helps build bones and teeth; important for blood-clotting, nerve and muscle function
Chlorine	Table salt; soy sauce; processed foods	Helps maintain water balance; aids in digestion
Fluorine	Fluoridated drinking water; fish	Helps form bones and teeth
Iodine	Seafood; iodized salt	Makes up part of hormones that regulate the release of energy
Iron	Red meats; seafood; green, leafy vegetables; legumes; dried fruits	Forms an important part of red blood cells
Magnesium	Green, leafy vegetables; legumes; nuts; whole-grain foods	Needed for normal muscle and nerve function; helps in the release of energy
Phosphorus	Meat; poultry; eggs; fish; dairy products	Needed for healthy bones and teeth; helps in the release of energy
Potassium	Grains; fruits; vegetables; meat; fish	Helps maintain water balance; needed for normal muscle and nerve function
Sodium	Table salt; soy sauce; processed foods	Helps maintain water balance; needed for normal nerve function

Source of sodium ▶

need. As you know from Chapter 17, calcium is needed for strong bones and teeth. Iron is needed for the proper function of red blood cells.

Water

Imagine that a boat is sinking. The people are getting into a lifeboat. They have room for one of the following: a bag of fruit, a can of meat, a loaf of bread, or a jug of water. Which item should they choose?

You might be surprised to learn that the lifeboat passengers should choose the water. Although people can probably survive for weeks without food, they will die within days without fresh water. Water is the most abundant substance in the body. It accounts for about 65 percent of the average person's body weight.

Water is the most important nutrient because the body's vital processes—including chemical reactions such as the breakdown of nutrients—take place in water. Water makes up most of the body's fluids, including blood. Nutrients and other important substances are carried throughout the body dissolved in the watery part of the blood. Your body also needs water to produce perspiration.

Under normal conditions, you need to take in about 2 liters of water every day. You can do this by drinking water and other beverages, and by eating foods with lots of water, such as fruits and vegetables. If the weather is hot or you are exercising, you need to drink even more to replace the water that you lose in sweat.

Figure 7 Like all living things, you need water. Without regular water intake, your body cannot carry out the processes that keep you alive.

Section 1 Review

1. List the six nutrients that are needed by the body.
2. Give three reasons why water is necessary for the body to function.
3. Why should you eat more complex carbohydrates than simple carbohydrates?
4. What is the difference between fat-soluble vitamins and water-soluble vitamins?
5. **Thinking Critically Applying Concepts** Why is it especially important that vegetarians eat a varied diet?

Check Your Progress

CHAPTER PROJECT

By now, you should have given your teacher your plan for keeping your food log. Adjust the plan as your teacher suggests. Then start your three days of record-keeping. If possible, your record-keeping should span two weekdays and one weekend day. Be sure to keep an accurate record of all the foods and beverages you consume. (*Hint:* Either make your log portable, or plan a method for recording your food intake when you're away from home.)

Iron for Breakfast

Have you ever looked at the nutrition facts on a cereal box? Some of the listed nutrients occur naturally in the cereal. Others are added as it is processed. In this lab, you will look for evidence that extra iron has been added to some cereals.

Problem

How can you test whether iron has been added to cereals?

Skills Focus

observing, predicting, interpreting data

Materials

long bar magnet
white paper towels
instant oatmeal
watch or clock
wooden dowel
2 dry breakfast cereals
3 sealable plastic freezer bags
plastic jar with sealable cover

balance
plastic spoon
warm water

Procedure

1. Read the nutrition facts listed on the packages of the cereals that you'll be testing. Record the percent of iron listed for each of the cereals.
2. Put a paper towel on the pan of a balance. Use a spoon to measure out 50 grams of instant oatmeal. **CAUTION:** *Do not eat any of the cereals in this lab.*
3. Place the oatmeal in a plastic bag. Push down gently on the bag to remove most of the air, then seal the bag. Roll a dowel over the cereal repeatedly to crush it into a fine powder.

4. Pour the powdered cereal into a plastic jar. Cover the cereal with warm water. Cover the jar tightly and shake it for about 15 minutes.
5. Move a bar magnet along the outside of the jar. Observe the results.
6. Repeat Steps 2 through 5 with your other cereal samples.

Analyze and Conclude

1. Describe the material you saw inside the jar near the magnet. What evidence do you have that this material is iron?
2. Which sample appeared to have the most added iron? The least? Were those results consistent with the listed amounts?
3. Why is it likely that any iron metal present in the cereal was added during the processing?
4. What roles does iron play in the body?
5. **Apply** Why might adding iron to breakfast cereal be a good way to ensure that children receive an adequate amount of that mineral?

More to Explore

Read the labels on five snack foods. Make a bar graph showing their iron content.

SECTION 2 Healthy Eating

DISCOVER ·ACTIVITY· · · · ·

Do Snack Foods Contain Fat?

1. Cut four small squares from a brown paper bag. Label them *A, B, C,* and *D.*

2. Rub some crushed potato chips on square A.
   CAUTION: *Do not eat any of the foods in this activity.*

3. Repeat Step 2 using crushed pretzels (on square B), a piece of chocolate (on square C), and an apple slice (on square D).

4. Remove any food. Allow the paper squares to dry.

5. Note which squares have spots of oil on them.

Think It Over
Classifying If a food contains fat, it will leave oily spots on the brown paper. What does this tell you about the foods you tested?

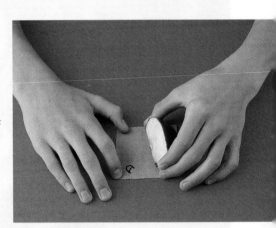

What does healthy eating mean to you? Eating more fresh fruits and vegetables? Not skipping breakfast? Cutting down on soft drinks and chips? You have just learned about the six types of nutrients—carbohydrates, fats, proteins, vitamins, minerals, and water—that are part of a healthy diet. You may now be wondering how you can use this information to make healthful changes in your diet.

With so many foods available, it may seem more difficult, not easier, to establish a healthful diet. Luckily, nutritionists have developed some aids—the Food Guide Pyramid and food labels.

GUIDE FOR READING

◆ How can the Food Guide Pyramid help you plan a healthy diet?

◆ What kind of information is included on food labels?

Reading Tip Before you read, preview *Exploring the Food Guide Pyramid* on page 573. Write a list of questions about the pyramid. As you read, try to answer your questions.

Figure 8 Fruits and vegetables are essential parts of a healthy diet. Some people enjoy picking these foods right off the plant.

The Food Guide Pyramid

The **Food Guide Pyramid** was developed by nutritionists to help people plan a healthy diet. **The Food Guide Pyramid classifies foods into six groups. It also indicates how many servings from each group should be eaten every day to maintain a healthy diet.** You can combine the advice within the pyramid with knowledge of your own food preferences. By doing this, you can have a healthy diet containing foods you like.

You can see the six food groups in *Exploring the Food Guide Pyramid*. Notice that the food group at the base of the pyramid includes foods made from grains, such as bread, cereal, rice, and pasta. This bottom level is the widest part of the pyramid. The large size indicates that these foods should make up the largest part of the diet.

The second level in the pyramid is made of two food groups, the Fruit group and the Vegetable group. Notice that this level is not as wide as the bottom level. This size difference indicates that people need fewer servings of these foods than of foods from the bottom level. The third level of the pyramid contains the Milk, Yogurt, and Cheese group, and the Meat, Poultry, Fish, Dry Beans, Eggs, and Nuts group. People need still smaller amounts of food from the third level.

At the top of the pyramid are foods containing large amounts of fat, sugar, or both. Notice that this is the smallest part of the pyramid. The small size indicates that intake of these foods should be limited. There is a good reason for this advice. Foods in the other groups already contain fats and sugars. Limiting intake of *additional* fats and sugars can help you prevent heart disease and other problems.

☑ *Checkpoint* *What types of foods should make up the largest portion of a person's diet?*

Food Labels

After a long day, you and your friends stop into a store on your way home from school. What snack should you buy? How can you make a wise choice? One thing you can do is to read the information provided on food labels. The United States Food and Drug Administration (FDA) requires that all food items except meat, poultry, fresh vegetables, and fresh fruit must be labeled with specific nutritional information.

Figure 9 If you are very active, you need to eat more servings within the ranges specified for each food group in the Food Guide Pyramid.

EXPLORING *the Food Guide Pyramid*

The Food Guide Pyramid recommends the number of servings that a person should eat each day from six food groups. Note that each number of servings is listed as a range. Active, growing teenagers may need to eat the larger number of servings for each group.

Fats, Oils, and Sweets (Use sparingly.)
Soft drinks, candy, ice cream, mayonnaise, and other foods in this group have few valuable nutrients. In addition, these foods are high in Calories. They should be eaten only in small quantities.

Milk, Yogurt, and Cheese Group (2–3 servings) Milk and other dairy products are rich in proteins, carbohydrates, vitamins, and minerals. Try to select low-fat dairy foods, such as low-fat milk.

Meat, Poultry, Fish, Dry Beans, Eggs, and Nuts Group (2–3 servings)
These foods are high in protein. They also supply vitamins and minerals. Since eggs, nuts, and some meats are high in fat, they should be eaten sparingly.

Vegetable Group (3–5 servings)
Vegetables are low-fat sources of carbohydrates, fiber, vitamins, and minerals.

Fruit Group (2–4 servings)
Fruits are good sources of carbohydrates, fiber, vitamins, and water.

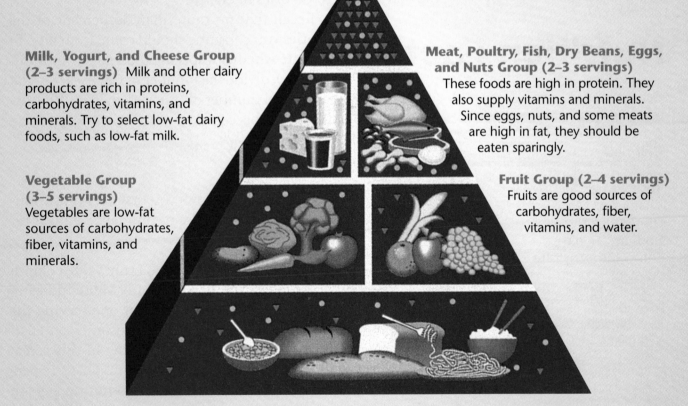

Bread, Cereal, Rice, and Pasta Group (6–11 servings)
The foods at the base of the pyramid are rich in complex carbohydrates and also provide proteins, fiber, vitamins, and some minerals.

● *Fat (naturally occurring and added)*
▲ *Sugars (naturally occurring and added)*

Figure 10 shows a food label that might appear on a box of cereal. Refer to that label as you read about some of the important nutritional information it contains.

Serving Size Notice that the serving size and the number of servings in the container are listed at the top of the label. The FDA has established standard serving sizes for all types of foods. This means that all containers of ice cream, for example, use the same serving size on their labels. The information on the rest of the label, including Calorie counts and nutrient content, is based on the serving size. Therefore, if you eat a portion that's twice as large as the serving size, you'll consume twice the number of Calories and nutrients listed on the label.

Calories from Fat The next item on the food label is the number of Calories in a serving and the number of Calories that come from fat. Notice that a single serving of this cereal supplies the body with 110 Calories of energy.

Recall that no more than 30 percent of the Calories you consume should come from fats. To calculate whether a specific food falls within this guideline, divide the number of Calories from fat by the total number of Calories, then multiply by 100%. For this cereal,

$$\frac{15}{110} \times \frac{100\%}{1} = 13.6\%.$$

That number shows you that a serving of this cereal is well within the recommended limits for fat intake.

Daily Values Locate the % Daily Value column on the label. The **Percent Daily Value** indicates how the nutritional content of one serving fits into the diet of a person who consumes a total of 2,000 Calories a day. One serving of this cereal contains 280 milligrams of sodium. That's 12 percent of the total amount of sodium a person should consume in one day.

As you have learned, the number of Calories you need daily depends on your age, size, and level of activity. An active teenager may require 2,500 Calories or more each day. If your needs exceed 2,000 Calories, you should take in more of each nutrient in your daily diet. Some food labels include a list of the nutrient needs for both a 2,000-Calorie and a 2,500-Calorie diet.

Figure 10 By law, specific nutritional information must be listed on food labels. *Calculating How many servings of this product would you have to eat to get 90 percent of the Daily Value for iron?*

Nutrition Facts

Serving Size	1 cup (30g)
Servings Per Container	About 10

Amount Per Serving

Calories 110	Calories from Fat 15

% Daily Value*

Total Fat 2g	3%
Saturated Fat 0g	0%
Cholesterol 0mg	0%
Sodium 280mg	12%
Total Carbohydrate 22g	7%
Dietary Fiber 3g	12%
Sugars 1g	
Protein 3g	

Vitamin A	10%	•	Vitamin C	20%
Calcium	4%	•	Iron	45%

* Percent Daily Values are based on a 2,000 Calorie diet. Your daily values may be higher or lower depending on your caloric needs:

		Calories	2,000	2,500
Total Fat	Less than		65g	80g
Sat. Fat	Less than		20g	25g
Cholesterol	Less than		300mg	300mg
Sodium	Less than		2,400mg	2,400mg
Total Carbohydrate			300g	375g
Fiber			25g	30g

Calories per gram:
Fat 9   •   Carbohydrate 4   •   Protein 4

Ingredients: Whole grain oats, sugar, salt, milled corn, oat fiber, dried whey, hone almonds, d

574

Ingredients Packaged foods, such as crackers and soup mixes, usually contain a mixture of ingredients. The food label lists those ingredients in order by weight, starting with the main ingredient. In a breakfast cereal, for example, that may be corn, oats, rice, or wheat. Often, sugar and salt are added for flavor. The list can alert you to substances that have been added to a food to improve its flavor or color, or to keep it from spoiling. In addition, some people can become sick or break out in a rash if they eat certain substances. By reading ingredients lists, people can avoid foods that contain those substances.

Using Food Labels You can use food labels to help you make healthful food choices. **Food labels allow you to evaluate a single food as well as to compare the nutritional value of two foods.** Suppose you are shopping for breakfast cereals. By reading the labels, you might find that one cereal contains little fat and a high percentage of the Daily Value for valuable nutrients such as complex carbohydrates and several vitamins. Another cereal might have fewer complex carbohydrates and vitamins and contain significant amounts of fat. You can see that the first cereal would be a better choice as a regular breakfast food. If you really enjoy the other cereal, however, you might make it an occasional treat rather than an everyday choice.

Figure 11 Food labels allow you to compare the nutritional content of similar kinds of foods.

Section 2 Review

1. What information does the Food Guide Pyramid provide? Into how many groups are foods classified?
2. Explain how food labels can help a person make healthy food choices.
3. Why are foods in the Bread, Cereal, Rice, and Pasta group placed at the bottom of the Food Guide Pyramid?
4. **Thinking Critically** **Applying Concepts** Why might a runner need more servings from the Bread, Cereal, Rice, and Pasta group than a less active person?

Check Your Progress CHAPTER PROJECT
By this point, you should have completed three full days of record keeping. Now create bar graphs to compare your food intake to the recommended numbers of servings in the Food Guide Pyramid. Analyze your graphs to identify changes you could make in your diet.

The Digestive Process Begins

How Can You Speed up Digestion?

1. Obtain two plastic jars with lids. Fill the jars with equal amounts of water.

2. At the same time, place a whole sugar cube into one jar. Place a crushed sugar cube into the other jar.

3. Fasten the lids on the jars. Holding one jar in each hand, shake the two jars gently and equally.

4. Place the jars on a flat surface. Observe whether the whole cube or the crushed cube dissolves faster.

Think It Over

Predicting Use the results of this activity to predict which would take longer to digest: a large piece of food or one that has been cut up into many small pieces. Explain your answer.

GUIDE FOR READING

◆ What general functions are carried out in the digestive system?

Reading Tip Before you read, preview the headings in this section. Predict the functions of the mouth, the esophagus, and the stomach.

Dr. William Beaumont ▼

In June of 1822, nineteen-year-old Alexis St. Martin was wounded in the stomach while hunting. William Beaumont, a doctor with the United States Army, saved St. Martin's life. However, the wound left an opening in St. Martin's stomach that never closed completely. Beaumont realized that by looking through the opening, he could observe what was happening inside St. Martin's stomach.

Beaumont observed that milk changed chemically inside the stomach. He hypothesized that chemical reactions inside the stomach broke down foods into smaller particles. To test his hypothesis, Beaumont removed liquid from St. Martin's stomach. He had the liquid analyzed to determine what materials it contained. The stomach liquid contained an acid that could break down foods into simpler substances.

Functions of the Digestive System

Beaumont's observations helped scientists understand the role of the stomach in the digestive system. The digestive system has three main functions. **First, it breaks down food into molecules the body can use. Then, the molecules are absorbed into the blood and carried throughout the body. Finally, wastes are eliminated from the body.**

The process by which your body breaks down food into small nutrient molecules is called **digestion.** There are two kinds of digestion—mechanical and chemical. In mechanical digestion, foods are physically broken down into smaller pieces. Mechanical digestion occurs when you bite into a sandwich and chew it into small pieces. In chemical digestion, chemicals produced by the body break foods into their smaller chemical building blocks. For example, the starch in bread is broken down into individual sugar molecules.

After your food is digested, the molecules are ready to be transported throughout your body. **Absorption** (ab SAWRP shun) is the process by which nutrient molecules pass through the wall of your digestive system into your blood. Materials that are not absorbed, such as fiber, are eliminated from the body as wastes.

Figure 12 shows the organs of the digestive system, which is about nine meters long from beginning to end. As food moves through the digestive system, the processes of digestion, absorption, and elimination occur one after the other in an efficient, continuous process.

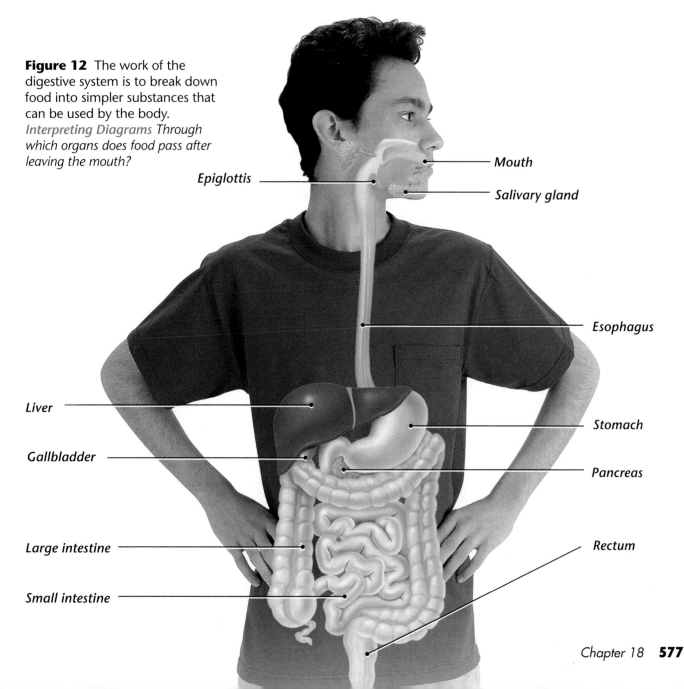

Figure 12 The work of the digestive system is to break down food into simpler substances that can be used by the body.
Interpreting Diagrams Through which organs does food pass after leaving the mouth?

Epiglottis

Mouth

Salivary gland

Esophagus

Liver

Stomach

Gallbladder

Pancreas

Large intestine

Rectum

Small intestine

Figure 13 Mechanical digestion begins in the mouth, where the teeth cut and tear food into smaller pieces. *Observing* *Which teeth are specialized for biting into a juicy apple?*

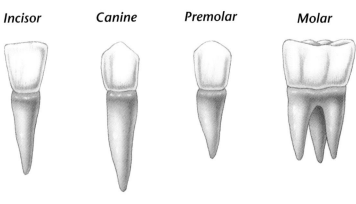

Incisor *Canine* *Premolar* *Molar*

The Mouth

Have you ever walked past a bakery or restaurant and noticed your mouth watering? Smelling or even just thinking about food when you're hungry is enough to start your mouth watering. This response isn't accidental. Your body is responding to hunger and thoughts of food by preparing for the delicious meal it expects. The fluid released when your mouth waters is called **saliva** (suh LY vuh). Saliva plays an important role in both the mechanical and chemical digestive processes that take place in the mouth.

Mechanical Digestion The process of mechanical digestion begins as you take your first bite of food. Your teeth carry out the first stage of mechanical digestion. Your center teeth, or incisors (in SY zurz), cut the food into bite-sized pieces. On either side of the incisors are sharp, pointy teeth called canines (KAY nynz). These teeth tear and slash the food in your mouth into smaller pieces. Behind the canines are the premolars and molars, which crush and grind the food. As the teeth do their work, saliva mixes with the pieces of food, moistening them into one slippery mass.

Chemical Digestion Like mechanical digestion, chemical digestion begins in the mouth. If you take a bite of a cracker and roll it around your mouth, the cracker begins to taste sweet. It tastes sweet because a chemical in the saliva has broken down the starch in the cracker into sugar molecules. Chemical digestion—the breakdown of complex molecules into simpler ones—has taken place. Chemical digestion is accomplished by enzymes. An **enzyme** is a protein that speeds up chemical reactions in the body. The chemical in saliva that digests starch is an enzyme. Your body produces many different enzymes. Each enzyme has a specific chemical shape. Its shape enables it to take part in only one kind of chemical reaction. For example, the enzyme that breaks down starch into sugars cannot break down proteins into amino acids.

INTEGRATING CHEMISTRY

The Esophagus

If you've ever choked on food, someone may have said that your food "went down the wrong way." That's because there are two openings at the back of your mouth. One opening leads to your windpipe, which carries air into your lungs. Usually, your body keeps food out of your windpipe. As you swallow, muscles in your throat move the food downward. While this happens, a flap of tissue called the **epiglottis** (ep uh GLAHT is) seals off your windpipe, preventing the food from entering. As you swallow, food goes into the **esophagus** (ih SAHF uh gus), a muscular tube that connects the mouth to the stomach. The esophagus is lined with mucus. **Mucus** is a thick, slippery substance produced by the body. In the digestive system, mucus makes food easier to swallow and to be moved along.

Food remains in the esophagus for only about 10 seconds. After food enters the esophagus, contractions of smooth muscles push the food toward the stomach. These involuntary waves of muscle contraction are called **peristalsis** (pehr ih STAWL sis). The action of peristalsis is shown in Figure 14. Peristalsis also occurs in the stomach and farther down the digestive system. These muscular waves keep food moving in one direction.

✓ *Checkpoint* **How is food prevented from entering the windpipe?**

Modeling Peristalsis

1. Obtain a clear, flexible plastic straw.

2. Put on your goggles. Hold the straw vertically and insert a small bead into the top of the straw. The bead should fit snugly into the straw. Do not blow into the straw.

3. Pinch the straw above the bead so that the bead begins to move down the length of the tubing.

4. Repeat Step 3 until the bead exits the straw.

Making Models How does this action compare with peristalsis? What do the bead and the straw represent in this model?

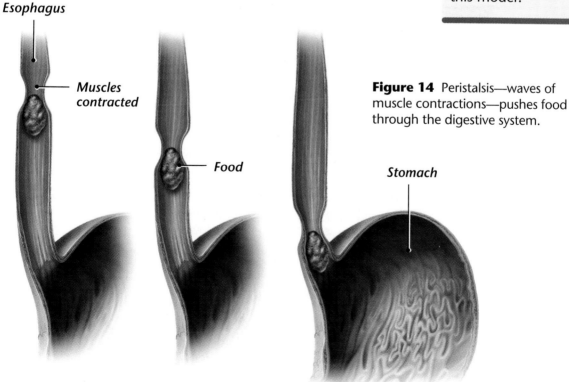

Esophagus

Muscles contracted

Food

Stomach

Figure 14 Peristalsis—waves of muscle contractions—pushes food through the digestive system.

The Stomach

When food leaves the esophagus, it enters the **stomach,** a J-shaped, muscular pouch located in the abdomen. As you eat, your stomach expands to hold all of the food that you swallow. An average adult's stomach holds about 2 liters of food.

Most mechanical digestion occurs in the stomach. Three strong layers of muscle contract to produce a churning motion. This action squeezes the food, mixing it with fluids in somewhat the same way that clothes and soapy water are mixed in a washing machine.

 INTEGRATING CHEMISTRY While mechanical digestion is taking place, so too is chemical digestion. The churning of the stomach mixes food with digestive juice, a fluid produced by cells in the lining of the stomach.

Digestive juice contains the enzyme pepsin. Pepsin chemically digests the proteins in your food, breaking them down into amino acids. Digestive juice also contains hydrochloric acid, a very strong acid. This acid would burn a hole in clothes if it were spilled on them. Without this strong acid, however, your stomach could not function properly. First, pepsin works best in an acid environment. Second, the acid kills many bacteria that you swallow along with your food.

Since the acid is so strong, you may wonder why it doesn't burn a hole in your stomach. The reason is that digestive juice

Figure 15 As food passes through the digestive system, the digestive juices gradually break down large food molecules into smaller molecules. *Interpreting Charts Which enzymes aid in protein digestion?*

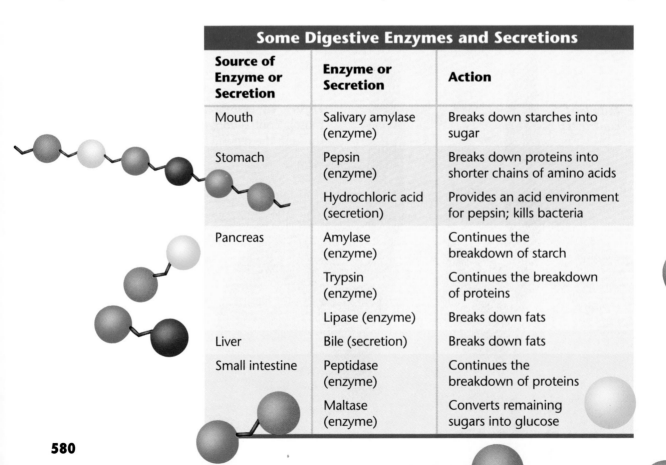

Some Digestive Enzymes and Secretions		
Source of Enzyme or Secretion	**Enzyme or Secretion**	**Action**
Mouth	Salivary amylase (enzyme)	Breaks down starches into sugar
Stomach	Pepsin (enzyme)	Breaks down proteins into shorter chains of amino acids
	Hydrochloric acid (secretion)	Provides an acid environment for pepsin; kills bacteria
Pancreas	Amylase (enzyme)	Continues the breakdown of starch
	Trypsin (enzyme)	Continues the breakdown of proteins
	Lipase (enzyme)	Breaks down fats
Liver	Bile (secretion)	Breaks down fats
Small intestine	Peptidase (enzyme)	Continues the breakdown of proteins
	Maltase (enzyme)	Converts remaining sugars into glucose

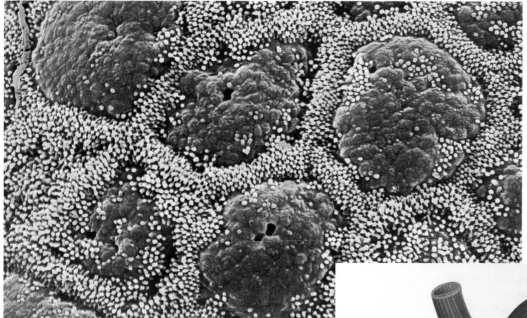

Figure 16 The stomach walls (left) produce mucus, shown here in yellow. Mucus protects the stomach from its own acid and enzymes. The stomach has powerful muscles (below) that help grind up food.

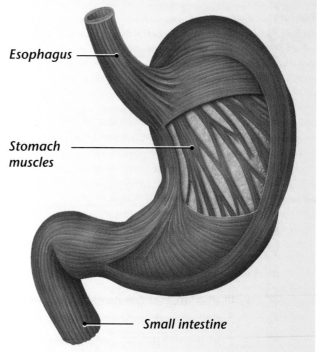

Esophagus

Stomach muscles

Small intestine

also contains mucus, which coats and protects the lining of your stomach. In addition, the cells that line the stomach are quickly replaced when they are damaged or worn out.

Food remains in the stomach until all of the solid material has been digested into liquid form. A few hours after you finish eating, the stomach completes mechanical digestion of the food. By that time, most of the proteins have been chemically digested into shorter chains of amino acids. The food, now a thick liquid, is released into the next part of the digestive system. That is where final chemical digestion and absorption will take place.

Section 3 Review

1. List the functions of the digestive system.
2. What role does saliva play in digestion?
3. Describe peristalsis and explain its function in the digestive system.
4. What is the function of pepsin?
5. **Thinking Critically** Predicting If your stomach could no longer produce acid, how do you think that would affect digestion?

Science at Home

Explain to your family what happens when people choke on food. With your family, find out how to recognize when a person is choking and what to do to help the person. Learn about the Heimlich maneuver and how it is used to help someone who is choking.

Skills Lab

AS THE STOMACH CHURNS

The proteins you eat are constructed of large, complex molecules. Your body begins to break down those complex molecules in the stomach. In this lab, you will draw conclusions about the process by which proteins are digested.

Problem

What conditions are needed for the digestion of proteins in the stomach?

Materials

test tube rack   marking pencil
pepsin   dilute hydrochloric acid
water   plastic stirrers
litmus paper
cubes of boiled egg white
10-mL plastic graduated cylinder
4 test tubes with stoppers

Procedure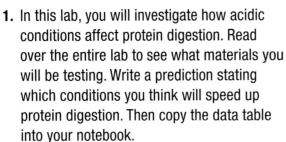

1. In this lab, you will investigate how acidic conditions affect protein digestion. Read over the entire lab to see what materials you will be testing. Write a prediction stating which conditions you think will speed up protein digestion. Then copy the data table into your notebook.

2. Label four test tubes *A, B, C,* and *D* and place them in a test tube rack.

3. In this lab, the protein you will test is boiled egg white, which has been cut into cubes about 1 cm on each side. Add 3 cubes to each test tube. Note and record the size and overall appearance of the cubes in each test tube. **CAUTION:** *Do not put any egg white into your mouth.*

4. Use a graduated cylinder to add 10 mL of the enzyme pepsin to test tube A. Observe the egg white cubes to determine whether an immediate reaction takes place. Record your observations under *Day 1* in your data table. If no changes occur, write "no immediate reaction."

5. Use a clean graduated cylinder to add 5 mL of pepsin to test tube B. Then rinse the graduated cylinder and add 5 mL of water to test tube B. Observe whether or not an immediate reaction takes place.

6. Use a clean graduated cylinder to add 10 mL of hydrochloric acid to test tube C. Observe whether or not an immediate reaction takes place. **CAUTION:** *Hydrochloric acid can burn skin and clothing. Avoid direct contact with it. Wash any splashes or spills with plenty of water, and notify your teacher.*

DATA TABLE

Test Tube	Egg White Appearance		Litmus Color	
	Day 1	Day 2	Day 1	Day 2
A				
B				
C				
D				

7. Use a clean graduated cylinder to add 5 mL of pepsin to test tube D. Then rinse the graduated cylinder and add 5 mL of hydrochloric acid to test tube D. Observe whether or not an immediate reaction takes place. Record your observations.

8. Obtain four strips of blue litmus paper. (Blue litmus paper turns pink in the presence of an acid.) Dip a clean plastic stirrer into the solution in each test tube, and then touch the stirrer to a piece of litmus paper. Observe what happens to the litmus paper. Record your observations.

9. Insert stoppers in the four test tubes and store the test tube rack as directed by your teacher.

10. The next day, examine the contents of each test tube. Note any changes in the size and overall appearance of the egg white cubes. Then test each solution with litmus paper. Record your observations in your data table.

Analyze and Conclude

1. Which material(s) were the best at digesting the egg white? What observations enabled you to determine this?

2. Do you think that the chemical digestion of protein in food is a fast reaction or a slow one? Explain.

3. What did this lab demonstrate about the ability of pepsin to digest protein?

4. Why was it important that the cubes of egg white all be about the same size?

5. **Think About It** How did test tubes A and C help you draw conclusions about protein digestion in this investigation?

Design an Experiment

Design a way to test whether protein digestion is affected by the size of the food pieces. Write down the hypothesis that you will test. Then create a data table for recording your observations. Obtain your teacher's permission before carrying out your plan.

4 Final Digestion and Absorption

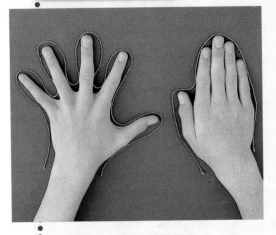

Which Surface Is Larger?

1. Work with a partner to carry out this investigation.

2. Begin by placing your hand palm-side down on a table. Keep your thumb and fingers tightly together. Lay string along the outline of your hand. Have your partner help you determine how long a string you need to outline your hand.

3. Use a metric ruler to measure the length of that string.

Think It Over
Predicting How long would you expect your hand outline to be if you spread out your thumb and fingers? Use string to test your prediction. Compare the two string lengths.

◆ What roles do the small intestine and large intestine play in digestion?

Reading Tip As you read, create a table with the headings *Small Intestine, Liver, Pancreas,* and *Large Intestine.* Under each heading, list that organ's digestive function.

Have you ever been part of a huge crowd attending a concert or sports event? Barriers and passageways often guide people in the right direction. Ticket takers make sure that only those with tickets get in, and that they enter in an orderly fashion.

In some ways, the stomach can be thought of as the "ticket taker" of the digestive system. Once the food has been changed into a thick liquid, the stomach releases a little liquid at a time into the next part of the digestive system. This slow, smooth passage of food through the digestive system ensures that digestion and absorption take place smoothly.

The Small Intestine

After the thick liquid leaves the stomach, it enters the small intestine. The **small intestine** is the part of the digestive system where most of the chemical digestion takes place. If you look back at Figure 12, you may wonder how the small intestine got its name. After all, at about 6 meters—longer than some full-sized cars— it makes up two thirds of the digestive system. The small intestine was named for its small diameter. It is about two to three centimeters wide, about half the diameter of the large intestine.

When food reaches the small intestine, it has already been mechanically digested into a thick liquid. But chemical digestion has just begun. Although starches and proteins have been partially broken down, fats haven't been digested at all. **Almost all chemical digestion and absorption of nutrients takes place in the small intestine.**

The small intestine is bustling with chemical activity. As the liquid moves into the small intestine, it mixes with enzymes and secretions. The enzymes and secretions are produced in three different organs—the small intestine, the liver, and the pancreas. The liver and the pancreas deliver their substances to the small intestine through small tubes.

The Role of the Liver The **liver** is located in the upper portion of the abdomen. It is the largest and heaviest organ inside the body. You can think of the liver as an extremely busy chemical factory that plays a role in many body processes. For example, the liver breaks down medicines and other substances, and it helps eliminate nitrogen from the body. As part of the digestive system, the liver produces **bile,** a substance that breaks up fat particles. Bile flows from the liver into the **gallbladder,** the organ that stores bile. After you eat, bile passes through a tube from the gallbladder into the small intestine.

Bile is not an enzyme. It does not chemically digest foods. It does, however, break up large fat particles into smaller fat droplets. You can compare the action of bile on fats with the action of soap on oily skin. Soap physically breaks up the oil into small droplets that can mix with the soapy water and be washed away. Bile mixes with the fats in food to form small fat droplets. The droplets can then be chemically broken down by enzymes produced in the pancreas.

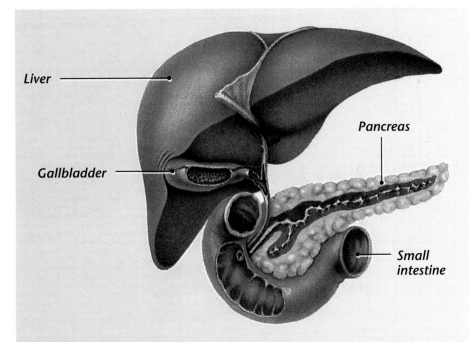

Figure 17 Substances produced by the liver and pancreas aid in the digestion of food.
Applying Concepts Where is bile produced? Where is it stored before it is released into the small intestine?

Liver

Pancreas

Gallbladder

Small intestine

Help From the Pancreas The **pancreas** is a triangular organ that lies between the stomach and the first part of the small intestine. Like the liver, the pancreas plays a role in many body processes. As part of the digestive system, the pancreas produces enzymes that flow into the small intestine. These enzymes help break down starches, proteins, and fats.

The digestive enzymes produced by the pancreas and other organs do not break down all food substances, however. Recall that the fiber in food isn't broken down. Instead, fiber thickens the liquid material in the intestine. This makes it easier for peristalsis to push the material forward.

✓ *Checkpoint* *How does the pancreas aid in digestion?*

Absorption in the Small Intestine After chemical digestion takes place, the small nutrient molecules are ready to be absorbed by the body. The structure of the small intestine makes it well suited for absorption. As you can see in Figure 18, the inner surface, or lining, of the small intestine looks bumpy. Millions of tiny finger-shaped structures called **villi** (VIL eye) (singular *villus*) cover the surface. Notice that tiny blood vessels run through the center of each villus. Nutrient molecules pass from cells on the surface of a villus into blood vessels. The blood carries the nutrients throughout the body for use by body cells.

The presence of villi increases the surface area of the small intestine. If all of the villi were laid out flat, the total surface area of the small intestine would be about as large as a tennis court.

Figure 18 Tiny finger-shaped projections called villi line the inside of the small intestine. In the diagram, you can see that the blood vessels in the villi are covered by a single layer of cells. The photograph shows a closeup view of villi. *Interpreting Diagrams How does the structure of the villi help them carry out their function?*

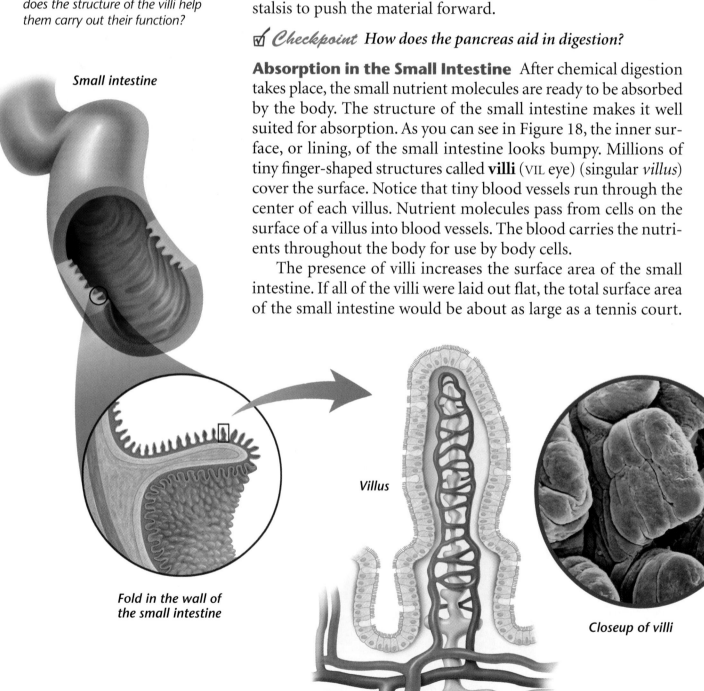

Small intestine

Fold in the wall of the small intestine

Villus

Closeup of villi

This greatly increased surface enables digested food to be absorbed faster than if the walls of the small intestine were smooth.

The Large Intestine

By the time material reaches the end of the small intestine, most nutrients have been absorbed. The remaining material moves from the small intestine into the large intestine. The **large intestine** is the last section of the digestive system. It is about one and a half meters long—about as long as the average bath-tub. As you can see in Figure 19, the large intestine is shaped somewhat like a horseshoe. It runs up the right-hand side of the abdomen, across the upper abdomen, and then down the left-hand side. The large intestine contains bacteria that feed on the material passing through. These bacteria normally do not cause disease. In fact, they are helpful because they make certain vitamins, including vitamin K.

The material entering the large intestine contains water and undigested food such as fiber. **As the material moves through the large intestine, water is absorbed into the bloodstream. The remaining material is readied for elimination from the body.**

The large intestine ends in a short tube called the **rectum.** Here waste material is compressed into a solid form. This waste material is eliminated from the body through the **anus,** a muscular opening at the end of the rectum.

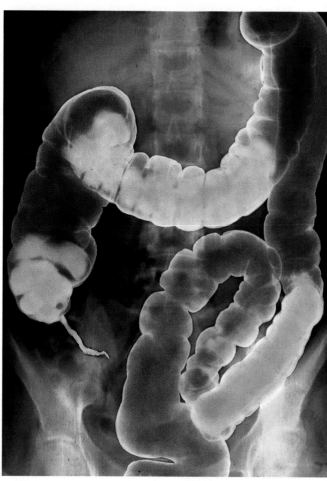

Figure 19 Notice the shape of the large intestine. As material passes through this structure, most of the water is absorbed by the body.

Section 4 Review

1. What two digestive processes occur in the small intestine? Briefly describe each process.
2. Which nutrient is absorbed in the large intestine?
3. How do the liver and pancreas function in the digestive process?
4. **Thinking Critically Relating Cause and Effect** Some people are allergic to a protein in wheat. When these people eat foods made with wheat, a reaction destroys the villi in the small intestine. What problems would you expect these people to experience?

Check Your Progress **CHAPTER PROJECT**
You should now be trying to eat a more healthful diet. Be sure you keep an accurate log of your food intake during this three-day period. Then graph the results. (*Hint:* You might find it helpful to focus on one food category when trying to improve your eating habits.)

Advertising and Nutrition

Millions of children enjoy Saturday morning television programs. As they watch, they see advertisements for high-sugar cereals, candy, soft drinks, and fat-filled foods. Such foods are not healthy choices. For example, in some cereals marketed to children, added sugar makes up almost half the cereal's weight. How greatly are children's eating habits influenced by food ads? Should these ads be allowed on children's television programs?

The Issues

Does Advertising Influence Children?
Advertising products to children between the ages of four and twelve works. Overall, companies spend more than $300 million a year advertising to that age group. In turn, children influence adults to spend more than 500 times that amount—at least $165 billion a year.

Should Food Companies Advertise on Children's Television? Some people want to regulate food ads on children's shows. Evidence indicates that children choose particular foods based on ads. The foods children eat can affect their health not just during childhood but for the rest of their lives.

Other people point out that children don't try to buy every food they see advertised. It is usually parents, not children, who decide what foods to buy. In addition, companies pay for advertisements. Without this money, television producers might not be able to afford to make good programs.

What Responsibilities Do Families and Schools Have? Many people believe that parents and teachers should teach children about nutrition. These people argue that adults should teach children to read food labels and to recognize misleading advertisements. For the rest of children's lives, they will be surrounded by advertising. If they learn to analyze ads critically, children will become wise consumers as adults.

You Decide

1. Describe the Issue

Summarize the debate about food advertisements on children's television.

2. Analyze the Options

List some possible solutions to the problem of food advertisements on children's television. How would each solution affect children and advertisers?

3. Find a Solution

Prepare a leaflet proposing one solution to the problem. Use persuasive arguments to support your proposal.

SECTION 1 — Food and Energy

Key Ideas

◆ Nutrients in food provide the body with energy and materials needed for growth, repair, and other life processes. The energy in foods is measured in Calories.

◆ The six nutrients necessary for human health are carbohydrates, fats, proteins, vitamins, minerals, and water.

◆ Water is the most important nutrient because it is necessary for all body processes.

Key Terms

nutrient	fat	protein
calorie	unsaturated fat	amino acid
carbohydrate	saturated fat	vitamin
glucose	cholesterol	mineral
fiber		

SECTION 2 — Healthy Eating

INTEGRATING HEALTH

Key Ideas

◆ The Food Guide Pyramid classifies foods into six major groups and tells how many servings from each group to eat.

◆ Food labels list the nutrients in foods and shows how the foods fit into your daily diet.

Key Terms

Food Guide Pyramid   Percent Daily Value

SECTION 3 — The Digestive Process Begins

Key Ideas

◆ The functions of the digestive system are to break down food, absorb food molecules into the blood, and eliminate wastes.

◆ During mechanical digestion, food is ground into small pieces. During chemical digestion, large food molecules are broken into small molecules by enzymes.

◆ Food first passes from the mouth into the esophagus, and then into the stomach. Waves of muscle contractions, known as peristalsis, keep the food moving in one direction.

Key Terms

digestion	enzyme	mucus
absorption	epiglottis	peristalsis
saliva	esophagus	stomach

SECTION 4 — Final Digestion and Absorption

Key Ideas

◆ Almost all chemical digestion and absorption of nutrients takes place in the small intestine.

◆ Nutrients are absorbed into the bloodstream through the villi of the small intestine.

◆ As material moves through the large intestine, water is absorbed. The remaining material is readied for elimination.

Key Terms

small intestine	gallbladder	large intestine
liver	pancreas	rectum
bile	villus	anus

USING THE INTERNET

www.science-explorer.phschool.com

California Test Prep: Reviewing Content

Multiple Choice

Choose the letter of the best answer.

1. Which nutrient makes up about 65 percent of the body's weight?
   a. carbohydrate
   b. protein
   c. water
   d. fat

2. According to the Food Guide Pyramid, from which group should you eat the most servings?
   a. Milk, Yogurt, and Cheese
   b. Meat, Poultry, Fish, Beans, Eggs, and Nuts
   c. Vegetables
   d. Bread, Cereal, Rice, and Pasta

3. Most mechanical digestion takes place in the
   a. mouth.   b. esophagus.
   c. stomach.   d. small intestine.

4. The enzyme in saliva chemically breaks down
   a. fats.   b. proteins.
   c. sugars.   d. starches.

5. Bile is produced by the
   a. liver.   b. pancreas.
   c. small intestine.   d. large intestine.

True or False

If the statement is true, write true. If it is false, change the underlined word or words to make the statement true.

6. Proteins that come from animal sources are <u>incomplete</u> proteins.

7. Vitamins that are stored in the fatty tissue of the body are <u>water-soluble</u>.

8. To determine which of two cereals supplies more iron, you can check the <u>Percent Daily Value</u> on the food label.

9. The physical breakdown of food is called <u>mechanical</u> digestion.

10. Most materials are absorbed into the bloodstream in the <u>large</u> intestine.

Checking Concepts

11. How does a person's level of physical activity affect his or her daily energy needs?

12. Why is fiber necessary in a diet even though it's not considered a nutrient?

13. Why does the Food Guide Pyramid give the recommended daily servings as a range instead of a single number?

14. Describe the function of the epiglottis.

15. Explain the role of peristalsis in the digestive system.

16. What is the function of villi? Where are villi located?

17. **Writing to Learn** Imagine that you are a bacon, lettuce, and tomato sandwich. Describe your journey through a person's digestive system, ending with absorption.

Thinking Visually

18. **Flowchart** Copy the incomplete flowchart onto a separate sheet of paper. Complete the flowchart with the names and functions of the missing organs. (For more on flowcharts, see the Skills Handbook.)

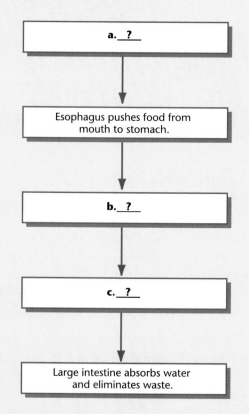

a. ?

↓

Esophagus pushes food from mouth to stomach.

↓

b. ?

↓

c. ?

↓

Large intestine absorbs water and eliminates waste.

Test Prep: Skills

Use the chart below to answer Questions 19–21.

Food (1 cup)	Calcium (% Daily Value)	Calories	Calories from Fat
Chocolate milk	30	230	80
Low-fat milk	35	110	20
Plain Yogurt	35	110	35

19. Classifying To which group in the Food Guide Pyramid do the foods in the chart belong? What is the recommended range of daily servings for that group?

20. Interpreting Data How many cups of low-fat milk provide the daily recommended amount of calcium?

21. Calculating Which of the foods meet the recommendation that no more than 30 percent of a food's Calories come from fat? Explain.

Thinking Critically

22. Applying Concepts Before winter arrives, animals that hibernate often prepare by eating foods that contain a lot of fat. How is this behavior helpful?

23. Comparing and Contrasting The digestive system is sometimes said to be "an assembly line in reverse." Identify some similarities and some differences between your digestive system and an assembly line.

24. Relating Cause and Effect "Heartburn" occurs when stomach acid enters the esophagus. Use your knowledge of the digestive system to explain how this condition affects the esophagus and how "heartburn" got its name.

25. Inferring Why is it important to chew your food thoroughly before swallowing?

26. Relating Cause and Effect Suppose a medicine killed all the bacteria in your body. How might this affect vitamin production in your body? Explain.

Performance Assessment

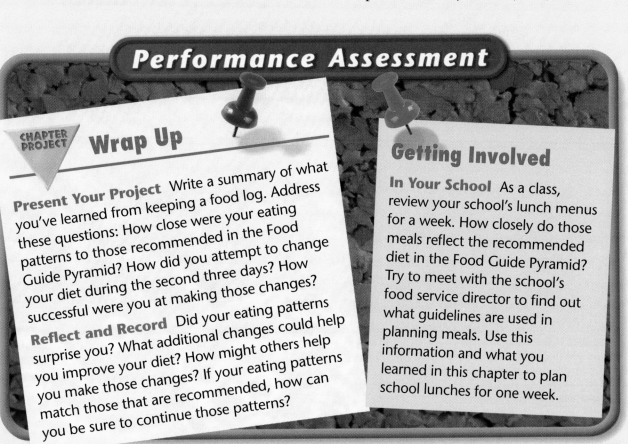

CHAPTER PROJECT **Wrap Up**

Present Your Project Write a summary of what you've learned from keeping a food log. Address these questions: How close were your eating patterns to those recommended in the Food Guide Pyramid? How did you attempt to change your diet during the second three days? How successful were you at making those changes?

Reflect and Record Did your eating patterns surprise you? What additional changes could help you improve your diet? How might others help you make those changes? If your eating patterns match those that are recommended, how can you be sure to continue those patterns?

Getting Involved

In Your School As a class, review your school's lunch menus for a week. How closely do those meals reflect the recommended diet in the Food Guide Pyramid? Try to meet with the school's food service director to find out what guidelines are used in planning meals. Use this information and what you learned in this chapter to plan school lunches for one week.

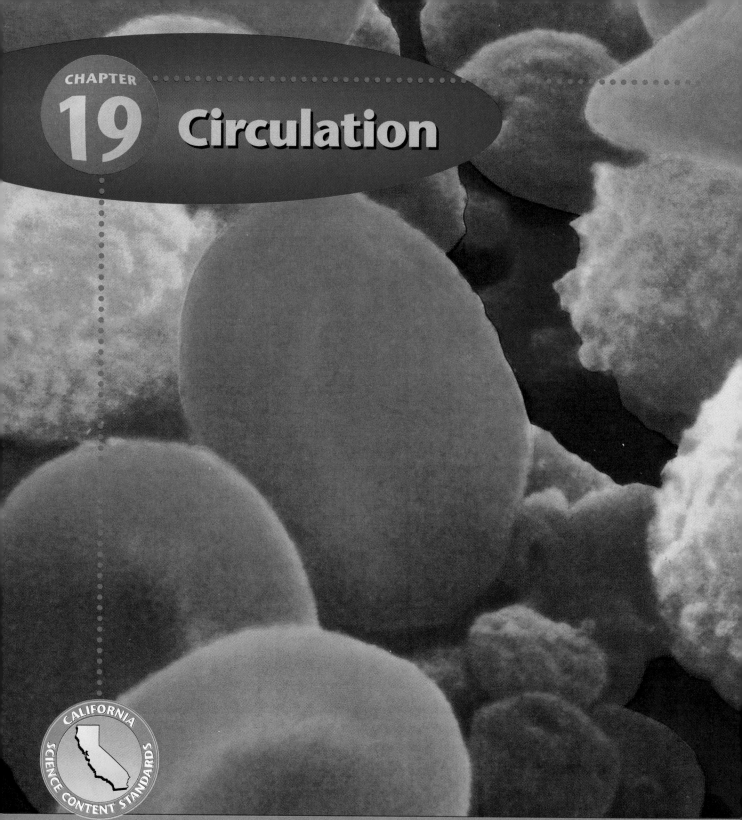

CALIFORNIA
SCIENCE CONTENT STANDARDS

The following California Science Content Standards are addressed in this chapter:

1. All living organisms are composed of cells, from just one to many trillions, whose details usually are visible only through a microscope.

   a. Cells function similarly in all living organisms.

5. The anatomy and physiology of plants and animals illustrate the complementary nature of structure and function.

a. Plants and animals have levels of organization for structure and function, including cells, tissues, organs, organ systems, and the whole organism.

b. Organ systems function because of the contributions of individual organs, tissues, and cells. The failure of any part can affect the entire system.

6. Physical principles underlie biological structures and functions.

   j. Contractions of the heart generate blood pressure, and heart valves prevent backflow of blood in the circulatory system.

7. Scientific progress is made by asking meaningful questions and conducting careful investigations.

Travels of a Red Blood Cell

Every day, you travel from home to school and then back home again. Your path makes a loop, or circuit, ending where it began. In this chapter, you'll learn how your blood also travels in circuits. You'll find out how your heart pumps your blood throughout your body, bringing that essential fluid to all your living cells. As you learn more about the heart and circulatory system, you'll create a display to show how blood circulates throughout the body.

Your Goal To design and construct a display showing a complete journey of a red blood cell through the human body.

To complete the project successfully, your display must
◆ show a red blood cell that leaves from the heart and returns to the same place
◆ show where the red blood cell picks up and delivers oxygen and carbon dioxide
◆ provide written descriptions of the circuits made by the red blood cell, either with captions or in a continuous story
◆ be designed following the safety guidelines in Appendix A

Get Started Look ahead at the diagrams in the chapter. Then discuss the kinds of displays you could use, including a three-dimensional model, posters, a series of drawings, a flip-book, or a video animation. Write down any content questions you'll need to answer.

Check Your Progress You'll be working on this project as you study this chapter. To keep your project on track, look for Check Your Progress boxes at the following points.
Section 1 Review, page 600: Make a sketch of your display.
Section 2 Review, page 605: Begin to construct your display.
Section 3 Review, page 612: Add a written description to your display.

Wrap Up At the end of the chapter (page 621), you will use your display to show how blood travels through the body.

Blood cells travel in blood vessels to all parts of the body.

b. Utilize a variety of print and electronic resources (including the World Wide Web) to collect information as evidence as part of a research project.

c. Communicate the logical connection among hypothesis, science concepts, tests conducted, data collected, and conclusions drawn from the scientific evidence.

d. Construct scale models, maps and appropriately labeled diagrams to communicate scientific knowledge.

① The Body's Transportation System

How Hard Does Your Heart Work?

1. Every minute, your heart beats about 75 to 85 times. With each beat, it pumps about 60 milliliters of blood. Can you work as hard and fast as your heart does?

2. Cover a table or desk with newspapers. Place two large plastic containers side by side on the newspapers. Fill one with 2.5 liters of water, which is about the volume of blood that your heart pumps in 30 seconds. Leave the other container empty.

3. With a plastic cup that holds about 60 milliliters, transfer water as quickly as possible into the empty container without spilling any. Have a partner time you for 30 seconds. As you work, count how many transfers you make in 30 seconds.

4. Multiply your results by 2 to find the number of transfers for one minute.

Think It Over

Inferring Compare your performance with the number of times your heart beats every minute. What do your results tell you about the strength and speed of a heartbeat?

GUIDE FOR READING

◆ What is the function of the cardiovascular system?

◆ What role does the heart play in the cardiovascular system?

◆ What path does blood take through the circulatory system?

Reading Tip As you read, create a flowchart that shows the path that blood follows as it circulates through the body.

In the middle of the night, a truck rolls rapidly through the darkness. Loaded with fresh fruits and vegetables, the truck is headed for a city supermarket. The driver steers off the interstate and onto a smaller highway. Finally, after driving through narrow city streets, the truck reaches its destination. As dawn begins to break, store workers unload the cargo. They work quickly, because other trucks—carrying meats, canned goods, and freshly baked breads—are waiting to be unloaded. And while workers fill the store with products to be sold, a garbage truck removes yesterday's trash. All these trucks have traveled long distances over roads. Without a huge network of roads, big and small, the supermarket couldn't stay in business.

Movement of Materials

Like the roads that link all parts of the country, your body has a "highway" network, called the cardiovascular system, that links all parts of your body. The **cardiovascular system,** or circulatory system, consists of the heart, blood vessels, and blood. **The cardiovascular system carries needed substances to cells and carries waste products away from cells.** In addition, blood contains cells that fight disease.

Needed Materials Most substances that need to get from one part of the body to another are carried by blood. For example, blood carries oxygen from your lungs to your body cells. Blood also transports the glucose your cells use to produce energy.

Waste Products The cardiovascular system also picks up wastes from cells. For example, when cells use glucose, they produce carbon dioxide as a waste product. The carbon dioxide passes from the cells into the blood. The cardiovascular system then carries carbon dioxide to the lungs, where it is exhaled.

Disease Fighters The cardiovascular system also transports cells that attack disease-causing microorganisms. This process can keep you from becoming sick. If you do get sick, these disease-fighting blood cells will kill the microorganisms to help you get well.

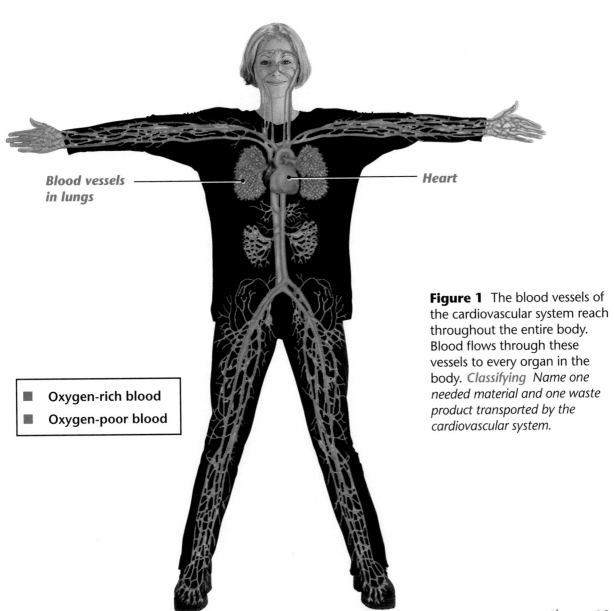

Blood vessels in lungs

Heart

■ Oxygen-rich blood
■ Oxygen-poor blood

Figure 1 The blood vessels of the cardiovascular system reach throughout the entire body. Blood flows through these vessels to every organ in the body. *Classifying Name one needed material and one waste product transported by the cardiovascular system.*

Figure 2 This small stone sculpture, created by ancient Egyptians, represents the heart. Ancient Egyptians believed that feelings, thoughts, and memories were created by the heart.

The Heart

Without the heart, blood wouldn't go anywhere. The **heart** is a hollow, muscular organ that pumps blood throughout the body. Your heart, which is about the size of your fist, is located in the center of your chest. The heart lies beneath the breastbone and inside the ribs. These bones protect the heart from injury.

Each time the heart beats, it pushes blood through the blood vessels of the cardiovascular system. As you learned in Chapter 17, the heart is made of cardiac muscle, which can contract over and over without getting tired. The heart beats continually throughout a person's life, resting only between beats. During your lifetime, your heart may beat over 3 billion times. In a year, it pumps enough blood to fill over 30 competition-size swimming pools.

The Heart's Structure Look closely at *Exploring the Heart* as you read about the structure of the heart. Notice that the heart has two sides—a right side and a left side—completely separated from each other by a wall of tissue. Each side has two compartments, or chambers—an upper and a lower chamber. Each of the two upper chambers, called an **atrium** (AY tree um) (plural *atria*), receives blood that comes into the heart. Each lower chamber, called a **ventricle**, pumps blood out of the heart. The atria are separated from the ventricles by valves. A **valve** is a flap of tissue that prevents blood from flowing backward. Valves are also located between the ventricles and the large blood vessels that carry blood away from the heart.

How the Heart Works The action of the heart has two main phases. In one phase, the heart muscle relaxes and the heart fills with blood. In the other phase, the heart muscle contracts and pumps blood forward. A heartbeat, which sounds something like *lub-dup*, can be heard during the pumping phase.

Figure 3 As blood flows out of the heart and toward the lungs, it passes through the valve shown in the photograph. The illustration shows how blood flows through the open valve.
Applying Concepts What is the function of the valves in the heart?

When the heart muscle relaxes, blood flows into the chambers. Then the atria contract. This muscle contraction squeezes blood out of the atria, through the valves, and then into the ventricles. Next the ventricles contract. This contraction closes the valves between the atria and ventricles, making the *lub* sound and squeezing blood into large blood vessels. As the valves between the ventricles and the blood vessels snap shut, they make the *dup* sound. All of this happens in less than a second.

☑ *Checkpoint* **Contrast the functions of atria and ventricles.**

EXPLORING *the Heart*

Every second of your life, your heart pumps blood through your body. The right side of the heart pumps blood to the lungs, while the left side pumps blood to the rest of the body.

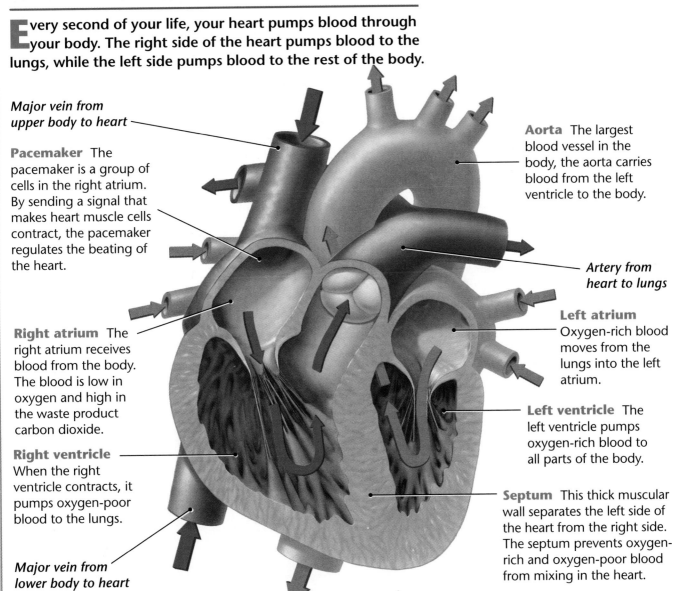

Major vein from upper body to heart

Pacemaker The pacemaker is a group of cells in the right atrium. By sending a signal that makes heart muscle cells contract, the pacemaker regulates the beating of the heart.

Right atrium The right atrium receives blood from the body. The blood is low in oxygen and high in the waste product carbon dioxide.

Right ventricle When the right ventricle contracts, it pumps oxygen-poor blood to the lungs.

Major vein from lower body to heart

Aorta The largest blood vessel in the body, the aorta carries blood from the left ventricle to the body.

Artery from heart to lungs

Left atrium Oxygen-rich blood moves from the lungs into the left atrium.

Left ventricle The left ventricle pumps oxygen-rich blood to all parts of the body.

Septum This thick muscular wall separates the left side of the heart from the right side. The septum prevents oxygen-rich and oxygen-poor blood from mixing in the heart.

Regulation of Heartbeat

A group of cells called the **pacemaker,** which is located in the right atrium, sends out signals that make the heart muscle contract. The pacemaker constantly receives messages about the body's oxygen needs. It then adjusts the heart rate to match. Your heart beats much faster when you are exercising than when you are sitting quietly. When you are exercising, the entire process from the beginning of one heartbeat to the beginning of the next can take less than half a second. Your muscles need more oxygen during exercise. Your rapid heartbeat supplies blood that carries the oxygen.

INTEGRATING TECHNOLOGY In some people, the pacemaker becomes damaged as a result of disease or an accident. This often results in an irregular or slow heartbeat. In the 1950s, doctors and engineers developed an artificial, battery-operated pacemaker. The artificial pacemaker is implanted beneath the skin and connected by wires to the heart. Tiny electric impulses travel from the battery through the wires. These impulses make the heart contract at a normal rate.

☑ *Checkpoint* *What is the function of the pacemaker?*

Two Loops

After leaving the heart, blood travels in blood vessels through the body. Your body has three kinds of blood vessels—arteries, capillaries, and veins. **Arteries** are blood vessels that carry blood away from the heart. From the arteries, blood flows into tiny vessels called **capillaries.** In the capillaries, substances are exchanged between the blood and body cells. From capillaries, blood flows into **veins,** which are the vessels that carry blood back to the heart.

The overall pattern of blood flow through the body is something like a figure eight. The heart is at the center where the two

Figure 4 Activities such as swimming require a lot of energy. A person's heart beats fast in order to supply the muscles with the blood they need. The heart's pacemaker regulates the speed at which the heart beats.

loops cross. **In the first loop, blood travels from the heart to the lungs and then back to the heart. In the second loop, blood is pumped from the heart throughout the body and then returns again to the heart.** The heart is really two pumps, one on the right and one on the left. The right side pumps blood to the lungs, and the left side pumps blood to the rest of the body.

Blood travels in only one direction. If you were a drop of blood, you could start at any point in the figure eight and eventually return to the same point. The entire trip would take less than a minute. As you read about the path that blood takes through the cardiovascular system, trace the path in Figure 5.

Loop One: to the Lungs and Back When blood from the body flows into the right atrium, it contains little oxygen but a lot of carbon dioxide. This oxygen-poor blood is dark red. The blood then flows from the right atrium into the right ventricle. Then the ventricle pumps blood into the arteries that lead to the lungs.

As blood flows through the lungs, large blood vessels branch into smaller ones. Eventually, blood flows through tiny capillaries that are in close contact with the air that comes into the lungs. The air in the lungs has more oxygen than the blood in the capillaries, so oxygen moves from the lung into the blood. In contrast, carbon dioxide moves in the opposite direction—from the blood into the lung. As the blood leaves the lungs, it is now rich in oxygen and poor in carbon dioxide. This blood, which is bright red, flows to the left side of the heart to be pumped through the second loop.

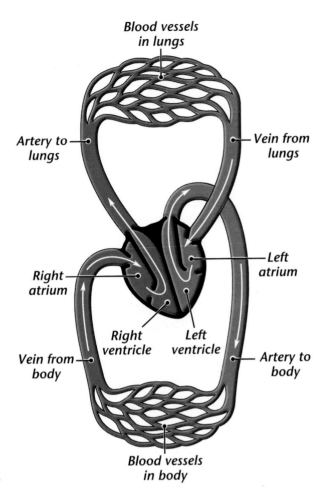

Figure 5 Blood circulates through the body in two loops with the heart at the center. Use the arrows to trace the path of blood, beginning at the right atrium. *Interpreting Diagrams Where does the blood that enters the left atrium come from?*

Loop Two: to the Body and Back   The second loop begins as the left atrium fills with oxygen-rich blood coming from the lungs. The blood then moves into the left ventricle. From the left ventricle, the blood is pumped into the **aorta** (ay AWR tuh), the largest artery in the body.

Eventually, after passing through branching arteries, blood flows through tiny capillaries in different parts of your body, such as your brain, liver, and legs. These vessels are in close contact with body cells. Oxygen moves out of the blood and into the body cells. At the same time, carbon dioxide passes from the body cells and into the blood. The blood then flows back to the right atrium of the heart through veins, completing the second loop.

The Force of the Ventricles

 When the ventricle muscles contract, they exert a force on the blood that is inside them. A **force** is a push or a pull. You see examples of forces all around you. When you lift a book off a table, for example, you exert a force on the book, making it move upward. The force exerted by the ventricles moves blood out of your heart and into arteries.

The contraction of the left ventricle exerts much more force than the contraction of the right ventricle. The right ventricle only pumps blood to the lungs. In contrast, the left ventricle pumps blood throughout the body. As a way of understanding this, think of the force it would take to bunt a baseball. Then think about how hard you would need to hit the ball if you wanted to hit a home run.

Figure 6   If the batter hits the ball, the bat will exert a force on the ball. This force will make the ball zoom through the air. Similarly, when the ventricles of the heart contract, they exert a force on the blood inside them. This force pushes blood through the blood vessels.

Section 1 Review

1. What is the function of the cardiovascular system?
2. What function does the heart perform?
3. Describe the route that blood takes through the cardiovascular system. Begin with blood leaving the left ventricle.
4. What is the heart's pacemaker? What causes the pacemaker to change the rate at which the heart beats?
5. **Thinking Critically Comparing and Contrasting** Most of the arteries in the body carry oxygen-rich blood away from the heart. One artery, however, carries blood that has little oxygen away from the heart. From which ventricle does that artery carry blood? To where does that artery carry blood?

CHAPTER PROJECT

Check Your Progress
At this point, you should have sketched out the two loops your red blood cell will travel. Make sure each pathway forms a complete circuit back to the heart. Begin to plan how you will construct your display. Keep a running list of the materials or equipment you'll need. (Hint: Think about how you will show the movement of the blood cell in your display.)

SECTION
2 A Closer Look at Blood Vessels

DISCOVER

ACTIVITY

How Does Pressure Affect the Flow of Blood?

1. Spread newspapers over a table or desktop. Then fill a plastic squeeze bottle with water.

2. Hold the bottle over a dishpan. Squeeze the bottle with one hand. Observe how far the water travels.

3. Now grasp the bottle with both hands and squeeze again. Observe how far the water travels this time.

Think It Over

Inferring Blood is pushed through arteries with much more force than it is pushed through veins. Which part of the activity models an artery? Which part models a vein? Which organ in the body provides the pushing force?

Like corridors in a large building, blood vessels run through all of the tissues of your body. While some blood vessels are as wide as your thumb, most of them are much finer than a human hair. If all the arteries, capillaries, and veins in your body were hooked together, end to end, they would stretch a distance of almost 100,000 kilometers. That's long enough to wrap around Earth twice—with a lot left over!

Arteries

When blood leaves the heart, it travels through arteries. The right ventricle pumps blood into the arteries that go to the lungs. The left ventricle pumps blood into the aorta, the largest artery in your body. Every organ receives blood from arteries that branch off the aorta. The first branches, called the **coronary arteries,** carry blood to the heart itself. Other branches carry blood to the brain, intestines, and other organs. Each artery branches into smaller and smaller arteries.

Artery Structure The walls of arteries are generally very thick. In fact, artery walls consist of three layers. The innermost layer, which is made up of epithelial

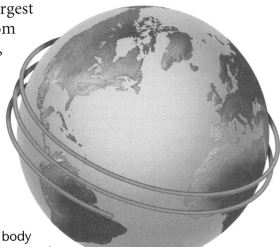

Figure 7 If all the blood vessels in your body were joined end to end, they would wrap around the world almost two and a half times.

GUIDE FOR READING

◆ What are the functions of arteries, capillaries, and veins?

◆ What causes blood pressure?

Reading Tip As you read, use the text headings to make an outline of the information in this section.

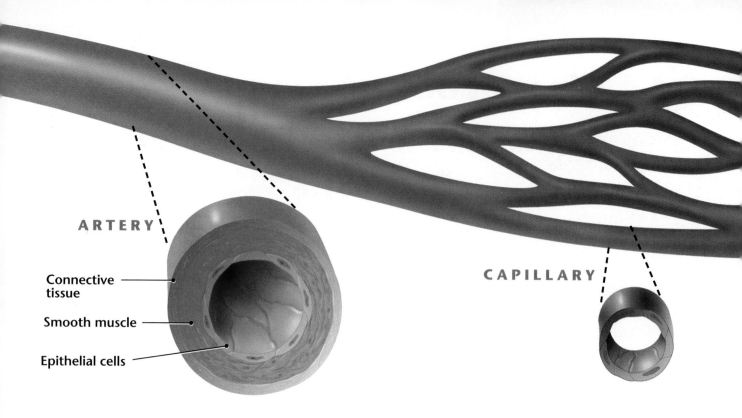

ARTERY

Connective tissue

Smooth muscle

Epithelial cells

CAPILLARY

Math TOOLBOX

Pulse Rate

A rate is the speed at which something happens. When you calculate a rate, you compare the number of events with the time period in which they occur. Here is how you can calculate the pulse rate of a person whose heart beats 142 times in 2 minutes.

1. Write the comparison as a fraction.

$$\frac{142 \text{ heartbeats}}{2 \text{ minutes}}$$

2. Divide the numerator and the denominator by the denominator.

$$\frac{142 \div 2}{2 \div 2} = \frac{71}{1}$$

The person's pulse rate is 71 heartbeats per minute.

tissue, is smooth. This smooth surface enables blood to flow freely. The middle layer consists mostly of muscle tissue. The outer wall is made up of flexible connective tissue. Because of this layered structure, arteries have both strength and flexibility. Arteries are able to withstand the enormous pressure of blood pumped by the heart, and to expand and relax in response to that pumping.

Pulse If you lightly touch the inside of your wrist, you can feel the artery in your wrist rise and fall repeatedly. The pulse that you feel is caused by the alternating expansion and relaxation of the artery wall. Every time the heart's ventricles contract, they send a spurt of blood out through all the arteries in your body. As this spurt travels through the arteries, it pushes the artery walls and makes them expand. After the spurt passes, the artery walls become narrower again. When you count the number of times an artery pulses beneath your fingers, you are counting heartbeats. By taking your pulse rate, you can determine how fast your heart is beating.

Regulating Blood Flow The muscles in the middle wall of an artery are involuntary muscles, which contract without your thinking about it. When they contract, the opening in the artery becomes smaller. When they relax, the opening becomes larger. These muscles act as control gates, adjusting the amount of blood sent to different organs. For example, after you eat, your stomach

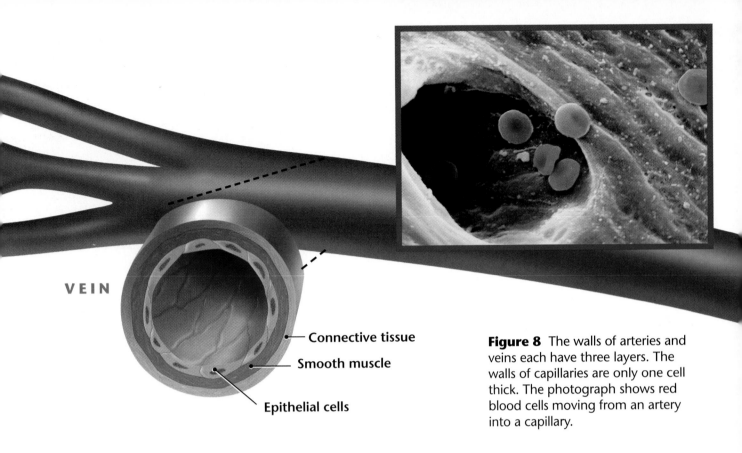

VEIN

Connective tissue

Smooth muscle

Epithelial cells

Figure 8 The walls of arteries and veins each have three layers. The walls of capillaries are only one cell thick. The photograph shows red blood cells moving from an artery into a capillary.

and intestines need a greater blood supply to help power digestion. The arteries leading to those organs become larger, so that more blood flows through them. In contrast, when you are running, your stomach and intestines need less blood than the muscles in your legs. The arteries leading to the stomach and intestines become narrower, decreasing the blood flow to those organs.

☑ *Checkpoint* *What causes the pulse that you feel in your wrist?*

Capillaries

Eventually, blood flows from small arteries into the tiny capillaries. **In the capillaries, materials are exchanged between the blood and the body's cells.** Capillary walls are only one cell thick. Because capillaries have thin walls, materials can pass easily through them. Materials such as oxygen and glucose pass from blood, through the thin capillary walls, to the cells. Cellular waste products travel in the opposite direction—from cells, through the capillary walls, and into blood.

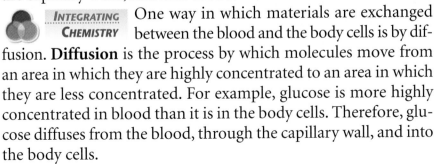 **INTEGRATING CHEMISTRY** One way in which materials are exchanged between the blood and the body cells is by diffusion. **Diffusion** is the process by which molecules move from an area in which they are highly concentrated to an area in which they are less concentrated. For example, glucose is more highly concentrated in blood than it is in the body cells. Therefore, glucose diffuses from the blood, through the capillary wall, and into the body cells.

Figure 9 The wall of the artery (left) is much thicker than that of the vein (right).
Making Generalizations Why is it important for artery walls to be both strong and flexible?

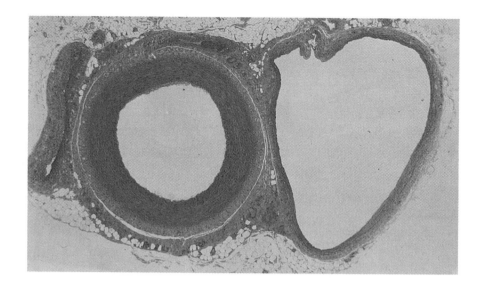

Veins

After blood moves through capillaries, it enters larger blood vessels called veins, which carry blood back to the heart. The walls of veins, like those of arteries, have three layers, with muscle in the middle layer. However, the walls of veins are generally thinner than those of arteries.

By the time blood flows into veins, the pushing force of the heart has less effect than it did in the arteries. Several factors help move blood through veins. First, because many veins are located near skeletal muscles, the contraction of the muscles helps push the blood along. For example, as you run or walk, the skeletal muscles in your legs contract and squeeze the veins in your legs. Second, larger veins in your body have valves in them that prevent blood from flowing backward. Third, breathing movements, which exert a squeezing pressure against veins in the chest, also force blood toward the heart.

 Checkpoint How do skeletal muscles help move blood in veins?

Blood Pressure

INTEGRATING PHYSICS Suppose that you are washing a car. You attach the hose to the faucet and turn on the faucet. The water flows out in a slow, steady stream. Then, while your back is turned, your little brother turns the faucet on all the way. Suddenly, the water spurts out rapidly, and the hose almost jumps out of your hand.

As water flows through a hose, it pushes against the walls of the hose, creating pressure on the walls. **Pressure** is the force that something exerts over a given area. When your brother turned on the faucet all the way, the additional water flow increased the pressure exerted on the inside of the hose. The extra pressure made the water spurt out of the nozzle faster.

What Causes Blood Pressure? Blood traveling through blood vessels behaves in a manner similar to that of water moving through a hose. Blood exerts a pressure, called **blood pressure,** against the walls of blood vessels. **Blood pressure is caused by the force with which the ventricles contract.** In general, as blood moves away from the heart, its pressure decreases. This happens because the farther away from the heart the blood moves, the lower the force of the ventricles. Blood flowing through arteries exerts the highest pressure. Blood pressure in the capillaries and veins is much lower than in the arteries.

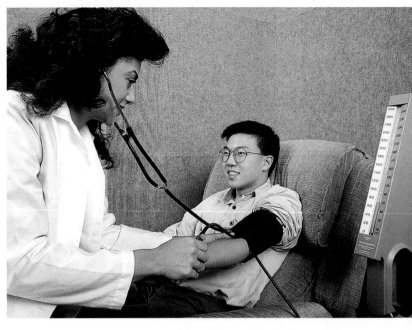

Figure 10 Blood pressure is measured with a sphygmomanometer. The cuff is wrapped around the patient's arm. His blood pressure is recorded by the height of the mercury column in the instrument on the right.

Measuring Blood Pressure Blood pressure can be measured with an instrument called a **sphygmomanometer** (sfig moh muh NAHM uh tur). Many sphygmomanometers contain a tube of mercury. Blood pressure is expressed in millimeters of mercury and is recorded as two numbers. The first number is a measure of the blood pressure while the ventricles contract and pump blood into the arteries. The second number, which is lower, measures the blood pressure while the ventricles relax between heartbeats. The two numbers are expressed as a fraction: the contraction pressure over the relaxation pressure. A typical blood pressure reading for a young adult is 120/80. You will learn about the effects of high blood pressure in Section 4.

Section 2 Review

1. Contrast the functions of arteries, capillaries, and veins.
2. What causes blood pressure?
3. Explain the factors that enable blood in your leg veins to return to the heart in spite of the downward pull of gravity.
4. **Thinking Critically** **Applying Concepts** Arteries adjust the amount of blood flowing to different parts of the body, depending on where blood is needed. Use this fact to explain why it may not be a good idea to exercise vigorously shortly after you eat.

CHAPTER PROJECT

By now you should have begun constructing your display. Make sure that the blood vessels are depicted accurately. Also check that your display correctly shows the path of a red blood cell and identifies the place where the red blood cell picks up oxygen. (*Hint:* Start to prepare a rough draft of your written description at the same time as you begin constructing your display.)

Heart Beat, Health Beat

Problem

How does physical activity affect your pulse rate?

Materials

watch or clock with
    second hand
graph paper

Procedure

1. Predict how your pulse rate will change as you go from resting to being active, then back to resting again. Then copy the data table into your notebook.

2. Locate your pulse by placing the index and middle finger of one hand on your other wrist at the base of your thumb. Move the two fingers slightly until you feel your pulse.

3. Work with a partner for the rest of this lab. Begin by determining your resting pulse rate. Count the number of beats in your pulse for exactly one minute while your partner times you. Record the number in your data table.
CAUTION: *Do not complete the rest of these procedures if there is any medical reason why you should avoid physical activities.*

4. Walk in place for one minute while your partner times you. Stop and immediately take your pulse for one minute. Record the number in your data table.

5. Run in place for one minute. Take your pulse again, and record the result.

6. Sit down right away, and have your partner time you as you rest for one minute. Then take your pulse rate again.

7. Have your partner time you as you rest for 3 more minutes. Then take your pulse rate again and record it.

Analyze and Conclude

1. Use the data you obtained to create a bar graph of your pulse rate under the different conditions you tested.

2. What conclusion can you draw about the relationship between physical activity and a person's pulse rate?

3. What happens to the pulse rate when the physical activity has stopped?

4. What can you infer about the heartbeat when the pulse rate increases?

5. **Think About It** Do you think the pulse measurements you made are completely accurate? Why or why not? How could you improve the accuracy of your measurements?

Design an Experiment

Do the resting pulse rates of adults, teens, and young children differ? Write a plan to answer this question. Obtain your teacher's permission before carrying out your plan.

DATA TABLE

Activity	Pulse Rate
Resting	
Walking	
Running	
Resting after Exercise	
(1 min) Resting after Exercise	
(3+ min) Resting after Exercise	

DISCOVER

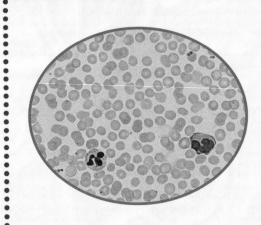

What Kinds of Cells Are in Blood?

1. Obtain a microscope slide of human blood. Look at the slide under the microscope, first under low power and then under high power.

2. Look carefully at the different kinds of cells that you see.

3. Make several drawings of each kind of cell. Use red pencil for the red blood cells.

Think It Over

Observing How many kinds of cells did you see? How do they differ from each other?

If someone fills a test tube with blood and lets it sit for a while, the blood separates into layers. The top layer is a clear, yellowish liquid. A dark red material rests on the bottom. The top layer is **plasma,** which is the liquid part of blood. The red material at the bottom is a mixture of blood cells. **Blood is made up of four components: plasma, red blood cells, white blood cells, and platelets.** About 45 percent of the volume of blood is made up of cells. The rest consists of plasma.

Plasma

Blood, as you have learned, transports materials from one part of the body to another. Most of those materials travel in plasma. In fact, 10 percent of plasma is made up of these dissolved materials. The other 90 percent of plasma is water.

Plasma carries molecules that come from the breakdown of digested food, such as glucose and fats. The vitamins and minerals your body needs also travel in plasma. Plasma also carries chemical messengers that direct body activities such as the uptake of glucose by your cells. In addition, many wastes produced by cell processes are carried away by plasma.

Protein molecules give plasma its yellow color. There are three groups of plasma proteins. One group helps to regulate the amount of water in blood. The second group, which is produced by white blood cells, helps fight disease. The third group of proteins interacts with platelets to form blood clots.

GUIDE FOR READING

◆ What are the four components of blood?

◆ What determines the type of blood that a person can receive in transfusion?

Reading Tip As you read, write definitions for each boldfaced term in your own words.

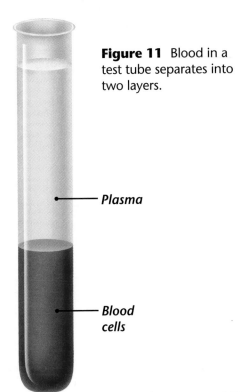

Figure 11 Blood in a test tube separates into two layers.

Plasma

Blood cells

Red Blood Cells

Without red blood cells, your body could not use the oxygen that you breathe in. **Red blood cells** take up oxygen in the lungs and deliver it to cells elsewhere in the body. Red blood cells, like most blood cells, are produced in bone marrow.

Exploring Blood Cells shows what red blood cells look like. Under a microscope, these cells look like disks with pinched-in centers. Because they are thin, red blood cells can bend and twist easily. This flexibility enables them to squeeze through narrow capillaries.

A red blood cell is made mostly of **hemoglobin** (HEE muh gloh bin), which is an iron-containing protein that binds chemically to oxygen molecules. When hemoglobin combines with oxygen, the cells become bright red. Without oxygen, they are dark red. Hemoglobin picks up oxygen in the lungs and releases it as blood travels through capillaries in the rest of the body. Hemoglobin also picks up some of the carbon dioxide produced by cells. However, most of the carbon dioxide is carried by plasma. The blood carries the carbon dioxide to the lungs, where it is released from the body.

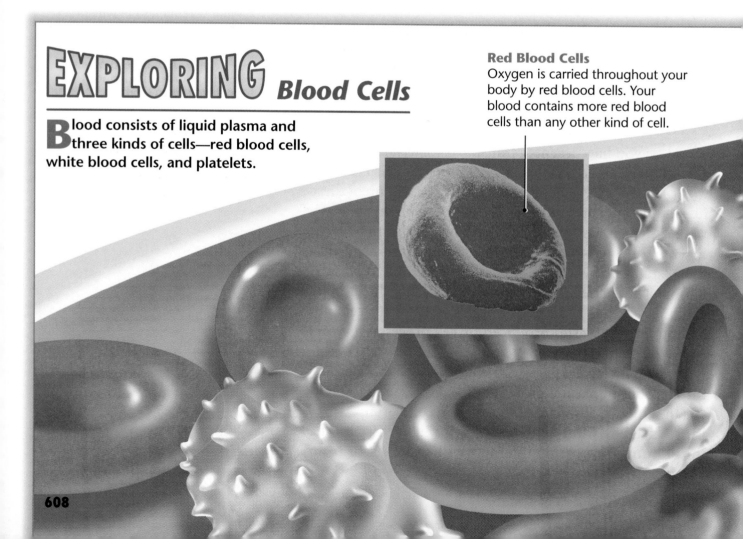

EXPLORING *Blood Cells*

Blood consists of liquid plasma and three kinds of cells—red blood cells, white blood cells, and platelets.

Red Blood Cells
Oxygen is carried throughout your body by red blood cells. Your blood contains more red blood cells than any other kind of cell.

Red blood cells have no nuclei. Without a nucleus, a red blood cell cannot live very long. In fact, red blood cells live only about 120 days. Every second, about 2 million red blood cells in your body die. Fortunately, your bone marrow produces new red blood cells at the same rate.

☑ *Checkpoint* *What is the shape of a red blood cell?*

White Blood Cells

Like red blood cells, white blood cells begin their existence in bone marrow. **White blood cells** are the body's disease fighters. Some white blood cells recognize disease-causing organisms such as bacteria, and alert the body that it has been invaded. Other white blood cells produce chemicals to fight the invaders. Still others surround and kill the organisms. You will learn more about the functions of white blood cells in Chapter 21.

White blood cells are different from red blood cells in several important ways. There are fewer of them—only about one white blood cell for every 500 to 1,000 red blood cells. White blood cells are also bigger than red blood cells, and they have nuclei. And most white blood cells live for months or even years.

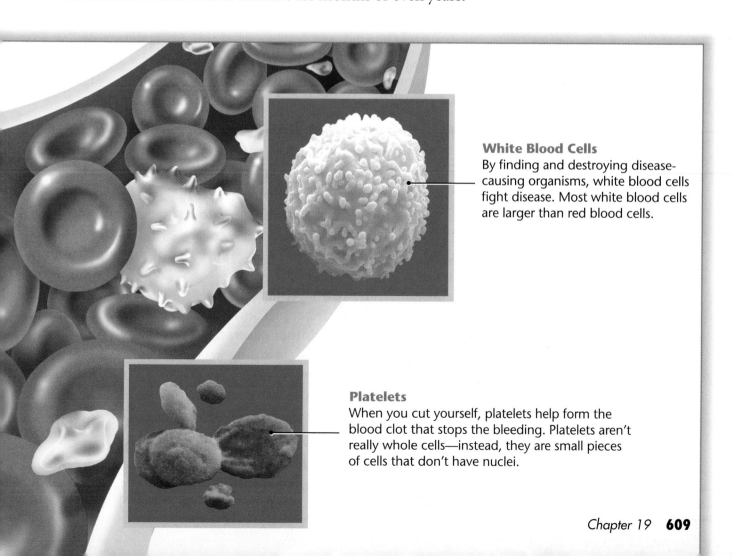

White Blood Cells
By finding and destroying disease-causing organisms, white blood cells fight disease. Most white blood cells are larger than red blood cells.

Platelets
When you cut yourself, platelets help form the blood clot that stops the bleeding. Platelets aren't really whole cells—instead, they are small pieces of cells that don't have nuclei.

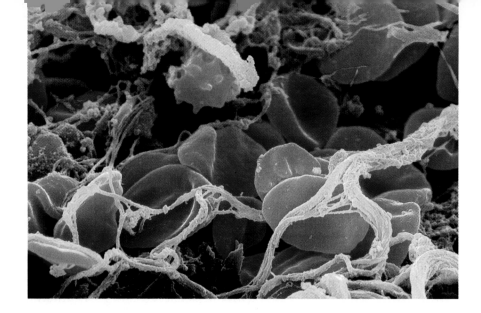

Figure 12 When you cut your skin, a blood clot forms. The blood clot consists of blood cells trapped in a fiber net. Platelets produce the material of which the fibers are made.

Caught in the Web

ACTIVITY

In this activity, you will model part of the process by which a blood clot forms.

1. Cover the opening of a sturdy plastic cup with a piece of cheesecloth. Use a rubber band to hold the cheesecloth in place.

2. Put some water, paper clips, and coins in another cup.

3. Carefully pour the water, coins, and paper clips into the middle of the cheesecloth.

Making Models The paper clips and coins represent blood cells. What does the cheesecloth represent? What starts the production of the substance that the cheesecloth represents?

Platelets

When you cut your finger, blood flows out of the cut. After a short time, however, a blood clot forms, stopping the blood flow. **Platelets** (PLAYT lits) are cell fragments that play an important part in forming blood clots.

When a blood vessel is cut, platelets collect and stick to the vessel at the site of the wound. The platelets release chemicals that start a chain reaction. This series of reactions eventually produces a chemical called **fibrin** (FY brin). Fibrin gets its name from the fact that it weaves a net of tiny fibers across the cut in the blood vessel. The fiber net traps blood cells. As more and more platelets and blood cells become trapped in the net, a blood clot forms. A scab is a dried blood clot on the skin surface.

☑ *Checkpoint* *What role do platelets play in forming blood clots?*

Blood Types

If a person loses a lot of blood—from a wound or during surgery—he or she may be given a **blood transfusion**. A blood transfusion is the transference of blood from one person to another. Most early attempts at blood transfusion failed, but no one knew why until the early 1900s. At that time Karl Landsteiner, an Austrian American physician, tried mixing blood samples from pairs of people. Sometimes the two blood samples blended smoothly. In other cases, however, the red blood cells clumped together. This clumping accounted for the failure of many blood transfusions. If clumping occurs within the body, it clogs the capillaries and may kill the person.

Marker Molecules Landsteiner went on to discover that there are four types of blood—A, B, AB, and O. Blood types are determined by marker molecules on red blood cells. If your blood type is A, you have the A marker. If your blood type is B, you have the B marker. People with type AB blood have both A and B markers. The red blood cells of people with type O blood contain neither A nor B markers.

Your plasma contains clumping proteins that recognize red blood cells with "foreign" markers and make those cells clump together. For example, if you have blood type A, your blood contains clumping proteins that act against cells with B markers. So if you receive a transfusion of type B blood, your clumping proteins will make the "foreign" type B cells clump together.

Safe Transfusions Landsteiner's work led to a better understanding of transfusions. **The marker molecules on your red blood cells determine your blood type and the type of blood that you can safely receive in transfusions.** A person with type A blood can receive transfusions of either type A or type O blood. Neither of these two blood types has B markers. Thus they would not be recognized as foreign by the clumping proteins in type A blood. A person with type AB blood can receive all blood types in transfusion, because type AB blood has no clumping proteins. Figure 13 shows which transfusions are safe for each blood type.

If you ever receive a transfusion, your blood type will be checked. Then donated blood that you can safely receive will be found. This process is called cross matching. You may have heard a doctor on a television show give the order to "type and cross." The doctor wants to find out what blood type the patient has and then cross match it against donated blood.

Blood Types

Blood Type	Marker Molecules on Red Blood Cells	Clumping Proteins	Blood Types That Can Be Safely Received in a Transfusion
A	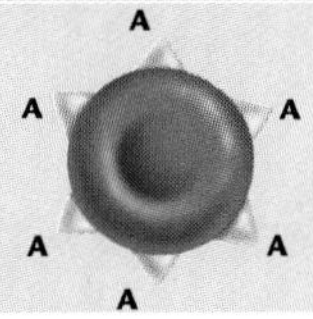	anti-B	A and O
B	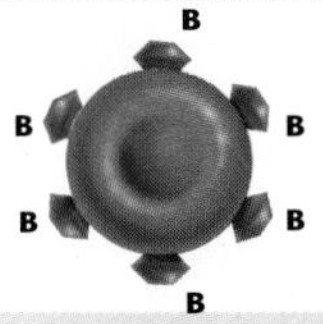	anti-A	B and O
AB	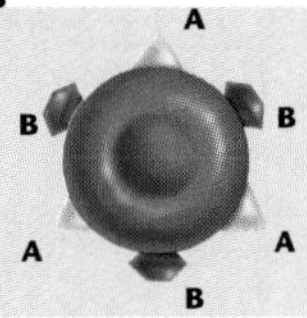	no clumping proteins	A, B, AB, and O
O		anti-A and anti-B	O

Figure 13 The chemical markers on a person's red blood cells determine the types of blood he or she can safely receive in a transfusion. *Interpreting Charts What types of blood can be given safely to a person with blood type AB? Who can safely receive blood type O?*

The Lymphatic System

As blood travels through the capillaries in the car-diovascular system, some of the fluid leaks out. It moves through the walls of capillaries and into surrounding tissues. This fluid carries materials that the cells in the tissues need.

After bathing the cells, this fluid moves into the lymphatic system. The **lymphatic system** (lim FAT ik) is a network of veinlike vessels that returns the fluid to the bloodstream. The lymphatic system acts something like rain gutters after a rainstorm, carrying the fluid away.

Lymph Once the fluid is inside the lymphatic sys-tem, it is called **lymph.** Lymph consists of water and dissolved materials such as glucose. It also contains some white blood cells that have left the capillaries.

The lymphatic system has no pump, so lymph moves slowly. Lymphatic vessels, which are part of the cardiovascular system, connect to large veins in the chest. Lymph empties into these veins and once again becomes part of blood plasma.

Lymph Nodes As lymph flows through the lym-phatic system, it passes through small knobs of tissue called **lymph nodes.** Lymph nodes filter the lymph, trapping bacteria and other microorgan-isms that cause disease. When the body is fighting an infection, the lymph nodes enlarge. If you've ever had "swollen glands" when you've been sick, you've actually had swollen lymph nodes.

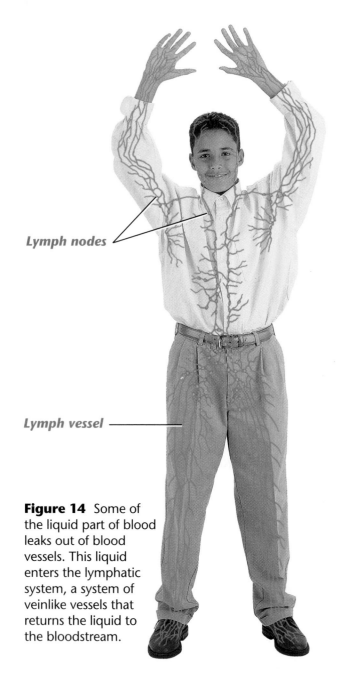

Lymph nodes

Lymph vessel

Figure 14 Some of the liquid part of blood leaks out of blood vessels. This liquid enters the lymphatic system, a system of veinlike vessels that returns the liquid to the bloodstream.

Section 3 Review

1. List the four components of blood. Identify whether each is a cell, a part of a cell, or a liquid.
2. Explain why a person with type O blood cannot receive a transfusion of type A blood.
3. Where does lymph come from? What happens to lymph after it travels through the lymphatic system?
4. **Thinking Critically Relating Cause and Effect** People with the disease hemophilia do not produce the chemical fibrin. Explain why hemophilia is a serious disease.

CHAPTER PROJECT

Check Your Progress
By now, you should be completing your display. Write out your description using the correct names of blood vessels and other terms that you've learned in this chapter. *(Hint:* If your display has moving parts, test it to make sure that it works the way you expect it to.)

Do You Know Your A-B-O's?

Donated blood is used for blood transfusions. But not every type of blood can be safely donated to every individual. In this lab, you'll investigate why type O blood is especially useful in blood transfusions.

Problem

Which blood types can safely receive transfusions of type A blood? Which can receive type O blood?

Materials

4 paper cups
4 plastic droppers
white paper
four model "blood" types

marking pen
8 plastic petri dishes
toothpicks

Procedure

1. Write down your ideas about why type O blood might be in higher demand than other blood types. Then make two copies of the data table in your notebook.

2. Label 4 paper cups A, B, AB, and O. Fill each cup about one-third full with the model "blood" supplied by your teacher. Insert one clean plastic dropper into each cup. Use each dropper to transfer only that one type of blood.

3. Label the side of each of 4 petri dishes with a blood type: A, B, AB, or O. Place the petri dishes on a sheet of white paper.

4. Use the plastic droppers to place 10 drops of each type of blood in its labeled petri dish. Each sample represents the blood of a potential receiver of a blood transfusion. Record the original color of each sample in your data table as yellow, blue, green, or colorless.

DATA TABLE

Donor: Type _____

Potential Receiver	Original Color	Final Color of Mixture	Safe or Unsafe?
A			
B			
AB			
O			

5. Label your first data table Donor: Type A. To test whether each potential receiver can safely receive type A blood, add 10 drops of type A blood to each sample. Stir each mixture with a separate, clean toothpick.

6. Record the final color of each mixture in the data table. If the color stayed the same, write "safe" in the last column. If the color of the mixture changed, write "unsafe."

7. Label your second data table Donor: Type O. Obtain four clean petri dishes, and repeat Steps 3 through 6 to determine who could safely receive type O blood.

Analyze and Conclude

1. Which blood types can safely receive a transfusion of type A blood? Type O blood?

2. If some blood types are not available, how might type O blood be useful?

3. **Apply** Why should hospitals have an adequate supply of different types of blood?

More to Explore

Repeat this activity to find out which blood types can safely receive donations of type B and type AB blood.

DISCOVER • **ACTIVITY** • •

Which Foods Are "Heart Healthy"?

1. Your teacher will give you an assortment of foods. If they have nutrition labels, read the information.

2. Sort the foods into three groups. In one group, put those foods that you think are good for your cardiovascular system. In the second group, put foods that you think might damage your cardiovascular system if eaten often. Place foods you aren't sure about in the third group.

Think It Over
Forming Operational Definitions How did you define a "heart-healthy" food?

GUIDE FOR READING

◆ What behaviors can help maintain cardiovascular health?

Reading Tip Before you read, rewrite the headings in the section as questions that begin with *how, why,* or *what.* Write short answers to these questions as you read.

Shortly after sunrise, when most people are just waking up, the rowers are already out on the river. Rhythmically, with perfectly coordinated movement, the rowers pull on the oars, making the boat glide swiftly through the water. Despite the chilly morning air, sweat glistens on the rowers' faces and arms. And inside their chests, their hearts are pounding, delivering blood to the arm and chest muscles that power the oars.

Rowers cannot perform at their peaks unless their cardiovascular systems are in excellent condition. But cardiovascular health is important to all people, not just athletes. Cardiovascular

disease is the leading cause of death in the United States. However, people can practice behaviors that decrease their risks of developing cardiovascular problems.

Cardiovascular Disease

Compare the two arteries shown in Figure 15. The one on the left is a healthy artery. It has a large space in the center through which blood can flow easily. The artery on the right, in contrast, has a thick wall and only a small space in the middle. This artery exhibits **atherosclerosis** (ath uh roh skluh ROH sis), a condition in which an artery wall thickens as a result of the buildup of fatty materials. One of these fatty materials is **cholesterol** (kuh LES tuh rahl), a waxy, fatlike substance. Atherosclerosis restricts the flow of blood in the arteries.

Atherosclerosis can develop in the coronary arteries that supply the heart. When that happens, the heart muscle receives less blood and therefore less oxygen. This condition may lead to a heart attack. A **heart attack** occurs when blood flow to part of the heart muscle is blocked. Cells die in the part of the heart that does not receive blood. This permanently damages the heart.

Treatment for mild atherosclerosis usually includes a low-fat diet and a moderate exercise program. In addition, medications that lower the levels of cholesterol and fats in the blood may be prescribed. People with severe atherosclerosis may need to undergo surgery or other procedures to unclog blocked arteries.

☑ *Checkpoint* *Why is atherosclerosis especially serious when it affects the coronary arteries?*

Hypertension

High blood pressure, or **hypertension** (hy pur TEN shun), is a disorder in which a person's blood pressure is consistently higher than normal—greater than 140/90. Hypertension makes the heart work harder. It also may damage the walls of the blood

Blocking the Flow

Use this activity to find out how **ACTIVITY** fatty deposits affect the flow of blood through an artery.

1. Put a funnel in the mouth of a plastic jar. The funnel will represent an artery.

2. To model blood flowing through the artery, slowly pour 100 mL of water into the funnel. Have your partner time how many seconds it takes for all the water to flow through the funnel. Then discard the water.

3. Use a plastic knife to spread a small amount of peanut butter along the bottom of the funnel's neck. Then, with a toothpick, carve out a hole in the peanut butter so that the funnel is partly, but not completely, clogged.

4. Repeat Steps 1 and 2.

Predicting If the funnels were arteries, which one—blocked or unblocked—would do a better job of supplying blood to tissues? Explain.

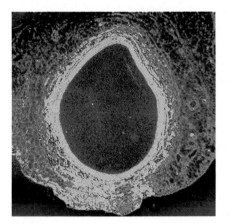
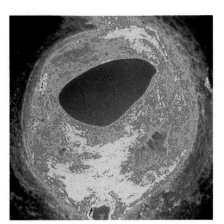

Figure 15 The healthy artery on the left is unblocked. In contrast, notice the narrow opening in the artery on the right. This person has atherosclerosis, which is caused by fatty deposits on the artery walls. *Relating Cause and Effect* *What kind of diet can lead to atherosclerosis?*

vessels. Over time, both the heart and arteries can be severely harmed by hypertension. Because people with hypertension often have no obvious symptoms to warn them, hypertension is sometimes called the "silent killer."

Hypertension and atherosclerosis are closely related. As the arteries narrow, blood pressure increases. Being overweight and failing to get enough exercise can also increase a person's risk of developing hypertension.

SCIENCE & History

Cardiovascular Advances in the Twentieth Century

Scientists today have an in-depth understanding of how the cardiovascular system works and how to treat cardiovascular problems. This time line describes some advances of the twentieth century.

1944
Treatment for "Blue Babies"

Helen Taussig identified the heart defect that causes the skin of some newborn babies to be bluish in color. The blood of these "blue babies" does not receive an adequate amount of oxygen. Taussig and another surgeon, Alfred Blalock, developed an operation to correct the defect and save these babies' lives.

1900	1920	1940

1901
Discovery of Blood Types

Karl Landsteiner demonstrated that people have different blood types, which are determined by marker molecules on their red blood cells. Landsteiner's discovery enabled blood transfusions to be done safely.

1930s–1940s
Blood Banks

Charles Drew demonstrated that emergency transfusions could successfully be done with plasma if whole blood was not available. During World War II, Drew established blood banks for storing donated blood. His work helped save millions of lives on and off the battlefield.

For mild hypertension, regular exercise and careful food choices may be enough to lower blood pressure. People with hypertension need to limit their intake of sodium, which can increase their blood pressure. Sodium is found in salt and in processed foods such as soups and packaged snack foods. For some people who have hypertension, however, medications are needed to reduce their blood pressure.

☑ *Checkpoint* **Why is hypertension called the "silent killer"?**

In Your Journal

Choose one of the scientists whose work is described here. Imagine that you are on a committee that has chosen him or her to receive an award. Write the speech you would give at the award ceremony. The speech should explain the importance of the scientist's contributions.

1967

First Heart Transplant

Christiaan Barnard, a South African surgeon, performed the first transplant of a human heart. Louis Washkansky, the man who received the heart, lived for only 18 days after the transplant. But Barnard's work paved the way for future successes in transplanting hearts and other organs.

1992

Laser Beam Unclogs Arteries

The United States government approved a device that uses a laser beam to burn away the material causing blockage in some arteries. This device can help some people with atherosclerosis.

1960	1980	2000

1982

Artificial Heart

An artificial heart, developed by Robert Jarvik, was implanted into a patient by surgeon William DeVries at the University of Utah. Barney Clark, the man who received the artificial heart, lived for 112 days. Today artificial hearts are sometimes used temporarily in people waiting for heart transplants.

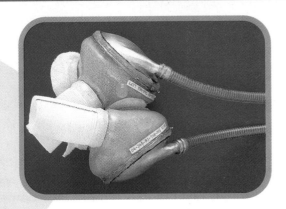

Keeping Your Cardiovascular System Healthy

Few young people have heart attacks, but atherosclerosis can begin to develop in people as young as 20 years old. You can establish habits now that will lessen your risk of developing atherosclerosis and hypertension. **To help maintain cardiovascular health, people should exercise regularly; eat a balanced diet that is low in fat, cholesterol, and sodium; and avoid smoking.**

Exercise Do you participate in sports, ride a bike, swim, dance, or climb stairs instead of taking the elevator? Every time you do one of those activities, you are helping to maintain your cardiovascular health. Exercise strengthens your heart muscle and also helps prevent atherosclerosis.

A Balanced Diet Foods that are high in cholesterol and fats can lead to a buildup of fatty deposits on artery walls. In addition, eating too many high-fat foods can lead to excessive weight gain. Foods such as red meats, eggs, and cheese are high in cholesterol. These foods also contain substances that your body needs. Therefore, a smart approach might be to eat them, but only in small quantities. Some foods that are especially high in fat include butter and margarine, potato chips, doughnuts, and fried foods such as French fries. Eat high-fat foods only occasionally, if at all.

Figure 16 Eating foods that are low in fat can help keep your cardiovascular system healthy.

Avoid Smoking Smokers are more than twice as likely to have a heart attack than are nonsmokers. Every year, almost 180,000 people in the United States die from cardiovascular disease caused by smoking. If smokers quit, however, their risk of death from cardiovascular disease decreases.

Section 4 Review

1. List three things you can do to help your cardiovascular system stay healthy.
2. What is atherosclerosis?
3. How does hypertension affect blood vessels?
4. **Thinking Critically Relating Cause and Effect** Coronary heart disease is much less common in some countries than it is in the United States. What factors might account for this difference?

Science at Home

With your family, discuss some things that you all can do to maintain healthy cardiovascular systems. Make a list of exercise activities, such as bicycling and swimming, that family members can enjoy together. You might also work with your family to cook and serve a "heart-healthy," low-fat meal.

SECTION 1 The Body's Transportation System

Key Ideas
- The cardiovascular system consists of the heart, blood vessels, and blood.
- The heart pumps blood through the blood vessels. The heart has four chambers. The two atria receive blood, and the two ventricles pump blood out of the heart.
- Blood travels from the heart to the lungs and back to the heart. It is then pumped to the body and returns again to the heart.
- A group of cells called the pacemaker regulates the rate at which the heart beats.

Key Terms
cardiovascular system   artery
heart   capillary
atrium   vein
ventricle   aorta
valve   force
pacemaker

SECTION 2 A Closer Look at Blood Vessels

Key Ideas
- Arteries carry blood from the heart to capillaries. In the capillaries, materials are exchanged between the blood and the body's cells. From the capillaries, blood flows into veins that carry it back to the heart.
- Blood pressure is caused by the force with which the ventricles contract. Blood pressure is highest in arteries.

Key Terms
coronary artery   blood pressure
diffusion   sphygmomanometer
pressure

SECTION 3 Blood and Lymph

Key Ideas
- Plasma, the liquid part of blood, transports materials such as glucose, vitamins, and waste products.
- Red blood cells, which contain hemoglobin, carry oxygen and deliver it to body cells. White blood cells fight disease. Platelets are important in forming blood clots.
- There are four blood types—A, B, AB, and O. A person's blood type determines the types of blood he or she can receive in transfusions.
- Some fluid escapes from blood vessels. The lymphatic system transports this fluid, called lymph, and empties it back into the blood.

Key Terms
plasma   fibrin
red blood cell   blood transfusion
hemoglobin   lymphatic system
white blood cell   lymph
platelet   lymph node

SECTION 4 Cardiovascular Health

INTEGRATING HEALTH

Key Ideas
- Atherosclerosis is a condition in which an artery wall thickens due to the buildup of cholesterol and other fatty materials.
- Hypertension is a disorder in which the blood pressure is higher than normal.
- To help prevent atherosclerosis and hypertension, people need to exercise regularly; eat a diet low in fat, cholesterol, and salt; and avoid smoking.

Key Terms
atherosclerosis   heart attack
cholesterol   hypertension

USING THE INTERNET

ACTIVITY

www.science-explorer.phschool.com

C H A P T E R

19

A S S E S S M E N T

California Test Prep: Reviewing Content

Multiple Choice

Choose the letter of the best answer.

1. The heart's upper chambers are called
   a. ventricles.
   b. atria.
   c. valves.
   d. hemoglobins.

2. Oxygen-rich blood enters the heart through the
   a. left atrium.
   b. right atrium.
   c. left ventricle.
   d. right ventricle.

3. Which of the following is *not* important in moving blood through veins?
   a. the force with which the atria contract
   b. valves
   c. breathing movements of the chest
   d. the contraction of skeletal muscles

4. Platelets help the body to
   a. control bleeding.
   b. carry oxygen.
   c. fight infection.
   d. regulate the amount of water in plasma.

5. Cholesterol is a fatlike substance associated with
   a. lymph nodes.
   b. fibrin.
   c. atherosclerosis.
   d. salt.

True or False

If the statement is true, write true. If it is false, change the underlined word or words to make the statement true.

6. The two lower heart chambers are called <u>ventricles</u>.
7. <u>White blood cells</u> contain hemoglobin.
8. The <u>capillaries</u> are the narrowest blood vessels in the body.
9. A person with blood type B can receive a transfusion of blood types B and <u>AB</u>.
10. Elevated blood pressure is called <u>hypertension</u>.

Checking Concepts

11. A red blood cell is moving through an artery in your leg. Describe the path that blood cell will follow back to your heart. Identify the chamber of the heart to which it will return.
12. Contrast the forces with which the right and left ventricles contract. How does this relate to each ventricle's function?
13. How is a capillary's structure adapted to its function?
14. What is the function of hemoglobin?
15. Give two reasons why the food choices that people make are important to their cardiovascular health.
16. **Writing to Learn** Write an ad that encourages teenagers to exercise. Your ad will appear in a teen magazine. The ad should point out the health benefits of exercise and identify some ways that teenagers can exercise.

Thinking Visually

17. **Compare/Contrast Table** Compare the three types of blood vessels by copying and completing the table below. (For more on compare/contrast tables, see the Skills Handbook.)

Blood Vessel	Function	Structure of Wall
Artery	a. ?	3 layers: inner–epithelial tissue middle–muscle outer–connective tissue
b. ?	exchange of materials between cells and blood	c. ?
Vein	d. ?	e. ?

Test Prep: Skills

The graph below shows how average blood pressure, measured when the ventricles contract, changes as men and women grow older. Use the graph to answer Questions 18–20.

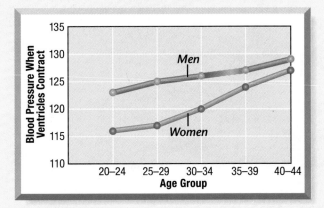

18. Interpreting Data At age 20, who is likely to have the higher blood pressure—a man or a woman?

19. Drawing Conclusions In general, what happens to people's blood pressure as they age?

20. Predicting Do you think that there is some age at which both men and women have about the same blood pressure? Use the graph lines to explain your prediction.

Thinking Critically

21. Predicting Some babies are born with an opening between the left and right ventricles. How would this heart defect affect the ability of the cardiovascular system to deliver oxygen to body cells?

22. Comparing and Contrasting Contrast the direction of movement of oxygen in lung capillaries and other capillaries in the body.

23. Relating Cause and Effect People who do not have enough iron in their diets sometimes develop a condition in which their blood cannot carry a normal amount of oxygen. Explain why this is so.

24. Making Generalizations Why are atherosclerosis and hypertension sometimes called "lifestyle diseases"?

Performance Assessment

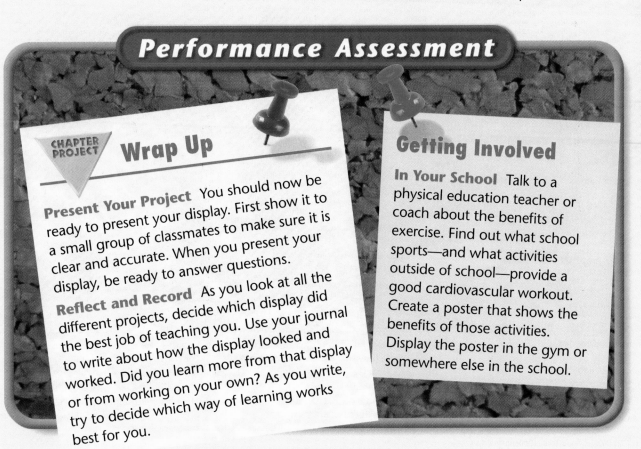

CHAPTER PROJECT **Wrap Up**

Present Your Project You should now be ready to present your display. First show it to a small group of classmates to make sure it is clear and accurate. When you present your display, be ready to answer questions.

Reflect and Record As you look at all the different projects, decide which display did the best job of teaching you. Use your journal to write about how the display looked and worked. Did you learn more from that display or from working on your own? As you write, try to decide which way of learning works best for you.

Getting Involved

In Your School Talk to a physical education teacher or coach about the benefits of exercise. Find out what school sports—and what activities outside of school—provide a good cardiovascular workout. Create a poster that shows the benefits of those activities. Display the poster in the gym or somewhere else in the school.

The following California Science Content Standards are addressed in this chapter:

1. All living organisms are composed of cells, from just one to many trillions, whose details usually are visible only through a microscope.

   a. Cells function similarly in all living organisms.

   d. Mitochondria liberate energy for the work that cells do, and chloroplasts capture sunlight energy for photosynthesis.

5. The anatomy and physiology of plants and animals illustrate the complementary nature of structure and function.

   a. Plants and animals have levels of organization for structure and function, including cells, tissues, organs, organ systems, and the whole organism.

   b. Organ systems function because of the contributions of individual organs, tissues, and cells. The failure of any part can affect the entire system.

   c. How bones and muscles work together to provide a structural framework for movement.

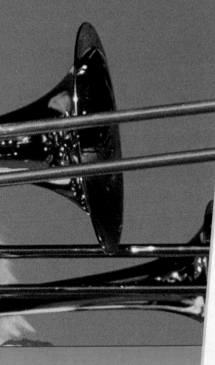

Trombone players in a marching band need strong, healthy lungs.

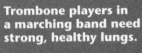

PROJECT 20

Get the Message Out

Lively music fills the air as the band marches along the parade route. To play many musical instruments, you need powerful, healthy lungs, which are part of the respiratory system. In this chapter, you will learn about the respiratory and excretory systems.

One way that people can keep their respiratory systems healthy is by choosing not to smoke. You've probably seen antismoking advertisements on television and in magazines. Imagine that you're part of a team of writers and designers who create advertisements. You've just been given the job of creating antismoking ads for different age groups. As you learn about the respiratory system, you can use your knowledge in your ad campaign.

Your Goal To create three different antismoking ads: one telling young children about the dangers of smoking; the second one discouraging teenagers from trying cigarettes; and the third encouraging adult smokers to quit.

To complete the project successfully, each ad must
- accurately communicate at least three health risks associated with smoking
- address at least two pressures that influence people to start or continue smoking
- use images and words in convincing, creative ways that gear your message to each audience

Get Started Brainstorm a list of reasons why people smoke. Consider the possible influence of family and friends as well as that of ads, movies, videos, and television. Also decide which types of ads you will produce, such as magazine ads or billboards. Begin to plan your ads.

Check Your Progress You'll be working on this project as you study this chapter. To keep your project on track, look for Check Your Progress boxes at the following points.
Section 2 Review, page 638: Plan your ads.
Section 3 Review, page 644: Design and produce your ads.

Wrap Up At the end of the chapter (page 647), you will display your completed ads. Be prepared to discuss your reasons for choosing the images and persuasive messages that you used.

7. Scientific progress is made by asking meaningful questions and conducting careful investigations.

　b. Utilize a variety of print and electronic resources (including the World Wide Web) to collect information as evidence as part of a research project.

DISCOVER • ACTIVITY

How Big Can You Blow Up a Balloon?

1. Take a normal breath, then blow as much air as possible into a balloon. Twist the end and hold it closed. Have your partner measure around the balloon at its widest point.

2. Let the air out of the balloon. Repeat Step 1 and calculate the average of the two measurements.

3. Compare your results with those of your classmates. The bigger the circumference, the greater the volume of air exhaled.

Think It Over
Inferring What factors might affect the volume of air a person can exhale?

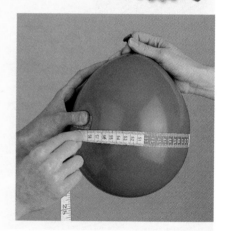

GUIDE FOR READING

◆ What are the functions of the respiratory system?

◆ What structures does air pass through as it travels to the lungs?

◆ How do oxygen, carbon dioxide, and water move in the lungs?

Reading Tip Before you read, preview *Exploring the Respiratory System* on page 627. Write down any unfamiliar terms.

Jerry, the main character in Doris Lessing's story "Through the Tunnel," is on vacation at the seaside. Day after day, he watches some older boys dive into deep water on one side of a huge rock. The boys mysteriously reappear on the other side. Jerry figures out that there must be an underwater tunnel in the rock. He finds the tunnel beneath the water and decides to swim through it. Once inside, though, he is terrified. The walls are slimy, and rocks scrape his body. He can barely see where he is going. But worst of all, Jerry has to hold his breath for far longer than ever before. The author describes Jerry this way: "His head was swelling, his lungs were cracking."

Jerry's behavior could have killed him. No one can go for very long without breathing. Your body cells need oxygen, and they get that oxygen from the air you breathe. **The respiratory system moves oxygen from the outside environment into the body. It also removes carbon dioxide and water from the body.**

Why the Body Needs Oxygen

The energy-releasing chemical reactions that take place inside your cells require oxygen. As a result of these reactions, your cells are able to perform all the tasks that keep you alive. Like a fire, which cannot burn without oxygen, your cells cannot "burn" enough substances to keep you alive without oxygen.

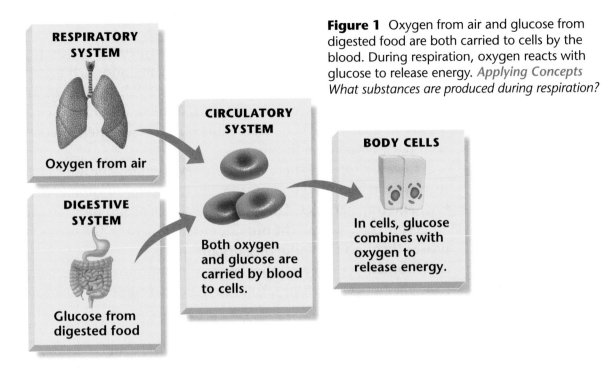

Figure 1 Oxygen from air and glucose from digested food are both carried to cells by the blood. During respiration, oxygen reacts with glucose to release energy. *Applying Concepts* *What substances are produced during respiration?*

RESPIRATORY SYSTEM

Oxygen from air

DIGESTIVE SYSTEM

Glucose from digested food

CIRCULATORY SYSTEM

Both oxygen and glucose are carried by blood to cells.

BODY CELLS

In cells, glucose combines with oxygen to release energy.

Respiration is the process in which oxygen and glucose undergo a complex series of chemical reactions inside cells. These chemical reactions release the energy that fuels growth and other cell processes. Besides releasing energy, respiration produces carbon dioxide and water. Your body eliminates the carbon dioxide and some of the water through your lungs. To a scientist, *breathing* and *respiration* mean different things. Respiration, which is also called cellular respiration, refers to the chemical reactions inside cells. Breathing refers to the movement of air into and out of the lungs.

Your respiratory system gets oxygen into your lungs. However, respiration could not take place without your circulatory and digestive systems. The digestive system absorbs glucose from food. The circulatory system carries both oxygen from your lungs and glucose from food to your cells.

☑ *Checkpoint* *Why does your body need oxygen?*

The Air You Breathe

INTEGRATING EARTH SCIENCE The oxygen your body needs comes from the atmosphere, which is the blanket of gases that surrounds Earth. The atmosphere is made up of a mixture of gases. Only about 21 percent of air is oxygen. Nitrogen makes up about 78 percent, and the remaining 1 percent includes carbon dioxide, helium, and other gases. Your body doesn't use most of the air that you breathe into your lungs. When you exhale, most of the air goes back into the atmosphere.

The Path of Air

If you look toward a window on a bright day, you may see tiny particles dancing in the air. These particles include such things as floating grains of dust, plant pollen, and ash from fires. In addition, air contains microorganisms, some of which can cause disease in humans. When you breathe in, all these materials enter your body along with the air.

However, most of these materials never enter your lungs. On its way to the lungs, air passes through a series of organs that filter and trap particles. These organs also warm and moisten the air. **As air travels from the outside environment to the lungs, it passes through the following organs: nose, pharynx, trachea, and bronchi.** It takes air only a few seconds to complete the route from the nose to the lungs. You can trace that route in *Exploring the Respiratory System.*

The Nose Your nose has two openings, or nostrils, which are separated by a thin wall. Air enters the body through the nostrils and then moves into the nose cavities, or nasal cavities. The lining of the nasal cavities contains many blood vessels. Warm blood flowing through these vessels heats the air. Some of the cells lining the cavities produce mucus. This sticky material moistens the air and keeps the delicate tissue from drying out. Mucus also traps particles, such as dust and bacteria. The cells that line the nasal cavities have **cilia** (SIL ee uh), tiny hairlike extensions that can move together like whips. The whiplike motion of these cilia sweeps the mucus into the throat, where you swallow it. In the stomach, the mucus, along with the particles and bacteria trapped in it, is destroyed by stomach acid.

Some particles and bacteria never make it to your stomach. They irritate the lining of your nose or throat, and you sneeze. The powerful force of a sneeze shoots the particles and bacteria out of your nose and into the air.

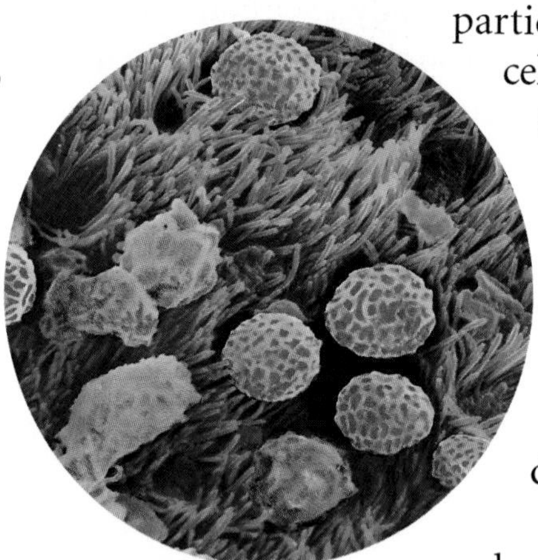

Figure 2 The cilia that line the nasal passages help remove trapped particles. The brown particles in the photograph are dust; the orange particles are pollen grains. When a person sneezes, many of the trapped particles are shot out into the air.

The Pharynx After flowing through the nasal cavities, air enters the **pharynx** (FAR ingks), or throat. The pharynx is the only part of the respiratory system that is shared with another system—the digestive system. If you look at *Exploring the Respiratory System,* you can see that both the nose and the mouth connect to the pharynx.

☑ *Checkpoint* *To what two body systems does the pharynx belong?*

The Trachea From the pharynx, air moves into the **trachea** (TRAY kee uh), or windpipe. You can feel your trachea if you gently run your fingers down the center of your neck. The trachea feels like a tube with a series of ridges. The firm ridges are rings of cartilage that strengthen the trachea and keep it open.

The trachea, like the nose, is lined with cilia and mucus. The cilia in the trachea sweep upward, moving mucus toward the pharynx, where it is swallowed. The trachea's cilia and mucus

EXPLORING *the Respiratory System*

On its path from outside the body into the lungs, air passes through several structures that clean, warm, and moisten it. Once in the lungs, the oxygen in the air can enter your bloodstream.

Pharynx Air moves from the nose downward into the throat, or pharynx. Part of the pharynx is also a passageway for food.

Nose Air enters the body through two nostrils. The lining of the nose is coated with cilia and mucus, which trap particles and warm and moisten the air.

Epiglottis

Larynx

Trachea The trachea leads from the pharynx toward the lungs. The walls of the trachea are made up of rings of cartilage which protect the trachea and keep it from collapsing.

Bronchi Air moves from the trachea into the right and left bronchi. One bronchus leads to each lung. Part of each bronchus is outside the lung and part is inside.

Lungs After it reaches the lungs, air moves through smaller and smaller bronchi until it reaches the alveoli. In the alveoli, oxygen passes into the blood and carbon dioxide passes out of the blood.

continue the cleaning and moistening of air that began in the nose. If particles irritate the lining of the trachea, you cough. A cough, like a sneeze, sends harmful materials flying out of your body and into the air.

Normally, only air—not food—enters the trachea. If food does enter the trachea, the food can block the opening and prevent air from getting to the lungs. When that happens, a person chokes. Fortunately, food rarely gets into the trachea. Remember from Chapter 18 that the epiglottis is a small flap of tissue that folds over the trachea. The epiglottis seals the trachea off while you swallow.

The Bronchi and Lungs Air moves from the trachea to the **bronchi** (BRAHNG ky)(singular *bronchus*), the passages that direct air into the lungs. The **lungs** are the main organs of the respiratory system. The left bronchus leads into the left lung, and the right bronchus leads into the right lung. Inside the lungs, each bronchus divides into smaller and smaller tubes in a pattern that resembles the branches of a tree.

At the end of the smallest tubes are small structures that look like bunches of grapes. The "grapes" are **alveoli** (al VEE uh ly) (singular *alveolus*), tiny sacs of lung tissue specialized for the movement of gases between air and blood. Notice in Figure 3 that each alveolus is surrounded by a network of capillaries. It is here that the blood picks up its cargo of oxygen from the air.

✓ *Checkpoint* *Describe the structure of the bronchi.*

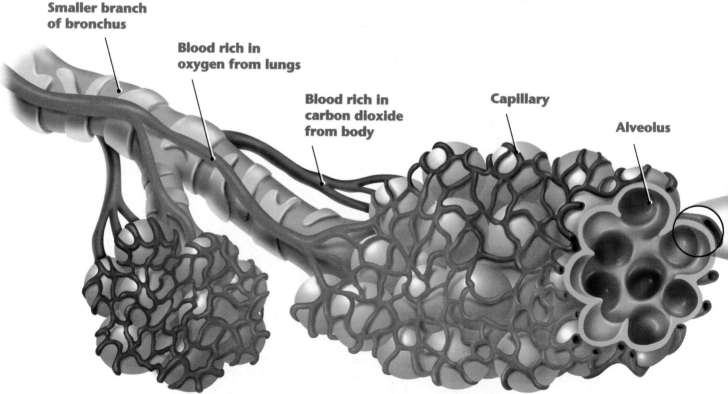

Smaller branch
of bronchus

Blood rich in
oxygen from lungs

Blood rich in
carbon dioxide
from body

Capillary

Alveolus

Gas Exchange

Because the walls of both the alveoli and the capillaries are very thin, materials can pass through them easily. **After air enters an alveolus, oxygen passes through the wall of the alveolus and then through the capillary wall into the blood. Carbon dioxide and water pass from the blood into the alveoli.** This whole process is known as gas exchange.

How Gas Exchange Occurs Imagine that you are a drop of blood beginning your journey through a capillary that wraps around an alveolus. When you begin that journey, you are carrying a lot of carbon dioxide and little oxygen. As you move through the capillary, oxygen gradually attaches to the hemoglobin in your red blood cells. At the same time, you are getting rid of carbon dioxide. At the end of your journey around the alveolus, you are rich in oxygen and poor in carbon dioxide.

A Large Surface Area Your lungs can absorb a large amount of oxygen because of the large surface area of the alveoli. An adult's lungs contain about 300 million alveoli. If you removed the alveoli, opened them, and spread them out on a flat surface, you would have a surface area of about 70 square meters. That's about the area of three lanes in a bowling alley!

The huge surface area of the alveoli enables the lungs to absorb a large amount of oxygen. The lungs can therefore supply the oxygen that people need—even when they are performing strenuous activities. When you play a musical instrument or a fast-paced game of basketball, you have your alveoli to thank.

Your lungs are not the only organs that provide a large surface area in a relatively small space. Remember that the small intestine contains numerous, tiny villi that increase the surface available to absorb food molecules.

Do You Exhale Carbon Dioxide?

ACTIVITY

Learn whether carbon dioxide is present in exhaled air.

1. Put on your goggles. Label two test tubes A and B.

2. Fill each test tube with 10 mL of water and a few drops of bromthymol blue solution. Bromthymol blue solution turns green or yellow in the presence of carbon dioxide.

3. Using a straw, blow air into the liquid in test tube A for a few seconds. Blow gently—if you blow hard, the liquid will bubble out of the test tube. **CAUTION:** *Use the straw to exhale only. Do not suck the solution back through the straw.*

4. Compare the solutions in the test tubes. Wash your hands when you have finished.

Predicting Suppose you had exercised immediately before you blew into the straw. Predict how this would have affected the results.

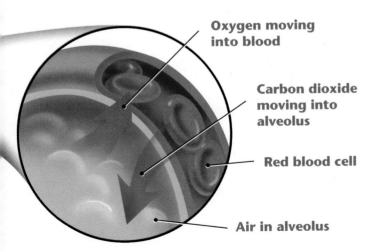

Oxygen moving into blood

Carbon dioxide moving into alveolus

Red blood cell

Air in alveolus

Figure 3 Alveoli are hollow air sacs surrounded by capillaries. As blood flows through the capillaries, oxygen moves from the alveoli into the blood. At the same time, carbon dioxide moves from the blood into the alveoli. *Interpreting Diagrams How is the structure of the alveoli important for gas exchange?*

How You Breathe

In an average day, you may breathe more than 20,000 times. The rate at which you breathe depends on your body's need for oxygen. When you exercise, your body needs a lot of oxygen to supply energy. The more oxygen you need, the faster you breathe.

Muscles for Breathing Pay attention to your breathing as you read this paragraph. Can you feel the air flowing in and out through your nose? Do you notice the gentle lift and fall of your chest?

Breathing, like other body movements, is controlled by muscles. Figure 5 shows the structure of the chest, including the muscles that enable you to breathe. Notice that the lungs are surrounded by the ribs, which have muscles attached to them. At the base of the lungs is the **diaphragm** (DY uh fram), a large, dome-shaped muscle that plays an important role in breathing.

The Process of Breathing Here is what happens when you

INTEGRATING PHYSICS

inhale, or breathe in. The rib muscles contract, lifting the chest wall upward and outward. At the same time, the diaphragm contracts and moves downward. The combined action of these muscles makes the chest cavity larger, providing extra space for the lungs to expand.

When the chest cavity has expanded, there is more room for air. For a brief moment, however, there is no extra air to fill the space. Because the same amount of air now occupies a larger

Figure 4 These people live high in the Andes Mountains in Ecuador. Despite the low oxygen levels, these people experience no symptoms of mountain sickness. Their respiratory systems have adjusted in order to get enough oxygen into their bodies.

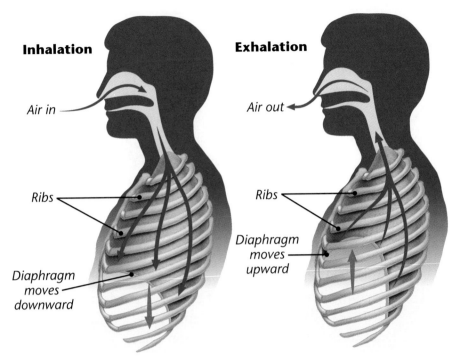

Inhalation

Air in

Ribs

Diaphragm moves downward

Exhalation

Air out

Ribs

Diaphragm moves upward

Figure 5 When you inhale, the diaphragm moves downward, allowing more room in the lungs for air. In contrast, when you exhale, the diaphragm moves upward. This upward movement increases the pressure in the lungs and pushes the air out.
Interpreting Diagrams How does the downward movement of the diaphragm affect the pressure of air inside the chest cavity?

space, the pressure of the air inside your lungs decreases. This means that the pressure of air inside the chest cavity is lower than the pressure of the atmosphere pushing on the body. Because of this difference in air pressure, air rushes into your chest, in the same way that air is sucked into a vacuum cleaner. You have inhaled.

In contrast, when you exhale, or breathe out, the rib muscles and diaphragm relax, and the chest cavity becomes smaller. This decrease in size squeezes air out of the lungs, the way squeezing a container of ketchup pushes ketchup out of the opening.

☑ *Checkpoint* *What muscles cause the chest to expand during breathing?*

How You Speak

The **larynx** (LAR ingks), or voice box, is located in the top part of the trachea, underneath the epiglottis. You can see the larynx if you look back at *Exploring the Respiratory System* on page 627. Place your fingers on your Adam's apple, which sticks out from the front of your neck. You can feel some of the cartilage that makes up the larynx. Two **vocal cords,** which are folds of connective tissue that produce your voice, stretch across the opening of the larynx.

How the Vocal Cords Work If you've ever let air out of a balloon while stretching its neck, you've heard the squeaking sound that the air makes. The neck of the balloon is something like your vocal cords. The vocal

INTEGRATING PHYSICS

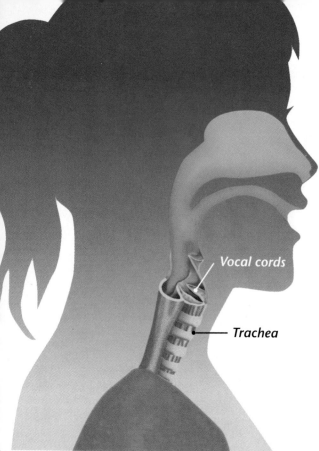

Figure 6 Air moving over this singer's vocal cords causes them to vibrate and produce sound. When her vocal cords contract, or shorten, she sings higher notes. When her vocal cords lengthen, she sings lower notes.

cords have a slitlike opening between them. When you speak, muscles make the vocal cords contract, narrowing the opening. Air from the lungs rushes through this opening. The movement of the vocal cords makes the air particles vibrate, or move rapidly back and forth. This vibration creates a sound—your voice.

High and Low Tones The length of the vocal cords affects whether you produce low or high tones. When the vocal cords contract and shorten, you speak in a higher voice. When they are longer and in a relaxed position, you speak in a lower voice.

The length of vocal cords changes during a person's lifetime. Small children have high-pitched voices because their larynxes are small and their vocal cords are short. The vocal cords of both boys and girls are about the same length. During the teenage years, however, the vocal cords of boys grow longer than those of girls. This is why men have deeper voices than women.

Section 1 Review

1. List the functions of the respiratory system.
2. Describe the path that a molecule of oxygen takes as it moves from the air into the alveoli.
3. Explain what happens to carbon dioxide in the blood that flows through capillaries in the alveoli.
4. Why does air rush into your body when you inhale?
5. **Thinking Critically Relating Cause and Effect** When there is a lot of dust in the air, people often cough and sneeze. Explain why this happens.

Science at Home

Use a shoe box and a set of blocks to show your family how the alveoli increase the surface area of the lungs. The shoe box represents a lung, and each block represents an alveolus. Fill the box with as many blocks as will fit inside. Then have your family imagine how much surface would be covered if all of the blocks were opened up and put together to form a large sheet. How would the surface area of the blocks compare with that of the shoe box?

A Breath of Fresh Air

How does air get into your lungs? In this lab, you will make a model of the lungs to demonstrate how breathing takes place.

Problem

What causes your body to inhale and exhale air?

Materials

small balloon   large balloon
scissors
transparent plastic bottle with narrow neck

Procedure

1. In your notebook, explain how you think air gets into the lungs during the breathing process.
2. Cut off and discard the bottom of a small plastic bottle. Trim the cut edge so there are no rough spots.
3. Stretch a small balloon, then blow it up a few times to stretch it further. Insert the round end of the balloon through the mouth of the bottle. Then, with a partner holding the bottle, stretch the neck of the balloon and pull it over the mouth of the bottle.
4. Stretch a large balloon, then blow it up a few times to stretch it further. Cut off the balloon's neck, and discard it.
5. Have a partner hold the bottle while you stretch the remaining part of the balloon over the bottom opening of the bottle, as shown in the photo.

6. Use one hand to hold the bottle firmly. With the knuckles of your other hand, push upward on the large balloon, causing it to form a dome. Remove your knuckles from the balloon, letting the balloon flatten. Repeat this procedure a few times. Observe what happens to the small balloon. Record your observations in your notebook.

Analyze and Conclude

1. Make a diagram of the completed model in your notebook. Add labels to show which parts of your model represent the chest cavity, diaphragm, lungs, and trachea.
2. In this model, what is the position of the diaphragm just after you have exhaled? What do the lungs look like just after you have exhaled?
3. In this model, how does the diaphragm move? How do these movements of the diaphragm affect the lungs?
4. **Think About It** How does this model show that pressure changes are responsible for breathing?

More to Explore

How could you improve on this model to more closely show what happens in the chest cavity during the process of breathing? Obtain your teacher's permission before making a new model.

SECTION 2 Smoking and Your Health

DISCOVER

What Are the Dangers of Smoking?

Pair up with a partner. Read each question below and decide on a reasonable answer based on your current knowledge.

1. In the United States, about how many people die each year from smoking-related illnesses?

2. What percentage of lung cancer deaths are related to smoking?

3. On the average, how much longer do nonsmokers live than smokers?

4. What percentage of smokers say they want to quit smoking?

5. What percentage of smokers actually succeed in quitting?

Think It Over

Inferring Why do you think people start smoking when they know that smoking can cause serious health problems?

GUIDE FOR READING

◆ What harmful chemicals are contained in tobacco smoke?

◆ How does tobacco smoke harm the respiratory and circulatory systems?

Reading Tip Before you read, make a list of smoking-related health problems that you already know about. Add to your list as you read.

Whoosh! Millions of tiny but dangerous aliens are invading the respiratory system. The aliens are pulled into the nose with an inhaled breath. The cilia in the nasal cavities trap some aliens, and others get stuck in mucus. But many aliens get past these defenses. After tumbling in air currents, thousands of the invaders enter the lungs. The aliens implant themselves in the alveoli!

The "aliens" are not tiny creatures from space. They are the substances found in cigarette smoke. In this section you will learn how tobacco smoke damages the respiratory system.

Chemicals in Tobacco Smoke

With each puff, a smoker inhales over 4,000 different chemicals. **Some of the most deadly chemicals in tobacco smoke are tar, carbon monoxide, and nicotine.**

Tar The dark, sticky substance that forms when tobacco burns is called **tar.** When someone inhales tobacco smoke, some tar settles on cilia that line the trachea and other respiratory organs. Tar makes cilia clump together so they can't function to prevent harmful materials from getting into the lungs. Tar also contains chemicals that have been shown to cause cancer.

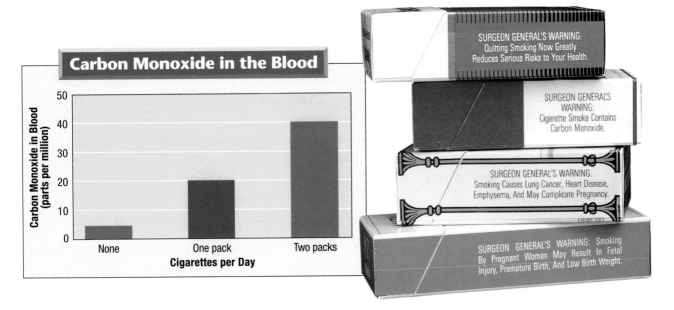

Carbon Monoxide in the Blood

Carbon Monoxide in Blood (parts per million)

| Cigarettes per Day | |
| None | One pack | Two packs |

Figure 7 The more cigarettes a person smokes, the more carbon monoxide he or she inhales. *Relating Cause and Effect How does carbon monoxide deprive the body of oxygen?*

Carbon Monoxide   When substances—including tobacco—are burned, a colorless, odorless gas called **carbon monoxide** is produced. Carbon monoxide is dangerous to inhale because its molecules bind to hemoglobin in red blood cells. When carbon monoxide binds to hemoglobin, it takes the place of some of the oxygen that the red blood cells normally carry. The carbon monoxide molecules are something like cars that have taken parking spaces reserved for other cars.

When carbon monoxide binds to hemoglobin, red blood cells carry less than their normal load of oxygen throughout the body. To make up for the decrease in oxygen, the breathing rate increases and the heart beats faster. Smokers' blood may contain too little oxygen to meet their bodies' needs.

Nicotine   Another dangerous chemical found in tobacco smoke is **nicotine.** Nicotine is a drug that speeds up the activities of the nervous system, heart, and other organs. It makes the heart beat faster and blood pressure rise. Nicotine produces an **addiction,** or physical dependence. Smokers feel an intense need, or craving, for a cigarette if they go without one. Addiction to nicotine is one reason why smokers have difficulty quitting.

✓ *Checkpoint*   *How does the tar in cigarette smoke affect the body?*

Respiratory System Problems

Tobacco smoke harms the respiratory system in several ways. For example, because their cilia can't sweep away mucus, many smokers have a frequent cough. The mucus buildup also limits the space for air flow, and this decreases oxygen intake. Because they are not getting enough oxygen, smokers may not be able to participate in vigorous sports. Long-term or heavy smokers may be short of breath during even light exercise.

Some serious respiratory problems can result from long-term smoking. **Over time, smokers can develop chronic bronchitis, emphysema, and lung cancer.** Every year in the United States, more than 400,000 people die from smoking-related illnesses. That's one out of every five deaths. Tobacco smoke is the most important preventable cause of major illness and death.

Chronic Bronchitis   Over time, mucus buildup can lead to long-term, or chronic, bronchitis. **Bronchitis** (brahng KY tis) is an irritation of the breathing passages in which the small passages become narrower than normal and may be clogged with mucus. People with bronchitis have a hard time breathing. If bronchitis lasts a long time, it can cause permanent damage to the breathing passages. Chronic bronchitis is often accompanied by infection with disease-causing microorganisms. Chronic bronchitis is five to ten times more common in heavy smokers than in nonsmokers.

Emphysema   The chemicals in tobacco smoke damage lung tissue as well as breathing passages. **Emphysema** (em fuh SEE muh) is a serious disease that destroys lung tissue and causes difficulty in breathing. People with emphysema do not get enough oxygen and cannot adequately eliminate carbon dioxide. Therefore, they are always short of breath. Some people with emphysema even have trouble blowing out a match. Unfortunately, the damage caused by emphysema is permanent, even if a person stops smoking.

Lung Cancer   About 140,000 Americans die each year from lung cancer caused by smoking. Cigarette smoke contains over 40 different chemicals that cause cancer, including chemicals in tar. Cancerous growths, or tumors, take away space in the lungs that should be used for gas exchange. Unfortunately, lung cancer is difficult to detect early, when treatment would be most effective.

☑ *Checkpoint*   *How does emphysema affect a person's lungs?*

Figure 8 These people stay healthy by exercising and by choosing not to smoke.

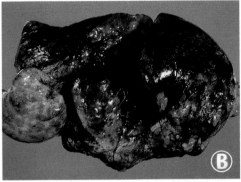

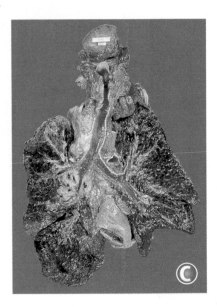

Figure 9 Over time, smoking damages the lungs and leads to serious health problems. Compare the lungs of a nonsmoker (A) to those of a person with emphysema (B) and a person with lung cancer (C).

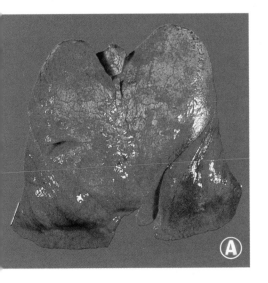

Circulatory System Problems

The chemicals in tobacco smoke that damage the lungs also harm the circulatory system. Some of the chemicals get into the blood and are absorbed by the blood vessels. The chemicals then irritate the walls of the blood vessels. This irritation contributes to the buildup of the fatty material that causes atherosclerosis. Atherosclerosis can lead to heart attacks. **Compared to nonsmokers, smokers are more than twice as likely to have heart attacks.**

Conditions that harm the lungs, such as bronchitis and emphysema, also strain the circulatory system. The respiratory and circulatory systems work together to get oxygen to the cells and to remove carbon dioxide from the body. If either system is damaged, the other one must work harder.

Passive Smoking

Smokers are not the only people to suffer from the effects of tobacco smoke. In **passive smoking,** people involuntarily inhale the smoke from other people's cigarettes, cigars, or pipes. Since this smoke contains the same harmful chemicals that smokers inhale, it can cause health problems. Each year, passive smoking causes about 300,000 young children in the United States to develop respiratory problems such as bronchitis. In addition, long-term exposure to cigarette smoke increases people's risks of heart disease and cancer.

Calculating

Heavy smokers may smoke two packs of cigarettes every day. Find out what one pack of cigarettes costs. Then use that price to calculate how much a person would spend on cigarettes if he or she smoked two packs a day for 30 years.

Figure 10 This antismoking advertisement was created by a teenager to encourage smokers to quit.

Choosing Not to Smoke

Today about 50 million Americans are smokers. Of those people, more than 90 percent began smoking when they were teenagers. Studies show that if people do not start smoking when they are teenagers, they probably will not start smoking later in life.

You may be tempted to try smoking. Friends may pressure you, or advertisements may appeal to you. Tobacco advertisements show smokers as young, attractive, popular people. The ads try to make you think that you will be like these people if you use tobacco products.

It is important to remember that it's very hard to quit smoking once you start. Many teenage smokers think that they will quit when they are older—but because nicotine is addictive, they have trouble doing so. And smoking hurts people right away, not just later in life. The lungs of teenagers who smoke develop more slowly than those of nonsmokers and may never reach the same peak level of functioning. In addition, teenage smokers may develop coughs and bronchitis. If someone asks you to try a cigarette, think of your health and politely refuse.

Section 2 Review

1. Name three harmful substances in tobacco smoke. Describe the effects of each substance.
2. Identify three respiratory problems caused by smoking.
3. Describe the effect of smoking on the circulatory system.
4. Identify two factors that may pressure teenagers to try smoking.
5. **Thinking Critically Relating Cause and Effect** Scientists estimate that about 3,000 nonsmoking Americans die every year from smoking-related lung cancer. Explain why.

Check Your Progress

CHAPTER PROJECT

By now you should have sketched what your ads might look like and written what they might say. In planning your ads, be sure to consider all the effects of smoking, not just those related to health—for example, the expense of smoking. Plan to use ideas and images that are appropriate for each age group. (*Hint:* Look through a variety of magazines to find ads aimed at different age groups. Which techniques seem to work best? How can you use those techniques in your ads?)

SECTION 3 The Excretory System

DISCOVER ··········· ACTIVITY

How Does Filtering a Liquid Change What Is in It?

1. Your teacher will give you 50 milliliters of a liquid in a small container. Pour a small amount of sand into the liquid.

2. Use a glucose-test strip to determine whether glucose is present in the liquid.

3. Put filter paper in a funnel. Then put the funnel into the mouth of a second container. Slowly pour the liquid through the funnel into the second container.

4. Look for any solid material on the filter paper. Remove the funnel and carefully examine the liquid that passed through the filter.

5. Test the liquid again to see whether it contains glucose.

Think It Over

Observing Which substances passed through the filter, and which did not? How might a filtering device be useful in the body?

The human body faces a challenge that is a bit like trying to keep a home clean. You learned in Chapter 18 that the body takes in foods through the digestive system and breaks them down into nutrients. As cells use those nutrients in respiration and other processes, wastes are created. **The excretory system is the system in the body that collects wastes produced by cells and removes the wastes from the body.** The removal process is known as **excretion.**

If wastes were not taken away, they would pile up and make you sick. Excretion helps maintain homeostasis by keeping the body's internal environment stable and free of harmful materials.

GUIDE FOR READING

◆ What is the function of the excretory system?

◆ How is urine produced in the kidneys' nephrons?

◆ In addition to the kidneys, what other organs play a role in excretion?

Reading Tip As you read, write a brief summary of the information under each heading.

The Kidneys

As you already know, some wastes that your body must eliminate are carbon dioxide and excess water. Another waste product is urea. **Urea** (yoo REE uh) is a chemical that comes from the breakdown of proteins. Your two **kidneys,** which are the major organs of the excretory system, eliminate urea, excess water, and some other waste materials. These wastes are eliminated in **urine,** a watery fluid produced by your kidneys.

The kidneys act something like filters. As blood flows through the kidneys, they remove wastes from the blood. After the process is complete, urine flows from the kidneys through two narrow tubes called **ureters** (yoo REE turz). The ureters carry the urine to the **urinary bladder,** a sacklike muscular organ that stores urine. When the bladder is full enough that its walls are stretched, you feel a need to urinate. Urine flows from the body through a small tube called the **urethra** (yoo REE thruh), which you can see in *Exploring a Kidney.*

☑ *Checkpoint* *What is the role of the ureters?*

The Filtering Process

The kidneys are champion filters. Every drop of blood in your body passes through your kidneys and is filtered more than 300 times a day. Contrast this to a typical swimming-pool filter, which only cleans the pool water about 5 times a day.

Each of your kidneys contains about a million tiny filtering factories called **nephrons.** The nephrons are the tiny structures that remove wastes from blood and produce urine. **Urine formation takes place in a number of stages. First, both wastes and needed materials, such as glucose, are removed from the blood. Then, much of the needed material is returned to the blood.**

Filtering Out Wastes After entering the kidneys, blood flows through smaller and smaller arteries. Eventually it reaches a cluster of capillaries in a nephron. These capillaries are surrounded

EXPLORING a Kidney

Each kidney contains about a million tiny filtering units called nephrons. Urine is produced in the nephrons.

EXCRETORY SYSTEM

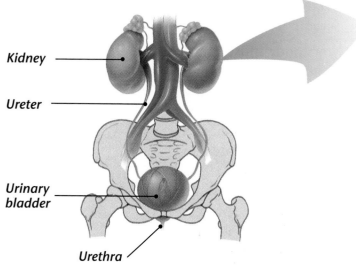

Kidney

Ureter

Urinary bladder

Urethra

KIDNEY

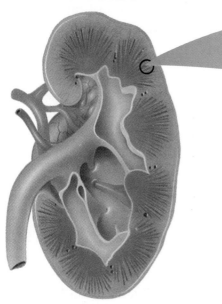

by a thin-walled, hollow capsule that is connected to a long tube. Find the capillary cluster, the capsule, and the tube in *Exploring a Kidney*. In the capillary cluster, urea, glucose, other chemicals, and some water move out of the blood and into the capsule. In contrast, blood cells and most protein molecules do not move into the capsule. Instead, they remain in the capillaries.

Formation of Urine Urine forms from the filtered material that passes into the capsule. This filtered material flows through the long, twisting tube. Some of the substances that collect in the capsule are needed by the body. As the liquid moves through the tube, many of these substances are reabsorbed, or returned to the blood. Normally all the glucose, most of the water, and small amounts of other materials pass back into the blood in the capillaries that surround the tube. In contrast, urea and other wastes remain in the tube.

The filtering process is something like cleaning your locker by throwing everything in your locker into a wastebasket, and then putting back the things that you want to keep. You can think of the locker as your blood and the wastebasket as the capsule. After the entire filtering and reabsorbing process is complete, the fluid that remains in the tube is urine.

NEPHRON

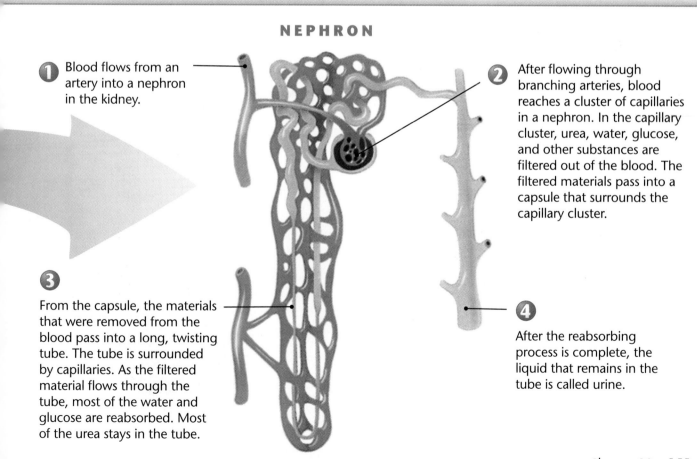

① Blood flows from an artery into a nephron in the kidney.

② After flowing through branching arteries, blood reaches a cluster of capillaries in a nephron. In the capillary cluster, urea, water, glucose, and other substances are filtered out of the blood. The filtered materials pass into a capsule that surrounds the capillary cluster.

③ From the capsule, the materials that were removed from the blood pass into a long, twisting tube. The tube is surrounded by capillaries. As the filtered material flows through the tube, most of the water and glucose are reabsorbed. Most of the urea stays in the tube.

④ After the reabsorbing process is complete, the liquid that remains in the tube is called urine.

Analyzing Urine for Signs of Disease When people go to a

doctor for a medical checkup, they usually have their urine analyzed. A chemical analysis of urine can be useful in detecting some medical problems. Normally, urine contains almost no glucose or protein. If glucose is present in urine, it may indicate that a person has diabetes, a condition in which body cells cannot absorb enough glucose from the blood. Protein in urine can be a sign that the kidneys are not functioning properly.

Real-World Lab

You Solve the Mystery

CLUES ABOUT HEALTH

In this lab, you'll become a medical detective as you carry out urine tests to uncover evidence of disease.

Problem

How can you test urine for the presence of glucose and protein?

Skills Focus

observing, interpreting data, drawing conclusions

Materials

test tubes, 6
plastic droppers, 6
glucose solution
marking pencil
glucose test strips
simulated urine samples, 3

test tube rack
water
protein solution
white paper towels
Biuret solution

Procedure

Part 1 Testing for Glucose

1. Label six test tubes as follows: "W" for water, "G" for glucose, "P" for protein, and "A," "B," and "C" for three patients' "urine samples."

2. Place the test tubes in a test tube rack. Label six glucose test strips with the same letters.
3. Copy the data table into your notebook.
4. Fill each test tube about 3/4 full with the solution that corresponds to its label.
5. Place the W glucose test strip on a clean, dry section of a paper towel. Then use a clean plastic dropper to place 2 drops of the water from test tube W on the test strip. Record the resulting color of the test strip in your data table. If no color change occurs, write "no reaction."

Water Balance in the Body

The kidneys also help maintain homeostasis by regulating the amount of water in your body. Remember that as urine is being formed, water passes from the tube back into the bloodstream. The exact amount of water that is reabsorbed depends on conditions both outside and within the body. Suppose that it's a hot day. You've been sweating a lot, and you haven't had much to drink. In that situation, almost all of the water in the tube will be reabsorbed, and you will excrete only a small amount of urine. If,

| | | | | DATA TABLE | | |
| | | | | Test Tube | | |
Test for	W (water)	G (glucose)	P (protein)	A (Patient A)	B (Patient B)	C (Patient C)
Glucose						
Protein						

6. Use the procedure in Step 5 to test each of the other five solutions with the correctly labeled glucose test strip. Record the color of each test strip in the data table.

Part 2 Testing for Protein

7. Obtain a dropper bottle containing Biuret solution. Record the original color of the solution in your notebook.

8. Carefully add 10 drops of Biuret solution to test tube W. **CAUTION:** *Biuret solution can harm skin and damage clothing. Handle it with care.* Gently swirl the test tube to mix the two solutions together. Hold the test tube against a white paper towel to help you detect any color change. Observe the color of the final mixture, and record that color in your data table.

9. Repeat Step 8 for each of the other test tubes.

Analyze and Conclude

1. Which of the three patients' urine samples tested normal? How do you know?
2. Which urine sample(s) indicated that diabetes might be present? How do you know?
3. Which urine sample(s) indicated that kidney disease might be present? How do you know?
4. When a person's health is normal, how are the kidneys involved in keeping glucose and protein out of urine?
5. Apply Do you think a doctor should draw conclusions about the presence of a disease based on a single urine sample? Explain.

More to Explore

Propose a way to determine whether a patient with glucose in the urine could reduce the level through changes in diet.

Figure 11 Your skin and lungs also function as excretory organs. Water and some chemical wastes are excreted in perspiration. And when you exhale on a cold morning, you can see the water in your breath. *Applying Concepts* *What other waste product does your exhaled breath contain?*

however, the day is cool and you've drunk a lot of water, less water will be reabsorbed. Your body will produce a larger volume of urine.

Every day, you need to take at least 2 liters of water into your body. You can do this either by drinking or by eating foods such as apples that contain a lot of water. This helps your kidneys maintain the proper water balance in your body.

Other Organs of Excretion

Most of the wastes produced by the body are removed through the kidneys, but not all. **The other organs of excretion are the lungs, skin, and liver.** You've already learned how the lungs and skin remove wastes. When you breathe out, carbon dioxide and some water are removed from the body. Sweat glands also function in excretion, because water and some chemical wastes are excreted in perspiration.

Have you ever torn apart a large pizza box so that it could fit in a wastebasket? If so, then you can understand that some wastes need to be broken down before they can be excreted. The liver performs this function. For example, urea, which comes from the breakdown of proteins, is produced by the liver. The liver also converts part of the hemoglobin molecule from old red blood cells into substances such as bile. Recall from Chapter 18 that bile helps break down fats during digestion. Because the liver produces a usable material from old red blood cells, you can think of the liver as a recycling factory.

Section 3 Review

1. What is the function of the excretory system?
2. Describe the two stages of urine formation.
3. What roles do the lungs, skin, and liver play in excretion?
4. How do the kidneys help regulate the amount of water in the body?
5. **Thinking Critically** **Predicting** On a long bus trip, Laura does not drink any water for several hours. How will the volume of urine she produces that day compare to the volume on a day when she drinks several glasses of water? Explain.

SECTION 1 The Respiratory System

Key Ideas

◆ The respiratory system moves oxygen into the body and removes carbon dioxide from the body.

◆ In the process of respiration in cells, glucose is broken down using oxygen to produce energy.

◆ As air travels from the outside environment to the lungs, it passes through the nose, pharynx, trachea, and bronchi. The air is warmed, moistened, and filtered.

◆ In the alveoli, oxygen moves from the air into the blood, while carbon dioxide and water pass from the blood into the air. This process is known as gas exchange.

◆ During inhalation, the diaphragm and rib muscles make the chest cavity expand. The air pressure inside the lungs decreases, and air rushes into the lungs. During exhalation, the chest cavity becomes smaller, pushing air out of the body.

◆ When air passes over the vocal cords, which are folds of tissue in the larynx, they vibrate to produce sound.

Key Terms

respiration	bronchi	diaphragm
cilia	lungs	larynx
pharynx	alveoli	vocal cords
trachea		

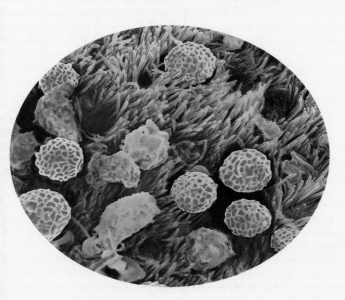

SECTION 2 Smoking and Your Health

INTEGRATING HEALTH

Key Ideas

◆ The most harmful substances in tobacco smoke are tar, carbon monoxide, and nicotine.

◆ When people inhale tobacco smoke, they increase their chances of developing respiratory diseases such as chronic bronchitis, emphysema, and lung cancer.

◆ Smokers are more likely to have heart attacks than are nonsmokers.

Key Terms

tar	bronchitis
carbon monoxide	emphysema
nicotine	passive smoking
addiction	

SECTION 3 The Excretory System

Key Ideas

◆ The excretory system removes carbon dioxide, urea, water, and other wastes from the body.

◆ The kidneys are the major organs of excretion. By filtering the blood, the kidneys produce urine.

◆ Urine travels from the kidneys through the ureters to the urinary bladder. Urine is eliminated through the urethra.

◆ In the kidney's nephrons, wastes and other materials are filtered from the blood. Some useful substances, such as glucose and water, are then reabsorbed into the blood.

◆ The lungs, skin, and liver are also organs of excretion.

Key Terms

excretion	ureters
urea	urinary bladder
kidney	urethra
urine	nephron

USING THE INTERNET ACTIVITY

www.science-explorer.phschool.com

California Test Prep: Reviewing Content

Multiple Choice

1. The process in which glucose and oxygen react in cells to release energy is called
   a. digestion.
   b. respiration.
   c. breathing.
   d. gas exchange.

2. The trachea divides into two tubes called
   a. bronchi.
   b. alveoli.
   c. windpipes.
   d. diaphragms.

3. Your voice is produced by the
   a. pharynx.
   b. larynx.
   c. trachea.
   d. alveoli.

4. The disease in which the respiratory passages become narrower than normal is called
   a. bronchitis.
   b. lung cancer.
   c. diabetes.
   d. emphysema.

5. Normal urine contains both
   a. water and carbon monoxide.
   b. water and large amounts of glucose.
   c. urea and proteins.
   d. urea and water.

True or False

If the statement is true, write true. If it is false, change the underlined word or words to make the statement true.

6. Dust particles trapped in mucus are swept away by tiny, hairlike <u>blood vessels</u>.

7. The clusters of air sacs in the lungs are called <u>alveoli</u>.

8. <u>Tar</u> is a chemical in tobacco smoke that makes the heart beat faster.

9. The <u>ureter</u> is the tube through which urine leaves the body.

10. The <u>lungs</u> are excretory organs.

Checking Concepts

11. Explain the difference between breathing and respiration.

12. Explain how the alveoli provide a large surface area for gas exchange.

13. Describe how the diaphragm and rib muscles control inhaling and exhaling.

14. Why do men have deeper voices than women?

15. Describe what happens when carbon monoxide enters the body. How does this affect the body?

16. Explain two ways in which the kidneys maintain homeostasis.

17. **Writing to Learn** Imagine that you are a molecule of oxygen. Write an adventure story that describes what happens to you between the time you are inhaled through someone's nose and the time you are used in respiration in a body cell.

Thinking Visually

18. **Flowchart** The kidneys eliminate wastes from the body in a series of steps. Copy the flowchart below and complete it by filling in the missing steps. (For more on flowcharts, see the Skills Handbook.)

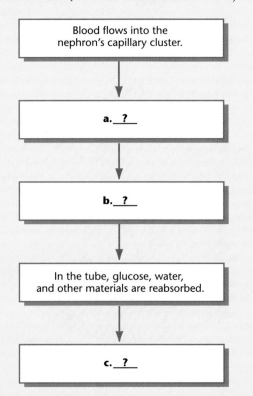

Blood flows into the nephron's capillary cluster.

↓

a. ___?___

↓

b. ___?___

↓

In the tube, glucose, water, and other materials are reabsorbed.

↓

c. ___?___

Test Prep: Skills

Use your knowledge of the respiratory system and the information in the data table to answer Questions 19–21.

Gases in Inhaled and Exhaled Air		
Gas	Inhaled Air	Exhaled Air
Nitrogen	78%	78%
Oxygen	21%	16%
Carbon dioxide	0.03%	4%

19. Interpreting Data Which gas makes up a higher percentage of exhaled air than inhaled air? How can you account for this difference?

20. Drawing Conclusions Based on the data, which gas is used by the body? How is this gas used?

21. Inferring Explain why the percentage of nitrogen is the same in both inhaled air and exhaled air.

Thinking Critically

22. Inferring If you exhale onto a mirror, the mirror will become clouded with a thin film of moisture. Explain why this happens.

23. Applying Concepts Explain how babies can develop smoking-related respiratory problems.

24. Predicting If the walls of the capillary cluster in a nephron were damaged or broken, what substance might you expect to find in urine that is not normally present? Explain.

25. Making Judgments Do you think that drugstores, which sell medicines, should also sell cigarettes and other tobacco products? Why or why not?

26. Comparing and Contrasting How is respiration similar to the burning of fuel? How is it different?

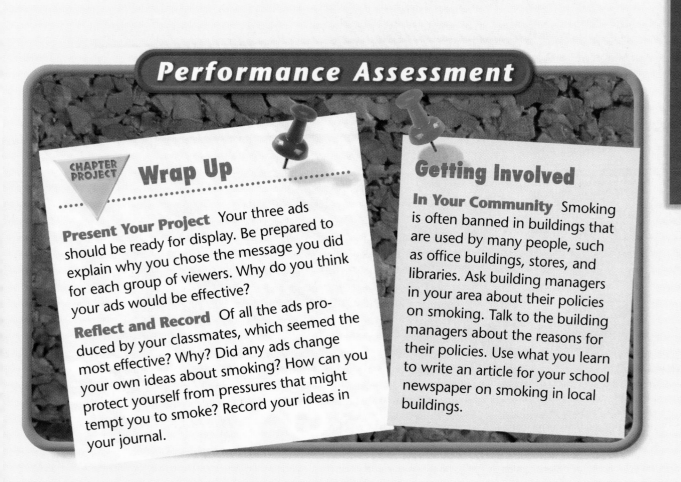

Performance Assessment

CHAPTER PROJECT Wrap Up

Present Your Project Your three ads should be ready for display. Be prepared to explain why you chose the message you did for each group of viewers. Why do you think your ads would be effective?

Reflect and Record Of all the ads produced by your classmates, which seemed the most effective? Why? Did any ads change your own ideas about smoking? How can you protect yourself from pressures that might tempt you to smoke? Record your ideas in your journal.

Getting Involved

In Your Community Smoking is often banned in buildings that are used by many people, such as office buildings, stores, and libraries. Ask building managers in your area about their policies on smoking. Talk to the building managers about the reasons for their policies. Use what you learn to write an article for your school newspaper on smoking in local buildings.

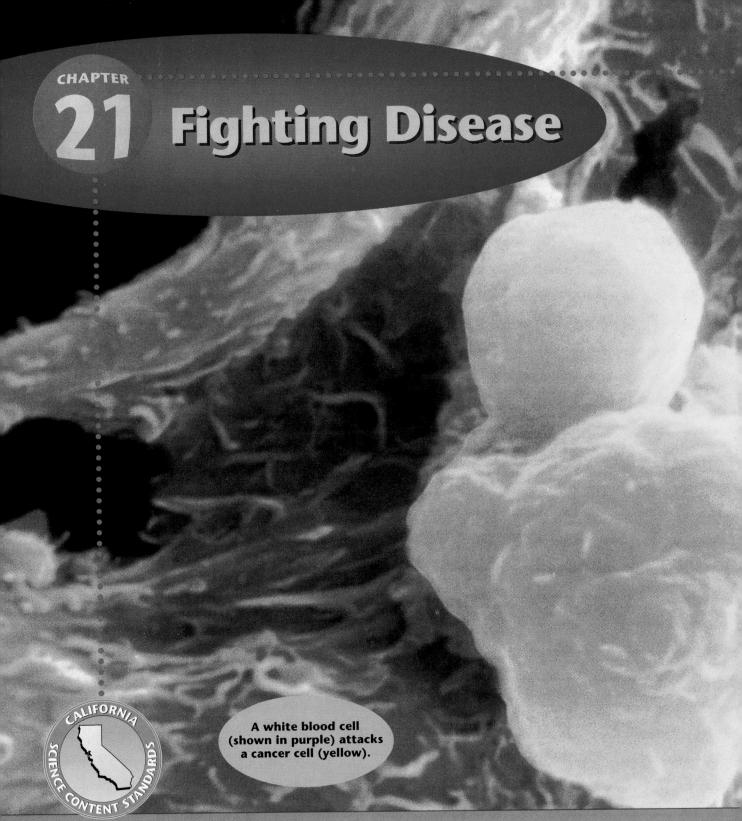

CHAPTER 21 Fighting Disease

A white blood cell (shown in purple) attacks a cancer cell (yellow).

CALIFORNIA SCIENCE CONTENT STANDARDS

The following California Science Content Standards are addressed in this chapter:

1. All living organisms are composed of cells, from just one to many trillions, whose details usually are visible only through a microscope.

   a. Cells function similarly in all living organisms.

   e. Cells divide to increase their numbers through a process of mitosis, which results in two daughter cells with identical sets of chromosomes.

5. The anatomy and physiology of plants and animals illustrate the complementary nature of structure and function.

   a. Plants and animals have levels of organization for structure and function, including cells, tissues, organs, organ systems, and the whole organism.

   b. Organ systems function because of the contributions of individual organs, tissues, and cells. The failure of any part can affect the entire system.

6. Physical principles underlie biological structures and functions.

   a. Visible light is a small band within a very broad electromagnetic spectrum.

Stop the Invasion!

When you catch a cold, your body is being attacked. The attackers are cold viruses. If they're not stopped, they'll multiply in great numbers and cause infection. Many other diseases are also caused in this way—by viruses or bacteria that invade your body. In this chapter, you'll learn how your body defends itself against such invasions. And you'll put that knowledge to use as you develop a series of informative news reports in this chapter project.

Your Goal To create a series of imaginary news broadcasts from "battlefield sites" where the body is fighting an infectious disease.

To complete the project successfully you must
- choose a specific disease and represent the sequence of events that occur when that disease strikes the body
- describe the stages of the disease as if they were battles between two armies
- present your story creatively in at least three reports using newspaper, radio, or television news-reporting techniques

Get Started With some classmates, list your ideas about delivering a good newspaper, radio, or television news report. Think about what techniques reporters use to make stories interesting or to explain complicated information. Also, recall the times you've had a cold, flu, or other infectious disease. Write down how your body responded, how long you were sick, and any other information.

Check Your Progress You'll be working on this project as you study this chapter. To keep your project on track, look for Check Your Progress boxes at the following points.

Section 1 Review, page 654: Select a specific disease to research. Learn how it affects the body and how the body responds.
Section 2 Review, page 661: Write scripts for your news reports.
Section 5 Review, page 678: Make any necessary revisions, and practice your presentation.

Wrap Up At the end of the chapter (page 681), you will "broadcast" your news reports for the rest of the class.

---

f. Light interacts with matter by transmission (including refraction), absorption, or scattering (including reflection).

7. Scientific progress is made by asking meaningful questions and conducting careful investigations.

a. Select and use appropriate tools and technology to perform tests, collect data, and display data.

b. Utilize a variety of print and electronic resources (including the World Wide Web) to collect information as evidence as part of a research project.

c. Communicate the logical connection among hypothesis, science concepts, tests conducted, data collected, and conclusions drawn from the scientific evidence.

d. Construct scale models, maps and appropriately labeled diagrams to communicate scientific knowledge.

1 Infectious Disease

DISCOVER ··· ACTIVITY

How Does a Disease Spread?

1. On a sheet of paper, write three headings: *Round 1, Round 2,* and *Round 3.*

2. Everyone in the class should shake hands with two people. Under *Round 1,* record the names of the people whose hand you shook.

3. Now shake hands with two different people. Record the name of each person whose hand you shook under *Round 2.*

4. Once again, shake hands with two additional people. Under *Round 3,* record the names of the people whose hand you shook.

Think It Over

Calculating Suppose you had a disease that was spread by shaking hands. Everyone whose hand you shook has caught the disease. So has anyone who later shook those people's hands. Calculate how many people you "infected."

GUIDE FOR READING

◆ What kinds of organisms cause disease?

◆ Where do pathogens come from?

Reading Tip As you read, use the headings in the section to make an outline. Write the important concepts under each heading.

Before the twentieth century, surgery was a very risky business. Even if people lived through an operation, they were not out of danger. After the operation, many patients' wounds became infected, and the patients often died. No one knew what caused these infections.

In the 1860s, a British surgeon named Joseph Lister hypothesized that microorganisms caused the infections. To protect his patients, Lister used carbolic acid, a chemical that kills microorganisms. Before performing an operation, Lister washed his hands and surgical instruments with carbolic acid. After the surgery, he covered the patient's wounds with bandages dipped in carbolic acid.

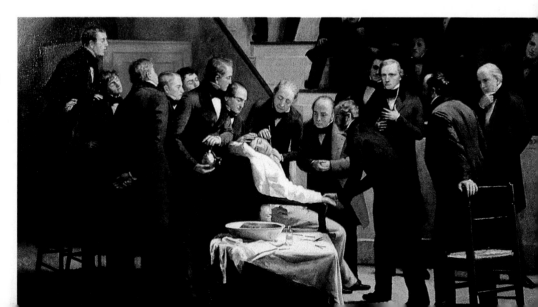

Figure 1 Doctors at Massachusetts General Hospital perform surgery on a patient in 1846. In the 1800s, surgery was performed under conditions that were very different from those used today.

Lister's results were dramatic. Before he used his new method, about 45 percent of his surgical patients died from infection. With Lister's new techniques, only 15 percent died.

Disease and Pathogens

Like the infections that Lister observed after surgery, many illnesses, such as ear infections and food poisoning, are caused by living things that are too small to see. Organisms that cause disease are called **pathogens.** Diseases caused by pathogens are infectious. An **infectious disease** is a disease that can pass from one organism to another.

When you have an infectious disease, pathogens have gotten inside your body and harmed it. Pathogens make you sick by damaging individual cells, even though you may feel pain in a whole organ or throughout your body. For example, when you have strep throat, pathogens have damaged cells in your throat.

✓ *Checkpoint* *What causes infectious disease?*

Understanding Infectious Disease

Until Lister's time, few people thought that living organisms could cause disease. Before that, people believed that things like evil spirits or swamp air made people sick.

Several scientists in the late 1800s contributed to the understanding of infectious diseases. Joseph Lister was influenced by the work of Louis Pasteur, a French scientist. In the 1860s, Pasteur showed that microorganisms cause certain kinds of diseases. In addition, Pasteur showed that killing the microorganisms could prevent the spread of those diseases. In the 1870s and 1880s, a German physician named Robert Koch demonstrated that each infectious disease is caused by a specific kind of pathogen. In other words, one kind of pathogen causes pneumonia, another kind causes chicken pox, and still another kind causes rabies.

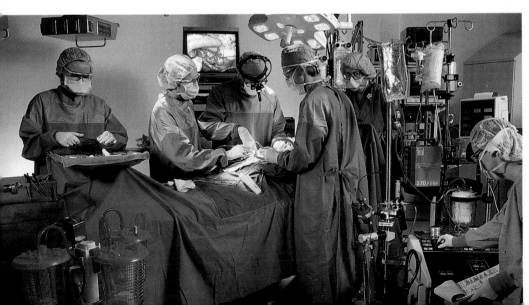

Figure 2 Surgery today is performed in operating rooms that have been cleaned thoroughly to eliminate disease-causing organisms.
Comparing and Contrasting Contrast Figures 1 and 2. How does surgery today differ from surgery in 1846?

Kinds of Pathogens

You share Earth with many kinds of organisms. Most are harmless, but some can make you sick. Some diseases are caused by many-celled animals, such as worms. However, most pathogens are too small to be seen without a microscope. **The four major groups of human pathogens are bacteria, viruses, fungi, and protists.** Look at Figure 3 to see examples of pathogens.

Bacteria Bacteria are one-celled microorganisms. They cause a wide variety of diseases, including ear infections, food poisoning, and tuberculosis, which is a disease of the lungs. Some bacterial pathogens damage body cells directly. Strep throat, for example, is caused by streptococcus bacteria that invade cells in your throat. Other bacterial pathogens do not enter cells, but instead produce a poison, or **toxin,** that damages cells. For example, when the bacteria that cause tetanus get into a wound, they can produce a toxin that damages the nervous system. Tetanus is also called lockjaw because the nerve damage can lock the muscles that control the jaws.

Viruses Viruses are tiny particles, much smaller than bacteria and other pathogens. Viruses cannot reproduce unless they are inside living cells. The cells are damaged or destroyed in the process, releasing new viruses to infect other cells. Both colds and influenza—or flu—are caused by viruses that invade cells in the respiratory system. In fact, there are over 200 different kinds of cold viruses, and each of them can give you a sore throat and a runny nose! Chicken pox and AIDS are also caused by viruses. You will learn more about AIDS later in the chapter.

Figure 3 Most infectious diseases are caused by microscopic organisms. **A.** Bacteria like this rod-shaped one cause tetanus, a disease that harms the nervous system. **B.** When you have a cough and a sore throat, this round virus, called an adenovirus may be to blame. **C.** This fungus causes ringworm, a skin disease.

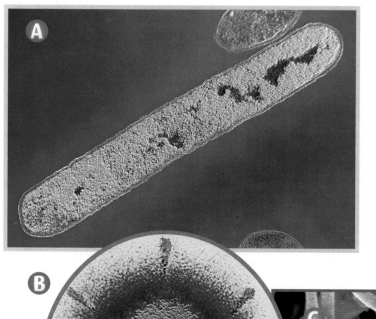

Fungi and Protists Fungi, which include molds, yeasts, and other organisms, cause some infectious diseases, including athlete's foot. Malaria, an infection of the blood that is common in tropical areas, is one disease caused by protists.

✓ Checkpoint What are two ways in which bacteria cause disease?

How Diseases Are Spread

Pathogens are something like ants at a picnic. They aren't trying to harm you. However, like the ants, pathogens need food. They also need a place to live and reproduce. Unfortunately, your body may be just the right place for a pathogen to meet those needs.

You can become infected by a pathogen in one of several ways. **Sources of pathogens include another person, a contaminated object, an animal bite, and the environment.**

Person-to-Person Transfer Many pathogens are transferred from one person to another person. Pathogens often pass from one person to another through direct physical contact, such as kissing, hugging, and shaking hands. For example, if you kiss someone who has a cold sore, cold-sore viruses can then get into your body.

Diseases are also spread through indirect contact with an infected person. For example, if a person with pneumonia sneezes, pathogens shoot into the air. Pathogens from a sneeze can travel most of the way across a small room! Other people may catch pneumonia if they inhale these pathogens. Colds, flu, and tuberculosis can be spread through coughing and sneezing.

Sharpen your Skills

Posing Questions

Cholera is a deadly disease **ACTIVITY** that is spread through food or water contaminated with cholera bacteria. In 1854, cholera spread through London, England. Dr. John Snow analyzed where most of the cholera victims lived, as well as the locations of the water pumps in the area. The map in Figure 4 shows Dr. Snow's findings. Dr. Snow hypothesized that the disease was spread by water that came from one of the pumps. Which pump was probably the source of the contaminated water?

Suppose that Dr. Snow just learned that two additional people had died of cholera. What questions would Dr. Snow most likely ask about the additional cholera cases?

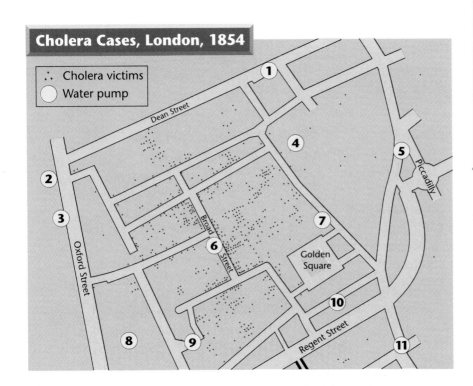

Figure 4 The map shows the location of cholera cases in the 1854 epidemic in London, England.

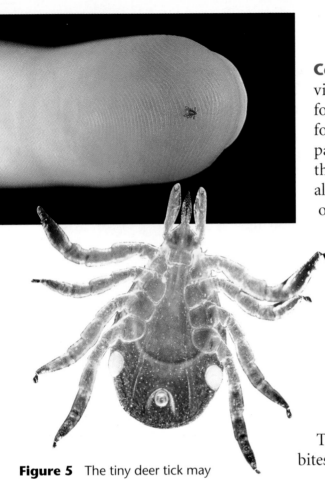

Figure 5 The tiny deer tick may carry the bacteria that cause Lyme disease, a serious condition that can damage the joints. If a deer tick that is carrying Lyme disease bacteria bites a person, the person may get Lyme disease. *Problem Solving How might people reduce their risk of catching Lyme disease?*

Contaminated Objects Some pathogens can survive for a time outside a person's body. Water and food can become contaminated. If people then eat the food or drink the water, they may become sick. Some pathogens that cause severe diarrhea are spread through contaminated food and water. People can also pick up pathogens by using objects, such as towels or silverware, that have been handled by an infected person. Colds and flu can be spread in this way. Tetanus bacteria can enter the body if a person steps on a contaminated nail.

Animal Bites If an animal is infected with certain pathogens and then bites a person, it can pass the pathogens to the person. People can get rabies, a serious disease that affects the nervous system, from the bite of an infected animal, such as a dog or a raccoon. Lyme disease and Rocky Mountain spotted fever are both spread by tick bites. The protist that causes malaria is transferred by the bites of mosquitoes that live in tropical regions.

Pathogens from the Environment Some pathogens occur naturally in the environment. The bacteria that cause tetanus live in soil or water. The bacteria that cause botulism, an especially severe form of food poisoning, also live in soil. Botulism bacteria can produce a toxin in foods that have been improperly canned. The toxin is extremely powerful.

 Section 1 Review

1. Name four kinds of pathogens that cause disease in humans.
2. Describe four ways that pathogens can infect humans.
3. Explain how Pasteur and Koch contributed to the understanding of infectious disease.
4. **Thinking Critically Applying Concepts** If you have a cold, what steps can you take to keep from spreading it to other people? Explain.

Check Your Progress CHAPTER PROJECT

At this stage, you should have chosen a specific infectious disease to research. You should also decide whether to do newspaper articles, radio programs, or a television series. Begin to plan how you will explain the way in which the body is invaded by pathogens. Also begin thinking about how you will make your show appropriate for your audience. (*Hint:* To get ideas on how to present news stories, read newspapers or watch or listen to real news programs about international conflicts.)

② The Body's Defenses

Your eyes are glued to the screen. The situation in the video game is desperate. Enemy troops have gotten through an opening in the wall. Your soldiers have managed to hold back most of the invaders. However, some enemy soldiers are breaking through the defense lines. You need your backup defenders. They can zap the invaders with their powerful weapons. If your soldiers can fight off the enemy until the backup team arrives, you can save your fortress.

Video games create fantasy wars, but in your body, real battles happen all the time. In your body, the "enemies" are invading pathogens. You are hardly ever aware of these battles. The body's disease-fighting system is so effective that most people get sick only occasionally. By eliminating pathogens that can destroy your cells, your body maintains homeostasis.

Figure 6 The pathogens that invade your body are something like the enemy soldiers in a video game. Your body has to defend itself against the pathogens.

Barriers That Keep Pathogens Out

Your body has three lines of defense against pathogens. The first line consists of barriers that keep pathogens from getting into the body. You do not wear a sign that says "Pathogens Keep Out," but that doesn't matter. **Barriers such as the skin, breathing passages, mouth, and stomach trap and kill most pathogens with which you come into contact.**

The Skin When pathogens land on the skin, they are exposed to destructive chemicals in oil and sweat. Even if these chemicals don't kill them, the pathogens may fall off with dead skin cells. If the pathogens manage to stay on the skin, they must get through the tightly packed dead cells that form a barrier on top of living skin cells. Most pathogens get through the skin only when it is cut. Scabs form over cuts so rapidly that the period in which pathogens can enter the body in this way is very short.

The Breathing Passages As you know, you can inhale pathogens when you breathe in. The nose, pharynx, trachea, and bronchi, however, contain mucus and cilia. Together, the mucus and cilia trap and remove most of the pathogens that enter the respiratory system. In addition, irritation by pathogens may make you sneeze or cough. Both actions force the pathogens out of your body.

Figure 7 Skin is covered with bacteria. The dots in the photo are colonies of bacteria living on a person's hand.
Relating Cause and Effect How can a cut in the skin lead to an infection?

The Mouth and Stomach Some pathogens are found in foods, even if the foods are handled safely. The saliva in your mouth contains destructive chemicals and your stomach produces acid. Most pathogens that you swallow are destroyed by saliva or stomach acid.

General Defenses

In spite of barriers, pathogens sometimes get into your body and begin to damage cells. When body cells are damaged, they release chemicals that trigger the **inflammatory response,** which is the second line of defense. **In the inflammatory response, fluid and certain types of white blood cells leak from blood vessels into nearby tissues. The white blood cells then fight the pathogens.** Because the inflammatory response is the same no matter what the pathogen, it is sometimes called the body's general defense.

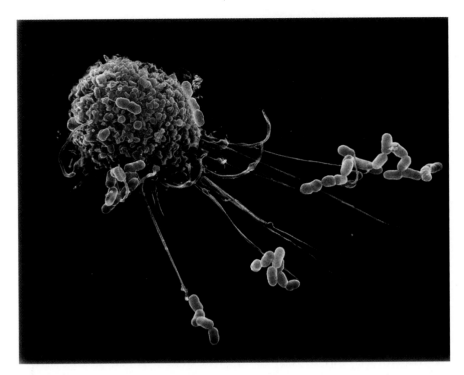

Figure 8 Caught! The bacteria, shown in green, don't stand a chance against the phagocyte, shown in red. Phagocytes are white blood cells that engulf and destroy bacteria.

All white blood cells are disease fighters, but there are different types, each with its own particular function. The kinds involved in the inflammatory response are called phagocytes. A **phagocyte** (FAG uh syt) is a white blood cell that engulfs pathogens and destroys them by breaking them down.

During the inflammatory response, blood vessels widen in the area affected by the pathogens. This enlargement increases the flow of blood to the area. The enlarged blood vessels—and the fluid that leaks out of them—make the affected area red and swollen. If you touch the swollen area, it will feel slightly warmer than normal. In fact, the term *inflammation* comes from a Latin word meaning "to set on fire."

In some cases, chemicals produced during the inflammatory response cause a fever, raising your body temperature above its normal temperature of 37° Celsius. Although fever makes you feel bad, it actually may help your body fight the infection. Some pathogens may not grow and reproduce well at higher temperatures.

☑ *Checkpoint* *What role do white blood cells play in the inflammatory response?*

The Immune System

If a pathogen infection is severe enough to cause a fever, it also triggers the third line of defense—the **immune response.** The immune response is controlled by the immune system, your body's disease fighting system. **The cells of the immune system can distinguish between different kinds of pathogens. The immune-system cells react to each kind of pathogen with a defense targeted specifically at that pathogen.** The white blood cells that do this are called **lymphocytes** (LIM fuh syts). There are two major kinds of lymphocytes—T lymphocytes and B lymphocytes, which are also called T cells and B cells. In *Exploring the Immune Response* , you can see how T cells and B cells work together to destroy flu viruses.

T Cells A major function of **T cells** is to identify pathogens and distinguish one kind of pathogen from another. You have tens of millions of T cells circulating in your blood. Each kind of T cell recognizes a different kind of pathogen. What T cells actually recognize are marker molecules, called antigens, found on each pathogen. **Antigens** are molecules on cells that the immune system recognizes either as part of your body or as coming from outside your body. All cells have antigens, and each person's antigens are different from those of all other people.

INTEGRATING CHEMISTRY

You can think of antigens as something like the uniforms that athletes wear. When you watch a track meet, you can look at the runners' uniforms to tell which school each runner comes from. Like athletes from different schools, each different pathogen has its own kind of antigen. Antigens differ from one another because each kind of antigen has a different chemical structure.

Figure 9 By looking at the runners' uniforms, you can tell that they come from different schools. Similarly, the immune system recognizes a pathogen by its antigens—marker molecules on the pathogen. *Applying Concepts What is the name of the cell that distinguishes one pathogen from another?*

EXPLORING the Immune Response

The immune system consists of T cells and B cells. The cells of the immune system work together to combat an infection, such as one caused by flu viruses.

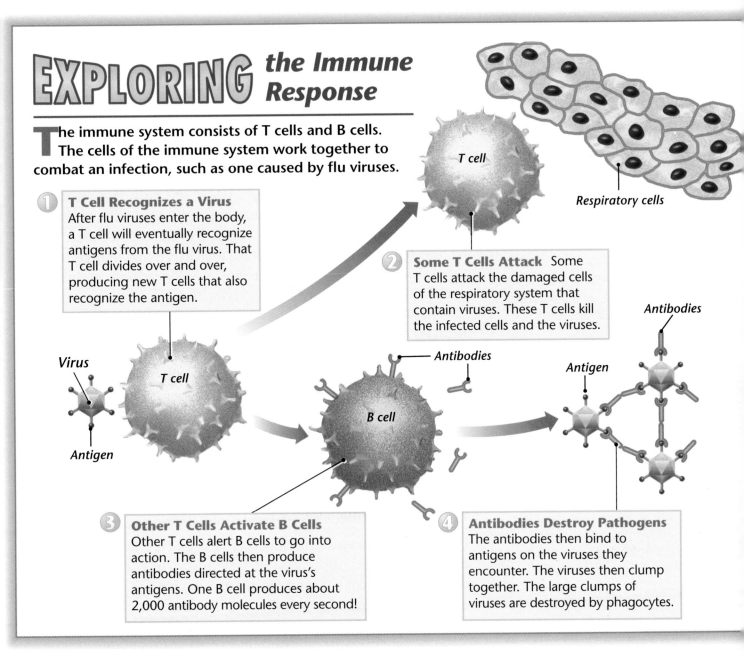

① T Cell Recognizes a Virus
After flu viruses enter the body, a T cell will eventually recognize antigens from the flu virus. That T cell divides over and over, producing new T cells that also recognize the antigen.

Respiratory cells

T cell

② Some T Cells Attack Some T cells attack the damaged cells of the respiratory system that contain viruses. These T cells kill the infected cells and the viruses.

Virus

T cell

Antigen

Antibodies

B cell

Antibodies

Antigen

③ Other T Cells Activate B Cells
Other T cells alert B cells to go into action. The B cells then produce antibodies directed at the virus's antigens. One B cell produces about 2,000 antibody molecules every second!

④ Antibodies Destroy Pathogens
The antibodies then bind to antigens on the viruses they encounter. The viruses then clump together. The large clumps of viruses are destroyed by phagocytes.

B Cells The lymphocytes called **B cells** produce chemicals that

INTEGRATING CHEMISTRY help destroy each kind of pathogen. These chemicals are called **antibodies.** Antibodies lock onto antigens. Each kind of B cell produces only one kind of antibody. Each kind of antibody has a different structure. Antigen and antibody molecules fit together, like pieces of a puzzle. An antigen on a flu virus will only bind to one kind of antibody—the antibody that acts against that flu virus.

When antibodies bind to the antigens on a pathogen, they mark the pathogen for destruction. Some antibodies make pathogens clump together. Others keep pathogens from attaching to the body cells that they might damage. Still other antibodies make it easier for phagocytes to destroy the pathogens.

✓ *Checkpoint* *What is the function of an antibody?*

AIDS, a Disease of the Immune System

Acquired immunodeficiency syndrome, or **AIDS,** is a disease caused by a virus that attacks the immune system. In the United States, AIDS is one of the leading causes of death in persons aged 25 to 44. The virus that causes AIDS is called human immunodeficiency virus, or HIV.

How HIV Affects the Body HIV is the only kind of virus known to attack the immune system directly. Once it invades the body, HIV enters T cells and reproduces inside them. People can be infected with HIV—that is, have the virus living in their body cells—for years before they become sick. More than 30 million people in the world may be infected with HIV.

Eventually HIV begins to destroy the T cells it has infected. Damage to the immune system is usually slow. But as the viruses destroy T cells, the body loses its ability to fight disease. Most persons infected with HIV eventually develop the disease AIDS.

Because their immune systems no longer function properly, people with AIDS become sick with diseases not normally found in people with healthy immune systems. Many people survive attack after attack of such diseases. But eventually their immune systems fail, ending in death. At this time, there is no cure for AIDS. However, new drug treatments allow people with the disease to survive much longer than in the past.

How HIV Is Spread Like all other viruses, HIV can only reproduce inside cells. In the case of HIV, the virus can only reproduce inside T cells. However, it can survive for a short time outside the human body in body fluids, such as blood and the fluids produced by the male and female reproductive systems.

HIV can spread from one person to another only if body fluids from an infected person come in contact with those of an uninfected person. Sexual contact is one way in which this can happen. HIV may also pass from an infected woman to her baby

Figure 10 The tiny red particles are HIV viruses emerging from a T cell. The viruses multiply inside the T cell and eventually cause the cell to die.
Relating Cause and Effect Why does the death of T cells interfere with the body's ability to fight disease?

Figure 11 You cannot get HIV, the virus that causes AIDS, by hugging someone infected with the virus.

during pregnancy or childbirth or through breast milk. In addition, when drug users share needles, some infected blood may get into the needle and then infect the next person who uses it. A person can also get HIV through a transfusion of blood that contains the virus. But since 1985, all donated blood in the United States has been tested for signs of HIV, and infected blood is not used in transfusions.

It is important to know the many ways in which HIV is *not* spread. HIV does not live on skin, so you cannot be infected by hugging or shaking hands with an infected person. You can't get infected by using a toilet seat after it has been used by someone with HIV. And HIV is not spread when you bump into someone while playing sports.

Section 2 Review

1. Name four barriers that prevent pathogens from getting into the body. Explain how each barrier prevents infection.
2. Describe the inflammatory response.
3. What is the function of the immune system?
4. How is HIV different from other virus pathogens?
5. **Thinking Critically Applying Concepts** Explain why you can't contract HIV by touching a doorknob that someone infected with the virus has touched.

Check Your Progress   CHAPTER PROJECT
At this point you should begin writing the newspaper articles or scripts for each of your broadcasts. Before you begin writing, outline the main ideas that you want to communicate. Work to make your descriptions sound like real news. (*Hint:* Make sure that your articles or scripts include information about each of the body's three lines of defense).

THE SKIN AS A BARRIER

Bacteria are all around you. Many of those bacteria can cause disease, yet you usually remain free of disease. In this lab, you will investigate how the skin protects you from infectious disease.

Problem

How does skin act as a barrier to pathogens?

Skills Focus

making models, controlling variables, drawing conclusions

Materials

sealable plastic bags, 4
fresh apples, 4
rotting apple
cotton swabs

marking pen
paper towels
toothpick
rubbing alcohol

Procedure 🧤 🔥 🚱

1. Read over the entire procedure to see how you will treat each of four fresh apples. Write a prediction in your notebook about the change(s) you expect to see in each apple. Then copy the data table into your notebook.

2. Label four plastic bags *1, 2, 3,* and *4.*

3. Gently wash four fresh apples with water, then dry them carefully with paper towels. Place one apple in plastic bag 1, and seal the bag.

4. Insert a toothpick tip into a rotting apple and withdraw it. Lightly draw the tip of the toothpick down the side of the second apple without breaking the skin. Repeat these actions three more times, touching the toothpick to different parts of the apple without breaking the skin. Insert the apple in plastic bag 2, and seal the bag.

5. Insert the toothpick tip into the rotting apple and withdraw it. Use the tip to make a long, thin scratch down the side of the third apple. Be sure to pierce the apple's skin. Repeat these actions three more times, making additional scratches on different parts of the apple. Insert the apple into plastic bag 3, and seal the bag.

6. Repeat Step 5 to make four scratches in the fourth apple. However, before you place the apple in the bag, dip a cotton swab in rubbing alcohol, and swab the scratches. Then place the apple in plastic bag 4, and seal the bag. **CAUTION:** *Alcohol and its vapors are flammable. Work where there are no sparks, exposed flames, or other heat sources.*

7. Store the four bags in a warm, dark place. Wash your hands thoroughly with soap and water.

8. Every day for one week, remove the apples from their storage place, and observe them without opening the bags. Record your observations, then return the bags to their storage location. At the end of the activity, dispose of the unopened bags as directed by your teacher.

Analyze and Conclude

1. How did the appearance of the four apples compare? Explain your results.
2. In this activity, what condition in the human body is each of the four fresh apples supposed to model?
3. What is the control in this experiment?
4. What is the role of the rotting apple in this activity?

5. **Apply** How does this investigation show why routine cuts and scrapes should be cleaned and bandaged?

Design an Experiment

Using apples as you did in this activity, design an experiment to model how washing hands can prevent the spread of disease. Obtain your teacher's permission before carrying out your investigation.

DATA TABLE

Date	Apple 1 (no contact with decay)	Apple 2 (contact with decay, unbroken skin)	Apple 3 (contact with decay, scratched, untreated)	Apple 4 (contact with decay, scratched, treated with alcohol)

DISCOVER

What Substances Can Kill Pathogens?

1. Your teacher will give you a variety of products, such as disinfectant soaps and mouthwashes, that claim to kill pathogens. Read the labels to learn the pathogens that each product is supposed to destroy.

2. Also note the ingredients in each product that act against pathogens. These are labeled "active ingredients."

Think It Over

Designing Experiments How could you determine which of two different soaps is more effective at killing bacteria? Design an experiment to find out. Do not perform the experiment without obtaining your teacher's approval.

GUIDE FOR READING

◆ What is active immunity?

◆ What is passive immunity?

Reading Tip Before you read, rewrite the headings in the section as questions that begin with *how, why,* or *what.* As you read, write short answers to those questions.

Itch, itch, itch. That's probably what you remember about chicken pox, if you ever had it. But once you got better, you could be pretty sure that you would never get that disease again. As people recover from some diseases, they develop immunity to the diseases. **Immunity** is the body's ability to destroy pathogens before they can cause disease. There are two basic types of immunity—active and passive.

Active Immunity

If you've been sick with chicken pox, your body was invaded by chicken pox viruses. Your immune system responded to the virus antigens by producing antibodies against them. The next time that chicken pox viruses invade your body, your immune system will probably produce antibodies so quickly that you won't become sick. You now have **active immunity** to chicken pox, because your own body has produced the antibodies that fight the chicken pox pathogens. **Active immunity occurs when a person's own immune system produces antibodies in response to the presence of a pathogen.**

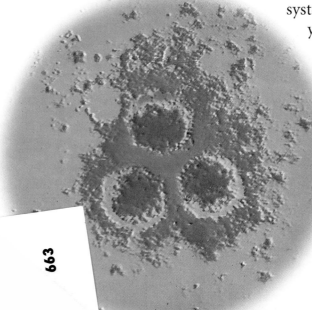

Figure 12 These virus particles cause chicken pox. Once you have had chicken pox you will probably never get that disease again.

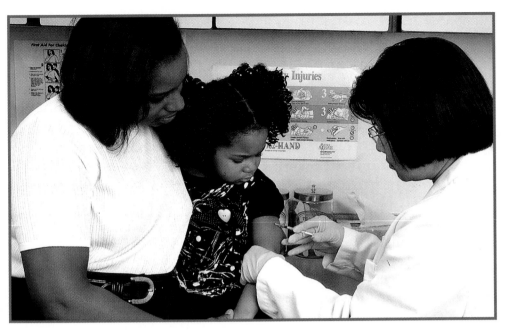

Figure 13 Ouch! The injection may sting a bit, but it is a vaccination that will protect the little girl against disease. Vaccinations consist of dead or weakened pathogens that do not make you sick. *Classifying Why does a vaccination produce active immunity to a disease?*

How Active Immunity Is Produced Active immunity is produced by the cells of a person's immune system as part of the immune response. Remember that during the immune response, T cells and B cells help destroy the disease-causing pathogens. After the person recovers, some of the T cells and B cells keep the "memory" of the pathogen's antigen. If that kind of pathogen enters the body again, these memory cells recognize the pathogen's antigen. The memory cells start the immune response so quickly that the person usually doesn't get sick. Active immunity usually lasts for many years, and sometimes it lasts for life.

Vaccination One way in which you can gain active immunity is by coming down with the disease. Another way is by being vaccinated against the disease. **Vaccination** (vac suh NAY shun), or immunization, is the process by which harmless antigens are deliberately introduced into a person's body to produce active immunity. Vaccinations are given by injection or by mouth. Vaccinations can prevent polio, chicken pox, and other diseases.

The substance that is used in a vaccination is called a vaccine. A **vaccine** (vak SEEN) usually consists of pathogens that have been weakened or killed but can still trigger the immune system to go into action. The T cells and B cells still recognize and respond to the antigens of the weakened or dead pathogen. When you receive a vaccination, the weakened pathogens usually do not make you sick. However, your immune system responds by producing memory cells and active immunity to the disease.

✓ Checkpoint *What are two ways in which a person can gain active immunity?*

Passive Immunity

Some diseases, such as rabies, are so uncommon that people rarely receive vaccinations against them. If a person is bitten by an animal that might have rabies, however, the person is usually given injections that contain antibodies to the rabies antigen. The protection that the person acquires this way is an example of passive immunity. This type of immunity is called **passive immunity** because the antibodies are given to the person—the person's own immune system did not make them.

Fighting Infectious Disease

From ancient times, people have practiced methods for preventing disease and caring for sick people. Ancient peoples, however, did not know what caused disease. About 200 years ago, people began to learn much more about the causes of infectious diseases and how to protect against them.

1854
Florence Nightingale

As an English nurse caring for British soldiers during the Crimean War, Florence Nightingale insisted that army hospitals be kept clean. By doing this, she saved many soldiers' lives. She is considered to be the founder of the modern nursing profession.

1800	1825	1850

1796
Edward Jenner

Edward Jenner, a country doctor in England, successfully vaccinated a child against smallpox, a deadly viral disease. Jenner used material from a sore of a person with cowpox, a mild but similar disorder. Although Jenner's procedure was successful, he did not understand why it worked.

1860s
Joseph Lister

Joseph Lister, an English surgeon, used carbolic acid to prevent infections in surgical patients. Because of Lister's techniques, far more people recovered from surgery than before.

Passive immunity occurs when the antibodies that fight the pathogen come from another source rather than from the person's own body. Unlike active immunity, which is long-lasting, passive immunity usually lasts no more than a few months.

A baby acquires passive immunity to some diseases before birth. This happens because antibodies from the mother's body pass into the baby's body. After birth, these antibodies protect the baby for a few months. After that time, the baby's own immune system has begun to function.

In Your Journal

Learn more about the work of one of these people. Then imagine that a new hospital is going to be dedicated to that person, and that you have been chosen to deliver the dedication speech. Write a speech that praises the person's contributions to fighting disease.

1882
Robert Koch

In Germany, Robert Koch identified one kind of microorganism in many samples of tissue taken from people with tuberculosis. Because he always found the same microorganism, Koch hypothesized that each infectious disease is caused by one specific pathogen.

1875 **1900** **1925**

1868
Louis Pasteur

In France, Louis Pasteur showed that microorganisms were the cause of a disease in silkworms. Pasteur reasoned that he could control the spread of disease by killing microorganisms. He also proposed that infectious diseases in humans are caused by microorganisms.

1928
Alexander Fleming

In Britain, Alexander Fleming observed that bacteria growing on laboratory plates were killed when some kinds of fungi grew on the same plate. He discovered that one fungus produced a substance—penicillin—that killed bacteria. Penicillin became the first antibiotic.

Preventing Infectious Diseases

◆ Don't share items that might carry pathogens, such as toothbrushes, drinking straws, or silverware.

◆ Keep clean. Wash your hands before eating and after using the bathroom.

◆ Cover your mouth when sneezing or coughing.

◆ Get eight hours of sleep every night.

◆ Eat a well-balanced diet.

◆ Get regular exercise.

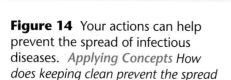

Figure 14 Your actions can help prevent the spread of infectious diseases. *Applying Concepts How does keeping clean prevent the spread of disease?*

Staying Healthy

 INTEGRATING HEALTH You almost certainly have immunity to some diseases, either because you have had the diseases or because you have been vaccinated against them. However, no one is immune to all diseases. But there are several steps you can take to decrease your risk of getting and spreading infectious diseases. Figure 14 summarizes these steps.

Unfortunately, you will probably become sick from time to time. When that happens, there are ways in which you can help yourself recover. Get plenty of rest. In addition, unless your stomach is upset, you should eat well-balanced meals. Drink plenty of fluids. These actions are all that you need to recover from most mild illnesses.

Sometimes when you are sick, medications can help you get better. If you have a disease that is caused by bacteria, you may be given an antibiotic. An **antibiotic** (an tih by AHT ik) is a chemical that kills bacteria or slows their growth without harming body cells. Unfortunately, there are no medications that cure viral illnesses, including the common cold. The best way to deal with most viral diseases is to get plenty of rest.

Some medicines don't kill pathogens but may help you feel more comfortable while you get better. Many of these are over-the-counter medications—drugs that can be purchased without a doctor's prescription. Such medications may reduce fever, clear your nose so you can breathe more easily, or stop a cough. Be sure you understand and follow the instructions for all types of medications. And if you don't start to feel better in a short time, you should see a doctor.

Section 3 Review

1. What is active immunity? How is it produced?
2. How is passive immunity produced? How does passive immunity differ from active immunity?
3. Identify four things that you can do that will help you avoid catching an infectious disease.
4. **Thinking Critically** **Applying Concepts** After receiving a vaccination, you may develop mild symptoms of the disease. Explain why.

Science at Home

With a family member, make a list of the vaccinations you have received. For each, note when you received the vaccination. Then, with your family member, learn about one of the diseases for which you were vaccinated. What kind of pathogen causes the disease? What are the symptoms of the disease? Is the disease still common in the United States?

SECTION 4 Noninfectious Disease

DISCOVER .... ACTIVITY ....

What Happens When Airflow Is Restricted?

1. Asthma is a disorder in which breathing passages become narrower than normal. This activity will help you understand how this condition affects breathing. Begin by breathing normally, first through your nose and then through your mouth. Observe how deeply you breathe.

2. Put one end of a drinking straw in your mouth. Then gently pinch your nostrils shut so that you cannot breathe through your nose.

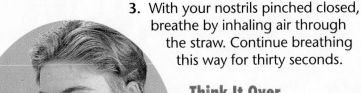

3. With your nostrils pinched closed, breathe by inhaling air through the straw. Continue breathing this way for thirty seconds.

Think It Over

Observing Compare your normal breathing pattern to that when breathing through the straw. Which way were you able to take deeper breaths? Did you ever feel short of breath?

Americans are living longer today than ever before. A person who was born in 1990 can expect to live about 75 years. In contrast, a person born in 1950 could expect to live only about 68 years.

Progress against infectious disease is one reason why life spans have increased. However, as infectious diseases have become less common, noninfectious diseases have grown more prevalent. **Noninfectious diseases** are diseases that are not spread from person to person. Unlike infectious diseases, noninfectious diseases are not caused by microorganisms. A noninfectious disease, cardiovascular disease, is the leading cause of death in America. Allergies, diabetes, and cancer are other noninfectious diseases.

Allergies

Spring has arrived. Flowers are in bloom, and the songs of birds fill the air. Unfortunately for some people, sneezing is another sound that fills the air. People who sneeze and cough in the spring may not have colds. Instead, they may be suffering from an **allergy** to plant pollen in the air. **An allergy is a disorder in which the immune system is overly sensitive to a foreign substance—something not normally found in the body.**

GUIDE FOR READING

◆ What is an allergy?

◆ How does diabetes affect the body?

◆ What is cancer?

Reading Tip As you read, create a table in which you record the characteristics of each noninfectious disease.

▼ Plant pollen

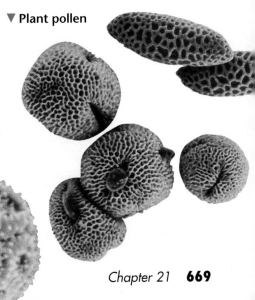

Chapter 21 **669**

ACTIVITY

Two weeks ago, after you ate strawberry shortcake with whipped cream, you broke out in an itchy rash. Besides strawberries, the ingredients in the dessert were sugar, flour, butter, eggs, vanilla, baking powder, salt, and cream. Then last night, you ate a strawberry custard tart with whipped cream and again broke out in a rash. The tart's ingredients were strawberries, sugar, cornstarch, milk, eggs, flour, shortening, salt, and vanilla.

You think that you may be allergic to strawberries. Do you have enough evidence to support this conclusion? If so, why? If not, what additional evidence do you need?

Allergens An **allergen** is any substance that causes an allergy. In addition to different kinds of pollen, people may be allergic to dust, molds, some foods, and even some medicines. If you are lucky, you have no allergies at all. However, many people are allergic to one or more substances.

Reaction to Allergens Allergens may get into your body when you inhale them, eat them in food, or touch them with your skin. When lymphocytes encounter the allergen, they produce antibodies. These antibodies, unlike the ones made during the immune response, signal cells in the body to release a chemical called histamine. **Histamine** (HIS tuh meen) is a chemical that is responsible for the symptoms of an allergy, such as sneezing and watery eyes. Drugs that interfere with the action of histamine, called antihistamines, may lessen this reaction. However, if you have an allergy, the best strategy is to try to avoid the substance to which you are allergic.

Asthma If some people inhale a substance to which they are allergic, they may develop a condition called asthma. **Asthma** (AZ muh) is a disorder in which the respiratory passages narrow significantly. This narrowing causes the person to wheeze and become short of breath. Asthma attacks may be brought on by factors other than allergies, such as stress and exercise. People who have severe asthma attacks may require emergency care. If you have asthma, avoid the substances or activities that trigger asthma attacks and learn how to treat an attack.

✓ *Checkpoint* *What is the effect of histamine on the body?*

Figure 15 Some people have allergic reactions to cats (left) or dust mites, tiny animals found in dust (below).

Diabetes

The pancreas produces a chemical called insulin. **Insulin** (IN suh lin) enables body cells to take in glucose from the blood and use it for energy. In the condition known as **diabetes** (dy uh BEE tis), either the pancreas fails to produce enough insulin or the body's cells can't use it properly. **As a result, a person with diabetes has high levels of glucose in the blood and excretes glucose in the urine. The person's body cells, however, do not have enough glucose.**

Effects of Diabetes People with diabetes may lose weight, feel weak, and be hungry all the time. These symptoms occur because the cells are unable to take in the glucose they need to function efficiently. In addition, these people may urinate frequently and feel thirsty as the kidneys work to eliminate the excess glucose from the body.

Diabetes is a serious condition that, if not treated properly, can result in death. Even with proper treatment, diabetes can have serious long-term effects. These effects can include blindness, kidney failure, and heart disease.

Figure 16 Many people with diabetes must test their blood frequently to determine the level of glucose in their blood. *Relating Cause and Effect What accounts for the high level of glucose in the blood of people with diabetes?*

Forms of Diabetes There are two main forms of diabetes. Type I diabetes, the more serious form, usually begins in childhood or early adulthood. In Type I diabetes, the pancreas produces little or no insulin. People with this condition must get insulin injections.

Type II diabetes usually develops during adulthood. In this condition, either the pancreas doesn't make enough insulin or body cells do not respond normally to insulin. People with Type II diabetes may not need to take insulin. Instead, they may be able to control the symptoms of diabetes through proper diet, weight control, and exercise.

☑ *Checkpoint What are some symptoms of diabetes?*

Cancer

Under normal conditions, the body produces new cells at about the same rate that other cells die. In a condition known as cancer, however, the situation is quite different. **Cancer is a disease in which cells multiply uncontrollably, over and over, destroying healthy tissue in the process.** The word *cancer* is the Latin word for crab. Cancerous growths act something like a crab, pinching healthy tissues as they grow.

Tumor Formation As cancerous cells divide over and over, they often form abnormal tissue masses called **tumors.** Cancerous tumors invade the healthy tissue around them and destroy the tissue. Cancer cells can break away from a tumor and invade blood or lymph vessels. The blood or lymph then carries the cancer cells to other parts of the body, where they may begin to divide and form new tumors. Unless stopped by treatment, cancer progresses through the body.

Causes of Cancer Different factors may work together to determine what makes cells become cancerous. One such factor is the characteristics that people inherit from their parents. Because of their inherited characteristics, some people are more likely than others to develop certain kinds of cancer. For example, women whose mothers had breast cancer have a higher risk of developing breast cancer than do women with no family history of the disease.

Some substances or factors in the environment, called **carcinogens** (kahr SIN uh junz), can cause cancer. The tar in cigarette smoke is a carcinogen. Ultraviolet light, which is part of sunlight, can also be a carcinogen.

Cancer Treatment Surgery, drugs, and radiation are all used to treat cancer. If cancer is detected before it has spread, doctors remove the cancerous tumors through surgery. Sometimes, however, a surgeon can't remove all of the cancer. In some cases, drugs or radiation may be used to kill the cancer cells or slow their spread.

INTEGRATING PHYSICS Radiation treatment uses high-energy waves to kill cancer cells. X-rays and gamma rays are two types of radiation used in cancer treatment. These waves are similar to sunlight and the

Figure 17 The large orange mass in the X-ray is a cancerous tumor in the lung. The graph shows leading types of cancer that affect men and women in the United States. *Interpreting Graphs Do more women or men develop lung cancer each year?*

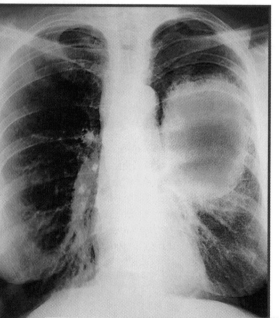

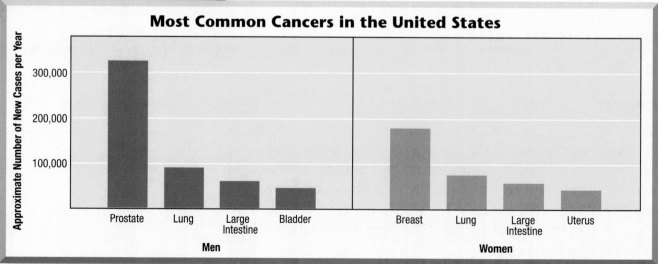

Most Common Cancers in the United States

Approximate Number of New Cases per Year

Men: Prostate, Lung, Large Intestine, Bladder

Women: Breast, Lung, Large Intestine, Uterus

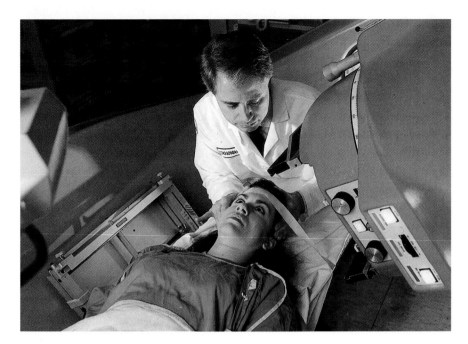

Figure 18 Radiation is one method that is used to treat cancer. The machine beams high-energy radiation at the tumor. This radiation kills cancer cells.

waves that make radios and microwave ovens work. However, X-rays and gamma rays have far more energy than sunlight, radio waves, or microwaves. When X-rays and gamma rays are aimed at tumors, they blast the cancer cells and kill them.

Cancer Prevention People can take steps to reduce their risk of developing cancer. For instance, they can avoid any form of tobacco, since tobacco and tobacco smoke contain carcinogens. Chewing tobacco and snuff contain carcinogens as well—they can cause cancers in the mouth. To prevent skin cancer, people can protect their skin from exposure to too much sunlight. A diet that is low in fat and includes plenty of fruits and vegetables can help people avoid some kinds of cancer, such as certain cancers of the digestive system.

Regular medical checkups are also important. Physicians or nurses may notice signs of cancer during a checkup. The earlier cancer is detected, the more likely it can be treated successfully.

Section 4 Review

1. What is an allergy? Describe how the body reacts to the presence of an allergen.
2. How does diabetes affect the level of glucose in the blood?
3. Describe how cancer cells harm the body.
4. **Thinking Critically Inferring** Doctors sometimes recommend that people with diabetes eat several small meals rather than three large ones. Why do you think doctors give this advice?

Science at Home

Explain to your family what allergies are and how allergens affect the body. Make a list of any substances your family members are allergic to. Use this list to determine whether certain allergies occur frequently in your family.

Causes of DEATH, Then and Now

In this lab you'll compare data on the leading causes of death in 1900 and today.

Problem

How do the leading causes of death today compare with those of a hundred years ago?

Materials

colored pencils
calculator (optional)
compass

ruler
protractor

Procedure

1. The data table on the next page shows the leading causes of death in the United States during two different years. Examine the data and note that two causes of death—accidents and suicides—are not diseases. The other causes are labeled either "I," indicating an infectious disease, or "NI," indicating a noninfectious disease.

Part 1 Comparing Specific Causes of Death

2. Look at the following causes of death in the data table: **(a)** pneumonia and influenza, **(b)** heart disease, **(c)** accidents, and **(d)** cancer. Construct a bar graph that compares the numbers of deaths from each of those causes in 1900 and today. Label the horizontal axis "Causes of Death." Label the vertical axis "Deaths per 100,000 People." Draw two bars side by side for each cause of death. Use a key to show which bars refer to 1900 and which refer to today.

Part 2 Comparing Infectious and Noninfectious Causes of Death

3. In this part of the lab, you will make two circle graphs showing three categories: infectious diseases, noninfectious diseases, and "other." You may want to review the information on creating circle graphs on page 769 of the Skills Handbook.

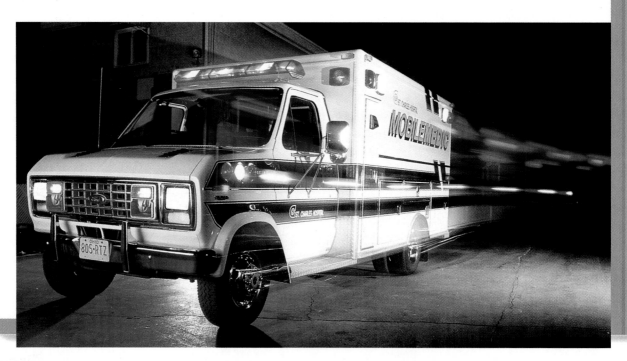

Ten Leading Causes of Death in the United States, 1900 and Today

1900		Today	
Cause of Death	Deaths per 100,000	Cause of Death	Deaths per 100,000
Pneumonia, influenza (I)*	215	Heart disease (NI)	281
Tuberculosis (I)	185	Cancer (NI)	205
Diarrhea (I)	140	Stroke (NI)	59
Heart disease (NI)	130	Lung disease (NI)	39
Stroke (NI)	110	Accidents	35
Kidney disease (NI)	85	Pneumonia (I)	31
Accidents	75	Diabetes (NI)	22
Cancer (NI)	65	HIV Infection (I)	16
Senility (NI)	55	Suicide	12
Diphtheria (I)	40	Liver disease (NI)	10
Total	**1,100**	**Total**	**710**

*"I" indicates an infectious disease. "NI" indicates a noninfectious disease.

4. Start by grouping the data from 1900 into the three categories—infectious diseases, noninfectious diseases, and other causes. Find the total number of deaths for each category. Then find the size of the "pie slice" (the number of degrees) for each category, and construct your circle graph. To find the size of the infectious disease slice for 1900, for example, use the following formula:

$$\frac{\text{number of deaths from infectious diseases}}{1{,}100 \text{ deaths total}} = \frac{x}{360°}$$

5. Calculate the percentage represented by each category using this formula:

$$\frac{\text{number of degrees in a slice}}{360°} \times 100 = \underline{\ ?\ } \%$$

6. Repeat Steps 4 and 5 using the data from today to make the second circle graph. What part of the formula in Step 4 do you need to change?

Analyze and Conclude

1. What kind of information did you learn just from examining the data table in Step 1?
2. According to your bar graph, which cause of death showed the greatest increase between 1900 and today? The greatest decrease?
3. In your circle graphs, which category decreased the most from 1900 to today? Which increased the most?
4. Suggest an explanation for the change in the number of deaths due to infectious diseases from 1900 to today.
5. **Think About It** How do graphs help you identify patterns and other information in data that you might otherwise overlook?

More to Explore

Write a question related to the data table that you have not yet answered. Then create a graph or work with the data in other ways to answer your question.

SECTION 5 Cancer and the Environment

DISCOVER ··· ACTIVITY

What Does Sunlight Do to the Beads?

1. Your teacher will give you beads that change color under certain conditions. Thread five beads on a pipe cleaner. Observe what the beads look like. Record your observations.

2. Wrap the pipe cleaner around your wrist. Go outdoors for one minute. Observe what happens to the beads.

Think It Over

Designing Experiments The ultraviolet light in sunlight causes the reaction you observed. How might you prevent the beads from reacting as they did? Describe the experiment you could perform to test your idea.

GUIDE FOR READING

◆ How can people's environments affect their chances of developing cancer?

Reading Tip As you read, write short summaries of the information under each heading.

You are trapped in a place that is dark, tight, and so warm that it is hard to breathe. You climb upwards, carefully feeling for footholds as you inch along. The surfaces are so warm that your knees begin to feel hot as they scrape against the walls. Grimy dirt falls on your face, and you blink to keep it out of your eyes. This story sounds like a nightmare. But it was real life for the boys who worked as chimney sweeps.

Chimney Sweeps and Skin Cancer

In 1775, about one million people lived in London, England. Their homes were heated by coal fires. Because burning coal produces lots of grimy black soot, the soot had to be cleaned out of the chimneys regularly. Chimney sweeps did this job by crawling into the chimneys and scraping the soot off the walls.

Because chimney sweeps had to be small and thin enough to fit inside a chimney, most were boys rather than men. Since the work was dangerous, only boys who badly needed a job were willing to do it. Therefore, chimney sweeps were usually poor. Their homes did not have a water supply, and bathing was difficult. At the end of a hard day, chimney sweeps were covered with soot, but few washed it off.

A Link Between Soot and Cancer Percivall Pott, a London doctor, saw many chimney sweeps at his medical clinic. Pott noticed that the chimney sweeps often had soot ground deeply into their skin. He also observed that an alarmingly high number of chimney sweeps developed skin cancer. Pott hypothesized that something in soot caused the cancer. He recommended frequent bathing to reduce the risk of skin cancer. Many years later, scientists identified the carcinogens in soot. They are the same substances that make up the tar in cigarette smoke.

Carcinogens in the Environment Percivall Pott was one of the first scientists to understand that the environment can affect people's health. Cancer is one disease that can be caused by harmful environmental factors. **People's environments may contain carcinogens. To reduce the risk of cancer, the carcinogens need to be removed or people need to be protected from them.**

Pott's work led to present-day efforts to control environmental carcinogens. In the United States, the Environmental Protection Agency (EPA) is in charge of enforcing environmental laws. The EPA identifies environmental carcinogens and develops strategies for protecting people from them.

☑ *Checkpoint* *What did Pott recommend that chimney sweeps do in order to reduce their risk of skin cancer?*

Figure 19 Percivall Pott followed scientific procedure as he figured out the cause of skin cancer in chimney sweeps.

1770s — Observations
Percivall Pott notices that chimney sweeps have a high rate of cancer.

1775 — Formation of hypothesis
Pott hypothesizes that something in soot causes skin cancer.

1775 — Testing of hypothesis
Pott recommends that chimney sweeps bathe frequently, thus removing the cancer-causing soot.

1892 — Result of testing
Evidence shows that chimney sweeps who bathe regularly develop skin cancer at a lower rate than sweeps who rarely bathe.

Early 1900s — Confirmation of hypothesis
Certain substances in soot are found to cause skin cancer in laboratory animals.

Figure 20 These asbestos ceiling panels were installed before people knew that asbestos can cause cancer. To protect the people who use the building, a worker is removing the panels.

Environmental Carcinogens Today

Scientists have identified many carcinogens found in the environment. Two important environmental carcinogens are asbestos and ultraviolet light.

Asbestos The mineral asbestos, which occurs in the form of fibers, is strong and does not burn. Because of these characteristics, asbestos was once widely used in materials such as roof shingles, brake linings, and insulation. However, scientists have since discovered that asbestos fibers can sometimes cause lung cancer when people inhale them repeatedly. Because of the dangers of asbestos, in 1989 the United States banned the manufacture and use of most asbestos products.

Ultraviolet Light As you learned in Chapter 17, skin cancer can result from overexposure to sunlight. Ultraviolet light is the part of sunlight that causes cancer. Fortunately, as sunlight travels from the sun to Earth, much of its ultraviolet light is absorbed high in the atmosphere, before it can reach Earth's surface. The gas ozone is the substance that absorbs most of the ultraviolet light.

In the 1970s and 1980s, scientists noticed that ozone levels in the upper atmosphere were decreasing. This decrease in ozone means that more ultraviolet light is reaching Earth's surface. At the same time, cases of skin cancer have been increasing. While the causes of the increase in skin cancer are complicated, some scientists believe that it is linked to the loss of ozone in the atmosphere.

Section 5 Review

1. How can the environment increase a person's risk for getting cancer?
2. What did Percivall Pott observe about the relationship between skin cancer and soot?
3. Why is asbestos dangerous?
4. **Thinking Critically** **Predicting** If ozone levels in the atmosphere decrease, what will probably happen to the number of skin cancers that develop each year? Explain.

CHAPTER PROJECT

Check Your Progress
Before your presentation, make your final revisions. If you are doing broadcasts, practice reading your scripts aloud. Experiment with different ways of bringing your series to a dramatic ending. Try to include answers to questions that might occur to your audience. For instance, are people around the patient at risk of invasion? If so, how can they defend themselves?

SECTION 1 — Infectious Diseases

Key Ideas

◆ Infectious diseases are caused by pathogens: bacteria, viruses, fungi, and protists.
◆ Pathogens that infect humans can come from another person, a contaminated object, an animal bite, or the environment.

Key Terms

pathogen   infectious disease   toxin

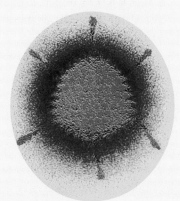

SECTION 2 — The Body's Defenses

Key Ideas

◆ The body has three lines of defense against pathogens. The first consists of barriers such as the skin that keep pathogens out. The second line of defense consists of the inflammatory response.
◆ The immune system, which is the third line of defense, targets specific pathogens. T lymphocytes, or T cells, identify pathogens and distinguish one kind from another. B lymphocytes, or B cells, produce antibodies that destroy pathogens.
◆ AIDS is a disease of the immune system. HIV, the virus that causes AIDS, infects and destroys T cells, and therefore destroys the body's ability to fight disease.

Key Terms

inflammatory response   antigen
phagocyte   B cell
immune response   antibody
lymphocyte   AIDS
T cell

SECTION 3 — Preventing Infectious Disease

Key Ideas

◆ In active immunity, a person's own immune system produces antibodies. A person can acquire active immunity by having the disease or by being vaccinated.
◆ In passive immunity, the antibodies come from a source other than the person's body.

Key Terms

immunity   vaccine
active immunity   passive immunity
vaccination   antibiotic

SECTION 4 — Noninfectious Disease

Key Ideas

◆ An allergy is a disorder in which the immune system is overly sensitive to a foreign substance, called an allergen.
◆ In diabetes, the body does not produce enough insulin or can't use it properly.
◆ In cancer, cells multiply uncontrollably, destroying healthy tissues.

Key Terms

noninfectious disease   insulin
allergy   diabetes
allergen   tumor
histamine   carcinogen
asthma

SECTION 5 — Cancer and the Environment

INTEGRATING ENVIRONMENTAL SCIENCE

Key Ideas

◆ In 1775, Percivall Pott hypothesized that soot caused cancer in chimney sweeps.
◆ Asbestos, which can cause lung cancer, and ultraviolet light, which can cause skin cancer, are environmental carcinogens.

ACTIVITY

USING THE INTERNET

www.science-explorer.phschool.com

California Test Prep: Reviewing Content

Multiple Choice

Choose the letter of the best answer.

1. Some pathogenic bacteria produce poisons called
   a. histamines.
   b. toxins.
   c. phagocytes.
   d. pathogens.

2. Antibodies are produced by
   a. phagocytes.
   b. B cells.
   c. T cells.
   d. pathogens.

3. Which disease is caused by HIV?
   a. diabetes
   b. flu
   c. AIDS
   d. tetanus

4. A carcinogen causes
   a. cancer.
   b. colds.
   c. allergies.
   d. food poisoning.

5. Ozone in the atmosphere absorbs
   a. allergens.
   b. T cells.
   c. soot.
   d. ultraviolet light.

True or False

If a statement is true, write true. If it is false, change the underlined word or words to make the statement true.

6. People can get Lyme disease from <u>animal bites</u>.

7. A <u>T cell</u> engulfs pathogens and destroys them.

8. Vaccination produces <u>active immunity</u>.

9. A <u>tumor</u> is a mass of cancer cells.

10. Percivall Pott linked soot to <u>stomach</u> cancer.

Checking Concepts

11. Explain why it is difficult for pathogens to get to a part of the body in which they can cause disease.

12. Why is it important not to share a drinking straw with someone else?

13. What is the relationship between antigens and antibodies?

14. How does diabetes harm the body?

15. Identify two factors that can make a person likely to develop cancer.

16. What evidence led Percivall Pott to hypothesize that something in soot causes cancer?

17. **Writing to Learn** A patient of Joseph Lister is angry because Lister has covered her surgery wound with a bandage dipped in carbolic acid. The acid stings and the bandage is uncomfortable. Write a conversation between Lister and the patient in which Lister explains why she shouldn't take the bandage off.

Thinking Visually

18. **Flowchart** Complete the flowchart, which shows what happens after tuberculosis bacteria begin to multiply in the lungs. (For more information on flowcharts, see the Skills Handbook.)

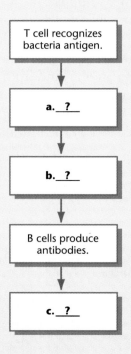

Test Prep: Skills

A person had an illness caused by bacteria. The table shows how the person's temperature and antibody level changed over the course of the disease. Use the table to answer Questions 19–21.

Week	Body Temperature (°C)	Antibody Level
0	37	low
1	39.8	low
2	39	medium
3	37	high
4	37	medium
5	37	low

19. **Graphing** Make a line graph of the temperature data. Label the horizontal axis "Week Number" and the vertical axis "Body Temperature."

20. **Interpreting Data** During what week did the person's temperature return to normal?

21. **Drawing Conclusions** When do antibody levels start to rise? What effect do antibodies have on the illness? Explain.

Thinking Critically

22. **Applying Concepts** Can you catch a cold by sitting in a chilly draft? Explain.

23. **Comparing and Contrasting** Compare the functions of T cells and B cells.

24. **Relating Cause and Effect** Why can the immune system successfully fight most pathogens, but not HIV?

25. **Inferring** Why did Pott think that frequent bathing would reduce chimney sweeps' risk of developing cancer?

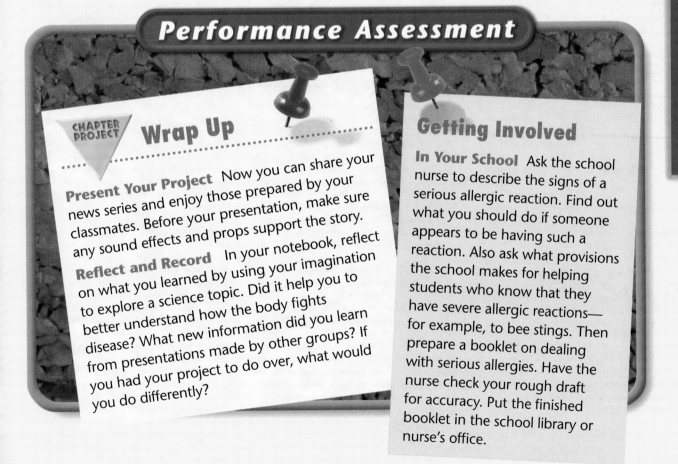

Performance Assessment

CHAPTER PROJECT ## Wrap Up

Present Your Project Now you can share your news series and enjoy those prepared by your classmates. Before your presentation, make sure any sound effects and props support the story.

Reflect and Record In your notebook, reflect on what you learned by using your imagination to explore a science topic. Did it help you to better understand how the body fights disease? What new information did you learn from presentations made by other groups? If you had your project to do over, what would you do differently?

Getting Involved

In Your School Ask the school nurse to describe the signs of a serious allergic reaction. Find out what you should do if someone appears to be having such a reaction. Also ask what provisions the school makes for helping students who know that they have severe allergic reactions—for example, to bee stings. Then prepare a booklet on dealing with serious allergies. Have the nurse check your rough draft for accuracy. Put the finished booklet in the school library or nurse's office.

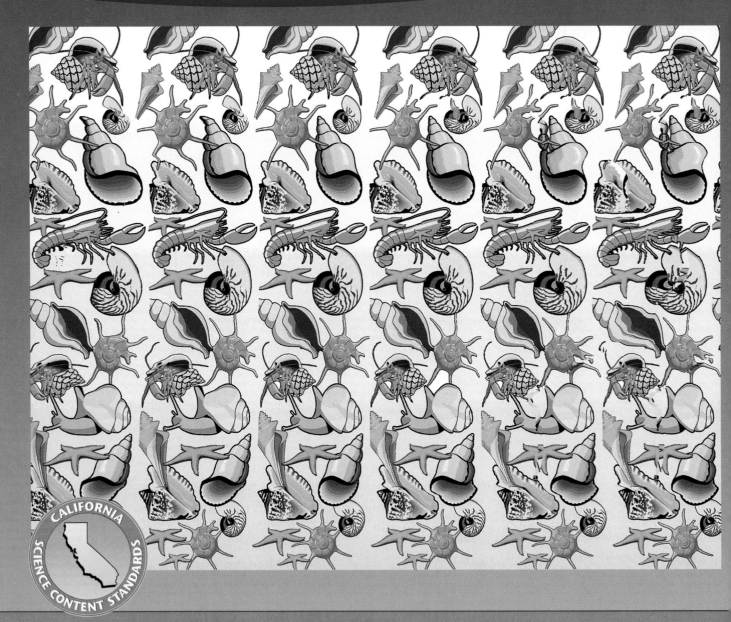

CALIFORNIA
SCIENCE CONTENT STANDARDS

The following California Science Content Standards are addressed in this chapter:

1. All living organisms are composed of cells, from just one to many trillions, whose details usually are visible only through a microscope.

   a. Cells function similarly in all living organisms.

5. The anatomy and physiology of plants and animals illustrate the complementary nature of structure and function.

   b. Organ systems function because of the contributions of individual organs, tissues, and cells. The failure of any part can affect the entire system.

   g. How to relate the structures of the eye and ear to their functions.

6. Physical principles underlie biological structures and functions.

   a. Visible light is a small band within a very broad electromagnetic spectrum.

   b. For an object to be seen, light emitted by or scattered from it must enter the eye.

   c. Light travels in straight lines except when the medium it travels through changes.

PROJECT 22

Tricks and Illusions

Can you be sure of what you see, hear, smell, taste, or touch? In this chapter, you'll learn how you experience your environment through your senses. You'll see how the senses send information to your nervous system and how your brain interprets the messages.

But things aren't always what they seem. For example, an optical illusion is a picture or other visual effect that tricks you into seeing something incorrectly. In this project, you'll investigate how your senses can sometimes be fooled by illusions.

Your Goal To set up a science fair booth to demonstrate how different people respond to one or more illusions.

To complete this project, you must

- try out a variety of illusions, including some that involve the senses of hearing or touch as well as sight
- select one or more illusions, and set up an experiment to monitor people's responses to the illusions
- learn why the illusions fool the senses
- follow the safety guidelines in Appendix A

Get Started In a small group, discuss optical illusions or other illusions that you know about. Look in books to learn about others. Try them out. Which illusions would make an interesting experiment? How could you set up such an experiment at a science fair?

Check Your Progress You'll be working on this project as you study this chapter. To keep your project on track, look for Check Your Progress boxes at the following points.

Section 2 Review, page 696: Plan the experiment you will perform.
Section 3 Review, page 709: Carry out your experiment.
Section 4 Review, page 718: Explain why the illusions trick the senses.

Wrap Up At the end of the chapter (page 721), be prepared to share your findings with your classmates. Then explain how your illusions work.

Now you see it. Now you don't. Sometimes your eyes can play tricks on you. The picture shows rows of seashells and sea animals. Or does it?

Stare at the picture for several seconds, as if it were far away. The picture should look slightly out of focus. After a while, does anything seem to pop out from the picture?

---

d. How simple lenses are used in a magnifying glass, the eye, camera, telescope, and microscope.

e. White light is a mixture of many wavelengths (colors), and that retinal cells react differently with different wavelengths.

f. Light interacts with matter by transmission (including refraction), absorption, or scattering (including reflection).

g. The angle of reflection of a light beam is equal to the angle of incidence.

7. Scientific progress is made by asking meaningful questions and conducting careful investigations.

b. Utilize a variety of print and electronic resources (including the World Wide Web) to collect information as evidence as part of a research project.

c. Communicate the logical connection among hypothesis, science concepts, tests conducted, data collected, and conclusions drawn from the scientific evidence.

1 How the Nervous System Works

DISCOVER •• ACTIVITY

How Simple Is a Simple Task?

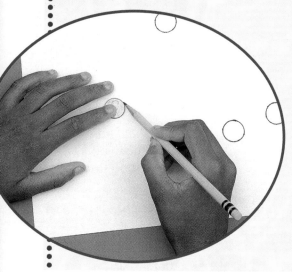

1. Trace the outline of a penny in twelve different places on a piece of paper.

2. Number the circles from 1 through 12. Write the numbers randomly, in no particular order.

3. Now pick up the penny again. Put it in each circle, one after another, in numerical order, beginning with 1 and ending with 12.

Think it Over

Inferring Make a list of all the sense organs, muscle movements, and thought processes in this activity. Compare your list with your classmates' lists. What organ system coordinated all the different processes involved in this task?

GUIDE FOR READING

◆ What are the functions of the nervous system?

◆ What are the three types of neurons and how do they interact?

Reading Tip Before you read, preview *Exploring the Path of a Nerve Impulse* on page 687. List any unfamiliar terms. Then, as you read, write a definition for each term.

The drums roll, and the crowd suddenly becomes silent. The people in the audience hold their breaths as the tightrope walker begins his long and dangerous journey across the wire. High above the circus floor, he inches along, slowly but steadily. One wrong movement could mean disaster.

To keep from slipping, tightrope performers need excellent coordination and a keen sense of balance. In addition, they must remember what they have learned from years of practice.

Even though you aren't a tightrope walker, you too need coordination, a sense of balance, memory, and the ability to learn. Your nervous system carries out all those functions. The nervous system consists of the brain, spinal cord, and nerves that run throughout the body. It also includes sense organs such as the eyes and ears.

Jobs of the Nervous System

The Internet lets people gather information from anywhere in the world with the click of a button. Like the Internet, your nervous system is a communications network. Your nervous system is much more efficient, however.

The nervous system receives information about what is happening both inside and outside your body. It also directs the way in which your body responds to this information. In addition, your nervous system helps maintain homeostasis. Without your nervous system, you could not move, think, feel pain, or taste a spicy taco.

Receiving Information Because of your nervous system, you are aware of what is happening in the environment around you. For example, you know that a soccer ball is zooming toward you, that the wind is blowing, or that a friend is telling a funny joke. Your nervous system also checks conditions inside your body, such as the level of glucose in your blood.

Responding to Information Any change or signal in the environment that can make an organism react is a **stimulus** (STIM yoo lus)(plural *stimuli*). A zooming soccer ball is a stimulus. After your nervous system analyzes the stimulus, it causes a response. A **response** is what your body does in reaction to a stimulus—you kick the ball toward the goal.

Some nervous system responses, such as kicking a ball, are voluntary, or under your control. However, many processes necessary for life, such as heartbeat rate, are controlled by involuntary actions of the nervous system.

Maintaining Homeostasis The nervous system helps maintain homeostasis by directing the body to respond appropriately to the information it receives. For example, when you are hungry, your nervous system directs you to eat. This action maintains homeostasis by supplying your body with nutrients and energy it needs.

✓ *Checkpoint* *What is a stimulus?*

Figure 1 The sparkling water is a stimulus. This toddler responds by thrusting her hands into the water and splashing.

The Neuron—A Message-Carrying Cell

The cells that carry information through your nervous system are called **neurons** (NOO rahnz), or nerve cells. The message that a neuron carries is called a **nerve impulse.** The structure of a neuron enables it to carry nerve impulses.

The Structure of a Neuron A neuron has a large cell body that contains the nucleus. The cell body has threadlike extensions. One kind of extension, a **dendrite,** carries impulses toward the cell body. An **axon** carries impulses away from the cell body. Nerve impulses begin in a dendrite, move toward the cell body, and then move down the axon. A neuron can have many dendrites, but it has only one axon. An axon, however, can have more than one tip, so the impulse can go to more than one other cell.

Axons and dendrites are sometimes called nerve fibers. Nerve fibers are often arranged in parallel bundles covered with connective tissue, something like a package of uncooked spaghetti wrapped in cellophane. A bundle of nerve fibers is called a **nerve.**

Kinds of Neurons Different kinds of neurons perform different functions. **Three kinds of neurons are found in the body— sensory neurons, interneurons, and motor neurons. Together they make up a chain of nerve cells that carry an impulse through the nervous system.** *Exploring the Path of a Nerve Impulse* shows how these three kinds of neurons work together.

A **sensory neuron** picks up stimuli from the internal or external environment and converts each stimulus into a nerve impulse. The impulse travels along the sensory neuron until it reaches an interneuron, usually in the brain or spinal cord. An **interneuron** is a neuron that carries nerve impulses from one neuron to another. Some interneurons pass impulses from sensory neurons to motor neurons. A **motor neuron** sends an impulse to a muscle, and the muscle contracts in response.

☑ *Checkpoint* *What is the function of an axon?*

Figure 2 A neuron, or nerve cell, has one axon and many dendrites that extend from the cell body. The dendrites carry a nerve message toward the cell body, and the axon carries the message away from the cell body. *Applying Concepts How many axons can a neuron have?*

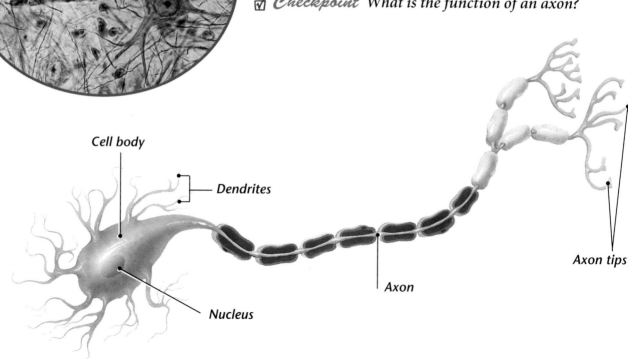

Cell body

Dendrites

Nucleus

Axon

Axon tips

EXPLORING the Path of a Nerve Impulse

When you hear the phone ring, you pick it up to answer it. Many sensory neurons, interneurons, and motor neurons are involved in this action.

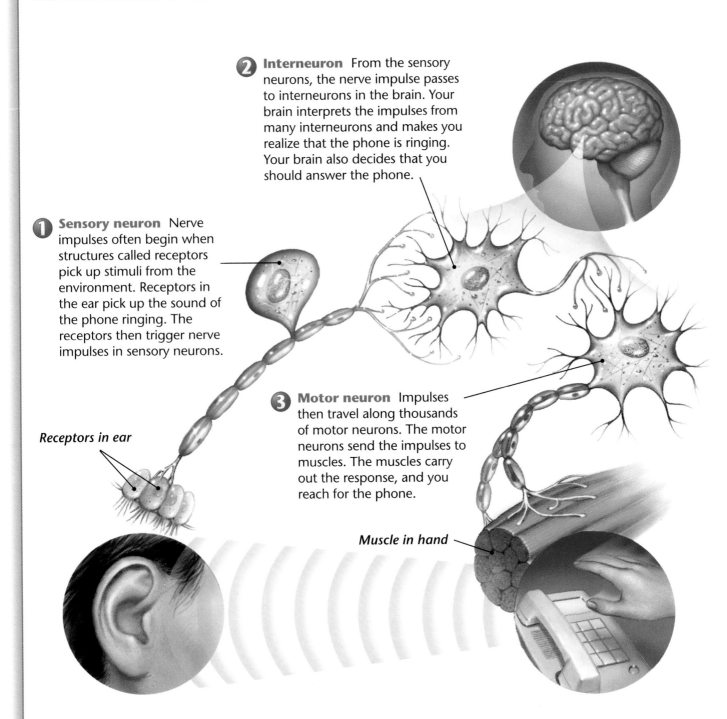

2 Interneuron From the sensory neurons, the nerve impulse passes to interneurons in the brain. Your brain interprets the impulses from many interneurons and makes you realize that the phone is ringing. Your brain also decides that you should answer the phone.

1 Sensory neuron Nerve impulses often begin when structures called receptors pick up stimuli from the environment. Receptors in the ear pick up the sound of the phone ringing. The receptors then trigger nerve impulses in sensory neurons.

Receptors in ear

3 Motor neuron Impulses then travel along thousands of motor neurons. The motor neurons send the impulses to muscles. The muscles carry out the response, and you reach for the phone.

Muscle in hand

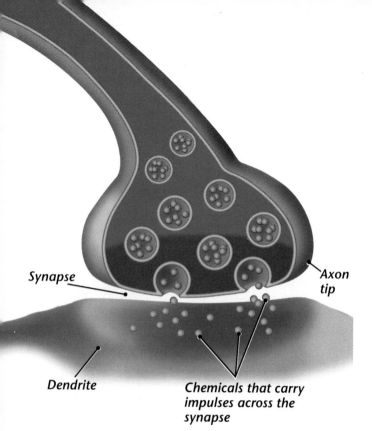

Synapse

Axon tip

Dendrite

Chemicals that carry impulses across the synapse

Figure 3 A synapse is the tiny space between the axon of one neuron and the dendrite of another neuron. When a nerve impulse reaches the end of an axon, chemicals are released into the synapse. These chemicals enable the nerve impulse to cross the synapse.

How a Nerve Impulse Travels

Every day of your life, millions of nerve impulses travel through your nervous system. Each of those nerve impulses begins in the dendrites of a neuron. The impulse moves rapidly toward the neuron's cell body and then down the axon until it reaches the axon tip. A nerve impulse travels along the neuron in the form of electrical and chemical signals. Nerve impulses can travel as fast as 120 meters per second!

There is a tiny space called a **synapse** (SIN aps) between each axon tip and the next structure. Sometimes this next structure is a dendrite of another neuron. Other times the next structure can be a muscle or a cell in another organ, such as a sweat gland. Figure 3 illustrates a synapse between the axon of one neuron and a dendrite of another neuron.

In order for a nerve impulse to be carried along, it must cross the gap between the axon and the next structure. The axon tips release chemicals that enable the impulse to cross the synapse. If that didn't happen, the impulse would stop at the end of the axon. The impulse would not be passed from sensory neuron, to interneuron, to motor neuron. Nerve impulses would never reach your brain or make your muscles contract.

You can think of a synapse as a river, and an axon as a road that leads up to the riverbank. The nerve impulse is like a car traveling on the road. To get to the other side, the car has to cross the river. The car gets on a ferry boat, which carries it across the river. The chemicals that the axon tips release are like a ferry that carries the nerve impulse across the synapse.

Section 1 Review

1. Describe three functions of the nervous system.
2. Identify the three kinds of neurons that are found in the nervous system. Describe how they interact to carry nerve impulses.
3. How does a nerve impulse cross a synapse?
4. **Thinking Critically Predicting** What would happen to a nerve impulse carried by an interneuron if the tips of the interneuron's axon were damaged? Explain.

Science at Home

During dinner, ask a family member to pass the salt and pepper to you. Observe what your family member then does. Explain that the words you spoke were a stimulus and that the family member's reaction was a response. Discuss other examples of stimuli and responses with your family.

688

Skills Lab

Ready or Not

Do people carry out tasks better at certain times of day? In this lab, you will design an experiment to answer this question.

Problem

Do people's reaction times vary at different times of day?

Materials

meter stick

Design a Plan

Part 1 Observing a Response to a Stimulus

1. Have your partner hold a meter stick with the zero end about 50 cm above a table.
2. Get ready to catch the meter stick by positioning the top of your thumb and forefinger just at the zero position as shown in the photograph.
3. Your partner should drop the meter stick without any warning. Using your thumb and forefinger only (no other part of your hand), catch the meter stick as soon as you can. Record the distance in centimeters that the meter stick fell. This distance is a measure of your reaction time.

Part 2 Design Your Experiment

4. With your partner, discuss how you can use the activity from Part 1 to find out whether people's reaction times vary at different times of day. Be sure to consider the questions below. Then write up your experimental plan.
   ◆ What hypothesis will you test?
   ◆ What variables do you need to control?
   ◆ How many people will you test? How many times will you test each person?

5. Submit your plan for your teacher's review. Make any changes your teacher recommends. Create a data table to record your results. Then perform your experiment.

Analyze and Conclude

1. In this lab, what is the stimulus? What is the response? Is this response voluntary or involuntary? Explain.
2. Why can you use the distance on the meter stick as a measure of reaction time?
3. Based on your results, do people's reaction times vary at different times of day? Explain.
4. **Think About It** In Part 2, why is it important to control all variables except the time of day?

More to Explore

Do you think people can do arithmetic problems more quickly and accurately at certain times of the day? Design an experiment to investigate this question. Obtain your teacher's permission before trying your experiment.

SECTION 2 Divisions of the Nervous System

DISCOVER ACTIVITY

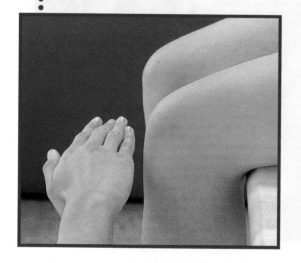

How Does Your Knee React?

1. Sit on a table or counter so that your legs dangle freely. Your feet should not touch the floor.

2. 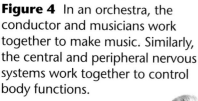 Have your partner use the side of his or her hand to *gently* tap one of your knees just below the kneecap. Observe what happens to your leg. Note whether you have any control over your reaction.

3. Change places with your partner. Repeat Steps 1 and 2.

Think It Over

Inferring When might it be an advantage for your body to react very quickly and without your conscious control?

GUIDE FOR READING

◆ What is the function of the central nervous system?

◆ What functions does the peripheral nervous system perform?

◆ What is a reflex?

Reading Tip As you read, make a list of main ideas and supporting details about the central and peripheral nervous systems.

A concert is about to begin. The conductor gives the signal, and the musicians begin to play. The sound of music, beautiful and stirring, fills the air.

To play music in harmony, an orchestra needs both musicians and a conductor. The musicians play the music, and the conductor directs the musicians and coordinates their playing.

Similarly, your nervous system has two divisions that work together—the central nervous system and the peripheral nervous system. The **central nervous system** consists of the brain and spinal cord. The **peripheral nervous system** consists of all the nerves located outside of the central nervous system. The central nervous system is like a conductor. The nerves of the peripheral nervous system are like the musicians.

Figure 4 In an orchestra, the conductor and musicians work together to make music. Similarly, the central and peripheral nervous systems work together to control body functions.

The Central Nervous System

You can see the central and peripheral nervous systems in Figure 5. **The central nervous system is the control center of the body.** All information about what is happening in the world inside or outside your body is brought to the central nervous system. The **brain,** located in the skull, is the part of the central nervous system that controls most functions in the body. The **spinal cord** is the thick column of nerve tissue that links the brain to most of the nerves in the peripheral nervous system.

Most impulses from the peripheral nervous system travel through the spinal cord to get to the brain. Your brain then directs a response. The response usually travels from the brain, through the spinal cord, and then to the peripheral nervous system.

For example, here is what happens when you reach under the sofa to find a lost quarter. Your fingers move over the floor, searching for the quarter. When your fingers finally touch the quarter, the stimulus of the touch triggers nerve impulses in sensory neurons in your fingers. These impulses travel through nerves of the peripheral nervous system to your spinal cord. Then the impulses race up to your brain. Your brain interprets the impulses, telling you that you've found the quarter. Your brain starts nerve impulses that move down the spinal cord. From the spinal cord, the impulses travel through motor nerves in your arm and hand. The impulses in the motor neurons cause your fingers to grasp the quarter.

☑ *Checkpoint* *What does the spinal cord do?*

The Brain

Your brain contains about 100 billion neurons, all of which are interneurons. Each of those neurons may receive messages from up to 10,000 other neurons and may send messages to about 1,000 more! Three layers of connective tissue cover the brain. The space between the outermost layer and the middle layer is filled with a watery fluid. The skull, layers of connective tissue, and fluid all help protect the brain from injury.

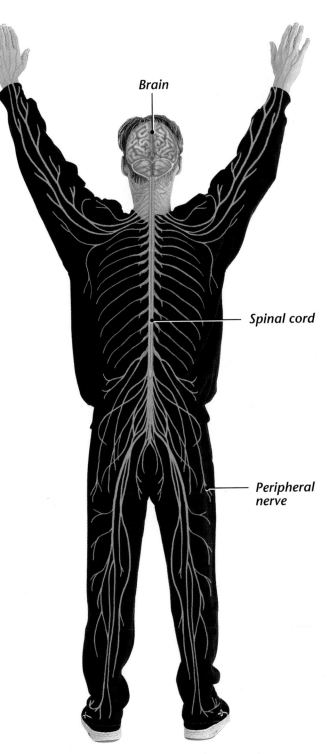

Brain

Spinal cord

Peripheral nerve

Figure 5 The central nervous system consists of the brain and spinal cord. The peripheral nervous system contains all the nerves that branch out from the brain and spinal cord.

Figure 6 The cerebrum, cerebellum, and brainstem are the three main parts of the human brain. The two halves of the cerebrum have been separated to show the cerebellum and the brainstem.
Applying Concepts What are three functions of the cerebrum?

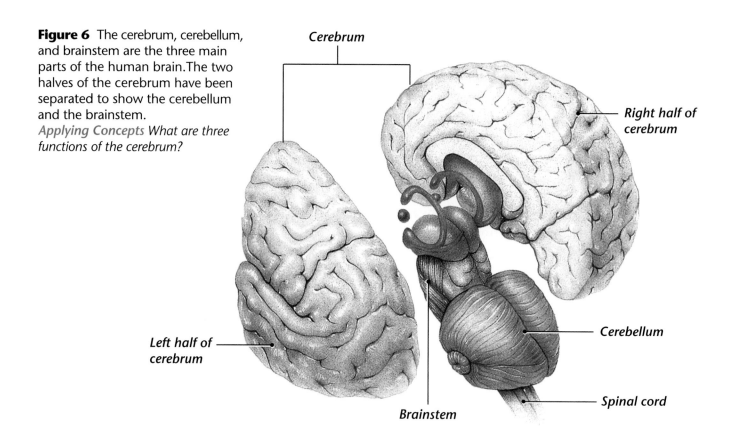

Cerebrum

Right half of cerebrum

Left half of cerebrum

Cerebellum

Spinal cord

Brainstem

Cerebrum There are three main regions of the brain. These are the cerebrum, the cerebellum, and the brainstem. Find each in Figure 6. The largest part of the brain is called the cerebrum. The **cerebrum** (suh REE brum) interprets input from the senses, controls the movement of skeletal muscles, and carries out complex mental processes such as learning, remembering, and making judgments. Because of your cerebrum, you can find the comics in a newspaper and locate your favorite comic strip on the page. Your cerebrum also enables you to read the comic strip and laugh at its funny characters.

Notice in Figure 6 that the cerebrum is divided into a right and a left half. The two halves have somewhat different functions. The right half of the cerebrum contains the neurons that send impulses to the skeletal muscles on the left side of the body. In contrast, the left half of the cerebrum controls the right side of the body. When you reach with your right hand for a pencil, the messages that tell you to do so come from the left half of your cerebrum.

In addition, each half of the cerebrum controls slightly different kinds of mental activity. The right half of the cerebrum is usually associated with creativity and artistic ability. The left half, in contrast, is associated with mathematical skills, speech, writing, and logical thinking.

Cerebellum and Brainstem The second largest part of your brain is called the cerebellum. The **cerebellum** (sehr uh BEL um) coordinates the actions of your muscles and helps you keep your balance. When you put one foot in front of the other as you walk, the motor neuron impulses that tell your feet to move start in your cerebrum. However, your cerebellum gives you the muscular coordination and sense of balance that keep you from falling down.

The **brainstem,** which lies between the cerebellum and spinal cord, controls your body's involuntary actions—those that occur automatically. For example, the brainstem regulates your breathing and helps control your heartbeat.

☑ *Checkpoint* *What part of your brain coordinates the contractions of your muscles?*

The Spinal Cord

Run your fingers down the center of your back to feel the bones of the vertebral column. The vertebral column surrounds and protects the spinal cord. The spinal cord is the link between your brain and the peripheral nervous system. The layers of connective tissue that surround and protect the brain also cover the spinal cord. In addition, like the brain, the spinal cord is further protected by a watery fluid.

Figure 7 This illustration, by the Dutch artist M. C. Escher, is called "Day and Night." Escher created this picture in 1938.

Visual Arts
CONNECTION

Some artists deliberately create works of art that can be interpreted by the brain in more than one way. The Dutch artist M. C. Escher (1898–1972) delighted in creating illustrations that played visual tricks on his viewers. Glance quickly at Escher's illustration in Figure 7. Then look at it again. Do you see the two different scenes in this single picture?

In Your Journal

Which scene did you see when you first looked at Figure 7? Did your brain interpret the picture differently the second time? Write a description of the visual trick that Escher has played in this illustration.

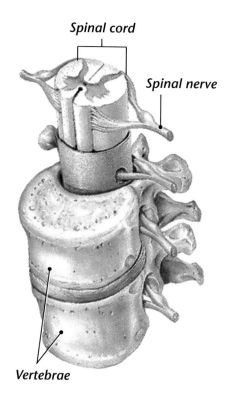

Spinal cord

Spinal nerve

Vertebrae

Figure 8 The spinal nerves, which connect to the spinal cord, emerge from spaces between the vertebrae. Each spinal nerve consists of both sensory and motor neurons.

The Peripheral Nervous System

The second division of the nervous system is the peripheral nervous system. **The peripheral nervous system consists of a network of nerves that branch out from the central nervous system and connect it to the rest of your body.** A total of 43 pairs of nerves make up the peripheral nervous system. Twelve pairs originate in the brain. The other 31 pairs—the spinal nerves—begin in the spinal cord. One nerve in each pair goes to the left side of the body, and the other goes to the right. As you can see in Figure 8, spinal nerves leave the spinal cord through spaces between the vertebrae.

Two-Way Traffic A spinal nerve is a little bit like a two-lane highway. Impulses travel on a spinal nerve in two directions—both to and from the central nervous system. Each spinal nerve contains axons of both sensory and motor neurons. The sensory neurons carry impulses from the body to the central nervous system. The motor neurons carry impulses in the opposite direction—from the central nervous system to the body.

Somatic and Autonomic Systems The nerves of the peripheral nervous system can be divided into two groups, called the somatic (soh MAT ik) and autonomic (awt uh NAHM ik) nervous systems. The nerves of the **somatic nervous system** control voluntary actions such as using a fork or tying your shoelaces. In contrast, nerves of the **autonomic nervous system** control involuntary actions. For example, the autonomic nervous system regulates the contractions of the smooth muscles that adjust the diameter of blood vessels.

Figure 9 The somatic nervous system controls voluntary actions. The girl's somatic nervous system is at work as she shapes the pot with her hands. *Classifying What part of the peripheral nervous system helps regulate the girl's heartbeat?*

Reflexes

Imagine that you are watching an adventure movie. The movie is so thrilling that you don't notice a fly circling above your head. When the fly zooms right in front of your eyes, however, your eyelids immediately blink shut. You didn't decide to close your eyes. The blink, which is an example of a **reflex,** happened automatically. **A reflex is an automatic response that occurs very rapidly and without conscious control.** If you did the Discover activity, you saw another example of a reflex.

As you have learned, the contraction of skeletal muscles is usually controlled by the brain. However, in some reflex actions, skeletal muscles contract with the involvement of the spinal cord only—not the brain. Figure 10 shows the reflex action that occurs when you touch a sharp object, such as a cactus thorn. When your finger touches the object, sensory neurons send impulses to the spinal cord. The impulses then pass to interneurons in the spinal cord. From there the impulses pass directly to motor neurons in your arm and hand. The muscles then contract, and your hand jerks up and away from the sharp object. By removing your hand quickly, this reflex protects you from getting badly cut.

At the same time that some nerve impulses make your arm muscles contract, other nerve impulses travel up your spinal cord and to your brain. When these impulses reach your brain, your brain interprets them. You then feel a sharp pain in your finger.

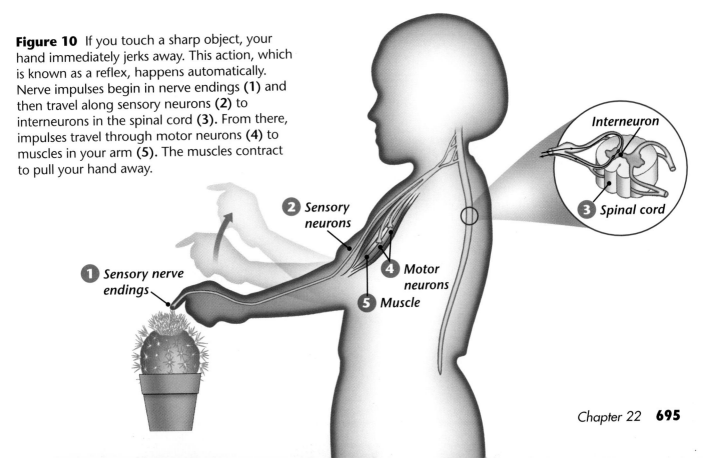

Figure 10 If you touch a sharp object, your hand immediately jerks away. This action, which is known as a reflex, happens automatically. Nerve impulses begin in nerve endings (1) and then travel along sensory neurons (2) to interneurons in the spinal cord (3). From there, impulses travel through motor neurons (4) to muscles in your arm (5). The muscles contract to pull your hand away.

Interneuron

1 *Sensory nerve endings*

2 *Sensory neurons*

3 *Spinal cord*

4 *Motor neurons*

5 *Muscle*

Figure 11 By wearing a helmet, this skateboarder is helping to prevent injury to his brain.

It takes longer for the pain impulses to get to the brain and be interpreted than it does for the reflex action to occur. By the time you feel the pain, you have already moved your hand away from the sharp object.

Safety and the Nervous System

INTEGRATING HEALTH Like other parts of the body, the nervous system can suffer injuries that interfere with its functioning. Concussions and spinal cord injuries are two ways in which the nervous system can be damaged.

A **concussion** is a bruiselike injury of the brain. A concussion occurs when soft tissue of the cerebrum bumps against the skull. Concussions can happen during a hard fall, an automobile accident, or contact sports such as football. With most concussions, you may have a headache for a short time, but the injured tissue heals by itself. However, if you black out, experience confusion, or feel drowsy after the injury, you should be checked by a doctor. To decrease your chances of getting a brain injury, wear a helmet when bicycling, skating, or performing other activities in which you risk bumping your head.

Spinal cord injuries occur when the spinal cord is cut or crushed. When the spinal cord is cut, all the nerve axons in that region are split, so impulses cannot pass through them. This type of injury results in paralysis, which is the loss of movement in some part of the body. Car crashes are the most common cause of spinal cord injuries. You can help protect yourself from a spinal cord injury by wearing a seatbelt when you travel in a car. Also, when you swim, make sure the water is deep enough before you dive in.

Section 2 Review

1. What is the function of the central nervous system? Which organs are part of this system?
2. What is the peripheral nervous system and what are its functions?
3. Explain what a reflex is. How do reflexes help protect the body from injury?
4. **Thinking Critically Relating Cause and Effect** What symptoms might indicate that a person's cerebellum has been injured?

Check Your Progress

CHAPTER PROJECT

At this point, you should have chosen one or more illusions to investigate. Now write up the plan for your experiment. List some questions that you will ask to monitor people's responses to the illusions. (*Hint:* Try out your illusions and your questions on classmates to find out what responses to expect.) With your classmates, make plans for setting up the science fair.

Should People Be Required to Wear Bicycle Helmets?

Bicycle riding is an enjoyable activity. But unfortunately, many bicycle riders become injured while riding. Each year about 150,000 children alone are treated in hospitals for head injuries that occur while bicycling. Head injuries can affect everything your brain does—thinking, remembering, seeing, and being able to move. Experts estimate that as many as 85 percent of bicycle-related head injuries could be prevented if all bicyclists wore helmets. But only about 18 percent of bicyclists wear helmets. What is the best way to get bicycle riders to protect themselves from head injury?

The Issues

Should Laws Require the Use of Bicycle Helmets? About 15 states have passed laws requiring bicycle riders to wear helmets. Nearly all of these laws, however, apply only to children. Some supporters of bicycle laws want to see the laws extended to all bicycle riders. Supporters point out that laws increase helmet use by 47 percent. In contrast, educational programs without laws to back them up increase bicycle helmet use by only 18 percent.

What Are the Drawbacks of Helmet Laws? Opponents of helmet laws believe it is up to the individual, not the government, to decide whether or not to wear a helmet. They say it is not the role of the government to stop people from taking risks. Rather than making people who don't

wear helmets pay fines, governments should educate people about the benefits of helmets. Car drivers should also be educated about safe driving procedures near bicycles.

Are There Alternatives to Helmet Laws? Instead of laws requiring people to wear helmets, some communities and organizations have set up educational programs that teach about the advantages of helmets. Effective programs teach about the dangers of head injuries and how helmets protect riders. In addition, they point out that safe helmets can be lightweight and comfortable. Effective education programs, though, can be expensive. They also need to reach a wide audience, including children, teens, and adults.

You Decide

1. Identify the Problem

In your own words, explain the issues concerning laws requiring people to wear bicycle helmets.

2. Analyze the Options

List two different plans for increasing helmet use by bicycle riders. List at least one advantage and one drawback of each plan.

3. Find a Solution

You are a member of the city government hoping to increase helmet use. Write a speech outlining your position for either a helmet law or an alternative plan. Support your position.

SECTION 3 Light

Why Does the Pencil Seem to Bend?

1. Put a pencil in a glass of water, as shown in the photograph.

2. Look at the pencil from the side. Describe what the pencil looks like.

Think It Over

Posing Questions What would you like to know about the properties of light that would help you explain the pencil's appearance? Write down a question about light to which you would like an answer.

GUIDE FOR READING

◆ What are the parts of the electromagnetic spectrum?

◆ What happens when light strikes an object?

Reading Tip Before you read, write down what you know about light. As you read, revise your list.

Imagine you are a famous photographer on location for a magazine. The scene is set—green, rolling hills and a clear blue sky as a background. The fashion models are in their places and you are ready to begin taking pictures. What factors should you take into consideration to produce the best possible photographs? Are there some color combinations that don't quite work? Are you in the correct position with respect to the sun? Is there enough light? Are some objects in the shade? Are there any reflections that are causing unwanted glare? All of these factors have one thing in common—light!

In this section, you will learn about the parts of the electromagnetic spectrum. You will also learn about the nature and behavior of visible light.

The Electromagnetic Spectrum

Sunlight travels to Earth in the form of electromagnetic waves. **Electromagnetic waves** are a form of energy that can travel through space. Electromagnetic waves are classified according to wavelength, or the length of the wave.

The **electromagnetic spectrum** is the name for the range of electromagnetic waves when they are placed in order of decreasing wavelength. Figure 12 shows the electromagnetic spectrum. **The electromagnetic spectrum is made up of radio waves, infrared rays, visible light, ultraviolet rays, X-rays, and gamma rays.**

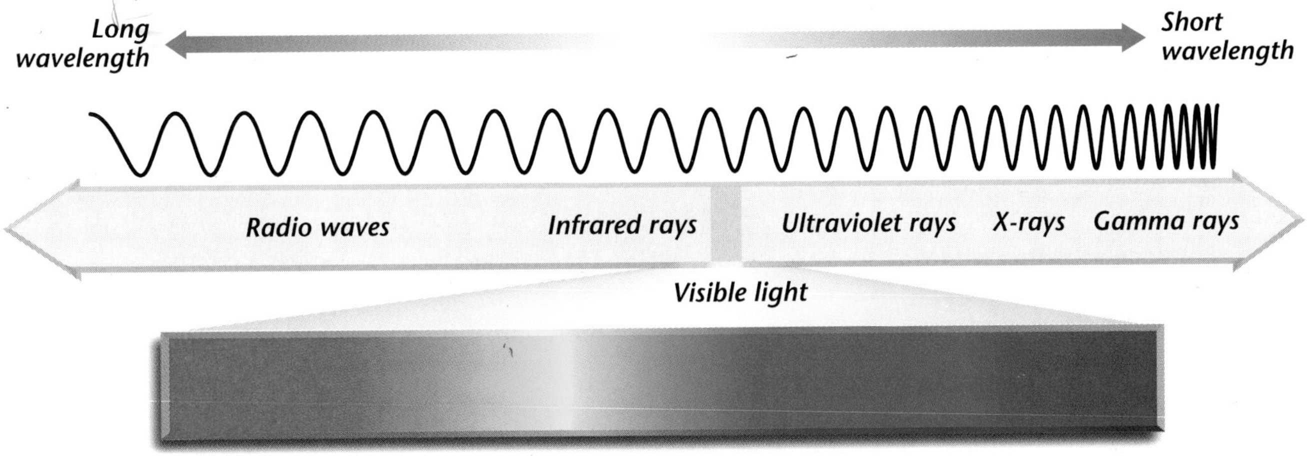

Long wavelength ← → Short wavelength

Radio waves   Infrared rays   Ultraviolet rays   X-rays   Gamma rays

Visible light

Figure 12 The electromagnetic spectrum shows the different electromagnetic waves in order of decreasing wavelength. *Interpreting Diagrams Which electromagnetic waves have the longest wavelengths?*

The part of the electromagnetic spectrum that you can see is called **visible light.** It makes up only a very small portion of the electromagnetic spectrum. Visible light is a mixture of all the colors that you see in a rainbow: red, orange, yellow, green, blue, and violet. The different colors are the result of different wavelengths of light. The longest wavelengths of visible light are seen as red, while the shortest wavelengths are seen as violet. The wavelengths are detected as different colors because they affect the eye differently. You will learn more about the eye and vision in Section 4.

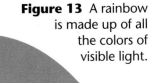

Figure 13 A rainbow is made up of all the colors of visible light.

The Behavior of Light

Light usually travels in straight lines unless it strikes an object. **When light strikes an object, the light can be absorbed, reflected, or transmitted.**

Absorption Some materials absorb, or take in and hold, light. Such materials include dark pavements and dark fabrics.

Reflection When light strikes a surface that it cannot enter, it bounces back. This is called **reflection.** There are many examples of reflection in your daily life. You have seen your own reflection in a mirror. Maybe you have worn sunglasses to guard against glare on a sunny day.

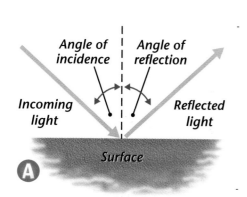

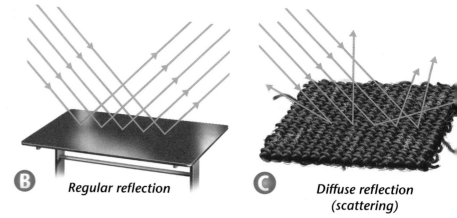

B *Regular reflection*

C *Diffuse reflection (scattering)*

Figure 14 When light strikes a surface through which it cannot pass, it is reflected. **A.** The angle of reflection is equal to the angle of incidence. **B.** When light strikes a smooth surface, regular reflection occurs. **C.** When light strikes an uneven surface, scattering occurs.

Figure 14A shows the reflection of a light ray. The **angle of incidence** is the angle between the incoming ray and an imaginary line that is perpendicular to the surface. The **angle of reflection** is the angle between the reflected wave and the imaginary line. The angle of reflection is always equal to the angle of incidence.

When parallel rays of light hit a smooth surface, regular reflection occurs. All of the rays are reflected at the same angle, as shown in Figure 14B. When you look in a mirror, you see yourself because of regularly reflected light. When parallel rays of light hit a bumpy or uneven surface, diffuse reflection occurs. Since the rays hit the surface at different angles, the rays are scattered, or reflected at different angles, as shown in Figure 14C. Some surfaces that appear to be smooth, such as a freshly painted wall, have small bumps that scatter light. You can see most objects because of scattering.

Transmission Glass and other transparent materials transmit light, or allow the light to pass through. When light is transmitted from one material to another, it changes speed. For example, light travels faster in air than in water. When a light ray that is traveling through air enters the surface of water at an angle, it changes speed and bends. The bending of light due to a change in speed is called **refraction.** Some materials cause light to bend more than others. Figure 15 shows how light passes from air to water to glass, and to air again.

Air

Water

Glass

Air

Figure 15 As light passes from one material to another, it changes speed and is refracted.

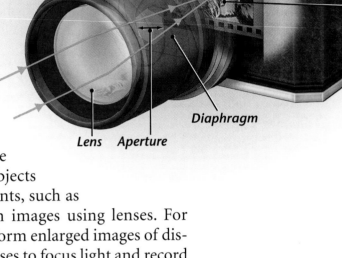

Figure 16 Light enters the camera through the lens and forms an image on the film.

Shutter control

Image on film

Diaphragm

Lens *Aperture*

Using Light

Have you ever looked through binoculars, used a magnifying glass or a telescope, or worn eyeglasses? If so, you have used lenses to refract light. A lens forms an image by refracting light rays that pass through it. In Chapter 1, you saw how a microscope uses convex lenses to make small objects look larger. Other optical instruments, such as telescopes and cameras, also form images using lenses. For example, a telescope uses lenses to form enlarged images of distant objects, while a camera uses lenses to focus light and record an image of an object on film.

Figure 16 shows the structure of a camera. To take a photograph, you press the shutter control button. This opens the shutter and allows light into the camera. The diaphragm controls the amount of light that enters by changing the size of the aperture, or opening. The lens then focuses the light rays to form an image on the film. The film is developed into negatives by treating it with chemicals. The negative is then used to print the photograph.

Section 3 Review

1. List the different types of electromagnetic waves.
2. What are the ways that light can behave when it strikes an object?
3. What is visible light?
4. **Thinking Critically Classifying** Explain what kind of reflection occurs when you look in a mirror and when you look at a wall.

Science at Home

Demonstrate to your family how light usually travels in a straight line. Punch holes in four index cards and stand them in front of a white screen. Run a piece of string through all four holes and pull it tight, then remove the string. Turn the room lights off and shine a flashlight through the holes. Move one of the cards and notice what happens on the screen.

SECTION 4 The Senses

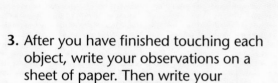

DISCOVER · ACTIVITY· · · ·

What's in the Bag?

1. Your teacher will give you a paper bag that contains several objects. Your challenge is to use only your sense of touch to identify each object. You will not look inside the bag.

2. Put your hand in the bag and carefully touch each object. Observe the shape of each object. Note whether its surface is rough or smooth. Also note other characteristics, such as its size, what it seems to be made of, and whether it can be bent.

3. After you have finished touching each object, write your observations on a sheet of paper. Then write your inference about what each object is.

Think It Over
Observing What could you determine about each object without looking at it? What could you not determine?

GUIDE FOR READING

◆ **What overall function do the senses perform?**

◆ **How do your eyes enable you to see?**

◆ **How do you hear?**

Reading Tip As you read, write an outline of this section. Use the headings in the section as the main topics in the outline.

You waited in line to get on the ride, and now it's about to begin. You grip the bars as the ride suddenly starts to move. Before you know it, you are lifted high above the ground and you feel the air whipping by. All you see is a dizzy blur.

You can thrill to the speed of amusement park rides because of your senses. **Each of your major senses—vision, hearing, balance, smell, taste, and touch—picks up a specific type of information about your environment. The sense organs change that information into nerve impulses and send the impulses to your brain.** Your brain then interprets the information. Because of the way in which your senses and brain work together, you learn a great deal about your environment.

Figure 17 Riders and bright lights whizzing by—that's what you see when you watch this amusement park ride.

702

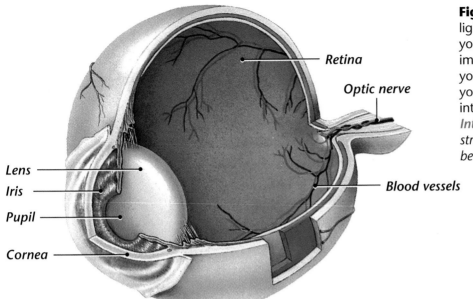

Retina

Optic nerve

Lens

Iris

Pupil

Cornea

Blood vessels

Figure 18 You see an object when light coming from the object enters your eye. The light produces an image on your retina. Receptors in your retina then send impulses to your cerebrum, and your cerebrum interprets these impulses. *Interpreting Diagrams What structures must light pass through before it reaches your retina?*

Vision

Your eyes are the sense organs that enable you to see the objects in your environment. They let you see this book in front of you, the window across the room, and the world outside the window. **Your eyes respond to the stimulus of light. They convert that stimulus into impulses that your brain interprets, enabling you to see.**

How Light Enters Your Eye When rays of light strike the eye, they pass through the structures shown in Figure 18. First, the light strikes the **cornea** (KAWR nee uh), the clear tissue that covers the front of the eye. The light then passes through a fluid-filled chamber behind the cornea and reaches the pupil. The **pupil** is the opening through which light enters the eye.

You may have noticed that people's pupils change size when they go from a dark room into bright sunshine. In bright light, the pupil becomes smaller. In dim light, the pupil becomes larger. The size of the pupil is adjusted by muscles in the iris. The **iris** is a circular structure that surrounds the pupil and regulates the amount of light entering the eye. The iris also gives the eye its color. If you have brown eyes, your irises are brown.

How Light Is Focused Light that passes through the pupil strikes the lens. The **lens** is a flexible structure that focuses light. The lens of your eye functions something like the lens of a camera, which focuses light on photographic film. Because of the way in which the lens of the eye bends the light rays, the image it produces is upside down and reversed. Muscles that attach to the lens adjust its shape. This adjustment produces an image that is clear and in focus.

Why Do You Need Two Eyes? In this activity, you will investigate how your two eyes work together to allow you to see.

1. With your arms fully extended, hold a plastic drinking straw in one hand and a pipe cleaner in the other.
2. With both eyes open, try to insert the pipe cleaner into the straw.
3. Now close your right eye. Try to insert the pipe cleaner into the straw.
4. Repeat Step 3, but this time close your left eye instead of your right eye.

Inferring How does closing one eye affect your ability to judge distances?

Figure 19 An upside-down image is focused on the retina. *Applying Concepts When you see an object, why does it appear right-side up?*

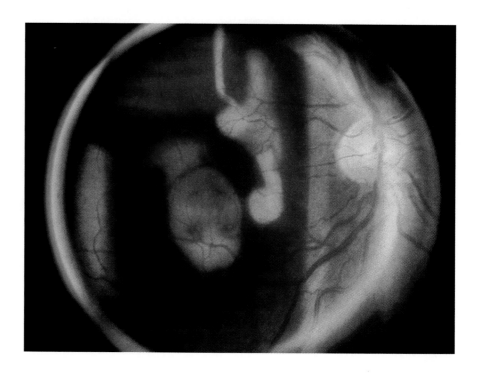

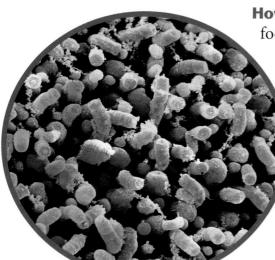

Figure 20 The retina of the eye contains light-sensitive cells. In this photograph, the rods have been colored pink, and the cones have been colored blue.

How You See an Image After passing through the lens, the focused light rays pass through a transparent, jellylike fluid. Then the light rays strike the **retina** (RET 'n uh), the layer of receptor cells that lines the back of the eye. The retina contains about 130 million receptor cells that respond to light. There are two types of receptors, rods and cones. Rod cells work best in dim light and enable you to see black, white, and shades of gray. In contrast, cone cells only work well in bright light and enable you to see colors. This difference between rods and cones explains why you see colors best in bright light, but you see only shadowy gray images in dim light.

When light strikes the rods and cones, nerve impulses begin. These nerve impulses travel to the cerebrum through the optic nerves. One optic nerve comes from the left eye and the other one comes from the right. In the cerebrum, two things happen. The brain turns the reversed image right-side up. In addition, the brain combines the images from each eye to produce a single image.

Correcting Vision Problems

INTEGRATING PHYSICS A lens—whether it is in your eye, in a camera, or in eyeglasses—is a curved, transparent object that bends light rays as they pass through it. If the lens of the eye does not focus light properly on the retina, vision problems result. The glass or plastic lenses in eyeglasses can help correct such vision problems.

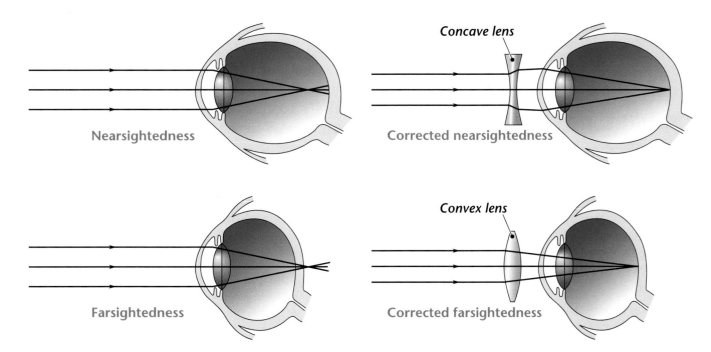

Nearsightedness People with **nearsightedness** can see nearby objects clearly. However, they have trouble seeing objects that are far away. Nearsightedness is caused by an eyeball that is too long. Because of the extra length that light must travel to reach the retina, distant objects do not focus sharply on the retina. Instead, the lens of the eye makes the image come into focus at a point in front of the retina, as shown in Figure 21.

To correct nearsightedness, a person needs to wear eyeglasses with concave lenses. A concave lens is a lens that is thicker at the edges than it is in the center. When light rays pass through a concave lens, they are bent away from the center of the lens. The concave lenses in glasses make light rays spread out before they reach the lens of the eye. Then, when these rays pass through the lens of the eye, they focus on the retina rather than in front of it.

Farsightedness People with **farsightedness** can see distant objects clearly. Nearby objects, however, look blurry. The eyeballs of people with farsightedness are too short. Because of this, the lens of the eye bends light from nearby objects so that the image does not focus properly on the retina. If light could pass through the retina, the image would come into sharp focus at a point behind the retina, as shown in Figure 21.

Convex lenses are used to help correct farsightedness. A convex lens is thicker in the middle than the edges. The convex lens makes the light rays bend toward each other before they reach the eye. Then the lens of the eye bends the rays even more. This bending makes the image focus exactly on the retina.

Figure 21 Nearsightedness and farsightedness are conditions in which images do not focus properly on the retina. The diagrams on the left show where the images are focused in both of these conditions. The diagrams on the right show how lenses in eyeglasses can help correct these conditions.

☑ *Checkpoint* *What type of lens is used to correct nearsightedness?*

Hearing

What wakes you up in the morning? Maybe an alarm clock buzzes, or perhaps your parent calls you. On a summer morning, you might hear birds singing. Whatever wakes you up, there's a good chance that it's a sound of some sort. **Your ears are the sense organs that respond to the stimulus of sound. The ears convert the sound to nerve impulses that your brain interprets.** So when you hear an alarm clock or other morning sound, your brain tells you that it's time to wake up.

How Sound Is Produced Sound is produced by vibrations. The material that is vibrating, or moving rapidly back and forth, may be almost anything—a guitar string, an insect's wings, or splashing water.

INTEGRATING PHYSICS

The vibrations create waves. The waves move outward from the source of the sound, something like ripples moving out from a stone dropped in water. The waves consist of moving particles, such as the molecules that make up air. When you hear a friend's voice, for example, sound waves have traveled from your friend's larynx to your ears. In addition to being able to travel through gases such as air, sound waves can also travel through liquids such as water and solids such as wood.

Sound Vibrations and the Ear The ear is structured to receive sound vibrations. As you can see in Figure 23, the ear consists of three parts—the outer ear, middle ear, and inner ear. The outer ear includes the part of the ear that you see. The visible part of the outer ear is shaped like a funnel.

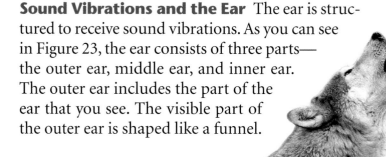

Figure 22 When a wolf howls, its vocal cords vibrate. The vibrating vocal cords produce sound waves. When the sound waves reach a person's ear, the person hears the wolf.

This funnel-like shape enables the outer ear to gather sound waves. The sound waves then travel down the ear canal, which is also part of the outer ear.

At the end of the ear canal, sound waves reach the eardrum. The **eardrum,** which separates the outer ear from the middle ear, is a membrane that vibrates when sound waves strike it. Your eardrum vibrates in much the same way that the surface of a drum vibrates when it is struck. Vibrations from the eardrum pass to the middle ear, which contains the three smallest bones in the body—the hammer, anvil, and stirrup. The names of these bones are based on their shapes. The vibrating eardrum makes the hammer vibrate. The hammer passes the vibrations to the anvil, and the anvil passes them to the stirrup.

How You Hear The stirrup vibrates against a thin membrane that covers the opening of the inner ear. The membrane channels the vibrations into the fluid in the cochlea. The **cochlea** (KAHK le uh) is a snail-shaped tube that is lined with receptors that respond to sound. When the fluid in the cochlea vibrates, it stimulates these receptors. Sensory neurons then send nerve impulses to the cerebrum through the auditory nerve. These impulses are interpreted as sounds that you hear.

✓ *Checkpoint* *Where in the ear is the cochlea located?*

Your Sense of Balance

Your ear also controls your sense of balance. Above the cochlea in your inner ear are the **semicircular canals,** which are the structures in the ear that are responsible for your sense of balance.

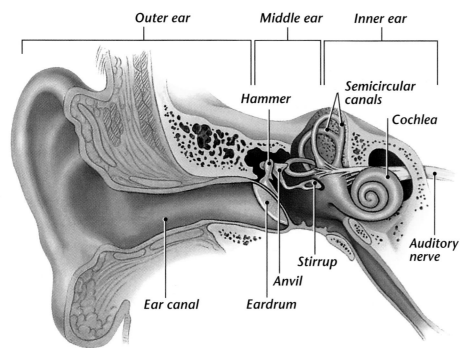

Outer ear   Middle ear   Inner ear

Hammer   Semicircular canals

Cochlea

Ear canal   Eardrum   Anvil   Stirrup   Auditory nerve

Figure 23 The ear has three regions—the outer ear, the middle ear, and the inner ear. Sound waves enter the outer ear and make structures in the middle ear vibrate. When the vibrations reach the inner ear, nerve impulses travel to the cerebrum through the auditory nerve. *Predicting What would happen if the bones of the middle ear were stuck together and could not move?*

Figure 24 The semicircular canals of the inner ear enable people to keep their balance—even in very tricky situations!

You can see how these structures got their name if you look at Figure 24. These canals, as well as two tiny sacs located behind them, are full of fluid. The canals and sacs are also lined with tiny cells that have hairlike extensions.

When your head moves, the fluid in the semicircular canals is set in motion. The moving fluid makes the cells' hairlike extensions bend. This bending produces nerve impulses in sensory neurons. The impulses travel to the cerebellum. The cerebellum then analyzes the impulses to determine the way your head is moving and the position of your body. If the cerebellum senses that you are losing your balance, it sends impulses to muscles that help you restore your balance.

Smell and Taste

You walk into the house and smell the aroma of freshly baked cookies. You bite into one and taste its rich chocolate flavor. When you smelled the cookies, receptors in your nose reacted to chemicals carried by the air from the cookies to your nose. When you took a bite of a cookie, taste buds on your tongue responded to chemicals in the food. These food chemicals were dissolved in saliva, which came in contact with your taste buds.

The senses of smell and taste work closely together, and both depend on chemicals. The chemicals trigger responses in receptors in the nose and mouth. Nerve impulses then travel to the brain, where they are interpreted as smells or tastes.

The nose can distinguish at least 50 basic odors. In contrast, there are only four main kinds of taste buds—sweet, sour, salty,

Designing Experiments

ACTIVITY

Can people tell one food from another if they can taste the foods but not smell them? Design an experiment to find out. Use these foods: a peeled pear, a peeled apple, and a peeled raw potato. Be sure to control all variables except the one you are testing. Write your hypothesis and a description of your procedure. Show these to your teacher. Do not perform your experiment until your teacher approves your procedure.

and bitter. When you eat, however, you experience a much wider variety of tastes. The flavor of food is determined by both the the senses of smell and taste. When you have a cold, your favorite foods may not taste as good as they usually do. That is because a stuffy nose can decrease your ability to smell food.

Touch

Unlike vision, hearing, balance, smell, and taste, the sense of touch is not found in one specific place. Instead, the sense of touch is found in all areas of your skin. Your skin is your largest sense organ!

Your skin contains different kinds of touch receptors. Some of these receptors respond to light touch and others to heavy pressure. Still other receptors pick up sensations of pain and temperature change.

The receptors that respond to light touch are in the upper part of the dermis. They tell you when something brushes against your skin. These receptors also let you feel the textures of objects, such as smooth glass and rough sandpaper. Receptors deeper in the dermis pick up the feeling of pressure. Press down hard on the top of your desk, for example, and you will feel pressure in your fingers.

The dermis also contains receptors that respond to temperature and pain. Pain is unpleasant, but it can be one of the body's most important feelings, because it alerts the body to possible danger. Have you ever stepped into a bathtub of very hot water and then immediately pulled your foot out? If so, you can appreciate how pain can trigger an important response in your body.

Figure 25 Blind people use their sense of touch to read. To do this, they run their fingers over words written in Braille. Braille uses raised dots to represent letters and numbers. Here a teacher shows a blind child how to read Braille.

 Section 4 Review

1. What overall role do the senses perform in the body?
2. Describe the process by which your eyes produce an image of your surroundings. Begin at the point at which light is focused by the lens.
3. How do sound vibrations affect structures in the ear to produce the sensation of hearing?
4. How are the senses of taste and smell similar? How are they different?
5. **Thinking Critically** **Relating Cause and Effect** Infections of the inner ear sometimes make people more likely to lose their balance and fall. Explain why this is so.

CHAPTER PROJECT

Check Your Progress
By now, you should have submitted your plans for your experiment to your teacher. Make any necessary changes in the plan. Prepare all the materials for the fair, including the illusions and questionnaire. Have a data table ready so you can record all responses. (*Hint:* Be sure the people you test cannot see or hear each other's responses. Also, test a large enough number of individuals.)

SECTION 5 Alcohol and Other Drugs

How Can You Best Say No?

1. In this activity, you will use candy to represent drugs. Your teacher will divide the class into groups of three students. In each group, your teacher will appoint two students to try to convince the other person to take the "drugs."

2. Depending on your role, you should think of arguments to get the person to accept the candy or arguments against accepting it. After everyone has had a chance to think of arguments, begin the discussion.

3. After a while, students in each group should exchange roles.

Think It Over

Inferring What role does peer pressure play in whether or not a person decides to abuse drugs?

GUIDE FOR READING

◆ How do commonly abused drugs affect the body?

◆ How does alcohol abuse harm the body?

Reading Tip Before you read, preview the table on page 713. List some ways in which drugs affect the central nervous system.

Drugs! You probably hear and see that word in a lot of places. Drugstores sell drugs to relieve headaches, soothe upset stomachs, and stop coughs. Radio and television programs and magazine articles explore drug-related problems. Your school probably has a program to educate students about drugs. When people talk about drugs, what do they mean? To a scientist, a **drug** is any chemical that causes changes in a person's body or behavior. Many drugs affect the functioning of the nervous system.

Medicines

Medicines are legal drugs that help the body fight disease and injury. Aspirin, for example, is a medicine that can relieve pain. To purchase some medicines, you need a doctor's prescription. Other medicines, however, can be bought in drugstores or supermarkets without a prescription. If medicines are used properly, they can help you stay healthy or speed your recovery from sickness. Whenever you take medicines of any kind, it is important to follow the directions for their proper use.

◀ Medicines in a drugstore

Drug Abuse

The deliberate misuse of drugs for purposes other than medical ones is called **drug abuse.** Medicines can be abused drugs if they are used in a way for which they were not intended. Many abused drugs, however, such as cocaine and heroin, are illegal under any circumstances. The use of these drugs is against the law because their effects on the body are almost always very dangerous.

Immediate Effects of Abused Drugs Abused drugs start to affect the body very shortly after they are taken. Different drugs have different effects. Some drugs cause nausea and a fast, irregular heartbeat. Others can cause sleepiness. Drug abusers may also experience headaches, dizziness, and trembling.

Most commonly abused drugs, such as marijuana, alcohol, and cocaine, are especially dangerous because they act on the brain and other parts of the nervous system. For example, alcohol can cause confusion, poor muscle coordination, and blurred vision. These effects are especially dangerous in situations in which an alert mind is essential, such as driving a car.

Most abused drugs can alter, or change, a person's mood and feelings. Because of this effect, these drugs are often called mood-altering drugs. For example, the mood of a person under the influence of marijuana may change from calm to anxious. Alcohol can sometimes make a person angry and even violent. Mood-altering drugs also affect patterns of thinking and the way in which the brain interprets information from the senses.

Tolerance If a person takes a drug regularly, the body may develop a tolerance to the drug. **Tolerance** is a state in which a drug user needs larger and larger amounts of the drug to produce the same effect on the body. Tolerance can cause people to take a very large amount of a drug, or an overdose. People who take an overdose may become unconscious or even die.

Figure 26 Abused drugs such as these can cause serious physical and emotional problems.
Applying Concepts List three ways in which drugs can affect the body.

Addiction   For many commonly abused drugs, repeated use can result in addiction. The body becomes physically dependent on the drug. If a drug addict misses a few doses of the drug, the body reacts to the lack of the drug. The person may experience headaches, fever, vomiting, body aches, and muscle cramps. The person is experiencing **withdrawal,** a period of adjustment that occurs when a person stops taking a drug.

Some drugs may also cause a person to become emotionally dependent on them. The person becomes accustomed to the feelings and moods produced by the drug. Therefore, the person has a strong desire to continue using the drug.

✓ *Checkpoint*   *What is meant by a tolerance to a drug?*

Other Effects of Drug Abuse

Drugs can also affect a person's health indirectly. Drug users sometimes share needles. When a person uses a needle to inject a drug, some of the person's blood remains in the needle after it is withdrawn. If the person has HIV or another pathogen in the blood, the next person to use the needle may become infected with the pathogen.

The abuse of drugs also has serious legal and social effects. A person who is caught using or selling an illegal drug may have to pay a fine or go to jail. Drug abuse can also make a person unable to get along with others. Drug abusers often have a hard time doing well in school or holding a job.

Kinds of Drugs

Figure 27 lists and describes the characteristics of some commonly abused drugs. Notice in the chart that some drugs are classified as depressants. **Depressants** are drugs that slow down the activity of the central nervous system. When people take depressants, their muscles relax and they may become sleepy. They may take longer than normal to respond to stimuli. For example, depressants may prevent people from reacting quickly to the danger of a car rushing toward them. Alcohol and narcotics, such as heroin, are depressants.

Stimulants, in contrast, speed up body processes. They make the heart beat faster and make the breathing rate increase. Cocaine and nicotine are stimulants, as are amphetamines. Amphetamines (am FET uh meenz) are prescription drugs that are sometimes sold illegally.

Some Effects of Commonly Abused Drugs

Drug Type	Short-Term Effects	Long-Term Effects	Addiction?	Emotional Dependence?
marijuana (including hashish)	anxiety, panic, excitement, sleepiness	difficulty with concentration and memory, respiratory disease and lung cancer	probably not	yes
nicotine (in cigarettes, cigars, chewing tobacco)	stimulant; nausea, loss of appetite, headache	heart and lung disease, difficulty breathing, heavy coughing	yes, strongly so	yes
alcohol	depressant; decreased alertness, poor reflexes, nausea, emotional depression	liver and brain damage, inadequate nutrition	yes	yes
inhalants (glue, nail polish remover, paint thinner)	sleepiness, nausea, headaches, emotional depression	damage to liver, kidneys, and brain; hallucinations	no	yes
cocaine (including crack)	stimulant; nervousness, disturbed sleep, loss of appetite	mental illness, damage to lining of nose, irregular heartbeat, heart or breathing failure, liver damage	yes	yes, strongly so
amphetamines	stimulant; restlessness, rapid speech, dizziness	restlessness, irritability, irregular heartbeat, liver damage	possible	yes
hallucinogens (LSD, mescaline, PCP)	hallucinations, anxiety, panic; thoughts and actions not connected to reality	mental illness; fearfulness; behavioral changes, including violence	no	yes
barbiturates (Phenobarbital, Nembutal, Seconal)	depressant; decreased alertness, slowed thought processes, poor muscle coordination	sleepiness, irritability, confusion	yes	yes
tranquilizers (Valium, Xanax)	depressant; blurred vision, sleepiness, unclear speech, headache, skin rash	blood and liver disease	yes	yes
narcotics (opium, codeine, morphine, heroin)	depressant; sleepiness, nausea, hallucinations	convulsion, coma, death	yes, very rapid development	yes, strongly so
anabolic steroids	mood swings	heart, liver, and kidney damage; hypertension; overgrowth of skull and facial bones	no	yes

Figure 27 Abused drugs can have many serious effects on the body. *Interpreting Charts What are the long-term effects of using inhalants?*

Some substances, called inhalants, produce mood-altering effects when they are inhaled, or breathed in. Inhalants include paint thinner, nail polish remover, and some kinds of cleaning fluids. Hallucinogens, such as LSD and mescaline, can make people see or hear things that do not really exist.

Some athletes try to improve their performance by taking drugs known as steroids. **Anabolic steroids** (an uh BAH lik steer oydz) are synthetic chemicals that are similar to hormones produced in the body. You will learn more about hormones in Chapter 23.

Anabolic steroids may increase muscle size and strength. However, steroids can cause mood changes that lead to violence.

Real-World Lab

You, the Consumer

With Caffeine or Without?

Caffeine is a stimulant found in some beverages and foods, such as coffee and cola drinks. In this lab, you'll observe the effect that caffeine has on a nonhuman organism to help understand how caffeine may affect your own body.

Problem

What body changes does caffeine produce in water fleas (*Daphnia*)?

Skills Focus

developing hypotheses, designing experiments

Materials

drinking straw	scissors
metric ruler	toothpick
petroleum jelly	microscope slide
Daphnia culture	microscope
plastic dropper	

adrenaline solution (about 0.01%)
clock or watch with second hand
beverages with and without caffeine

Procedure

Part 1 Observing Effects of a Known Stimulant

1. Cut off the tip of a drinking straw to form a tiny ring about 1 mm deep. With a toothpick, spread some petroleum jelly along the top rim of the ring.
2. Place the ring, jelly side down, on a microscope slide. This ring will be a chamber for your water fleas.
3. Using a plastic dropper, add a drop of *Daphnia* culture to the chamber. Then use the dropper to draw back most of the water. Leave the *Daphnia* and a small amount of water on the slide.
4. Use the low-power lens of a microscope to locate a water flea. Observe the heart, which you can see in the diagram.
5. Use a watch or clock with a second hand to count the number of heartbeats you observe in 1 minute. Record the heartbeat count in your notebook.

In addition, steroid abuse can cause serious health problems, such as heart damage, liver damage, and increased blood pressure. Steroid use is especially dangerous for teenagers, whose growing bodies can be permanently damaged.

Alcohol

Alcohol is a drug found in many beverages, including beer, wine, cocktails, and hard liquor. Alcohol is a powerful depressant. In the United States, it is illegal for people under the age of 21 to buy or possess alcohol. In spite of this fact, alcohol is the most commonly abused drug in people aged 12 to 17.

6. Remove the slide from the microscope. Use a plastic dropper to add 1 drop of adrenaline solution to the water flea chamber. (Adrenaline is a substance that is produced by the human body that acts in a manner similar to a stimulant.)

7. Place the slide on the microscope. Using low power, locate a water flea. Count and record the number of heartbeats in a minute.

Part 2 Testing the Effects of Caffeine

8. Using the procedures you followed in Part 1, design an experiment that tests the effect of caffeine on *Daphnia's* heartbeat. You can use beverages with and without caffeine in your investigation. Be sure to write a hypothesis and control all necessary variables.

9. Submit your experimental plan to your teacher for review. After making any necessary changes, carry out your experiment.

Analyze and Conclude

1. What effect does a stimulant have on the body?

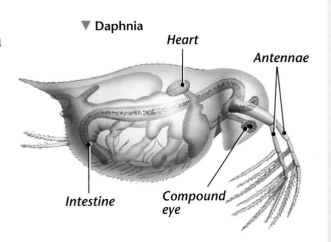

▼ Daphnia

Heart

Antennae

Intestine

Compound eye

2. In Part 1, how did you know that adrenaline acted as a stimulant?

3. In Part 2, did caffeine act as a stimulant?

4. **Apply** Based on your work in Part 2, how do you think your body would react to drinks with caffeine? To drinks without caffeine?

Design an Experiment

Do you think that "decaffeinated" products will act as a stimulant in *Daphnia?* Design a controlled experiment to find out. Obtain your teacher's approval before performing this experiment.

How Alcohol Affects the Body   Alcohol is absorbed by the digestive system quickly. If a person drinks alcohol on an empty stomach, the alcohol enters the blood and gets to the brain and other organs almost immediately. If alcohol is drunk with a meal, it takes longer to get into the blood.

To understand what alcohol does to the body, look at *Exploring the Effects of Alcohol.* The more alcohol in the blood, the more serious the effects. The amount of alcohol in the blood is usually expressed as blood alcohol concentration, or BAC. A BAC value of 0.1 percent means that one tenth of one percent of the fluid in the blood is alcohol. In some states, if car drivers have a BAC of 0.08 percent or more, they are legally drunk. In other states, drivers with a BAC of 0.1 are considered drunk.

Alcohol produces serious effects, including loss of normal judgment, at a BAC of less than 0.08 percent. This loss of judgment can have serious consequences. For example, people who have been drinking may not realize that they cannot drive a car safely. In the United States, alcohol is involved in about 40 percent of traffic-related deaths. About every two minutes, a person in the United States is injured in a car crash related to alcohol.

Long-Term Alcohol Abuse   Many adults drink occasionally, and in moderation, without serious safety or health problems. However, heavy drinking, especially over a long period, can result in significant health problems. **The abuse of alcohol can cause the destruction of cells in the brain and liver, and it can also lead to addiction and emotional dependence.** Damage to the brain can cause mental disturbances, such as hallucinations and

Figure 28 Alcohol is involved in many car crashes. Alcohol decreases a driver's ability to react quickly to traffic and road conditions.

loss of consciousness. The liver, which breaks down alcohol for elimination from the body, can become so scarred that it does not function properly. In addition, long-term alcohol abuse can increase the risk of getting certain kinds of cancer.

Abuse of alcohol can result in **alcoholism,** a disease in which a person is both physically addicted to and emotionally dependent on alcohol. To give up alcohol, alcoholics must go through withdrawal, as with any addictive drug. To give up drinking,

EXPLORING the Effects of Alcohol

Alcohol is a drug that affects every system of the body. It also impacts a person's thought processes and judgment.

Nervous system Vision becomes blurred. Speech becomes unclear. Control of behavior is reduced. Judgment becomes poor.

Skin Blood flow to the skin increases, causing rapid loss of body heat.

Cardiovascular system At first, heartbeat rate and blood pressure increase. Later, with large amounts of alcohol, the heartbeat rate and blood pressure may decrease.

Liver The liver breaks down alcohol. Over many years, liver damage can result.

Digestive system Alcohol is absorbed directly from the stomach and small intestine. The alcohol passes into the bloodstream quickly.

Excretory system Alcohol causes the kidneys to produce more urine. As a result, the drinker loses more water than usual.

Figure 29 The message is clear: drugs are dangerous, and you have the right to refuse to take them.

alcoholics need both medical and emotional help. Medical professionals and organizations such as Alcoholics Anonymous can help a person stop drinking.

Avoiding Drugs and Alcohol

The best way to avoid depending on drugs and alcohol is not to start using them. Many teenagers who start do so because of peer pressure from people who are abusing drugs. Try to avoid situations in which there is a possibility that drugs may be used.

If you are faced with pressure to use drugs, give a simple but honest reason for your refusal. For example, you might say that you don't want to risk getting into trouble with the law. You do not need to apologize for your decision. And remember that people who don't respect your feelings aren't very good friends.

To stay away from drugs, it is important to find healthy things to do with friends. Become involved in sports and other school or community activities in which you and your friends can have fun together. Such activities help you feel good about yourself. By deciding not to use drugs, you are protecting your health.

 Section 5 Review

1. How do abused drugs affect the nervous system? Why can these effects be dangerous?
2. What are the effects of long-term alcohol abuse?
3. What is alcoholism?
4. **Thinking Critically Comparing and Contrasting** Contrast the effects that stimulants and depressants have on the body.

Check Your Progress

CHAPTER PROJECT

By now you should have finished collecting your data and recording your observations. Now begin preparing a report about your findings. Think about the best way to communicate the procedures you followed and the results you obtained. Your report should explain how you think the illusions you chose trick the senses. Decide how to use graphs and other visuals in your report.

SECTION 1 How the Nervous System Works

Key Ideas

◆ The nervous system receives and responds to information about the external and internal environment, and helps to maintain homeostasis.

◆ Sensory neurons, interneurons, and motor neurons make up a chain of nerve cells that carry an impluse through the nervous system.

◆ To pass from an axon of a neuron to another structure, a nerve impulse must cross a space called a synapse.

Key Terms

stimulus • dendrite • interneuron
response • axon • motor neuron
neuron • nerve • synapse
nerve impulse • sensory neuron

SECTION 2 Divisions of the Nervous System

Key Ideas

◆ The central nervous system, which consists of the brain and spinal cord, is the control center of the body.

◆ The cerebrum in the brain receives input from the senses, controls voluntary muscles, and controls complex mental processes. The cerebellum coordinates muscle action and balance. The brain stem controls involuntary actions necessary for life.

◆ The peripheral nervous system links the central nervous system to the rest of the body.

◆ A reflex is an automatic response that occurs very rapidly and without conscious control.

Key Terms

central nervous system • cerebellum
peripheral nervous system • brainstem
brain • somatic nervous system
spinal cord • autonomic nervous system
cerebrum • reflex
• concussion

SECTION 3 Light

INTEGRATING PHYSICS

Key Ideas

◆ The electromagnetic spectrum is made up of radio waves, infrared rays, visible light, ultraviolet rays, X-rays, and gamma rays.

◆ When light strikes an object, the light can be absorbed, reflected, or transmitted.

Key Terms

electromagnetic waves • angle of incidence
electromagnetic spectrum • angle of reflection
visible light • refraction
reflection

SECTION 4 The Senses

Key Ideas

◆ The senses change information about the environment into nerve impulses.

◆ Your eyes convert light into nerve impulses that then travel to the brain.

◆ Your ears convert sound to nerve impulses that your brain interprets.

Key Terms

cornea • retina • eardrum
pupil • nearsightedness • cochlea
iris • farsightedness • semicircular canals
lens

SECTION 5 Alcohol and Other Drugs

INTEGRATING HEALTH

Key Ideas

◆ Abused drugs act on the nervous system.

◆ The long-term abuse of alcohol can damage the liver and brain and lead to alcoholism.

Key Terms

drug • withdrawal • anabolic steroid
drug abuse • depressant • alcoholism
tolerance • stimulant

USING THE INTERNET
www.science-explorer.phschool.com

California Test Prep: Reviewing Content

Multiple Choice

Choose the letter of the best answer.

1. A change or signal in the environment that makes the nervous system react is called a
   a. stimulus.
   b. response.
   c. receptor.
   d. synapse.

2. The structures that carry messages toward a neuron's cell body are
   a. axons.
   b. dendrites.
   c. nerves.
   d. impulses.

3. Which structure links the brain and the peripheral nervous system?
   a. the cerebrum
   b. the cerebellum
   c. the cochlea
   d. the spinal cord

4. Which structure adjusts the size of the pupil?
   a. the cornea
   b. the retina
   c. the lens
   d. the iris

5. Physical dependence on a drug is called
   a. withdrawal.
   b. response.
   c. addiction.
   d. tolerance.

True or False

If the statement is true, write true. If it is false, change the underlined word or words to make the statement true.

6. The <u>brainstem</u> is the part of the brain that controls involuntary actions.

7. When light changes speed as it enters a new material, it undergoes <u>reflection</u>.

8. In <u>nearsightedness</u>, a person cannot see nearby objects clearly.

9. The hammer, anvil, and <u>wrench</u> are the three bones in the middle ear.

10. Alcohol is a <u>depressant</u>.

Checking Concepts

11. Compare the functions of axons and dendrites.

12. What is the function of the autonomic nervous system?

13. What are some steps you can take to protect your central nervous system from injury?

14. Describe the difference between regular reflection and diffuse reflection.

15. Describe how lenses in eyeglasses correct nearsightedness and farsightedness.

16. List all the structures in your ear that must vibrate before you hear a sound. List them in the order in which they vibrate.

17. What are the effects of anabolic steroids on the body?

18. **Writing to Learn** Imagine that Earth has been invaded by space aliens who are exactly like humans except for the fact that they have no sense of touch. These aliens plan to take over Earth. Write a plan for fighting the aliens that makes use of the fact that they lack a sense of touch.

Thinking Visually

19. **Concept Map** Complete the following concept map about nerve cells and their functions. (For more on concept maps, see the Skills Handbook.)

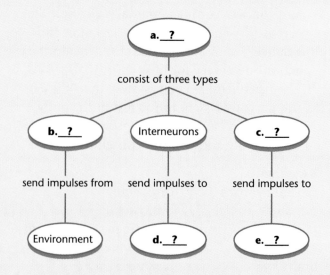

Test Prep: Skills

A person with normal vision stood at different distances from an eye chart and tried to identify the letters on the chart. The table gives the results. Use the table to answer Questions 20–22.

Distance from Eye Chart	Percent of Letters Identified Correctly
2 meters	100
4 meters	92
6 meters	80
8 meters	71
10 meters	60

20. Graphing Make a line graph of the data. Plot the distance from the chart on the horizontal axis. On the vertical axis, plot the percent of letters identified correctly.

21. Controlling Variables What was the manipulated variable in this experiment? What was the responding variable?

22. Predicting How would you expect the results to differ for a farsighted person? Explain.

Thinking Critically

23. Relating Cause and Effect When a person has a stroke, blood flow to part of the brain is reduced, and severe brain damage can result. Suppose that after a stroke, a woman is unable to move her right arm and right leg. In which side of her brain did the stroke occur? Explain.

24. Applying Concepts As a man walks barefoot along a beach, he steps on a sharp shell. His foot automatically jerks upward, even before he feels pain. What process is this an example of? How does it help protect the man?

25. Making Judgments If someone tried to convince you to take drugs, what arguments would you use as a way of refusing? Why do you think these arguments would be effective?

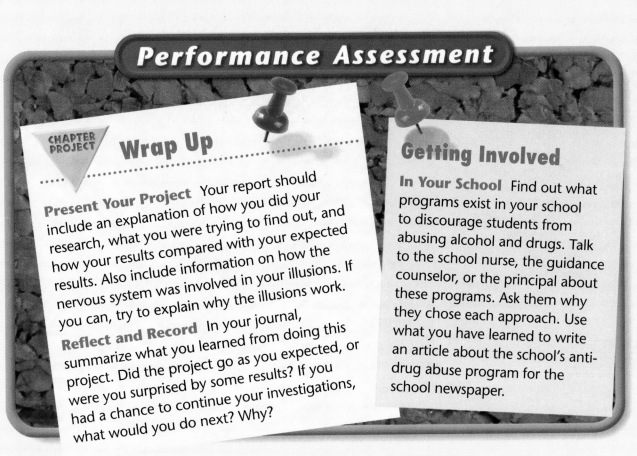

Performance Assessment

CHAPTER PROJECT Wrap Up

Present Your Project Your report should include an explanation of how you did your research, what you were trying to find out, and how your results compared with your expected results. Also include information on how the nervous system was involved in your illusions. If you can, try to explain why the illusions work.

Reflect and Record In your journal, summarize what you learned from doing this project. Did the project go as you expected, or were you surprised by some results? If you had a chance to continue your investigations, what would you do next? Why?

Getting Involved

In Your School Find out what programs exist in your school to discourage students from abusing alcohol and drugs. Talk to the school nurse, the guidance counselor, or the principal about these programs. Ask them why they chose each approach. Use what you have learned to write an article about the school's anti-drug abuse program for the school newspaper.

CHAPTER 23

The Endocrine System and Reproduction

CALIFORNIA SCIENCE CONTENT STANDARDS

The following California Science Content Standards are addressed in this chapter:

1. All living organisms are composed of cells, from just one to many trillions, whose details usually are visible only through a microscope.

   e. Cells divide to increase their numbers through a process of mitosis, which results in two daughter cells with identical sets of chromosomes.

   f. As multicellular organisms develop, their cells differentiate.

2. A typical cell of any organism contains genetic instructions that specify its traits. Those traits may be modified by environmental influences.

   b. Sexual reproduction produces offspring that inherit half their genes from each parent.

   e. DNA is the genetic material of living organisms, and is located in the chromosomes of each cell.

5. The anatomy and physiology of plants and animals illustrate the complementary nature of structure and function.

   b. Organ systems function because of the contributions of individual organs,

A Precious Bundle

With the arrival of their first baby, most new parents discover that their lives are totally changed. Their usual schedules are disrupted, and they suddenly need a new set of skills. Parents must begin to learn how to keep the infant comfortable and happy.

As you learn about reproduction and development, you'll experience what it's like to care for a "baby." Although your baby will be only a physical model, you'll have a chance to learn about the responsibilities of parenthood.

Your Goal To develop and follow a plan to care for a "baby" for three days and nights.

To complete this project, you must
- ◆ list all the essential tasks involved in caring for a young infant, and prepare a 24-hour schedule of those tasks
- ◆ make a model "baby" from a bag of flour, and care for the baby according to your schedule
- ◆ keep a journal of your thoughts and feelings as you care for your "baby," making entries at least twice a day

Get Started With classmates write down all the things that parents must do when caring for infants. Prepare a plan describing how to carry out those activities with your "baby." List the materials you'll need. If you require more information, write down your questions, then consult adult caregivers, day care facilities, or other resources.

Check Your Progress You'll be working on this project as you study this chapter. To keep your project on track, look for Check Your Progress boxes at the following points.

Section 1 Review, page 728: Present your child-care plan to your teacher for review.

Section 2 Review, page 734: Care for your "baby," and record your experiences in your journal.

Section 4 Review, page 747: Summarize your experiences.

Wrap Up At the end of the chapter (page 751), you'll share what you learned about parenthood.

"Breakfast now!" A baby may need care at any moment of the day or night.

tissues, and cells. The failure of any part can affect the entire system.

d. How the reproductive organs of the human female and male generate eggs and sperm, and how sexual activity may lead to fertilization and pregnancy.

e. The function of the umbilicus and placenta during pregnancy.

7. Scientific progress is made by asking meaningful questions and conducting careful investigations.

b. Utilize a variety of print and electronic resources (including the World Wide Web) to collect information as evidence as part of a research project.

c. Communicate the logical connection among hypothesis, science concepts,

tests conducted, data collected, and conclusions drawn from the scientific evidence.

SECTION 1 The Endocrine System

DISCOVER

What's the Signal?

1. Stand up and move around the room until your teacher says "Freeze!" Then stop moving immediately. Stay perfectly still until your teacher says "Start!" Then begin moving again.

2. Anyone who moves between the "Freeze!" command and the "Start!" command has to leave the game.

3. Play until only one person is left in the game. That person is the winner.

Think It Over

Inferring Why is it important for players in this game to respond to signals? What types of signals does the human body use?

GUIDE FOR READING

◆ What is the function of the endocrine system?

◆ How does negative feedback control hormone levels?

Reading Tip Before you read, preview *Exploring the Endocrine System* on pages 726–727. List the terms in the diagram that are new to you. Look for their meanings as you read.

You're playing softball on a hot afternoon. Without warning, thick, dark clouds form. Suddenly, there's a flash of lightning. Thunder cracks overhead. Someone screams, you jump, and everyone runs for cover. Your heart is pounding, your palms are sweaty, and your muscles are tight.

Your body's reaction to the sudden storm was caused mainly by your body's endocrine system. In this section, you will learn about the role of the endocrine system in many body processes—from the quick response to a thunder clap, to the slower body changes that turn a child into an adult.

The Role of the Endocrine System

The human body has two systems that regulate its activities. You learned about one, the nervous system, in Chapter 22. The endocrine system is the other regulating system. **The endocrine system controls many of the body's daily activities as well as long-term changes such as development.**

The endocrine system is made up of glands. Glands are organs that produce chemicals. You already know about some glands, such as those that produce saliva or sweat. Those glands release their chemicals into tiny tubes. The tubes deliver the chemicals to a specific location within the body or to the skin's surface.

The endocrine system does not have delivery tubes. **Endocrine glands** (EN duh krin) produce and release their chemical products directly into the bloodstream. The blood then carries those chemicals throughout the body.

Hormones

The chemical product of an endocrine gland is called a **hormone.** Hormones turn on, turn off, speed up, or slow down the activities of different organs and tissues. You can think of a hormone as a chemical messenger. Because hormones are carried by blood, they can regulate activities in tissues and organs far from the glands that produced them.

Hormone Production What causes the release of hormones? In situations such as a sudden storm, nerve impulses from the senses travel to the brain. There, information, such as the sound of thunder, is interpreted. The brain then sends a nerve impulse to a specific endocrine gland. That gland, in turn, releases the hormone adrenaline into the bloodstream. As you read in Chapter 16, adrenaline causes your heart rate to increase, makes you breathe faster and deeper, and releases sugars that power your muscles.

In contrast to the body's response to a nerve impulse, hormones cause a slower, but longer-lasting, response. For example, the brain sends a quick signal to an endocrine gland to release adrenaline into the bloodstream. When the adrenaline reaches the heart, it makes the heart beat more rapidly. The heart continues to race until the amount of adrenaline in the blood drops to a normal level.

Target Cells When a hormone enters the bloodstream, why does it affect some organs but not others? **INTEGRATING CHEMISTRY** The answer lies in its chemical structure. A hormone interacts only with certain **target cells,** cells that recognize the hormone's chemical structure. A hormone and its target cell fit together the way a key fits into a lock. Hormones not meant for a particular organ will travel through the bloodstream until they find the "lock" that they fit.

Figure 1 The endocrine system controls the body's response to an exciting situation (left) as well as the changes that occur as a child grows (right). *Applying Concepts What substances produced by endocrine glands control these body processes?*

Each endocrine gland releases different hormones and thus controls different processes. *Exploring the Endocrine System* shows the locations of the endocrine glands and describes some activities they control.

The Hypothalamus

The nervous system and the endocrine system work together. The **hypothalamus** (hy poh THAL uh mus), a tiny part of the brain near the middle of your head, is the link between the two systems. Nerve messages controlling sleep, hunger, and other conditions come from the hypothalamus. The hypothalamus also produces hormones that control other endocrine glands and organs. Through its nerve impulses and hormones, the hypothalamus plays a major role in maintaining homeostasis.

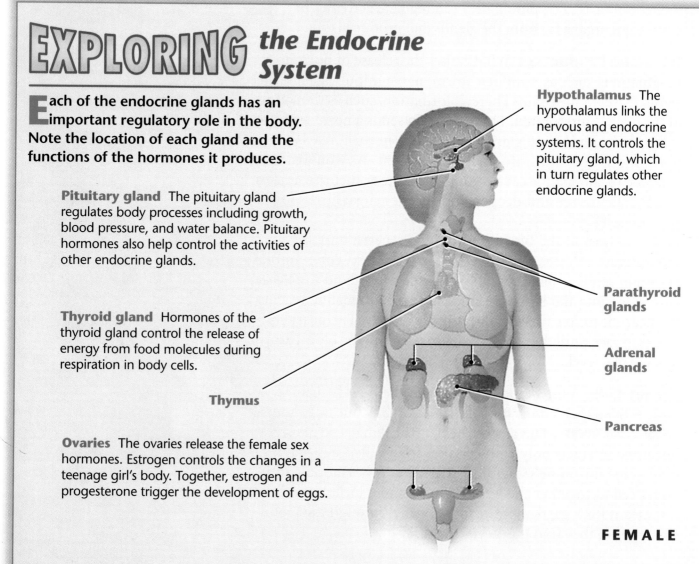

EXPLORING the Endocrine System

Each of the endocrine glands has an important regulatory role in the body. Note the location of each gland and the functions of the hormones it produces.

Pituitary gland The pituitary gland regulates body processes including growth, blood pressure, and water balance. Pituitary hormones also help control the activities of other endocrine glands.

Thyroid gland Hormones of the thyroid gland control the release of energy from food molecules during respiration in body cells.

Thymus

Ovaries The ovaries release the female sex hormones. Estrogen controls the changes in a teenage girl's body. Together, estrogen and progesterone trigger the development of eggs.

Hypothalamus The hypothalamus links the nervous and endocrine systems. It controls the pituitary gland, which in turn regulates other endocrine glands.

Parathyroid glands

Adrenal glands

Pancreas

FEMALE

The Pituitary Gland

Just below the hypothalamus is an endocrine gland about the size of a pea. The **pituitary gland** (pih TOO ih tehr ee) communicates with the hypothalamus to control many body activities. In response to nerve impulses or hormone signals from the hypothalamus, the pituitary gland releases its hormones. Some of those hormones act as an "on" switch for other endocrine glands. For example, one pituitary hormone signals the thyroid gland to produce hormones. Other pituitary hormones control body activities directly. Growth hormone regulates growth from infancy to adulthood. Another pituitary hormone directs the kidneys to regulate the amount of water in the blood.

✓ *Checkpoint* *What causes the pituitary gland to release hormones?*

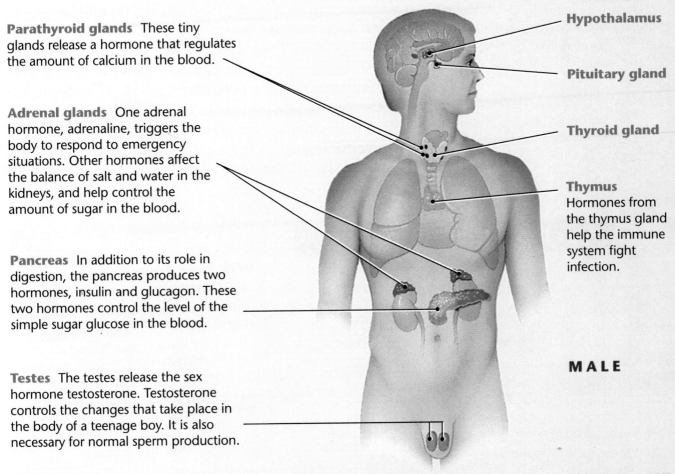

Parathyroid glands These tiny glands release a hormone that regulates the amount of calcium in the blood.

Adrenal glands One adrenal hormone, adrenaline, triggers the body to respond to emergency situations. Other hormones affect the balance of salt and water in the kidneys, and help control the amount of sugar in the blood.

Pancreas In addition to its role in digestion, the pancreas produces two hormones, insulin and glucagon. These two hormones control the level of the simple sugar glucose in the blood.

Testes The testes release the sex hormone testosterone. Testosterone controls the changes that take place in the body of a teenage boy. It is also necessary for normal sperm production.

Hypothalamus

Pituitary gland

Thyroid gland

Thymus Hormones from the thymus gland help the immune system fight infection.

MALE

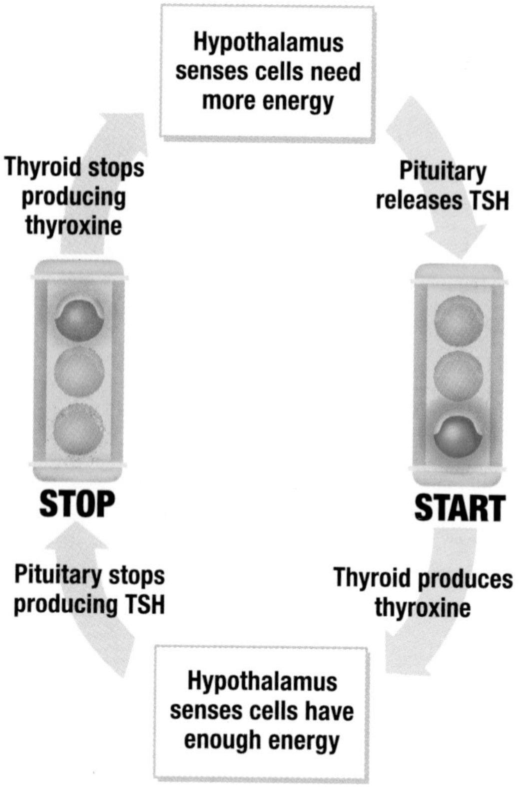

Hypothalamus senses cells need more energy

Pituitary releases TSH

Thyroid stops producing thyroxine

STOP

START

Pituitary stops producing TSH

Thyroid produces thyroxine

Hypothalamus senses cells have enough energy

Figure 2 The release of the hormone thyroxine is controlled through negative feedback. When enough thyroxine is present, the system signals the thyroid gland to stop releasing the hormone. *Predicting* *What happens when the amount of thyroxine becomes too low?*

Negative Feedback

One way that the endocrine system maintains homeostasis may remind you of the way a heating system works. Suppose you set a thermostat at 20°C. If the temperature falls below 20°, the thermostat signals the furnace to turn on. When the furnace heats the area to the proper temperature, information about the warm conditions "feeds back" to the thermostat. The thermostat then gives the furnace a negative signal that means "no more heat." That signal turns the furnace off.

The type of signal used in a heating system is called **negative feedback** because the system is turned off by the condition it produces. The endocrine system often works in this way. Through negative feedback, when the amount of a particular hormone in the blood reaches a certain level, the endocrine system sends signals that stop the release of that hormone. **Negative feedback is an important way that the body maintains homeostasis.**

You can see an example of negative feedback in Figure 2. Like a thermostat in a cool room, the endocrine system senses when there's not enough thyroxine in the blood. Thyroxine is a thyroid hormone. It controls how much energy is available to cells. When there's not enough energy available, the hypothalamus signals the pituitary gland to release thyroid-stimulating hormone (TSH). That hormone signals the thyroid gland to release thyroxine. When the amount of thyroxine reaches the right level, the endocrine system signals the thyroid gland to stop releasing thyroxine.

Section 1 Review

1. What role does the endocrine system play in the body? What are the organs of the endocrine system called?

2. Explain how negative feedback helps to maintain homeostasis in the body.

3. How do the hypothalamus and the pituitary gland interact?

4. **Thinking Critically** **Making Judgments** Years ago, one of the endocrine glands was called the "master gland." Which part of the endocrine system would you consider the master gland? Explain.

Check Your Progress

CHAPTER PROJECT

You should now be ready to turn in your plan for your teacher's review. Your plan should include your daily schedule and a list of the materials you'll need. Be sure to describe the kind of journal you plan to keep. (*Hint:* Discuss with your teacher any problems you foresee in caring for the "baby" for three full days and nights.)

SECTION 2 The Male and Female Reproductive Systems

DISCOVER .... ACTIVITY

What's the Big Difference?

1. Your teacher will provide prepared slides of eggs and sperm.
2. Examine each slide under the microscope, first under low power, then under high power. Be sure you view at least one sample of egg and sperm from the same species.
3. Sketch and label each sample.

Think It Over

Observing What differences did you observe between sperm cells and egg cells? What general statement can you make about eggs and sperm?

Many differences between an adult animal and its young are controlled by the endocrine system. In humans, two endocrine glands—the ovaries in girls and the testes in boys—control many of the changes that occur as a child matures. These glands release hormones that cause the body to develop as a person grows older.

Sex Cells

You may find it hard to believe that you began life as a single cell. That single cell was produced by the joining of two other cells, an egg and a sperm. An **egg** is the female sex cell. A **sperm** is the male sex cell.

The joining of a sperm and an egg is called **fertilization.** Fertilization is an important part of **reproduction,** the process by which living things produce new individuals of the same type. When fertilization occurs, a fertilized egg, or **zygote,** is produced. Every one of the trillions of cells in your body is descended from the single cell that formed during fertilization.

Figure 3 This gosling began its life as a single cell. When it is fully grown, it will be made up of millions of cells.

> **GUIDE FOR READING**
>
> ◆ What are the organs of the male and female reproductive systems?
>
> ◆ What events occur during the menstrual cycle?
>
> *Reading Tip* As you read, create a table comparing the male and female reproductive systems. Include the type of sex cells and primary reproductive organs of each.

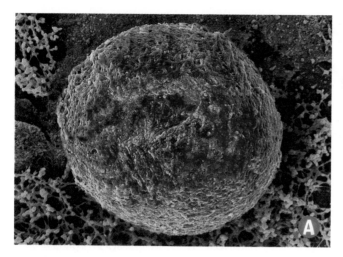

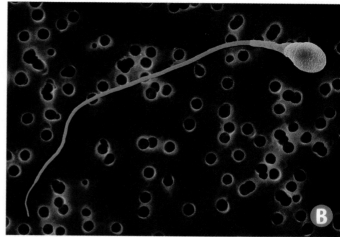

Figure 4 The human reproductive system produces either eggs or sperm. **A.** An egg is one of the largest cells in the body. **B.** A sperm, which is much smaller than an egg, has a tail that allows it to move.

Like other cells in the body, sex cells contain rod-shaped structures called chromosomes. **Chromosomes** (KROH muh sohmz) carry the information that controls inherited characteristics, such as eye color and blood type. Every cell in the human body, except the sex cells, contains 46 chromosomes. Each sex cell contains half that number, or 23 chromosomes. During fertilization, the 23 chromosomes in a sperm join the 23 chromosomes in an egg. The result is a zygote with 46 chromosomes. The zygote contains all of the information needed to produce a new human being.

✓ *Checkpoint* *What happens to the number of chromosomes when a male sex cell and a female sex cell join?*

The Male Reproductive System

The male reproductive system is shown in Figure 5. **The male reproductive system is specialized to produce sperm and the hormone testosterone.**

The Testes The oval-shaped **testes** (tes teez) (singular *testis*), are the organs of the male reproductive system in which sperm are produced. The testes are actually clusters of hundreds of tiny coiled tubes. Sperm are formed inside the tubes.

The testes also produce the hormone **testosterone** (tes TAHS tuh rohn). Testosterone controls the development of physical characteristics in men. Some of those characteristics include facial hair, a deep voice, broad shoulders, and the ability to produce sperm.

Notice in Figure 5 that the testes are located in an external pouch of skin called the **scrotum** (SKROH tum). That external location keeps the testes about 2° to 3°C below the usual body temperature of 37°C. That temperature difference is important. Sperm need the slightly cooler conditions to develop normally.

Sperm Production The production of sperm cells begins in males at some point during the teenage years. Each sperm is composed of a head that contains chromosomes and a long, whiplike tail. Basically, a sperm cell is a tiny package of chromosomes that can swim.

The Path of Sperm Cells Once sperm cells form in the testes, they travel through other structures in the male reproductive system. During this passage, sperm mix with fluids produced by nearby glands. This mix of sperm cells and fluids is called **semen** (SEE mun). Semen contains a huge number of sperm—about 5 to 10 million per drop! The fluids in semen provide an environment in which sperm can swim. Semen also contains nutrients that the moving sperm use as a source of energy.

Semen leaves the body through an organ called the **penis.** The male urethra runs through the penis. The urethra is the tube through which the semen travels as it leaves the body.

Urine also leaves the body through the urethra, as you learned in Chapter 20. When semen passes through the urethra, however, muscles near the bladder contract. Those muscles prevent urine and semen from mixing.

☑ *Checkpoint* *What is a sperm composed of?*

Figure 5 In the male reproductive system, the testes produce sperm and the hormone testosterone. *Interpreting Diagrams What pathway do sperm follow to reach the urethra?*

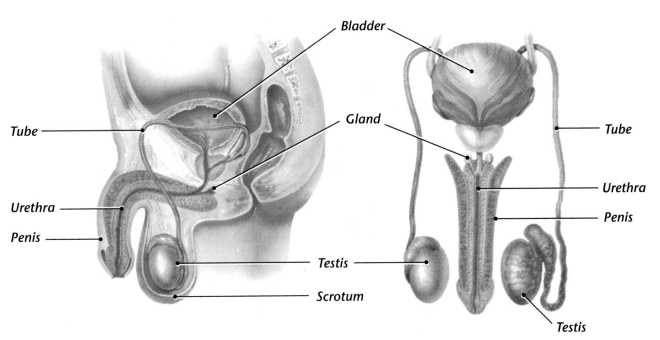

Bladder

Tube

Gland

Tube

Urethra

Urethra

Penis

Penis

Testis

Testis

Scrotum

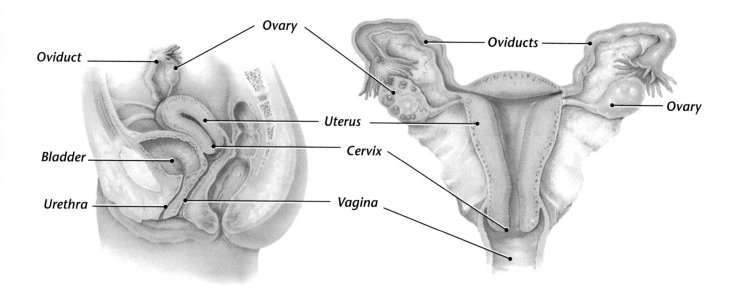

Figure 6 labels: Oviduct, Ovary, Uterus, Bladder, Cervix, Urethra, Vagina, Oviducts, Ovary

Figure 6 In the female reproductive system, the two ovaries produce eggs and hormones such as estrogen. From an ovary, an egg travels through an oviduct to the uterus. *Interpreting Diagrams Through what opening does an unfertilized egg pass when leaving the uterus?*

The Female Reproductive System

Unlike the male reproductive system, almost all of the female reproductive system is inside the body. **The role of the female reproductive system is to produce eggs and, if an egg is fertilized, to nourish a developing baby until birth.** The organs of the female reproductive system are shown in Figure 6.

The Ovaries Find the two ovaries in Figure 6. The **ovaries** (OH vuh reez) are located slightly below the waist, one on each side of the body. The name for these organs comes from the word *ova*, meaning "eggs." One major role of the ovaries is to produce egg cells.

Like the testes in males, the ovaries also are endocrine glands that produce hormones. One hormone, **estrogen** (ES truh jun), triggers the development of some adult female characteristics. For example, estrogen causes the hips to widen and the breasts to develop. Estrogen also plays a role in the process by which egg cells develop.

The Path of the Egg Cell As you can see in Figure 6, each ovary is located near an **oviduct** (OH vih duct). The two oviducts are passageways for eggs. They are also the places where fertilization usually occurs. Each month, one of the ovaries releases a mature egg, which enters the nearest oviduct. The egg moves through the oviduct, which leads to the uterus, or womb. The **uterus** (YOO tur us) is a hollow muscular organ about the size of a pear. If the egg has been fertilized, it remains in the uterus and begins to develop.

An egg that has not been fertilized starts to break down as it enters the uterus. It leaves the uterus through an opening at its base called the cervix. The egg then enters the vagina. The **vagina** (vuh JY nuh) is a muscular passageway leading to the outside of the body. The vagina is also called the birth canal. It is the passageway through which a baby leaves the mother's body during the birth process.

☑ *Checkpoint* *What is one of the roles of the ovaries?*

The Menstrual Cycle

When the female reproductive system becomes mature during the teenage years, there are about 400,000 undeveloped eggs in a woman's ovaries. However, only about 500 of those eggs will actually leave the ovaries and reach the uterus. An egg is released about once a month in a mature female's body. The monthly cycle of changes that occurs in the female reproductive system is called the **menstrual cycle** (MEN stroo ul).

During the menstrual cycle, an egg develops in an ovary. At the same time, the uterus prepares for the arrival of a fertilized egg. In this way, the menstrual cycle prepares the female's body for pregnancy, the condition that begins after fertilization has taken place.

Stages of the Cycle The menstrual cycle begins when an egg starts to mature in one of the ovaries. At the same time, the lining of the uterus begins to thicken. About halfway through a typical cycle, the mature egg is released from the ovary into an oviduct. This process is called **ovulation** (OH vyuh lay shun).

Sharpen your Skills

Graphing ACTIVITY

A woman's hormone levels change throughout the menstrual cycle. The table below shows the levels of one female hormone, known as LH, during the menstrual cycle.

Day	Level of LH
1	12
5	14
9	14
13	70
17	12
21	12
25	8

Construct a line graph using the information in the table. Label the horizontal axis *Day*. Label the vertical axis *Hormone Level*. What event takes place about the same time that LH reaches its highest level?

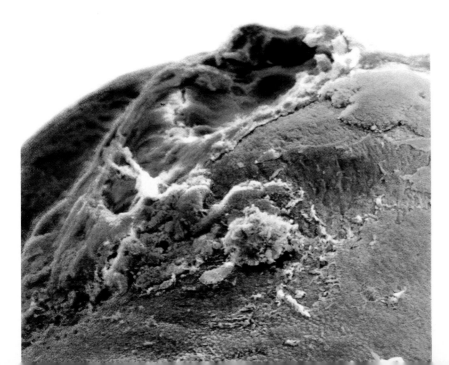

Figure 7 During ovulation an egg bursts from the side of an ovary. In this photograph, the egg is the round red structure on the right.

Once the egg is released, it can be fertilized for the next few days if sperm are present in the oviduct. If the egg is not fertilized, it begins to break down. The lining of the uterus also breaks down. The extra blood and tissue of the thickened lining pass out of the body through the vagina. This process is called **menstruation** (men stroo AY shun). On average, menstruation lasts about 4 to 6 days. At the same time that menstruation occurs, a new egg begins to mature in the ovary, and the cycle continues. You can follow the main steps in the cycle in Figure 8.

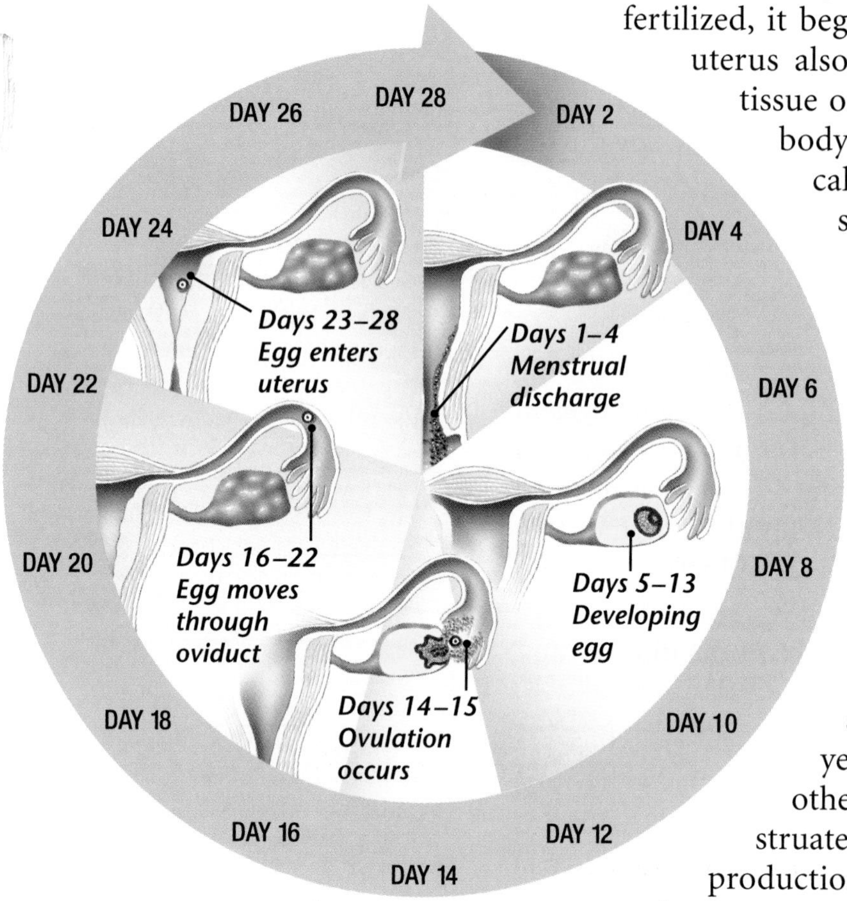

Endocrine Control The menstrual cycle is controlled by hormones of the endocrine system. Hormones also trigger a girl's first menstruation. Many girls begin menstruation between the ages of 10 and 14 years. Some girls start earlier, while others start later. Women continue to menstruate until about age 50. At around that age, production of sex hormones drops. As a result, the ovaries stop releasing mature egg cells.

DAY 26 DAY 28 DAY 2
DAY 24 DAY 4
Days 23–28 Egg enters uterus *Days 1–4 Menstrual discharge*
DAY 22 DAY 6
Days 16–22 Egg moves through oviduct *Days 5–13 Developing egg*
DAY 20 DAY 8
DAY 18 *Days 14–15 Ovulation occurs* DAY 10
DAY 16 DAY 12
DAY 14

Figure 8 During the menstrual cycle, the lining of the uterus builds up with extra blood and tissue. About halfway through a typical cycle, ovulation takes place. If the egg is not fertilized, menstruation occurs.

Section 2 Review

1. What specialized cells are produced in the male and female reproductive systems?
2. How does the uterus change during the menstrual cycle?
3. How does a sperm's structure help it function?
4. What is ovulation? How often does it occur?
5. **Thinking Critically Comparing and Contrasting** In what ways are the functions of the ovaries and the testes similar? How do their functions differ?

Check Your Progress

CHAPTER PROJECT

You should now be caring for your "baby," taking it with you everywhere or arranging for a responsible person to care for it. You or your substitute must continue to perform all the child-care tasks, such as feeding the baby, changing diapers, and playing with the baby. Whenever you travel, you must have a safe method for transporting the baby. Don't forget to make at least two journal entries each day.

Pregnancy, Birth, and Childhood

How Many Ways Does a Child Grow?

1. Compare the two photographs at the left. One shows a baby girl. The other shows the same girl at the age of five.

2. Make two lists—one of the similarities and the other of the differences you see.

3. Compare your lists with those of your classmates.

Think It Over

Observing Based on your observations, list three physical changes that occur in early childhood.

An egg can be fertilized during the first few days after ovulation. When sexual activity occurs, sperm are deposited into the vagina. Sperm then move through the uterus into the oviducts. If a sperm fertilizes an egg, pregnancy can occur. Then, the amazing process of human development begins.

A fertilized egg, or zygote, is no larger than the period at the end of this sentence. Yet after fertilization, the zygote undergoes changes that result in the formation of a new human. **The zygote develops first into an embryo and then into a fetus.** About nine months after fertilization, a baby is born.

GUIDE FOR READING

◆ What are the stages of human development that occur before birth?

◆ What happens during childbirth?

Reading Tip As you read, use the headings to outline the events that occur during pregnancy, birth, and childhood.

The Zygote

After an egg cell and sperm cell join, the zygote moves down the oviduct toward the uterus. During this trip, which takes about four days, the zygote begins to divide. The original cell divides to make two cells, these two cells divide to make four, and so on. Eventually, the growing mass of hundreds of cells forms a hollow ball. The ball attaches to the lining of the uterus. For the next eight weeks or so, the developing human is called an **embryo** (EM bree oh).

Figure 9 Only one sperm can fertilize an egg. Once fertilization occurs, the process of human development begins.

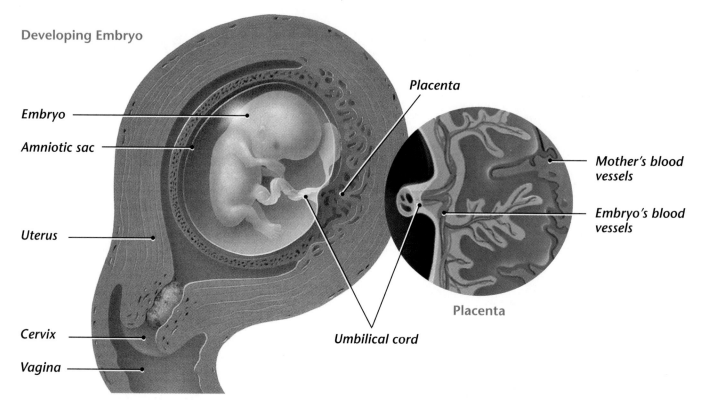

Embryo

Amniotic sac

Uterus

Cervix

Vagina

Placenta

Mother's blood vessels

Embryo's blood vessels

Placenta

Umbilical cord

Figure 10 The placenta connects the mother and the developing embryo. But the mother's and the embryo's blood vessels remain separate, as you can see in the closeup of the placenta. *Interpreting Diagrams What structure carries nutrients and oxygen from the placenta to the embryo?*

The Development of the Embryo

Soon after the embryo attaches to the uterus, many changes take place. The hollow ball of cells grows inward. Three cell layers form and the cells begin to differentiate. The outer layer of cells will eventually develop into cells of the nervous system and epidermis. The middle layer will develop into cells of the heart, bones, muscles, kidneys, and other organs. The inner layer will develop into parts of the digestive system.

New membranes also begin to form. One membrane surrounds the embryo and develops into a fluid-filled sac called the **amniotic sac** (am nee AHT ik). Locate the amniotic sac surrounding the embryo in Figure 10. The fluid in the amniotic sac cushions and protects the developing baby. Another membrane that forms is the **placenta** (pluh SEN tuh). The placenta becomes the link between the developing embryo and the mother.

In the placenta, the embryo's blood vessels flow next to the mother's blood vessels. Blood from the two systems does not mix, but many substances are exchanged. The embryo receives nutrients, oxygen, and other substances from the mother. It gives off carbon dioxide and other wastes.

The embryo soon moves a short distance from the placenta. A ropelike structure called the **umbilical cord** forms between the embryo and the placenta. It contains blood vessels that link the embryo to the mother, but the two circulatory systems remain separated by a thin barrier.

 **INTEGRATING HEALTH** The barrier that separates the embryo's and mother's blood prevents some diseases from spreading from the mother to the embryo. However, substances such as chemicals in tobacco smoke, alcohol, and some other drugs can pass through the barrier to the embryo. For this reason, pregnant women should not smoke tobacco, drink alcohol, or take any drug without a doctor's approval.

☑ *Checkpoint* *How does an embryo obtain oxygen?*

The Development of the Fetus

From the ninth week of development until birth, the embryo is called a **fetus** (FEE tus). Although the fetus starts out about as small as a walnut shell, it now looks more like a baby. Many internal organs have developed. The head is about half the body's total size. The fetus's brain is developing rapidly. It also has dark eye patches, fingers, and toes. By the end of the third month, the fetus is about 9 centimeters long and has a mass of about 26 grams.

Between the fourth and sixth months, the tissues of the fetus continue to develop into more recognizable shapes. Bones become distinct. A heartbeat can be heard with a stethoscope. A layer of soft hair grows over the skin. The arms and legs develop more completely. The fetus begins to move and kick, a sign that its muscles are growing. At the end of the sixth month, the mass of the fetus is approaching 700 grams. Its body is about 20 centimeters long.

The final 3 months prepare the fetus to survive outside the mother's body. The brain surface develops grooves and ridges. The lungs become developed enough to carry out the exchange of oxygen and carbon dioxide. The eyelids can open. Eyelashes and eyebrows grow. The fetus doubles in length. Its mass may reach 3 kilograms or more.

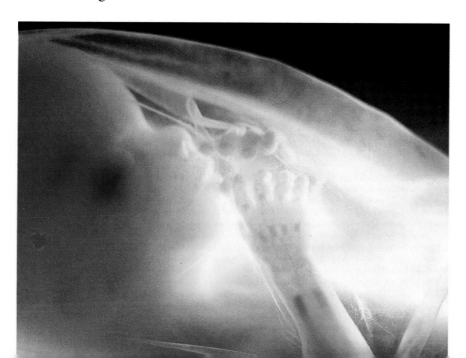

Way to Grow!

The table lists the average mass of a developing baby at different months of pregnancy.

ACTIVITY

Month of Pregnancy	Mass (grams)
1	0.02
2	2.0
3	26
4	150
5	460
6	640
7	1,500
8	2,300
9	3,200

1. Use a balance to identify an everyday object with a mass equal to each mass listed in the table. You may need to use different balances to cover the range of masses listed.

2. Arrange the objects in order by month.

Making Models What did you learn by gathering these physical models?

Figure 11 At the beginning of the fourth month of development, a fetus has developed internal organs, dark eye patches, fingers, and toes. Later, its eyes will open, and fingernails and toenails will form.

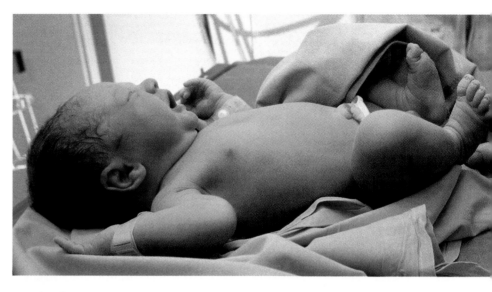

Figure 12 After about 9 months of growth and development inside the uterus, a baby is born. You can see where the umbilical cord of this newborn was clamped and cut.

Birth

After about 9 months of development inside the uterus, the baby is ready to be born. **The birth of a baby takes place in three stages—labor, delivery, and afterbirth.**

Labor During the first stage of birth, strong muscular contractions of the uterus begin. These contractions are called labor. The contractions cause the cervix to enlarge, eventually allowing the baby to fit through the opening. As labor progresses, the contractions become stronger and more frequent. Labor may last from about 2 hours to more than 20 hours.

Delivery The second stage of birth is called delivery. During delivery, the baby is pushed completely out of the uterus, through the vagina, and out of the mother's body. The head usually comes out first. At this time, the baby is still connected to the placenta by the umbilical cord. Delivery usually takes less time than labor does—from several minutes to a few hours.

Shortly after delivery, the umbilical cord is clamped, then cut about five centimeters from the baby's abdomen. Cutting the umbilical cord does not cause the baby any pain. Within 7 to 10 days, the remainder of the umbilical cord dries up and falls off, leaving a scar called the navel, or belly button.

Afterbirth About 15 minutes after delivery, the third stage of the birth process begins. Contractions push the placenta and other membranes out of the uterus through the vagina. This stage, called afterbirth, is usually completed in less than an hour.

Birth and the Baby The birth process is stressful for both the baby and the mother. The baby is pushed and squeezed as it travels out of the mother's body. Contractions put pressure on the placenta and umbilical cord, briefly cutting off the baby's supply of oxygen.

In response to the changes, the baby's endocrine system releases adrenaline. The baby's heart rate increases. Within a few seconds of delivery, a baby may cry or cough. This action helps rid the lungs of fluid and fills them with air. The newborn's heart rate then slows to a steady pace. Blood travels to the lungs and picks up oxygen from the air that the baby breathes in. The newborn's cry helps it adjust to the changes in its surroundings.

☑ *Checkpoint* *What events occur during labor?*

Multiple Births

The delivery of more than one baby from a single pregnancy is called a multiple birth. In the United States, a set of twins is born in about one out of every 90 births. Triplets are born in about one out of every 7,000 births.

There are two types of twins: identical twins and fraternal twins. Identical twins develop from a single fertilized egg, or zygote: Early in development, the embryo splits into two identical embryos. The two embryos have identical inherited traits and are the same sex. Fraternal twins develop when two eggs are released from the ovary and are fertilized by two different sperm. Fraternal twins are no more alike than any other brothers or sisters. Fraternal twins may or may not be the same sex.

Triplets and other multiple births can occur when three or more eggs are produced and fertilized by different sperm. Such births can also occur when an embryo splits into three or more identical embryos.

Sharpen your Skills

Designing Experiments

How does the frequency of twins in your school compare to the frequency given in the text? Develop a plan to find out. With your teacher's permission, carry out your plan. Then collect and analyze your data. Of the total number of students, how many are twins? Are your results close to 1 out of 90?

Figure 13 Identical twins (left) develop from the same zygote; they share identical characteristics. Fraternal twins (right) develop from two different fertilized eggs. *Applying Concepts Why can fraternal twins be different sexes while identical twins cannot?*

Figure 14 During infancy, many physical and mental skills develop. Babies can usually crawl by about seven months of age (left). By the age of two (right), most babies are coordinated enough to feed themselves. *Making Generalizations What other skills develop during infancy?*

Infancy

What can a newborn baby do? You might say "Not much!" A newborn can perform only simple actions, such as crying, sucking, yawning, and blinking. But during infancy—the first two years of life—babies undergo many changes and learn to do many things.

Physical Changes A baby's shape and size change greatly during infancy. When a baby is born, its head makes up about one fourth of its body length. As the infant develops, its head grows more slowly, and its body, legs, and arms begin to catch up. Its nervous and muscular systems become better coordinated. The baby then starts to develop new physical skills.

The exact ages at which physical skills develop vary from baby to baby. A newborn cannot lift its head. But after about 3 months, it can hold its head up and reach for objects. Within the next 2 months or so, the infant can grasp objects. At about 7 months, most infants can move around by crawling. Somewhere between 10 and 16 months, most infants begin to walk by themselves.

Other Changes How does an infant communicate? You may think that babies display feelings mostly by crying. But young infants can show pleasure by smiling and laughing. They can turn their heads or spit out food they don't like. Babies also begin to make babbling sounds. Sometime between the ages of one and three years, many children speak their first word. By the end of infancy, children can do many things for themselves, such as understand simple directions, feed themselves, and play with toys. However, infants are too young to know when something can hurt them. They must be watched carefully at all times.

Childhood

Infancy ends and childhood begins at about two years of age. Childhood continues until about the age of 13 years. Children gradually become more active and independent, and experience many physical and mental changes.

Physical Changes Throughout childhood, children continue to grow. They become taller and heavier as their bones and muscles increase in size. They become more coordinated as they practice skills such as walking, holding a fork, using a pencil, and playing games. Over a period of several years, baby teeth fall out and are replaced by permanent teeth. Toward the end of childhood, the bones, especially the legs, begin to grow faster. An increased appetite signals that the body needs more nutrients for its next stage of growth and development.

Other Changes As they develop, children show a growing curiosity and increasing mental abilities. Their curiosity helps them learn about their surroundings. With the help of family members and teachers, children learn to read and to solve problems. Language skills improve rapidly. For example, most four-year-olds can express themselves clearly and can carry on conversations.

Over time, children learn to make friends, care about others, and behave responsibly. Between the ages of 3 and 6, they learn to share and play with others. As children think about and care more for others, friends become more important. About the age of 10, children develop a strong wish to fit in with others of their age group. As their independence increases, children take on more responsibilities at home and school.

Figure 15 During childhood, children learn to get along with others. Their physical activities and games help them become stronger and more coordinated.

Section 3 Review

1. What three stages of development does a fertilized egg go through before birth?
2. Briefly describe what happens during each of the three stages of birth.
3. What is the function of the amniotic sac? What is the function of the placenta?
4. List two physical changes that occur during infancy.
5. **Thinking Critically** Relating Cause and Effect Why is it dangerous for a pregnant woman to drink alcohol or to smoke?

Science at Home

Discuss with a family member some of the physical and other changes that take place during infancy and childhood. If possible, find out about some of your own milestones—when you first smiled, walked, or talked, for example. Discuss how these milestones relate to the physical changes that occur at each stage.

SECTION 4 Adolescence—A Time of Change

DISCOVER ·················· ACTIVITY

How Do Ads Portray Teenagers?

1. Carefully examine an advertisement taken from a teen magazine. The ad should show one or more teenagers. Be sure to read the text and examine the picture.

2. Think about how the ad portrays the teenagers. How do they look and act? Do you think they are typical teens? How accurate is this "picture" of teenagers? Write down your thoughts.

Think It Over

Drawing Conclusions How does the ad use teenagers to try to influence people your age? Explain your opinion. Do you think the ad is effective?

GUIDE FOR READING

◆ What is the difference between adolescence and puberty?

◆ What mental and social changes are associated with adolescence?

Reading Tip As you read, make a list of the changes that take place during adolescence.

I f you compared a current photo of yourself with one taken three years ago, you would notice many changes. Starting at about the age of 12, you gradually begin to change from a child to an adult. Although many changes happen during infancy and childhood, some of the most significant changes occur during adolescence. **Adolescence** (ad ul ES uns) is the stage of development when children become adults physically and mentally.

By the end of adolescence, you will be able to do things you could not do during childhood. You will become eligible for privileges such as a driver's license and the right to vote. Along

Figure 16 During adolescence, teens mature both physically and mentally. It's a time when many teens try new experiences and take on more responsibilities. Working in the community is one way that teens can explore their interests while helping others.

with these privileges, you will be expected to take on adult responsibilities, such as driving safely. Adolescence is the time to work to become the healthy adult you want to be.

Physical Changes

Adolescence is a time of rapid physical growth. A person grows taller and heavier, and begins to look like an adult. However, some of the most important physical changes take place inside the body. These physical changes are controlled by the hormones of the endocrine system.

Puberty Sometime between the ages of about 9 and 14 years, a child enters puberty. **Puberty** (PYOO bur tee) is the period of sexual development in which the body becomes able to reproduce. Some people think that the term *puberty* is another word for adolescence, but that is not correct. **Adolescence includes more than just the physical changes of puberty. Many important mental and social changes take place as well.**

In girls, hormones produced by the pituitary gland and the ovaries control the physical changes of puberty. The sex organs develop. Ovulation and menstruation begin. The breasts begin to enlarge, and the hips start to widen. The skin begins to produce more oils, and body odor increases.

In boys, hormones from the testes and the pituitary gland govern the changes. The sex organs develop, and sperm production begins. The voice deepens. Hair appears on the face and sometimes on the chest. As with girls, more skin oils are produced, and body odor increases.

Figure 17 Despite their different sizes, each of these teens is developing normally. *Relating Cause and Effect What body system controls the rate at which changes occur during puberty?*

Bone and Muscle Growth Just as infants and children experience growth spurts, or periods of rapid growth, so do adolescents. Girls tend to experience their growth spurt slightly younger than boys do. Thus, during early adolescence girls tend to be taller than boys. Later in adolescence boys display rapid growth. Overall, boys tend to reach taller adult heights than girls.

Have you ever heard the phrase "growing pains"? Some adolescents grow so rapidly that they experience aches in their arms and legs. A sudden change in height or weight can cause a teen to feel clumsy or awkward at times. It takes time to adjust to a new body size and shape. Regular exercise can help a teen adjust more quickly. Teens should not over-exercise, however, as growing bones and muscles can be injured if overworked.

Another effect rapid growth can produce is hunger. It's normal for teens to go through periods when they eat huge amounts of food. The extra food provides the raw materials and energy required by the growing body. Nutritious meals and snacks can supply the body with the nutrients it needs.

When Puberty Begins As adolescents mature, they may compare their physical development with that of their peers. Teens of the same age can be at different stages of growth. This is because the age at which puberty begins varies from person to person.

These different rates of physical development may lead to misunderstandings. Adolescents whose bodies mature at a younger age may be expected to have adult judgment and take on more responsibilities than other teens. Those whose bodies develop later may face different challenges. They may be treated like children because of their young appearance.

☑ *Checkpoint* **What is a growth spurt?**

Mental and Social Changes

Adolescents may notice changes in the way they think, feel, and get along with others. Many teenagers have mixed feelings about the changes they are experiencing. They may feel excited and happy about them one day, and shy and confused the next day. **Adolescents undergo many mental and social changes as they become more mature.**

Mental Changes Between about the ages of 13 and 15, a teenager gradually becomes able to think and reason like an adult. Teens can think in ways that they could not as children. For example, young children think of hunger only when their stomachs are empty, or of pain only when they are hurt. They don't think beyond what's happening at the moment. Teenagers' thoughts are no longer limited to their immediate experiences. They begin to consider the consequences of their actions and make thoughtful judgments. Memory and problem-solving skills also improve. These and other mental abilities are often developed at school or through interests such as music or theater.

Adolescence is a time when individuals begin to question things that they accepted as children. Adolescents may wonder about the opinions and actions of friends and family members. They may also begin to ask themselves questions such as "Who am I?" and "What will I do with my life?" Often teens find answers by talking with parents, religious leaders, and other adults. Other times teens try out new experiences—from new hairstyles and clothes to volunteering their time to help others.

Social Studies CONNECTION

In many cultures, adolescence is seen as a passage from childhood to adulthood. In the Apache culture, girls who have entered puberty and begun their menstrual cycles undergo the Changing Woman ceremony. Often the whole community enjoys the feasting, dancing, and performances that are part of the ceremony. The girl dresses in a decorated buckskin dress and is sprinkled with cattail pollen. Other parts of the ceremony include fasting followed by special meals and prayer. After the ceremony, the girl is considered a woman by tribal members.

In Your Journal

Imagine you have just witnessed the Changing Woman ceremony. Write a short letter to a friend describing the event. Include information about the significance of the ceremony. Relate the experience to events with which you are familiar.

Figure 18 In the ceremony being celebrated here, tribal members help this 14-year-old Apache girl mark her passage to adulthood.

Figure 19 During the adolescent years, teens place a high value on friendships. *Making Judgments How can friends help each other develop skills that will be important throughout life?*

Social Changes It is common for adolescents to experience changes in their relationships with others. As they become more independent, teens spend more time with their friends. Because friends' opinions are very important, teens may worry whether friends approve of their clothing, looks, personality, and interests. Some teens may also become interested in members of the opposite sex.

As you learned in Chapter 16, peer pressure may influence the decisions and actions of teenagers. Peer pressure can produce both negative and positive results. Negative peer pressure can lead teens to do things that go against their values. The support of friends, on the other hand, can encourage teens to work toward their goals or develop new interests and skills.

☑ *Checkpoint* *What social changes occur during adolescence?*

Life as an Adult

At what point does adolescence end and adulthood begin? On a certain birthday? When people are physically mature? When people start to live on their own? If you look up the word *adult* in the dictionary, it is defined as being grown up, or mature. Legally, Americans are considered to be adults at the age of 16 or 18 for some activities and at the age of 21 for others. From a physical and mental standpoint, however, it is difficult to say when adulthood begins.

Physical changes continue to occur throughout adulthood. After about the age of 30, a process known as aging begins. Aging becomes more noticeable between the ages of 40 and 65. The skin starts to become wrinkled, the eyes lose their ability to focus on close objects, the hair may lose its coloring, and muscle strength decreases. During this period, females stop menstruating and ovulating. Males usually continue to produce sperm throughout their lives, although the number of sperm they produce decreases with age.

After age 65, aging intensifies, often leading to less efficient heart and lung action. But the effects of aging can be slowed if people follow sensible diets and good exercise plans. With the help of such healthy behaviors, more and more adults remain active throughout their lives.

Responsibilities—as well as opportunities, rights, and privileges—arrive with adulthood. During adolescence you learn to take care of yourself. Eventually, no one will tell you how to spend your money or what to eat. As an adult, you may need to make decisions that affect not just yourself, but your spouse and your children as well. You will need know what values are important to you, and make decisions that match those values.

Figure 20 Adulthood is a time when opportunities and choices expand. Adults can also share their knowledge and experience with younger people.

Section 4 Review

1. What is the difference between puberty and adolescence? Describe three physical changes that occur in boys and girls during puberty.
2. Name two mental changes and one social change that adolescents experience.
3. Why do adolescents sometimes feel clumsy or awkward?
4. What behaviors can adults practice to slow down the effects of aging?
5. **Thinking Critically Making Judgments** "Developing a sense of who you are is the most important part of adolescence." What does this statement mean? Do you agree with it? Explain.

Check Your Progress

CHAPTER PROJECT

By now, you should be preparing a summary of what you learned about being a parent. What skills do parents need? What are some of the rewards of parenthood? What are some of the challenges? How would you feel if you had to continue caring for the "baby" past the project deadline? Write answers to these questions as your final journal entry.

Growing Up

Problem

How do the proportions of the human body change during development?

Procedure

1. Examine the diagram below. Notice that the figures are drawn against a graph showing percents. You can use this diagram to determine how the lengths of major body parts compare to each figure's height. Make a data table in which to record information about each figure's head size and leg length.
2. Look at Figure D. You can use the graph to estimate that the head is about 15% of the figure's full height. Record that number in your data table.
3. Examine Figures A through C. Determine the percent of the total height that the head makes up. Record your results. (*Hint:* Figure A shows the legs folded. You will need to estimate the data for that figure.)
4. Now compare the length of the legs to the total body height for Figures A through D. Record your results.

Analyze and Conclude

1. How do the percents for head size and leg length change from infancy to adulthood?
2. What can you infer about the rate at which different parts of the body grow? Explain.
3. **Think About It** If you made a line graph using the data in the diagram, what would be on the horizontal axis? On the vertical axis? What additional information could you gain from this line graph?

Design an Experiment

Make a prediction about the relationship between the circumference of the head compared to body height. Then design an experiment to test your prediction, using people for test subjects. Obtain your teacher's permission before carrying out the experiment.

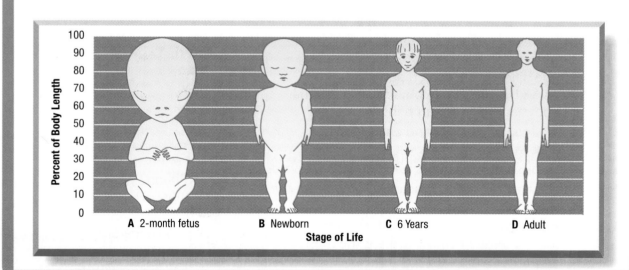

SECTION 1 — The Endocrine System

Key Ideas

◆ The endocrine system controls many of the body's daily activities, as well as the body's overall development.

◆ The endocrine system releases chemical messages called hormones. Hormones travel through the bloodstream to their target organs.

◆ Homeostasis in the body is maintained partly through negative feedback: the right amount of a particular hormone signals the body to stop producing that hormone.

Key Terms

endocrine gland	hypothalamus
hormone	pituitary gland
target cell	negative feedback

SECTION 2 — The Male and Female Reproductive Systems

Key Ideas

◆ The male reproductive system is specialized to produce sperm and the hormone testosterone.

◆ The role of the female reproductive system is to produce eggs and to nourish a developing baby until birth.

◆ Eggs are produced in the ovaries of the female. During the menstrual cycle, an egg develops, and the uterus prepares for the arrival of a fertilized egg.

Key Terms

egg	testosterone	oviduct
sperm	scrotum	uterus
fertilization	semen	vagina
reproduction	penis	menstrual cycle
zygote	ovary	ovulation
chromosome	estrogen	menstruation
testis		

SECTION 3 — Pregnancy, Birth, and Childhood

Key Ideas

◆ If an egg is fertilized, pregnancy begins. The zygote develops into an embryo and then a fetus.

◆ A baby develops inside the mother's uterus for about 9 months before it is born. Birth takes place in three stages—labor, delivery, and afterbirth.

◆ Infancy is a time of rapid physical growth and mastery of basic skills. During childhood, children become more independent.

Key Terms

embryo	placenta	fetus
amniotic sac	umbilical cord	

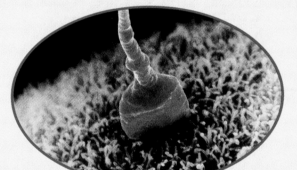

SECTION 4 — Adolescence— A Time of Change

INTEGRATING HEALTH

Key Ideas

◆ Adolescence includes the physical changes of puberty as well as mental and social changes.

◆ Puberty is the period of sexual development in which the body becomes able to reproduce. Males and females develop the physical characteristics of adult men and women.

Key Terms

adolescence	puberty

ACTIVITY

USING THE INTERNET

www.science-explorer.phschool.com

California Test Prep: Reviewing Content

Multiple Choice

Choose the letter of the best answer.

1. Which structure links the nervous system and the endocrine system?
   a. pituitary gland
   b. adrenal gland
   c. parathyroid gland
   d. hypothalamus

2. What is the male sex cell called?
   a. testis
   b. sperm
   c. egg
   d. ovary

3. The release of an egg from an ovary is known as
   a. ovulation.
   b. fertilization.
   c. menstruation.
   d. afterbirth.

4. Two individuals that develop from the same zygote are called
   a. embryos.
   b. fraternal twins.
   c. identical twins.
   d. triplets.

5. Sex organs develop rapidly during
   a. infancy.
   b. childhood.
   c. puberty.
   d. adulthood.

True or False

If the statement is true, write true. If it is false, change the underlined word or words to make the statement true.

6. The <u>pituitary</u> gland produces adrenaline.
7. The female reproductive glands are the <u>ovaries</u>.
8. The joining of a sperm and an egg is called <u>fertilization</u>.
9. An <u>oviduct</u> is the passageway through which an egg travels from the ovary to the uterus.
10. The physical changes of adolescence are controlled by the <u>nervous</u> system.

Checking Concepts

11. What is the function of the hypothalamus?
12. When enough thyroxine has been released into the blood, what signal is sent to the thyroid gland? How is that signal sent?
13. What changes occur in the uterus during the menstrual cycle?
14. How does a zygote form? What happens to the zygote about four days after it forms?
15. Describe how a fetus receives food and oxygen and gets rid of wastes.
16. Summarize the physical changes that take place during infancy.
17. List six changes a ten-year-old boy should expect to occur in the next five years. Include physical, mental, and social changes.
18. **Writing to Learn** Imagine you're a skeleton in the body of a sixteen-year-old person. Write about the changes you've experienced since infancy.

Thinking Visually

19. **Flowchart** Copy this flowchart and fill in the main stages that occur between fertilization and birth. (For more on flowcharts, see the Skills Handbook.)

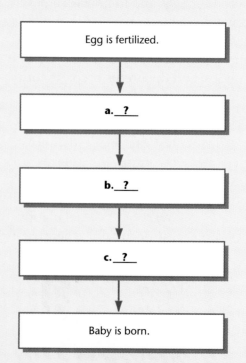

Egg is fertilized.

↓

a. __?__

↓

b. __?__

↓

c. __?__

↓

Baby is born.

Test Prep: Skills

The data table below shows how the length of a developing baby changes during pregnancy. Use the table to answer Questions 20–22.

Week of Pregnancy	Average Length (mm)	Week of Pregnancy	Average Length (mm)
4	7	24	300
8	30	28	350
12	75	32	410
16	180	36	450
20	250	38	500

20. Measuring Use a metric ruler to mark each length on a piece of paper. During which four-week period did the greatest increase in length occur?

21. Graphing Graph the data by plotting time on the horizontal axis and length on the vertical axis.

22. Interpreting Data At the twelfth week, a developing baby measures about 75 mm. By which week has the fetus grown to four times that length? Six times that length?

Thinking Critically

23. Applying Concepts The pancreas produces insulin, a hormone that lowers the level of sugar in the blood. Glucagon, another hormone of the pancreas, increases the level of sugar in the blood. Suggest how these two hormones might work together to maintain homeostasis in the body.

24. Relating Cause and Effect How can playing games help children develop important skills?

25. Comparing and Contrasting In what way is development during adolescence similar to development before birth? How are the two stages different?

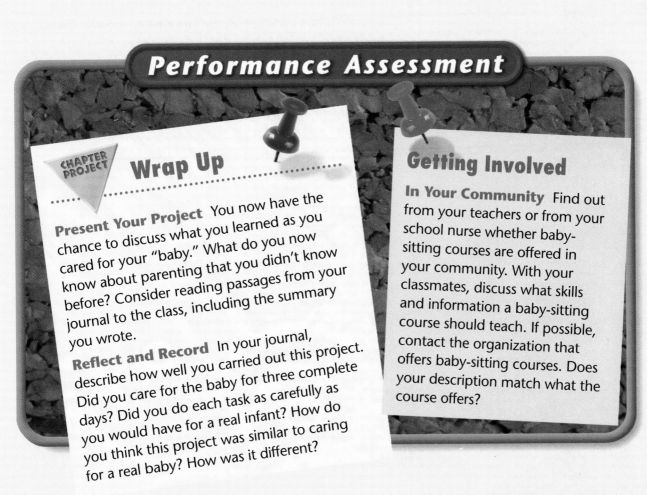

Performance Assessment

CHAPTER PROJECT Wrap Up

Present Your Project You now have the chance to discuss what you learned as you cared for your "baby." What do you now know about parenting that you didn't know before? Consider reading passages from your journal to the class, including the summary you wrote.

Reflect and Record In your journal, describe how well you carried out this project. Did you care for the baby for three complete days? Did you do each task as carefully as you would have for a real infant? How do you think this project was similar to caring for a real baby? How was it different?

Getting Involved

In Your Community Find out from your teachers or from your school nurse whether baby-sitting courses are offered in your community. With your classmates, discuss what skills and information a baby-sitting course should teach. If possible, contact the organization that offers baby-sitting courses. Does your description match what the course offers?

THE OLYMPIC GAMES

The Olympic flame is a symbol of the spirit of the Olympic Games.

WHAT EVENT —

◆ *began in the spirit of competition and fair play?*

◆ *has the motto "faster, higher, stronger"?*

◆ *supports amateur sports?*

◆ *is the dream of young athletes around the world?*

The Olympic Games began more than 2,500 years ago in Olympia, Greece. For one day every four years, the best athletes in Greece gathered to compete. The games honored the Greek god Zeus. The ancient Greeks valued both physical and intellectual achievement. A winning athlete at the Olympic Games was rewarded with a lifetime of honor and fame.

For more than a thousand years, the Greeks held the games at Olympia every four years. This four-year period was called an Olympiad. The games were discontinued in A.D. 394, when the Romans ruled Greece.

Centuries later, in the 1880s, Pierre de Coubertin, a Frenchman, convinced the United States and other nations to bring back the Olympic games. Coubertin hoped that the modern Olympics would promote world peace by bringing together athletes from all nations. The modern Olympics began in Athens in 1896.

Today the Summer and Winter Olympics alternate every two years. For several weeks, athletes from all around the world experience the excitement of competing. Only a few know the joy of winning. But all who participate learn about fair play, striving toward a goal, and becoming a little bit faster and stronger through training.

This ancient marble statue is called *Discobolus*, ancient Greek for "discus thrower." The statue is a Roman copy of a statue made in Greece about 2,500 years ago.

Sports in Ancient Greece

The ancient Greeks valued physical fitness as much as an educated mind. Men and boys exercised regularly by wrestling, sprinting, throwing the discus, and tossing the javelin. Greek philosophy taught that a sound mind and body created a well-balanced person. Greek art glorified the muscles and movement of the human body in magnificent sculptures and paintings.

Chariot racing became a popular sport in the ancient Olympics. This scene is painted on a Greek amphora, a pottery jar for olive oil or wine.

The first recorded Olympic Games were held in 776 B.C. That year a cook named Coroebus from Elis, Greece, won the only event in the games—a sprint of about 192 meters. The prize was a wreath of olive leaves. In ancient Greece an olive wreath was the highest mark of honor.

Over the next 130 years, other events were added to the games, including longer running events, wrestling, chariot racing, boxing, and the pentathlon. *Pent-* comes from the Greek word meaning "five." A pentathlon included five competitions: long jump, javelin toss, discus throw, foot race, and wrestling. Early records indicate that women were not allowed to compete in the games.

Ancient Greece

Ancient Greece was a land of many rival city-states, such as Athens and Sparta. Each city-state sent its best athletes to the games at Olympia.

Social Studies Activity

The Olympics encourage peaceful competition among athletes from many nations. But political conflicts sometimes have disrupted or canceled the games. For example, the 1916 games were canceled because of World War I. Other Olympics are remembered for the achievements of certain athletes, such as Babe Didrikson in 1932. Find out what political events affected particular Olympics during the twentieth century. Or find out who were the outstanding athletes at different games. Report your findings to the class.

Modern Olympic Games

At the 1988 Olympic games in Seoul, South Korea, Jackie Joyner-Kersee was one of the star athletes. She won two gold medals there. In total, between 1984 and 1996, she won six Olympic medals (three of them gold), making her one of the world's greatest athletes.

Jackie grew up in East St. Louis, Illinois, where she started running and jumping at age ten. Although she was a natural at the long jump, she wasn't a fast runner. But her coach, Mr. Fennoy, encouraged her. After her final Olympics, Jackie wrote an autobiography—a story of her life. Here is an excerpt from her book *A Kind of Grace.*

Jackie Joyner-Kersee throws the javelin, one of seven events in the Olympic heptathlon. She won the heptathlon twice, in 1988 and 1992.

After school the boys' and girls' teams jogged to Lincoln Park's irregular-shaped track and makeshift long-jump pit. The track was a 36-inch-wide strip of black cinders sprinkled amid the rest of the dirt and grass. We called it the bridle path because that's what it looked like. We ran over, around and through the potholes, rocks, glass and tree limbs that littered the track. . . . After practice, we jogged another two or three miles around the neighborhood to complete our workout.

In winter, when it was too cold to practice outside, we trained inside the Lincoln High building. Every afternoon after school and at 9:00 every Saturday morning, the team of twenty-five girls split into groups on the two floors and ran along the brown concrete corridors. When it was time for hurdling drills, Mr. Fennoy set up hurdles in the center of the hallway on the second floor, and put us through our paces. We sprinted and leaped past the doors to the math and science classrooms. We ran to the end of the hall, turned around and repeated the drill in the opposite direction. . . .

The running drills, exhausting as they were, eventually paid off. In 1977, between the ninth and tenth grade, I developed booster rockets and cut an astonishing four seconds off my 440 time. I surged to the front of the pack in practice heats. By the time we entered Lincoln High as tenth-graders, I was the fastest 440 runner on the team. The last was—at long last—first.

Language Arts Activity

What does Jackie mean by "the last was—at long last—first"? How did she get to be first? Some people say that Jackie was just a natural athlete. Jackie herself says, "I think it was my reward for all those hours of work on the bridle path, the neighborhood sidewalks and the schoolhouse corridors."

Think about a period in your life when you had to prepare for a math competition, a recital, a performance, a sports event, or other event. Write a short autobiographical sketch describing how you worked to improve your performance.

Olympic Records

To prepare for the Olympic Games, top athletes train for years. Sometimes they even move to climates that will help them prepare to compete in their sports. Skiers, for example, might move to a mountain region where they can train year-round. Athletes also use the most advanced equipment available in their sport. This scientific approach to training has helped athletes set new records for speed, height, and distance. In

addition, measurement tools such as timing clocks have become more precise. Sprinters and other athletes can now break records by just a few hundredths of a second.

The table and graph below show how the winning height in the women's high jump has changed over many Olympic Games. Notice that the high jump measures height in inches.

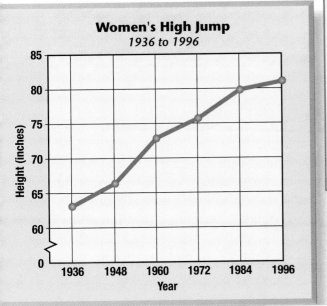

Women's High Jump (height in inches)	
1936	63
1948	66 $\frac{1}{8}$
1960	72 $\frac{3}{4}$
1972	75 $\frac{1}{2}$
1984	79 $\frac{1}{2}$
1996	80 $\frac{3}{4}$

Stefka Kostadinova of Bulgaria won the women's high jump at the 1996 Olympics in Atlanta, Georgia. How much higher did she jump than the 1936 winner?

Men's 400-Meter Run (time in seconds)	
1936	46.5
1948	46.2
1960	44.9
1972	44.66
1984	44.27
1996	43.49

Math Activity

The line graph above shows how the heights in the Olympic women's high jump have changed since 1936. Use the table showing times for the men's 400-meter run to create your own line graph.

How did the winning performance in the men's 400-meter run change over time? How does your graph differ from that of the women's high jump? Why do the graphs differ?

Getting Fit, Staying Fit

If you could be an Olympic athlete, would you be a runner, an ice skater, a gymnast, or some other athlete? Whatever their sport, Olympic athletes need to be physically fit to compete at their best. Physical fitness is the ability of the heart, blood vessels, lungs, and muscles to work together to meet the body's needs. Most people never compete in the Olympics. But if you are physically fit, you can reach your personal best.

The best way to boost your fitness is to exercise regularly. When you exercise, your heart, lungs, and muscles benefit. Team sports are good exercise, but so are activities such as walking, riding a bicycle, skating, swimming, and dancing. For the most benefit, people should exercise at least three times a week. Before you start an exercise program, have a physical examination to make sure that you do not have any health problems that rule out vigorous exercise.

A good exercise routine consists of stages, as shown in the flowchart below. Begin by warming up for five to ten minutes. To warm up, do your workout activity, but at a slower pace. If you plan to run, you can warm up by walking. You also should do exercises that gently stretch the muscles that you will use in your workout.

For the workout itself, you can choose exercises that will develop your heart and lungs, your muscular fitness, or both. A person whose heart and lungs function easily during vigorous exercise has good endurance. Endurance is the ability to exercise for a long time without getting tired. Walking, running, swimming, and bicycling all strengthen the heart and lungs and increase endurance. Team sports such as basketball and soccer also build endurance.

Stages in a Fitness Workout

Warm-up	Stretch	Workout	Cool-down	Stretch
Slowly move muscles to be used in workout.	Stretch muscles to be used in workout.	Do an activity such as walking, running, swimming, gymnastics, or riding a bicycle.	Move muscles used in workout at a reduced pace.	Stretch muscles used in workout.
5–10 minutes	5–10 minutes	20–45 minutes	5–10 minutes	5–10 minutes

These cross-country runners are about to test their physical fitness.

To improve muscular fitness, activities such as gymnastics and weight training are good choices. But many activities that are good for your heart and lungs contribute to muscular fitness too.

After you exercise vigorously, you should cool down by doing a gentler exercise. Stretching is also important for cooling down.

Science Activity

Your target heart rate is the approximate heart rate you need to maintain during a workout in order to increase your endurance. Target heart rate is usually expressed as a range—for example, 145 to 170 beats per minute.

1. To calculate your target heart rate, first take your pulse when you are at rest. Refer to page 112 for instructions on taking your pulse. Determine the number of times that your heart beats in one minute. This number is called your resting heart rate.

2. Subtract your resting heart rate from 210, which is about the maximum number of times your heart can beat in a minute.

3. To find the lower limit of your target heart rate, multiply the number you obtained in Step 2 by 0.6. Then add this number to your resting heart rate.

4. To get the upper limit of your target heart rate, multiply the number you obtained in Step 2 by 0.8. Then add this number to your resting heart rate.

Tie It Together

Plan an Olympic Day!

Design a competition that can be held at your school. Decide the time, place, and kind of contests to hold. Remember that the ancient Greeks honored intellect as well as athletics. So you could include games that test the mind as well as the body.

Research the decathlon, pentathlon, heptathlon, and marathon in the ancient and modern Olympics. You could design your own pentathlon that includes athletic and nonathletic events.

To organize the Olympic Day, you should:

◆ Set up the sports contests by measuring and marking the ground for each event.

◆ Find stopwatches, meter sticks, tape measures, and any necessary equipment.

◆ Locate or make prizes for first, second, and third place in each event.

◆ Enlist volunteers to compete in the events.

◆ Assign someone to take notes and to write a newspaper story on your Olympic Day.

Think Like a Scientist

*A*lthough you may not know it, you think like a scientist every day. Whenever you ask a question and explore possible answers, you use many of the same skills that scientists do. Some of these skills are described on this page.

Observing

When you use one or more of your five senses to gather information about the world, you are **observing.** Hearing a dog bark, counting twelve green seeds, and smelling smoke are all observations. To increase the power of their senses, scientists sometimes use microscopes, telescopes, or other instruments that help them make more detailed observations.

An observation must be factual and accurate—an exact report of what your senses detect. It is important to keep careful records of your observations in science class by writing or drawing in a notebook. The information collected through observations is called evidence, or data.

Inferring

When you explain or interpret an observation, you are **inferring,** or making an inference. For example, if you hear your dog barking, you may infer that someone is at your front door. To make this inference, you combine the evidence—the barking dog—and your experience or knowledge—you know that your dog barks when strangers approach—to reach a logical conclusion.

Notice that an inference is not a fact; it is only one of many possible explanations for an observation. For example, your dog may be barking because it wants to go for a walk. An inference may turn out to be incorrect even if it is based on accurate observations and logical reasoning. The only way to find out if an inference is correct is to investigate further.

Predicting

When you listen to the weather forecast, you hear many predictions about the next day's weather—what the temperature will be, whether it will rain, and how windy it will be. Weather forecasters use observations and knowledge of weather patterns to predict the weather. The skill of **predicting** involves making an inference about a future event based on current evidence or past experience.

Because a prediction is an inference, it may prove to be false. In science class, you can test some of your predictions by doing experiments. For example, suppose you predict that larger paper airplanes can fly farther than smaller airplanes. How could you test your prediction?

ACTIVITY Use the photograph to answer the questions below.

Observing Look closely at the photograph. List at least three observations.

Inferring Use your observations to make an inference about what has happened. What experience or knowledge did you use to make the inference?

Predicting Predict what will happen next. On what evidence or experience do you base your prediction?

Classifying

Could you imagine searching for a book in the library if the books were shelved in no particular order? Your trip to the library would be an all-day event! Luckily, librarians group together books on similar topics or by the same author. Grouping together items that are alike in some way is called **classifying.** You can classify items in many ways: by size, by shape, by use, and by other important characteristics.

Like librarians, scientists use the skill of classifying to organize information and objects. When things are sorted into groups, the relationships among them become easier to understand.

ACTIVITY

Classify the objects in the photograph into two groups based on any characteristic you choose. Then use another characteristic to classify the objects into three groups.

Making Models

Have you ever drawn a picture to help someone understand what you were saying? Such a drawing is one type of model. A model is a picture, diagram, computer image, or other representation of a complex object or process. **Making models** helps people understand things that they cannot observe directly.

Scientists often use models to represent things that are either very large or very small, such as the planets in the solar system, or the parts of a cell. Such models are physical models—drawings or three-dimensional structures that look like the real thing. Other models are mental models—mathematical equations or words that describe how something works.

ACTIVITY

This student is using a model to demonstrate what causes day and night on Earth. What do the flashlight and the tennis ball in the model represent?

Communicating

Whenever you talk on the phone, write a letter, or listen to your teacher at school, you are communicating. **Communicating** is the process of sharing ideas and information with other people. Communicating effectively requires many skills, including writing, reading, speaking, listening, and making models.

Scientists communicate to share results, information, and opinions. Scientists often communicate about their work in journals, over the telephone, in

letters, and on the Internet. They also attend scientific meetings where they share their ideas with one another in person.

ACTIVITY

On a sheet of paper, write out clear, detailed directions for tying your shoe. Then exchange directions with a partner. Follow your partner's directions exactly. How successful were you at tying your shoe? How could your partner have communicated more clearly?

Making Measurements

When scientists make observations, it is not sufficient to say that something is "big" or "heavy." Instead, scientists use instruments to measure just how big or heavy an object is. By measuring, scientists can express their observations more precisely and communicate more information about what they observe.

Measuring in SI

The standard system of measurement used by scientists around the world is known as the International System of Units, which is abbreviated as SI (in French, *Système International d'Unités*). SI units are easy to use because they are based on multiples of 10. Each unit is ten times larger than the next smallest unit and one tenth the size of the next largest unit. The table lists the prefixes used to name the most common SI units.

Common SI Prefixes

Prefix	Symbol	Meaning
kilo-	k	1,000
hecto-	h	100
deka-	da	10
deci-	d	0.1 (one tenth)
centi-	c	0.01 (one hundredth)
milli-	m	0.001 (one thousandth)

Length To measure length, or the distance between two points, the unit of measure is the **meter (m).** One meter is the approximate distance from the floor to a doorknob. Long distances, such as the distance between two cities, are measured in kilometers (km). Small lengths are measured in centimeters (cm) or millimeters (mm). Scientists use metric rulers and meter sticks to measure length.

Common Conversions

1 km = 1,000 m
1 m = 100 cm
1 m = 1,000 mm
1 cm = 10 mm

The larger lines on the metric ruler in the picture show centimeter divisions, while the smaller, unnumbered lines show millimeter divisions. How many centimeters long is the shell? How many millimeters long is it? **ACTIVITY**

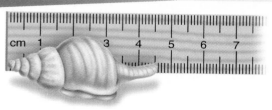

Liquid Volume To measure the volume of a liquid, or the amount of space it takes up, you will use a unit of measure known as the **liter (L).** One liter is the approximate volume of a medium-sized carton of milk. Smaller volumes are measured in milliliters (mL). Scientists use graduated cylinders to measure liquid volume.

Common Conversion

1 L = 1,000 mL

The graduated cylinder in the picture is marked in milliliter divisions. Notice that the water in the cylinder has a curved surface. This curved surface is called the *meniscus.* To measure the volume, you must read the level at the lowest point of the meniscus. What is the volume of water in this graduated cylinder? **ACTIVITY**

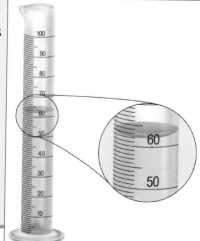

Mass To measure mass, or the amount of matter in an object, you will use a unit of measure known as the **gram (g)**. One gram is approximately the mass of a paper clip. Larger masses are measured in kilograms (kg). Scientists use a balance to find the mass of an object.

Common Conversion

1 kg = 1,000 g

The electronic balance displays the mass of an apple in kilograms. What is the mass of the apple? Suppose a recipe for applesauce called for one kilogram of apples. About how many apples would you need?

ACTIVITY

Temperature
To measure the temperature of a substance, you will use the **Celsius scale**. Temperature is measured in degrees Celsius (°C) using a Celsius thermometer. Water freezes at 0°C and boils at 100°C.

ACTIVITY

What is the temperature of the liquid in degrees Celsius?

Converting SI Units

To use the SI system, you must know how to convert between units. Converting from one unit to another involves the skill of **calculating**, or using mathematical operations. Converting between SI units is similar to converting between dollars and dimes because both systems are based on multiples of ten.

Suppose you want to convert a length of 80 centimeters to meters. Follow these steps to convert between units.

1. Begin by writing down the measurement you want to convert—in this example, 80 centimeters.
2. Write a conversion factor that represents the relationship between the two units you are converting. In this example, the relationship is *1 meter = 100 centimeters*. Write this conversion factor as a fraction, making sure to place the units you are converting from (centimeters, in this example) in the denominator.

3. Multiply the measurement you want to convert by the fraction. When you do this, the units in the first measurement will cancel out with the units in the denominator. Your answer will be in the units you are converting to (meters, in this example).

Example

80 centimeters = ___?___ meters

$$80 \text{ centimeters} \times \frac{1 \text{ meter}}{100 \text{ centimeters}} = \frac{80 \text{ meters}}{100}$$

$$= 0.8 \text{ meters}$$

Convert between the following units.
1. 600 millimeters = _?_ meters
2. 0.35 liters = _?_ milliliters
3. 1,050 grams = _?_ kilograms

ACTIVITY

Conducting a Scientific Investigation

In some ways, scientists are like detectives, piecing together clues to learn about a process or event. One way that scientists gather clues is by carrying out experiments. An experiment tests an idea in a careful, orderly manner. Although all experiments do not follow the same steps in the same order, many follow a pattern similar to the one described here.

Posing Questions

Experiments begin by asking a scientific question. A scientific question is one that can be answered by gathering evidence. For example, the question "Which freezes faster— fresh water or salt water?" is a scientific question because you can carry out an investigation and gather information to answer the question.

Developing a Hypothesis

The next step is to form a hypothesis. A **hypothesis** is a possible explanation for a set of observations or answer to a scientific question. In science, a hypothesis must be testable. Hypotheses are based on observations and previous knowledge. An example of a hypothesis is "*Salt water takes longer to freeze than fresh water.*"

You then use the words *If … then …* to make a prediction based on the hypothesis. An example is, "*If I add salt to fresh water, then the salt water will take longer to freeze.*" Such a prediction outlines a possible experiment.

Designing an Experiment

Next you need to plan a way to test your hypothesis. Your plan should be written out as a step-by-step procedure and should describe the observations or measurements you will make.

Two important steps involved in designing an experiment are controlling variables and forming operational definitions.

Controlling Variables In a well-designed experiment, you need to keep all variables the same except for one. A **variable** is any factor that can change in an experiment. The factor that you change is called the **manipulated variable.** In this experiment, the manipulated variable is the amount of salt added to the water. Other factors, such as the amount of water or the starting temperature, are kept constant.

The factor that changes as a result of the manipulated variable is called the responding variable. The **responding variable** is what you measure or observe to obtain your results. In this experiment, the responding variable is how long the water takes to freeze.

An experiment in which all factors except one are kept constant is a **controlled experiment.** Most controlled experiments include a test called the control. In this experiment, Container 3 is the control. Because no salt is added to Container 3, you can compare the results from the other containers to it. Any difference in results must be due to the addition of salt alone.

Forming Operational Definitions
Another important aspect of a well-designed experiment is having clear operational definitions. An **operational definition** is a statement that describes how a particular variable is to be measured or how a term is to be defined. For example, in this experiment, how will you determine if the water has frozen? You might decide to insert a stick in each container at the start of the experiment. Your operational definition of "frozen" would be the time at which the stick can no longer move.

EXPERIMENTAL PROCEDURE

1. Fill 3 containers with 300 milliliters of cold tap water.

2. Add 10 grams of salt to Container 1; stir. Add 20 grams of salt to Container 2; stir. Add no salt to Container 3.

3. Place the 3 containers in a freezer.

4. Check the containers every 15 minutes. Record your observations.

Interpreting Data

The observations and measurements you make in an experiment are called data. At the end of an experiment, you need to analyze the data to look for any patterns or trends. Patterns often become clear if you organize your data in a data table or graph. Then think through what the data reveal. Do they support your hypothesis? Do they point out a flaw in your experiment? Do you need to collect more data?

Drawing Conclusions

A conclusion is a statement that sums up what you have learned from an experiment. When you draw a conclusion, you need to decide whether the data you collected support your hypothesis or not. You may need to repeat an experiment several times before you can draw any conclusions from it. Conclusions often lead you to pose new questions and plan new experiments to answer them.

ACTIVITY

Is a ball's bounce affected by the height from which it is dropped? Using the steps just described, plan a controlled experiment to investigate this problem.

763

Thinking Critically

Has a friend ever asked for your advice about a problem? If so, you may have helped your friend think through the problem in a logical way. Without knowing it, you used critical-thinking skills to help your friend. Critical thinking involves the use of reasoning and logic to solve problems or make decisions. Some critical-thinking skills are described below.

Comparing and Contrasting

When you examine two objects for similarities and differences, you are using the skill of **comparing and contrasting.** Comparing involves identifying similarities, or common characteristics. Contrasting involves identifying differences. Analyzing objects in this way can help you discover details that you might otherwise overlook.

ACTIVITY
Compare and contrast the two animals in the photo. First list all the similarities that you see. Then list all the differences.

Applying Concepts

When you use your knowledge about one situation to make sense of a similar situation, you are using the skill of **applying concepts.** Being able to transfer your knowledge from one situation to another shows that you truly understand a concept. You may use this skill in answering test questions that present different problems from the ones you've reviewed in class.

ACTIVITY
You have just learned that water takes longer to freeze when other substances are mixed into it. Use this knowledge to explain why people need a substance called antifreeze in their car's radiator in the winter.

Interpreting Illustrations

Diagrams, photographs, and maps are included in textbooks to help clarify what you read. These illustrations show processes, places, and ideas in a visual manner. The skill called **interpreting illustrations** can help you learn from these visual elements. To understand an illustration, take the time to study the illustration along with all the written information that accompanies it. Captions identify the key concepts shown in the illustration. Labels point out the important parts of a diagram or map, while keys identify the symbols used in a map.

Bristles
Waste-removal organs
Intestine
Nerve cord
Digestive tract
Lower blood vessel
Upper blood vessel
Reproductive organs
Arches
Brain
Mouth

▲ **Internal anatomy of an earthworm**

ACTIVITY
Study the diagram above. Then write a short paragraph explaining what you have learned.

Relating Cause and Effect

If one event causes another event to occur, the two events are said to have a cause-and-effect relationship. When you determine that such a relationship exists between two events, you use a skill called **relating cause and effect.** For example, if you notice an itchy, red bump on your skin, you might infer that a mosquito bit you. The mosquito bite is the cause, and the bump is the effect.

It is important to note that two events do not necessarily have a cause-and-effect relationship just because they occur together. Scientists carry out experiments or use past experience to determine whether a cause-and-effect relationship exists.

ACTIVITY

You are on a camping trip and your flashlight has stopped working. List some possible causes for the flashlight malfunction. How could you determine which cause-and-effect relationship has left you in the dark?

Making Generalizations

When you draw a conclusion about an entire group based on information about only some of the group's members, you are using a skill called **making generalizations.** For a generalization to be valid, the sample you choose must be large enough and representative of the entire group. You might, for example, put this skill to work at a farm stand if you see a sign that says, "Sample some grapes before you buy." If you sample a few sweet grapes, you may conclude that all the grapes are sweet—and purchase a large bunch.

ACTIVITY

A team of scientists needs to determine whether the water in a large reservoir is safe to drink. How could they use the skill of making generalizations to help them? What should they do?

Making Judgments

When you evaluate something to decide whether it is good or bad, or right or wrong, you are using a skill called **making judgments.** For example, you make judgments when you decide to eat healthful foods or to pick up litter in a park. Before you make a judgment, you need to think through the pros and cons of a situation, and identify the values or standards that you hold.

ACTIVITY

Should children and teens be required to wear helmets when bicycling? Explain why you feel the way you do.

Problem Solving

When you use critical-thinking skills to resolve an issue or decide on a course of action, you are using a skill called **problem solving.** Some problems, such as how to convert a fraction into a decimal, are straightforward. Other problems, such as figuring out why your computer has stopped working, are complex. Some complex problems can be solved using the trial and error method—try out one solution first, and if that doesn't work, try another. Other useful problem-solving strategies include making models and brainstorming possible solutions with a partner.

Organizing Information

As you read this textbook, how can you make sense of all the information it contains? Some useful tools to help you organize information are shown on this page. These tools are called *graphic organizers* because they give you a visual picture of a topic, showing at a glance how key concepts are related.

Concept Maps

Concept maps are useful tools for organizing information on broad topics. A concept map begins with a general concept and shows how it can be broken down into more specific concepts. In that way, relationships between concepts become easier to understand.

A concept map is constructed by placing concept words (usually nouns) in ovals and connecting them with linking words. Often, the most general concept word is placed at the top, and the words become more specific as you move downward. Often the linking words, which are written on a line extending between two ovals, describe the relationship between the two concepts they connect. If you follow any string of concepts and linking words down the map, it should read like a sentence.

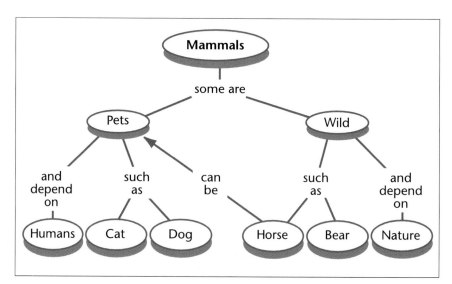

Some concept maps include linking words that connect a concept on one branch of the map to a concept on another branch. These linking words, called cross-linkages, show more complex interrelationships among concepts.

Compare/Contrast Tables

Compare/contrast tables are useful tools for sorting out the similarities and differences between two or more items. A table provides an organized framework in which to compare items based on specific characteristics that you identify.

To create a compare/contrast table, list the items to be compared across the top of a table. Then list the characteristics that will form the basis of your comparison in the left-hand

Characteristic	Baseball	Basketball
Number of Players	9	5
Playing Field	Baseball diamond	Basketball court
Equipment	Bat, baseball, mitts	Basket, basketball

column. Complete the table by filling in information about each characteristic, first for one item and then for the other.

Venn Diagrams

Another way to show similarities and differences between items is with a Venn diagram. A Venn diagram consists of two or more circles that partially overlap. Each circle represents a particular concept or idea. Common characteristics, or similarities, are written within the area of overlap between the two circles. Unique characteristics, or differences, are written in the parts of the circles outside the area of overlap.

To create a Venn diagram, draw two overlapping circles. Label the circles with the names of the items being compared. Write the

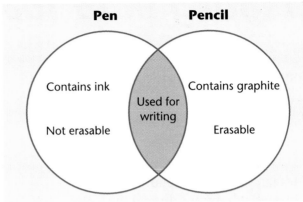

Pen **Pencil**

Contains ink

Contains graphite

Used for writing

Not erasable

Erasable

unique characteristics in each circle outside the area of overlap. Then write the shared characteristics within the area of overlap.

Flowcharts

A flowchart can help you understand the order in which certain events have occurred or should occur. Flowcharts are useful for outlining the stages in a process or the steps in a procedure.

To make a flowchart, write a brief description of each event in a box. Place the first event at the top of the page, followed by the second event, the third event, and so on. Then draw an arrow to connect each event to the one that occurs next.

Preparing Pasta

Boil water

Cook pasta

Drain water

Add sauce

Cycle Diagrams

A cycle diagram can be used to show a sequence of events that is continuous, or cyclical. A continuous sequence does not have an end because, when the final event is over, the first event begins again. Like a flowchart, a cycle diagram can help you understand the order of events.

To create a cycle diagram, write a brief description of each event in a box. Place one event at the top of the page in the center. Then, moving in a clockwise direction around an imaginary circle, write each event in its proper sequence. Draw arrows that connect each event to the one that occurs next, forming a continuous circle.

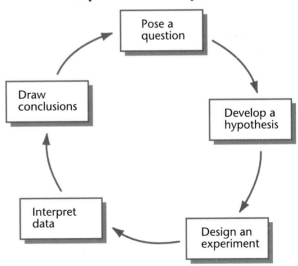

Steps in a Science Experiment

Pose a question

Develop a hypothesis

Design an experiment

Interpret data

Draw conclusions

Creating Data Tables and Graphs

How can you make sense of the data in a science experiment? The first step is to organize the data to help you understand them. Data tables and graphs are helpful tools for organizing data.

Data Tables

You have gathered your materials and set up your experiment. But before you start, you need to plan a way to record what happens during the experiment. By creating a data table, you can record your observations and measurements in an orderly way.

Suppose, for example, that a scientist conducted an experiment to find out how many Calories people of different body masses burn while doing various activities. The data table shows the results.

Notice in this data table that the manipulated variable (body mass) is the heading of one column. The responding variable (for Experiment 1, the number of Calories burned while bicycling) is the heading of the next column. Additional columns were added for related experiments.

CALORIES BURNED IN 30 MINUTES OF ACTIVITY			
Body Mass	Experiment 1 Bicycling	Experiment 2 Playing Basketball	Experiment 3 Watching Television
30 kg	60 Calories	120 Calories	21 Calories
40 kg	77 Calories	164 Calories	27 Calories
50 kg	95 Calories	206 Calories	33 Calories
60 kg	114 Calories	248 Calories	38 Calories

Bar Graphs

To compare how many Calories a person burns doing various activities, you could create a bar graph. A bar graph is used to display data in a number of separate, or distinct, categories. In this example, bicycling, playing basketball, and watching television are three separate categories.

To create a bar graph, follow these steps.

1. On graph paper, draw a horizontal, or *x*-, axis and a vertical, or *y*-, axis.
2. Write the names of the categories to be graphed along the horizontal axis. Include an overall label for the axis as well.
3. Label the vertical axis with the name of the responding variable. Include units of measurement. Then create a scale along the axis by marking off equally spaced numbers that cover the range of the data collected.
4. For each category, draw a solid bar using the scale on the vertical axis to determine the

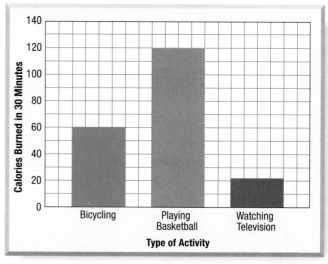

Calories Burned by a 30-kilogram Person in Various Activities

appropriate height. For example, for bicycling, draw the bar as high as the 60 mark on the vertical axis. Make all the bars the same width and leave equal spaces between them.
5. Add a title that describes the graph.

Line Graphs

To see whether a relationship exists between body mass and the number of Calories burned while bicycling, you could create a line graph. A line graph is used to display data that show how one variable (the responding variable) changes in response to another variable (the manipulated variable). You can use a line graph when your manipulated variable is *continuous*, that is, when there are other points between the ones that you tested. In this example, body mass is a continuous variable because there are other body masses between 30 and 40 kilograms (for example, 31 kilograms). Time is another example of a continuous variable.

Line graphs are powerful tools because they allow you to estimate values for conditions that you did not test in the experiment. For example, you can use the line graph to estimate that a 35-kilogram person would burn 68 Calories while bicycling.

To create a line graph, follow these steps.

1. On graph paper, draw a horizontal, or *x*-, axis and a vertical, or *y*-, axis.
2. Label the horizontal axis with the name of the manipulated variable. Label the vertical axis with the name of the responding variable. Include units of measurement.
3. Create a scale on each axis by marking off equally spaced numbers that cover the range of the data collected.
4. Plot a point on the graph for each piece of data. In the line graph above, the dotted lines show how to plot the first data point (30 kilograms and 60 Calories). Draw an imaginary vertical line extending up from the horizontal axis at the 30-kilogram mark. Then draw an imaginary horizontal line extending across from the vertical axis at the 60-Calorie mark. Plot the point where the two lines intersect.

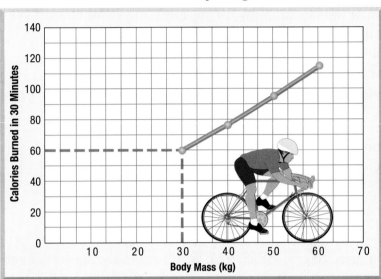

Effect of Body Mass on Calories Burned While Bicycling

5. Connect the plotted points with a solid line. (In some cases, it may be more appropriate to draw a line that shows the general trend of the plotted points. In those cases, some of the points may fall above or below the line. Also, not all graphs are linear. Sometimes it is more appropriate to draw a curve to connect the points. Such a graph is nonlinear.)
6. Add a title that identifies the variables or relationship in the graph.

Create line graphs to display the data from Experiment 2 and Experiment 3 in the data table. **ACTIVITY**

You read in the newspaper that a total of 4 centimeters of rain fell in your area in June, 2.5 centimeters fell in July, and 1.5 centimeters fell in August. What type of graph would you use to display these data? Use graph paper to create the graph. **ACTIVITY**

Circle Graphs

Like bar graphs, circle graphs can be used to display data in a number of separate categories. Unlike bar graphs, however, circle graphs can only be used when you have data for *all* the categories that make up a given topic. A circle graph is sometimes called a pie chart because it resembles a pie cut into slices. The pie represents the entire topic, while the slices represent the individual categories. The size of a slice indicates what percentage of the whole a particular category makes up.

The data table below shows the results of a survey in which 24 teenagers were asked to identify their favorite sport. The data were then used to create the circle graph at the right.

Sports That Teens Prefer

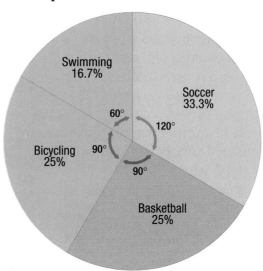

FAVORITE SPORTS	
Sport	Number of Students
Soccer	8
Basketball	6
Bicycling	6
Swimming	4

To create a circle graph, follow these steps.

1. Use a compass to draw a circle. Mark the center of the circle with a point. Then draw a line from the center point to the top of the circle.

2. Determine the size of each "slice" by setting up a proportion where x equals the number of degrees in a slice. (NOTE: A circle contains 360 degrees.) For example, to find the number of degrees in the "soccer" slice, set up the following proportion:

$$\frac{\text{students who prefer soccer}}{\text{total number of students}} = \frac{x}{\text{total number of degrees in a circle}}$$

$$\frac{8}{24} = \frac{x}{360}$$

Cross-multiply and solve for x.

$$24x = 8 \times 360$$
$$x = 120$$

The "soccer" slice should contain 120 degrees.

3. Use a protractor to measure the angle of the first slice, using the line you drew to the top of the circle as the 0° line. Draw a line from the center of the circle to the edge for the angle you measured.

4. Continue around the circle by measuring the size of each slice with the protractor. Start measuring from the edge of the previous slice so the wedges do not overlap. When you are done, the entire circle should be filled in.

5. Determine the percentage of the whole circle that each slice represents. To do this, divide the number of degrees in a slice by the total number of degrees in a circle (360), and multiply by 100%. For the "soccer" slice, you can find the percentage as follows:

$$\frac{120}{360} \times 100\% = 33.3\%$$

6. Use a different color to shade in each slice. Label each slice with the name of the category and with the percentage of the whole it represents.

7. Add a title to the circle graph.

ACTIVITY

In a class of 28 students, 12 students take the bus to school, 10 students walk, and 6 students ride their bicycles. Create a circle graph to display these data.

Laboratory Safety

Safety Symbols

These symbols alert you to possible dangers in the laboratory and remind you to work carefully.

Safety Goggles Always wear safety goggles to protect your eyes in any activity involving chemicals, flames or heating, or the possibility of broken glassware.

Lab Apron Wear a laboratory apron to protect your skin and clothing from damage.

Breakage You are working with materials that may be breakable, such as glass containers, glass tubing, thermometers, or funnels. Handle breakable materials with care. Do not touch broken glassware.

Heat-resistant Gloves Use an oven mitt or other hand protection when handling hot materials. Hot plates, hot glassware, or hot water can cause burns. Do not touch hot objects with your bare hands.

Heating Use a clamp or tongs to pick up hot glassware. Do not touch hot objects with your bare hands.

Sharp Object Pointed-tip scissors, scalpels, knives, needles, pins, or tacks are sharp. They can cut or puncture your skin. Always direct a sharp edge or point away from yourself and others. Use sharp instruments only as instructed.

Electric Shock Avoid the possibility of electric shock. Never use electrical equipment around water, or when the equipment is wet or your hands are wet. Be sure cords are untangled and cannot trip anyone. Disconnect the equipment when it is not in use.

Corrosive Chemical You are working with an acid or another corrosive chemical. Avoid getting it on your skin or clothing, or in your eyes. Do not inhale the vapors. Wash your hands when you are finished with the activity.

Poison Do not let any poisonous chemical come in contact with your skin, and do not inhale its vapors. Wash your hands when you are finished with the activity.

Physical Safety When an experiment involves physical activity, take precautions to avoid injuring yourself or others. Follow instructions from your teacher. Alert your teacher if there is any reason you should not participate in the activity.

Animal Safety Treat live animals with care to avoid harming the animals or yourself. Working with animal parts or preserved animals also requires caution. Wash your hands when you are finished with the activity.

Plant Safety Handle plants in the laboratory or during field work only as directed by your teacher. If you are allergic to certain plants, tell your teacher before doing an activity in which those plants are used. Avoid touching harmful plants such as poison ivy, poison oak, or poison sumac, or plants with thorns. Wash your hands when you are finished with the activity.

Flames You may be working with flames from a lab burner, candle, or matches. Tie back loose hair and clothing. Follow instructions from your teacher about lighting and extinguishing flames.

No Flames Flammable materials may be present. Make sure there are no flames, sparks, or other exposed heat sources present.

Fumes When poisonous or unpleasant vapors may be involved, work in a ventilated area. Avoid inhaling vapors directly. Only test an odor when directed to do so by your teacher, and use a wafting motion to direct the vapor toward your nose.

Disposal Chemicals and other laboratory materials used in the activity must be disposed of safely. Follow the instructions from your teacher.

Hand Washing Wash your hands thoroughly when finished with the activity. Use antibacterial soap and warm water. Lather both sides of your hands and between your fingers. Rinse well.

General Safety Awareness You may see this symbol when none of the symbols described earlier appears. In this case, follow the specific instructions provided. You may also see this symbol when you are asked to develop your own procedure in a lab. Have your teacher approve your plan before you go further.

Science Safety Rules

To prepare yourself to work safely in the laboratory, read over the following safety rules. Then read them a second time. Make sure you understand and follow each rule. Ask your teacher to explain any rules you do not understand.

Dress Code

1. To protect yourself from injuring your eyes, wear safety goggles whenever you work with chemicals, burners, glassware, or any substance that might get into your eyes. If you wear contact lenses, notify your teacher.
2. Wear a lab apron or coat whenever you work with corrosive chemicals or substances that can stain.
3. Tie back long hair to keep it away from any chemicals, flames, or equipment.
4. Remove or tie back any article of clothing or jewelry that can hang down and touch chemicals, flames, or equipment. Roll up or secure long sleeves.
5. Never wear open shoes or sandals.

General Precautions

6. Read all directions for an experiment several times before beginning the activity. Carefully follow all written and oral instructions. If you are in doubt about any part of the experiment, ask your teacher for assistance.
7. Never perform activities that are not assigned or authorized by your teacher. Obtain permission before "experimenting" on your own. Never handle any equipment unless you have specific permission.
8. Never perform lab activities without direct supervision.
9. Never eat or drink in the laboratory.
10. Keep work areas clean and tidy at all times. Bring only notebooks and lab manuals or written lab procedures to the work area. All other items, such as purses and backpacks, should be left in a designated area.
11. Do not engage in horseplay.

First Aid

12. Always report all accidents or injuries to your teacher, no matter how minor. Notify your teacher immediately about any fires.
13. Learn what to do in case of specific accidents, such as getting acid in your eyes or on your skin. (Rinse acids from your body with lots of water.)
14. Be aware of the location of the first-aid kit, but do not use it unless instructed by your teacher. In case of injury, your teacher should administer first aid. Your teacher may also send you to the school nurse or call a physician.
15. Know the location of emergency equipment, such as the fire extinguisher and fire blanket, and know how to use it.
16. Know the location of the nearest telephone and whom to contact in an emergency.

Heating and Fire Safety

17. Never use a heat source, such as a candle, burner, or hot plate, without wearing safety goggles.
18. Never heat anything unless instructed to do so. A chemical that is harmless when cool may be dangerous when heated.
19. Keep all combustible materials away from flames. Never use a flame or spark near a combustible chemical.
20. Never reach across a flame.
21. Before using a laboratory burner, make sure you know proper procedures for lighting and adjusting the burner, as demonstrated by your teacher. Do not touch the burner. It may be hot. Never leave a lighted burner unattended. Turn off the burner when not in use.
22. Chemicals can splash or boil out of a heated test tube. When heating a substance in a test tube, make sure that the mouth of the tube is not pointed at you or anyone else.
23. Never heat a liquid in a closed container. The expanding gases produced may blow the container apart.
24. Before picking up a container that has been heated, hold the back of your hand near it. If you can feel heat on the back of your hand, the container is too hot to handle. Use an oven mitt to pick up a container that has been heated.

Using Chemicals Safely

25. Never mix chemicals "for the fun of it." You might produce a dangerous, possibly explosive substance.

26. Never put your face near the mouth of a container that holds chemicals. Many chemicals are poisonous. Never touch, taste, or smell a chemical unless you are instructed by your teacher to do so.

27. Use only those chemicals needed in the activity. Read and double-check labels on supply bottles before removing any chemicals. Take only as much as you need. Keep all containers closed when chemicals are not being used.

28. Dispose of all chemicals as instructed by your teacher. To avoid contamination, never return chemicals to their original containers. Never simply pour chemicals or other substances into the sink or trash containers.

29. Be extra careful when working with acids or bases. Pour all chemicals over the sink or a container, not over your work surface.

30. If you are instructed to test for odors, use a wafting motion to direct the odors to your nose. Do not inhale the fumes directly from the container.

31. When mixing an acid and water, always pour the water into the container first and then add the acid to the water. Never pour water into an acid.

32. Take extreme care not to spill any material in the laboratory. Wash chemical spills and splashes immediately with plenty of water. Immediately begin rinsing with water any acids that get on your skin or clothing, and notify your teacher of any acid spill at the same time.

Using Glassware Safely

33. Never force glass tubing or thermometers into a rubber stopper or rubber tubing. Have your teacher insert the glass tubing or thermometer if required for an activity.

34. If you are using a laboratory burner, use a wire screen to protect glassware from any flame. Never heat glassware that is not thoroughly dry on the outside.

35. Keep in mind that hot glassware looks cool. Never pick up glassware without first checking to see if it is hot. Use an oven mitt. See rule 24.

36. Never use broken or chipped glassware. If glassware breaks, notify your teacher and dispose of the glassware in the proper broken-glassware container. Never handle broken glass with your bare hands.

37. Never eat or drink from lab glassware.

38. Thoroughly clean glassware before putting it away.

Using Sharp Instruments

39. Handle scalpels or other sharp instruments with extreme care. Never cut material toward you; cut away from you.

40. Immediately notify your teacher if you cut your skin when working in the laboratory.

Animal and Plant Safety

41. Never perform experiments that cause pain, discomfort, or harm to animals. This rule applies at home as well as in the classroom.

42. Animals should be handled only if absolutely necessary. Your teacher will instruct you as to how to handle each animal species brought into the classroom.

43. If you know that you are allergic to certain plants, molds, or animals, tell your teacher before doing an activity in which these are used.

44. During field work, protect your skin by wearing long pants, long sleeves, socks, and closed shoes. Know how to recognize the poisonous plants and fungi in your area, as well as plants with thorns, and avoid contact with them. Never eat any part of a plant or fungus.

45. Wash your hands thoroughly after handling animals or the cage containing animals. Wash your hands when you are finished with any activity involving animal parts, plants, or soil.

End-of-Experiment Rules

46. After an experiment has been completed, turn off all burners or hot plates. If you used a gas burner, check that the gas-line valve to the burner is off. Unplug hot plates.

47. Turn off and unplug any other electrical equipment that you used.

48. Clean up your work area and return all equipment to its proper place.

49. Dispose of waste materials as instructed by your teacher.

50. Wash your hands after every experiment.

Using the Microscope

The microscope is an essential tool in the study of life science. It allows you to see things that are too small to be seen with the unaided eye.

You will probably use a compound microscope like the one you see here. The compound microscope has more than one lens that magnifies the object you view.

Typically, a compound microscope has one lens in the eyepiece, the part you look through. The eyepiece lens usually magnifies 10 ×. Any object you view through this lens would appear 10 times larger than it is.

The compound microscope may contain one or two other lenses called objective lenses. If there are two objective lenses, they are called the low-power and high-power objective lenses. The low-power objective lens usually magnifies 10 ×. The high-power objective lens usually magnifies 40 ×.

To calculate the total magnification with which you are viewing an object, multiply the magnification of the eyepiece lens by the magnification of the objective lens you are using. For example, the eyepiece's magnification of 10 × multiplied by the low-power objective's magnification of 10 × equals a total magnification of 100 ×.

Use the photo of the compound microscope to become familiar with the parts of the microscope and their functions.

The Parts of the Compound Microscope

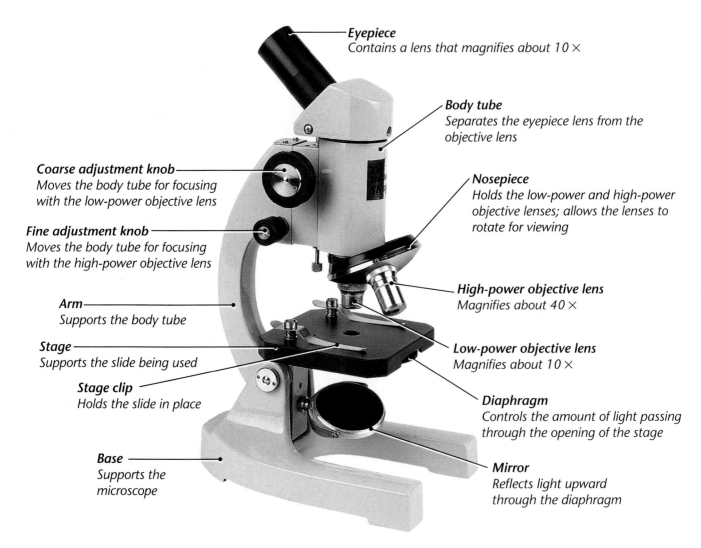

Eyepiece
Contains a lens that magnifies about 10 ×

Body tube
Separates the eyepiece lens from the objective lens

Coarse adjustment knob
Moves the body tube for focusing with the low-power objective lens

Fine adjustment knob
Moves the body tube for focusing with the high-power objective lens

Nosepiece
Holds the low-power and high-power objective lenses; allows the lenses to rotate for viewing

Arm
Supports the body tube

High-power objective lens
Magnifies about 40 ×

Stage
Supports the slide being used

Low-power objective lens
Magnifies about 10 ×

Stage clip
Holds the slide in place

Diaphragm
Controls the amount of light passing through the opening of the stage

Base
Supports the microscope

Mirror
Reflects light upward through the diaphragm

Using the Microscope

Use the following procedures when you are working with a microscope.

1. To carry the microscope grasp the microscope's arm with one hand. Place your other hand under the base.
2. Place the microscope on a table with the arm toward you.
3. Turn the coarse adjustment knob to raise the body tube.
4. Revolve the nosepiece until the low-power objective lens clicks into place.
5. Adjust the diaphragm. While looking through the eyepiece, also adjust the mirror until you see a bright white circle of light. **CAUTION:** *Never use direct sunlight as a light source.*
6. Place a slide on the stage. Center the specimen over the opening on the stage. Use the stage clips to hold the slide in place. **CAUTION:** *Glass slides are fragile.*
7. Look at the stage from the side. Carefully turn the coarse adjustment knob to lower the body tube until the low-power objective almost touches the slide.
8. Looking through the eyepiece, very slowly turn the coarse adjustment knob until the specimen comes into focus.
9. To switch to the high-power objective lens, look at the microscope from the side. Carefully revolve the nosepiece until the high-power objective lens clicks into place. Make sure the lens does not hit the slide.
10. Looking through the eyepiece, turn the fine adjustment knob until the specimen comes into focus.

Making a Wet-Mount Slide

Use the following procedures to make a wet-mount slide of a specimen.

1. Obtain a clean microscope slide and a coverslip. **CAUTION:** *Glass slides and coverslips are fragile.*
2. Place the specimen on the slide. The specimen must be thin enough for light to pass through it.
3. Using a plastic dropper, place a drop of water on the specimen.
4. Gently place one edge of the coverslip against the slide so that it touches the edge of the water drop at a 45° angle. Slowly lower the coverslip over the specimen. If air bubbles are trapped beneath the coverslip, tap the coverslip gently with the eraser end of a pencil.
5. Remove any excess water at the edge of the coverslip with a paper towel.

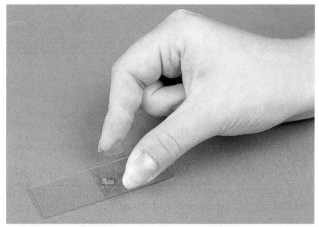

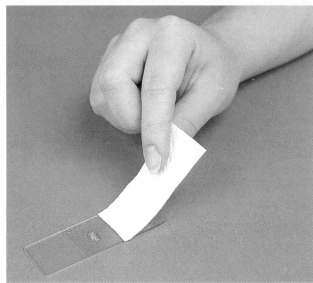

Glossary

········· A ·········

abdomen The hind section of an arachnid's body that contains its reproductive organs and part of its digestive trac; the hind section of an insect's body. (p. 408)

absolute age The age of a rock given as the number of years since the rock formed. (p. 169)

absorption The process by which nutrient molecules pass through the wall of the digestive system into the blood. (p. 577)

accessory pigment A yellow, orange, or red pigment found in plant cells. (p. 311)

acne A bacterial infection of the skin in which the oil glands become blocked and swollen. (p. 556)

active immunity Immunity that occurs when a person's own immune system produces antibodies in response to the presence of a pathogen. (p. 664)

active transport The movement of materials through a cell membrane using energy. (p. 33)

adaptation A characteristic that helps an organism survive in its environment or reproduce. (pp. 139, 369)

addiction A physical dependence on a substance; an intense need by the body for a substance. (p. 635)

adolescence The stage of development between childhood and adulthood when children become adults physically and mentally. (p. 742)

adrenaline A chemical that gives a burst of energy and causes changes in the body to prepare a person for quick action. (p. 520)

afterbirth The third stage of birth, in which contractions push the placenta out of the uterus through the vagina. (p. 738)

AIDS (acquired immunodeficiency syndrome) A disease caused by a virus that attacks the immune system. (p. 660)

alcoholism A disease in which a person is both physically addicted to and emotionally dependent on alcohol. (p. 717)

alga A plantlike protist. (p. 276)

algal bloom The rapid growth of a population of algae. (p. 280)

alleles The different forms of a gene. (p. 73)

allergen A substance that causes an allergy. (p. 670)

allergy A disorder in which the immune system is overly sensitive to a foreign substance. (p. 669)

alveoli Tiny sacs of lung tissue specialized for the movement of gases between the air and the blood. (p. 628)

amino acids Small units that are linked together chemically to form large protein molecules. (pp. 25, 566)

amniocentesis A technique by which a small amount of the fluid that surrounds a developing baby is removed; the fluid is analyzed to determine whether the baby will have a genetic disorder. (p. 112)

amniotic sac A fluid-filled sac that cushions and protects a developing fetus in the uterus. (p. 736)

amphibian An ectothermic vertebrate that spends its early life in water and its adulthood on land, returning to water to reproduce. (pp. 186, 446)

anabolic steroids Synthetic chemicals similar to hormones produced in the body; may increase muscle size and cause mood swings. (p. 714)

angiosperm A plant that produces seeds that are enclosed in a protective structure. (p. 346)

angle of incidence The angle between an incoming wave and an imaginary line drawn perpendicular to the surface of the new medium. (p. 700)

angle of reflection The angle between a reflected wave and an imaginary line drawn perpendicular to the surface of the new medium. (p. 700)

antenna An appendage on the head of an animal that contains sense organs. (p. 407)

antibiotic A chemical that kills bacteria or slows their growth without harming the body cells of humans. (pp. 262, 668)

antibody A chemical produced by a B cell of the immune system that destroys a specific kind of pathogen. (p. 659)

antigen A molecule on a cell that the immune system can recognize either as part of the body or as coming from outside the body. (p. 658)

anus A muscular opening at the end of the rectum through which digestive waste material is eliminated from the body. (pp. 389, 587)

aorta The largest artery in the body. (p. 600)

arachnid An arthropod with only two body sections. (p. 408)

artery A blood vessel that carries blood away from the heart. (p. 598)

arthropod An invertebrate that has an external skeleton, a segmented body, and jointed attachments called appendages. (p. 405)

asexual reproduction The reproductive process that involves only one parent and produces offspring that are identical to the parent. (pp. 249, 368)

asthma A disorder in which the respiratory passages narrow significantly. (p. 670)

atherosclerosis A condition in which an artery wall thickens as a result of the buildup of fatty materials. (p. 615)

atom The smallest unit of an element. (pp. 23, 175)

atrium Each of the two upper chambers of the heart that receives blood that comes into the heart. (pp. 446, 596)

autonomic nervous system The group of nerves that controls involuntary actions. (p. 694)

autotroph An organism that makes its own food. (pp. 44, 211, 367)

auxin The plant hormone that speeds up the rate of growth of plant cells. (p. 355)

axon A threadlike extension of a neuron that carries nerve impulses away from the cell body. (p. 686)

B cell A lymphocyte that produces chemicals that help destroy a specific kind of pathogen. (p. 659)

bacteriophage A virus that infects bacteria. (p. 240)

bacterium A single-celled organism that is a prokaryote. (p. 247)

bilateral symmetry Line symmetry; being divisible into two halves that are mirror images. (p. 374)

bile A substance produced by the liver that breaks up fat particles. (p. 585)

binary fission Asexual reproduction in which one cell divides to form two identical cells. (p. 249)

binomial nomenclature The naming system in which each organism is given a two-part name—a genus name and a species name. (p. 220)

bird An endothermic vertebrate that has feathers and a four-chambered heart, and lays eggs. (p. 471)

bivalve A mollusk that has two shells held together by hinges and strong muscles. (p. 400)

blood pressure The pressure that is exerted by the blood against the walls of blood vessels. (p. 605)

blood transfusion The transference of blood from one person to another. (p. 610)

bog A wetland where sphagnum moss grows on top of acidic water. (p. 317)

brain The part of the central nervous system that is located in the skull and controls most functions in the body. (p. 691)

brainstem The part of the brain that controls many body functions that occur automatically. (p. 693)

branching tree A diagram that shows how scientists think different groups of organisms are related. (p. 154)

bronchi The passages that branch from the trachea and direct air into the lungs. (p. 628)

bronchitis An irritation of the breathing passages in which the small passages become narrower than normal and may be clogged with mucus. (p. 636)

budding A form of asexual reproduction in which a new organism grows out of the body of a parent. (p. 288)

buoyant force The force that water exerts upward on any underwater object. (p. 442)

calorie The amount of energy needed to raise the temperature of one gram of water by one Celsius degree. (p. 563)

cambium The layer of cells in a plant that produces new phloem and xylem cells. (p. 337)

camouflage Protective coloration; a common animal defense. (p. 416)

cancer A disease in which some body cells grow and divide uncontrollably, damaging the parts of the body around them. (pp. 61, 555)

canine teeth Sharply pointed teeth that stab food and tear into it. (p. 486)

capillary A tiny blood vessel where substances are exchanged between the blood and the body cells. (p. 598)

carbohydrates Energy-rich organic compounds, such as sugars and starches, that are made of the elements carbon, hydrogen, and oxygen. They provide the raw materials to make parts of cells. (pp. 24, 563)

carbon film A type of fossil consisting of an extremely thin coating of carbon on rock. (p. 166)

carbon monoxide A colorless, odorless gas produced when substances are burned. (p. 635)

carcinogen A substance or a factor in the environment that can cause cancer. (p. 672)

cardiac muscle Muscle tissue found only in the heart. (p. 543)

cardiovascular system The body system that consists of the heart, blood vessels, and blood, and that carries needed substances to cells and carries waste products away from cells. (p. 594)

carnivore An animal that eats only other animals. (p. 369)

carrier A person who has one recessive allele for a trait and one dominant allele, but does not have the trait. (p. 106)

cartilage A connective tissue that is more flexible than bone and that gives support to some parts of the body. (pp. 433, 536)

cast A fossil that is a copy of an organism's shape, formed when minerals seep into a mold. (p. 165)

cell The basic unit of structure and function in living things. (pp. 6, 207, 512)

cell cycle The regular sequence of growth and division that cells undergo. (p. 52)

cell membrane The outside boundary of a cell; controls which substances can enter or leave the cell. (pp. 14, 512)

cell theory A widely accepted explanation of the relationship between cells and living things. (p. 10)

cell wall A rigid layer of nonliving material that surrounds the cells of plants and some other organisms. (pp. 14, 301)

cellulose A chemical that makes the cell walls of plants rigid and strong. (p. 301)

central nervous system The brain and spinal cord; the control center of the body. (p. 690)

cephalopod A mollusk with feet adapted to form tentacles around its mouth. (p. 402)

cerebellum The part of the brain that coordinates the actions of the muscles and helps maintain balance. (p. 693)

cerebrum The part of the brain that interprets input from the senses, controls the movement of skeletal muscles, and carries out complex mental processes. (p. 692)

chemotherapy The use of drugs to kill cancer cells. (p. 62)

chitin The tough, flexible material from which arthropod exoskeletons are made. (p. 405)

chlorophyll A green pigment found in the chloroplasts of plants, algae, and some bacteria. (pp. 42, 302)

chloroplast A structure in the cells of plants and some other organisms that captures energy from sunlight and uses it to produce food. (pp. 19, 301)

cholesterol A waxy, fatlike substance, found only in animal products, that is an important part of your body's cells; can build up on artery walls. (pp. 565, 615)

chordate The phylum whose members have a notochord, a nerve cord, and slits in their throat area at some point in their lives. (p. 432)

chromatid One of the identical rods of a chromosome. (p. 53)

chromatin Material in cells that contains DNA and carries genetic information. (p. 18)

chromosome(s) Rod-shaped cellular structures made of condensed chromatin; contain DNA that carries the genetic information which controls inherited characteristics such as eye color and blood type. (pp. 53, 730)

cilia The hairlike projections on the outside of cells that move in a wavelike manner. (pp. 273, 626)

classification The process of grouping things based on their similarities. (p. 218)

clone An organism that is genetically identical to the organism from which it was produced. (p. 118)

cnidarians Animals whose stinging cells are used to capture their prey and defend themselves, and who take their food into a hollow central cavity. (p. 381)

cochlea A snail-shaped tube in the inner ear lined with sound receptors; nerve impulses are sent from the cochlea to the brain. (p. 707)

codominance A condition in which neither of two alleles of a gene is dominant or recessive. (p. 82)

complete metamorphosis A type of metamorphosis characterized by four dramatically different stages: egg, larva, pupa, and adult. (p. 414)

compound Two or more elements that are chemically combined. (p. 23)

compound microscope A light microscope that has more than one lens. (p. 7)

concussion A bruiselike injury of the brain that occurs when the soft tissue of the cerebrum bumps against the skull. (p. 696)

cone The reproductive structure of a gymnosperm. (p. 342)

conjugation The process in which a unicellular organism transfers some of its genetic material to another unicellular organism. (p. 250)

connective tissue A body tissue that provides support for the body and connects all of its parts. (p. 513)

continuum A gradual progression through many stages between one extreme and another, as in the illness-wellness continuum. (p. 524)

contour feather A large feather that helps give shape to a bird's body. (p. 471)

contractile vacuole The cell structure that collects extra water from the cytoplasm and then expels it from the cell. (p. 272)

controlled experiment An experiment in which all factors are identical except one. (pp. 209, 763)

convex lens A curved lens in which the center is thicker than the edges. (p. 11)

cornea The clear tissue that covers the front of the eye. (p. 703)

coronary artery An artery that supplies blood to the heart itself. (p. 601)

cotyledon A seed leaf that stores food. (p. 332)

crop A bird's internal storage tank that allows it to store food inside its body after swallowing it. (p. 472)

crustacean An arthropod that has two or three body sections, five or more pairs of legs, two pairs of antennae, and usually three pairs of appendages for chewing. (p. 407)

cuticle The waxy, waterproof layer that covers the leaves and stems of some plants. (p. 303)

cytokinesis The final stage of the cell cycle, in which the cell's cytoplasm divides, distributing the organelles into each of the two new cells. (p. 56)

cytoplasm The region of a cell located inside the cell membrane (in prokaryotes) or between the cell membrane and nucleus (in eukaryotes); contains a gel-like material and cell organelles. (pp. 18, 247, 512)

decomposer An organism that breaks down large chemicals from dead organisms into small chemicals and returns important materials to the soil and water. (p. 253)

delivery The second stage of birth, in which the baby is pushed completely out of the uterus, through the vagina, and out of the mother's body. (p. 738)

dendrite A threadlike extension of a neuron that carries nerve impulses toward the cell body. (p. 686)

depressant A drug that slows down the activity of the central nervous system. (p. 712)

dermis The lower layer of the skin. (p. 553)

development The process of change that occurs during an organism's life to produce a more complex organism. (p. 208)

diabetes A condition in which either the pancreas fails to produce enough insulin, or the body's cells can't use it properly. (p. 671)

diaphragm A large, dome-shaped muscle that plays an important role in breathing. (pp. 486, 630)

dicot An angiosperm that has two seed leaves. (p. 350)

diffusion The process by which molecules move from an area in which they are highly concentrated to an area in which they are less concentrated. (pp. 31, 603)

digestion The process by which the body breaks down food into small nutrient molecules. (p. 576)

DNA Deoxyribonucleic acid; the genetic material that carries information about an organism and is passed from parent to offspring. (p. 26)

dominant allele An allele whose trait always shows up in the organism when the allele is present. (p. 73)

down feathers Short, fluffy feathers that trap heat and keep a bird warm. (p. 472)

drug Any chemical that causes changes in a person's body or behavior. (p. 710)

drug abuse The deliberate misuse of drugs for purposes other than appropriate medical ones. (p. 711)

eardrum The membrane that separates the outer ear from the middle ear, and that vibrates when sound waves strike it. (p. 707)

echinoderm A radially symmetrical invertebrate that lives on the ocean floor and has a spiny internal skeleton. (p. 423)

ectotherm An animal whose body does not produce much internal heat. (p. 434)

egg A female sex cell. (p. 729)

electromagnetic spectrum The range of electromagnetic waves placed in a certain order. (p. 698)

electromagnetic waves Transverse waves that transfer electric and magnetic energy. (p. 698)

element A type of matter in which all the atoms are the same; cannot be broken down into simpler substances. (pp. 23, 175)

embryo The young plant that develops from a zygote. (p. 332) Also, a developing human during the first eight weeks after fertilization has occurred. (p. 735)

emphysema A serious disease that destroys lung tissue and causes difficulty in breathing. (p. 636)

endocrine gland An organ of the endocrine system that produces and releases its chemical products directly into the bloodstream. (p. 724)

endoplasmic reticulum A cell structure that forms a maze of passageways in which proteins and other materials are carried from one part of the cell to another. (p. 19)

endoskeleton An internal skeleton. (p. 423)

endospore A small, rounded, thick-walled, resting cell that forms inside a bacterial cell. (p. 251)

endotherm An animal whose body controls and regulates its temperature by controlling the internal heat it produces. (p. 435)

enzyme A protein that speeds up chemical reactions in the bodies of living things. (pp. 25, 578)

epidermis The outermost layer of the skin. (p. 552)

epiglottis A flap of tissue that seals off the windpipe and prevents food from entering. (p. 579)

epithelial tissue A body tissue that covers the surfaces of the body, inside and out. (p. 513)

epochs Subdivisions of the periods of the geologic time scale. (p. 181)

era One of the three long units of geologic time between the Precambrian and the present. (p. 180)

esophagus A muscular tube that connects the mouth to the stomach. (p. 579)

estrogen A hormone produced by the ovaries that controls the development of adult female characteristics. (p. 732)

eukaryote An organism with cells that contain nuclei and other cell structures. (p. 231)

eutrophication The buildup over time of nutrients in freshwater lakes and ponds that leads to an increase in the growth of algae. (p. 282)

evolution The gradual change in a species over time. (pp. 139, 224)

excretion The process by which wastes are removed from the body. (p. 639)

exoskeleton A waxy, waterproof outer shell. (p. 405)

extinct A species that does not have any living members. (p. 148)

extrusion An igneous rock layer formed when lava flows onto Earth's surface and hardens. (p. 171)

F

farsightedness The condition in which distant objects can be seen clearly but nearby objects look blurry. (p. 705)

fats High-energy nutrients that are composed of carbon, oxygen, and hydrogen and contain more than twice as much energy as an equal amount of carbohydrates. (p. 565)

fault A break or crack in Earth's lithosphere along which the rocks move. (p. 171)

fermentation The process by which cells break down molecules to release energy without using oxygen. (p. 48)

fertilization The joining of a sperm cell and an egg cell. (pp. 306, 368, 729)

fetus A developing human from the ninth week of development until birth. (p. 737)

fiber A complex carbohydrate, found in plant foods, that cannot be broken down into sugar molecules by the body. (p. 564)

fibrin A chemical that is important in blood clotting because it forms a fiber net that traps red blood cells. (p. 610)

fish A vertebrate that lives in the water and has fins. (p. 437)

flagellum A long, whiplike structure that extends out through the cell membrane and cell wall. (p. 248)

flower The reproductive structure of an angiosperm. (p. 347)

follicle Structure in the dermis of the skin from which a strand of hair grows. (p. 553)

Food Guide Pyramid A chart that classifies foods into six groups to help people plan a healthy diet. (p. 572)

force A push or a pull exerted on an object. (pp. 546, 600)

fossil The preserved remains or traces of an organism that lived in the past. (pp. 147, 217, 462)

fossil record The millions of fossils that scientists have collected. (p. 148)

frond The leaf of a fern plant. (p. 323)

fruit The ripened ovary and other structures that enclose one or more seeds of an angiosperm. (p. 348)

fruiting body The reproductive hypha of a fungus. (p. 288)

fulcrum The fixed point around which the lever rotates. (p. 546)

G

gallbladder The organ that stores bile after it is produced by the liver. (p. 585)

gamete A sperm cell or an egg cell. (p. 307)

gametophyte The stage in the life cycle of a plant in which the plant produces gametes, or sex cells. (p. 307)

gastropod A mollusk with a single shell or no shell. (p. 400)

gene A segment of DNA on a chromosome that codes for a specific trait. (p. 73)

gene therapy The insertion of working copies of a gene into the cells of a person with a genetic disorder in an attempt to correct the disorder. (p. 120)

genetic disorder An abnormal condition that a person inherits through genes or chromosomes. (p. 109)

genetic engineering The transfer of a gene from the DNA of one organism into another organism, in order to produce an organism with desired traits. (pp. 118, 359)

genetics The scientific study of heredity. (p. 70)

genome All of the DNA in one cell of an organism. (p. 122)

genotype An organism's genetic makeup, or allele combinations. (p. 82)

genus A classification grouping that consists of a number of similar, closely related species. (p. 220)

geologic time scale A record of the geologic events and life forms in Earth's history. (p. 179)

germination The early growth stage of the embryo plant in a seed. (p. 334)

gestation period The length of time between fertilization and birth of a mammal. (p. 493)

gill An organism's breathing organ that removes oxygen from water. (p. 399)

gizzard A thick-walled, muscular part of a bird's stomach that squeezes and grinds partially digested food. (p. 473)

glucose A sugar that is the major source of energy for the body's cells. (p. 564)

Golgi body A structure in a cell that receives proteins and other newly formed materials from the endoplasmic reticulum, packages them, and distributes them to other parts of the cell. (p. 19)

gradual metamorphosis A type of metamorphosis in which an egg hatches into a nymph that resembles an adult, and which has no distinctly different larval stage. (p. 414)

gradualism The theory that evolution occurs slowly but steadily. (p. 148)

gymnosperm A plant that produces seeds that are not enclosed by a protective covering. (p. 340)

H

habitat The specific environment in which an animal lives. (p. 450)

half-life The time it takes for half of the atoms of a radioactive element to decay. (p. 176)

heart A hollow, muscular organ that pumps blood throughout the body. (p. 596)

heart attack A condition in which blood flow to a part of the heart muscle is blocked, which causes heart cells to die. (p. 615)

hemoglobin An iron-containing protein that binds chemically to oxygen molecules and makes up most of red blood cells. (p. 608)

herbivore An animal that eats only plants. (p. 369)

heredity The passing of traits from parents to offspring. (p. 70)

heterotroph An organism that cannot make its own food. (pp. 44, 212, 367)

heterozygous Having two different alleles for a trait. (p. 82)

histamine A chemical that is responsible for the symptoms of an allergy. (p. 670)

homeostasis The process by which an organism's internal environment is kept stable in spite of changes in the external environment. (pp. 213, 518)

homologous structures Body parts that are structurally similar in related species; provide evidence that the structures were inherited from a common ancestor. (p. 152)

homozygous Having two identical alleles for a trait. (p. 82)

hormone The chemical product of an endocrine gland that speeds up or slows down the activities of an organ or tissue. (pp. 355, 725)

host An organism that provides a source of energy or a suitable environment for a virus or for another organism to live. (pp. 239, 386)

hybrid An organism that has two different alleles for a trait; an organism that is heterozygous for a particular trait. (p. 74)

hybridization A selective breeding method in which two genetically different individuals are crossed. (p. 117)

hydroponics The method of growing plants in a solution of nutrients instead of in soil. (p. 360)

hypertension A disorder in which a person's blood pressure is consistently higher than normal. (p. 615)

hypha One of many branching, threadlike tubes that make up the body of a fungus. (p. 286)

hypothalamus A tiny part of the brain that links the nervous system and the endocrine system. (p. 726)

hypothesis A possible explanation for a set of observations or answer to a scientific question; must be testable. (p. 762)

igneous rock A type of rock that forms from the cooling of molten rock at or below the surface. (p. 162)

immune response Part of the body's defense against pathogens in which cells of the immune system react to each kind of pathogen with a defense targeted specifically at that pathogen. (p. 658)

immunity The ability of the immune system to destroy pathogens before they can cause disease. (p. 664)

inbreeding A selective breeding method in which two individuals with identical or similar sets of alleles are crossed. (p. 117)

incisors Flat-edged teeth used to bite off and cut parts of food. (p. 486)

index fossils Fossils of widely distributed organisms that lived during only one short period. (p. 172)

infectious disease A disease that can pass from one organism to another. (pp. 258, 651)

inflammatory response Part of the body's defense against pathogens, in which fluid and white blood cells leak from blood vessels into tissues; the white blood cells destroy pathogens by breaking them down. (p. 656)

inorganic compound A compound that does not contain carbon. (p. 24)

insect An arthropod with three body sections, six legs, one pair of antennae, and usually one or two pairs of wings. (p. 413)

insulator A material that does not conduct heat well and which therefore helps prevent it from escaping. (p. 472)

insulin A chemical produced in the pancreas that enables the body's cells to take in glucose from the blood and use it for energy. (p. 671)

interneuron A neuron that carries nerve impulses from one neuron to another. (p. 686)

interphase The stage of the cell cycle that takes place before cell division occurs; during this stage, the cell grows, copies its DNA, and prepares to divide. (p. 52)

intrusion An igneous rock layer formed when magma hardens beneath Earth's surface. (p. 171)

invertebrate An animal that does not have a backbone. (pp. 180, 372)

involuntary muscle A muscle that is not under conscious control. (p. 540)

iris The circular structure that surrounds the pupil and regulates the amount of light entering the eye. (p. 703)

joint A place where two bones come together. (p. 536)

karyotype A picture of all the chromosomes in a cell arranged in pairs. (p. 113)

kidney A major organ of the excretory system; eliminates urea, excess water, and other waste materials from the body. (pp. 399, 639)

L

labor The first stage of birth, in which strong muscular contractions of the uterus occur. (p. 738)

large intestine The last section of the digestive system, where water is absorbed from food and the remaining material is eliminated from the body. (p. 587)

larva The immature form of an animal that looks very different from the adult. (p. 380)

larynx The voice box, located in the top part of the trachea, underneath the epiglottis. (p. 631)

law of superposition The geologic principle that states that in horizontal layers of sedimentary rock, each layer is older than the layer above it and younger than the layer below it. (p. 170)

lens The flexible structure that focuses light that has entered the eye. (p. 703)

lever A rigid object that is free to pivot about a fixed point. (p. 546)

lichen The combination of a fungus and either an alga or an autotrophic bacteria that live together in a mutualistic relationship. (p. 294)

lift The difference in pressure between the upper and lower surfaces of a bird's wing that produces an upward force that causes the wing to rise. (p. 481)

ligament Strong connective tissue that holds together the bones in a movable joint. (p. 538)

lipids Energy-rich organic compounds, such as fats, oils, and waxes, that are made of carbon, hydrogen, and oxygen. (p. 26)

liver The largest and heaviest organ inside the body; it breaks down substances and eliminates nitrogen from the body. (p. 585)

lungs The main organs of the respiratory system. (p. 628)

lymph The fluid that the lymphatic system collects and returns to the bloodstream. (p. 612)

lymph node A small knob of tissue in the lymphatic system that filters lymph. (p. 612)

lymphatic system A network of veinlike vessels that returns the fluid that leaks out of blood vessels to the bloodstream. (p. 612)

lymphocyte White blood cell that reacts to each kind of pathogen with a defense targeted specifically at that pathogen. (p. 658)

lysosome A small round cell structure that contains chemicals that break down large food particles into smaller ones. (p. 20)

M

machine A device that helps do work. (p. 546)

magnification The ability to make things look larger than they are. (p. 11)

mammal An endothermic vertebrate with a four-chambered heart, skin covered with fur or hair, and has young fed with milk from the mother's body. (pp. 193, 483)

mammary glands The organs that produce the milk with which mammals feed their young. (p. 488)

manipulated variable The one factor that a scientist changes during an experiment. (p. 763)

marrow The soft tissue that fills the internal spaces in bone. (p. 536)

marsupial A mammal whose young are born alive at an early stage of development, and which usually continue to develop in a pouch on their mother's body. (p. 492)

mass extinction When many types of living things become extinct at the same time. (p. 187)

mechanical advantage The measure of how much easier it is to do work using the machine. (p. 547)

medusa The cnidarian body plan characterized by a bowl shape and which is adapted for a free-swimming life. (p. 382)

meiosis The process that occurs in sex cells (sperm and egg) by which the number of chromosomes is reduced by half. (p. 88)

melanin A pigment that gives the skin its color. (p. 553)

menstrual cycle The monthly cycle of changes that occurs in the female reproductive system, during which an egg develops and the uterus prepares for the arrival of a fertilized egg. (p. 733)

menstruation The process that occurs if fertilization does not take place, in which the thickened lining of the uterus breaks down and blood and tissue then pass out of the female body through the vagina. (p. 734)

mental health A component of wellness that involves a person's feelings, or emotions. (p. 523)

messenger RNA RNA that copies the coded message from DNA in the nucleus and carries the message into the cytoplasm. (p. 93)

metamorphic rock A type of rock that forms from an existing rock that is changed by heat, pressure, or chemical reactions. (p. 162)

metamorphosis A process in which an animal's body undergoes dramatic changes in form during its life cycle. (p. 408)

microscope An instrument that makes small objects look larger. (p. 7)

minerals Nutrients that are needed by the body in small amounts and are not made by living things. (p. 568)

mitochondria Rod-shaped cell structures that produce most of the energy needed to carry out the cell's functions. (p. 18)

mitosis The stage of the cell cycle during which the cell's nucleus divides into two new nuclei and one copy of the DNA is distributed into each daughter cell. (p. 53)

molars Teeth that, along with premolars, grind and shred food into tiny bits. (p. 486)

mold A fossil formed when an organism buried in sediment dissolves, leaving a hollow area. (p. 165)

molecule The smallest unit of most compounds. (p. 23)

mollusk An invertebrate with a soft, unsegmented body; most are protected by hard outer shells. (p. 398)

molting The process of shedding an outgrown exoskeleton. (p. 406)

monocot An angiosperm that has only one seed leaf. (p. 350)

monotreme A mammal that lays eggs. (p. 492)

motor neuron A neuron that sends an impulse to a muscle, causing the muscle to contract. (p. 686)

mucus A thick, slippery substance produced by the body. (p. 579)

multicellular A type of organism that is made up of many cells. (p. 207)

multiple alleles Three or more forms of a gene that code for a single trait. (p. 103)

muscle tissue A body tissue that contracts or shortens, making body parts move. (p. 512)

mutation A change in a gene or chromosome. (p. 61)

mutualism A type of symbiosis in which both partners benefit from living together. (p. 274)

natural selection The process by which individuals that are better adapted to their environment are more likely to survive and reproduce than other members of the same species. (p. 140)

nearsightedness The condition in which nearby objects can be seen clearly but distant objects look blurry. (p. 705)

negative feedback A process in which a system is turned off by the condition it produces; examples of negative feedback systems include regulation of temperature by a thermostat and the regulation of the levels of many hormones in the blood. (p. 728)

nephron One of a million tiny, filtering structures found in the kidneys that removes wastes from blood and produces urine. (p. 640)

nerve A bundle of nerve fibers. (p. 686)

nerve impulse The message carried by a neuron. (p. 685)

nerve tissue A body tissue that carries messages back and forth between the brain and every other part of the body. (p. 513)

neuron A cell that carries messages through the nervous system. (p. 685)

nicotine A drug in tobacco that speeds up the activities of the nervous system, heart, and other organs. (p. 635)

noninfectious disease A disease that is not spread from person to person. (p. 669)

nonvascular plant A low-growing plant that lacks vascular tissue. (p. 315)

notochord A flexible rod that supports a chordate's back. (p. 432)

nucleic acid A very large organic molecule made of carbon, oxygen, hydrogen, nitrogen, and phosphorus, that contains instructions that cells need to carry out all the functions of life. (p. 26)

nucleus The control center of a cell that directs the cell's activities; contains the chemical instructions that direct all the cell's activities and determine the cell's characteristics. (pp. 15, 231, 512)

nutrients Substances in food that provide the raw materials and energy the body needs to carry out all the essential life processes. (p. 562)

nymph A stage of gradual metamorphosis that usually resembles the adult insect. (p. 414)

omnivore An animal that eats both plants and animals. (p. 370)

operational definition A statement that describes how a particular variable is to be measured or how a term is to be defined. (p. 763)

organ A structure in the body that is composed of different kinds of tissue. (p. 514)

organ system A group of organs that work together to perform a major function in the body. (p. 514)

organelle A tiny cell structure that carries out a specific function within the cell. (p. 14)

organic compound A compound that contains carbon. (p. 24)

organism A living thing. (p. 206)

osmosis The diffusion of water molecules through a selectively permeable membrane. (p. 32)

osteoporosis A condition in which the body's bones become weak and break easily. (p. 539)

ovary A protective structure in plants that encloses the developing seeds. (p. 347) Also, an organ of the female reproductive system in which eggs and estrogen are produced. (p. 732)

oviduct A passageway for eggs from an ovary to the uterus; the place where fertilization usually occurs. (p. 732)

ovulation The process in which a mature egg is released from the ovary into an oviduct; occurs about halfway through a typical menstrual cycle. (p. 733)

ovule A plant structure in seed plants that contains an egg cell. (p. 343)

pacemaker A group of cells located in the right atrium that sends out signals that make the heart muscle contract and that regulates heartbeat rate. (p. 598)

paleontologist A scientist who studies fossils to learn about organisms that lived long ago. (pp. 164, 464)

pancreas A triangular organ that produces enzymes that flow into the small intestine. (p. 586)

parasite An organism that lives on or in a host and causes harm to the host. (pp. 239, 386)

passive immunity Immunity in which the antibodies that fight a pathogen come from another organism rather than from the person's own body. (p. 666)

passive smoking The involuntary inhalation of smoke from other people's cigarettes, cigars, or pipes. (p. 637)

passive transport The movement of materials through a cell membrane without using energy. (p. 33)

pathogen An organism that causes disease. (p. 651)

peat The blackish-brown material consisting of compressed layers of dead sphagnum mosses that grow in bogs. (p. 317)

pedigree A chart or "family tree" that tracks which members of a family have a particular trait. (p. 107)

peer pressure The pressure from friends and classmates to behave in certain ways. (p. 523)

penis The organ through which both semen and urine leave the male body. (p. 731)

Percent Daily Value An indication of how the nutritional content of a food fits into the diet of a person who consumes a total of 2,000 Calories a day. (p. 574)

period One of the units of geologic time into which geologists divide eras. (p. 181)

peripheral nervous system All the nerves located outside the central nervous system; connects the central nervous system to all parts of the body. (p. 690)

peristalsis Involuntary waves of muscle contraction that keep food moving along in one direction through the digestive system. (p. 579)

petal The colorful, leaflike structures of a flower. (p. 347)

petrified fossil A fossil in which minerals replace all or part of an organism. (p. 164)

phagocyte A white blood cell that destroys pathogens by engulfing them and breaking them down. (p. 657)

pharynx The throat; part of both the respiratory and digestive systems. (p. 626)

phenotype An organism's physical appearance, or visible traits. (p. 82)

phloem The vascular tissue through which food moves in some plants. (p. 331)

photosynthesis The process by which plants and some other organisms capture light energy and use it to make food from carbon dioxide and water. (pp. 41, 301)

phylum The second broadest classification level into which biologists group organisms. (pp. 222, 370)

physical health A component of wellness that consists of how well the body functions. (p. 522)

pigment A colored chemical compound that absorbs light, producing color. (pp. 42, 277)

pistil The female reproductive parts of a flower. (p. 348)

pituitary gland An endocrine gland just below the hypothalamus that communicates with the hypothalamus to control many body activities. (p. 727)

placenta A membrane that becomes the link between the developing embryo or fetus and the mother. (pp. 496, 736)

placental mammal A mammal that develops inside its mother's body until its body systems can function independently. (p. 493)

plasma The liquid part of blood. (p. 607)

platelet A cell fragment that plays an important part in forming blood clots. (p. 610)

pollen Tiny particles produced by plants that contain the microscopic cells that later become sperm cells. (p. 342)

pollination The transfer of pollen from male reproductive structures to female reproductive structures in plants. (p. 343)

polyp The cnidarian body plan characterized by a vaselike shape and which is usually adapted for life attached to an underwater surface. (p. 381)

pore An opening through which sweat reaches the surface of the skin. (p. 553)

predator A carnivore that hunts and kills other animals and has adaptations that help it capture the animals it preys upon. (p. 369)

premolars Teeth that, along with molars, grind and shred food into tiny bits. (p. 486)

pressure The force that something exerts over a given area. (p. 604)

prey An animal that a predator feeds upon. (p. 370)

probability The likelihood that a particular event will occur. (p. 78)

prokaryote An organism whose cells lack a nucleus and some other cell structures. (p. 231)

proteins Large organic molecules made of carbon, hydrogen, oxygen, nitrogen, and sometimes sulfur; they are needed for tissue growth and repair and play a part in chemical reactions within cells. (pp. 25, 566)

protozoan An animal-like protist. (p. 271)

pseudopod A "false foot" or temporary bulge of the cell membrane used for feeding and movement in some protozoans. (p. 271)

puberty The period of sexual development during the teenage years in which the body becomes able to reproduce. (p. 743)

punctuated equilibria The theory that species evolve during short periods of rapid change. (p. 150)

Punnett square A chart that shows all the possible combinations of alleles that can result from a genetic cross. (p. 80)

pupa The second stage of complete metamorphosis, in which an insect is enclosed in a protective covering and gradually changes from a larva to an adult. (p. 414)

pupil The opening through which light enters the eye. (p. 703)

purebred An organism that always produces offspring with the same form of a trait as the parent. (p. 71)

radial symmetry The quality of having many lines of symmetry that all pass through a central point. (p. 374)

radioactive decay The breakdown of a radioactive element, releasing particles and energy. (p. 176)

radula A flexible ribbon of tiny teeth in mollusks. (p. 399)

recessive allele An allele that is masked when a dominant allele is present. (p. 73)

rectum A short tube at the end of the large intestine where waste material is compressed into a solid form before being eliminated. (p. 587)

red blood cell A cell in the blood that takes up oxygen in the lungs and delivers it to cells elsewhere in the body. (p. 608)

red tide An algal bloom that occurs in salt water. (p. 281)

reflection The bouncing back of a wave when it hits a surface through which it cannot pass. (p. 699)

reflex An automatic response that occurs very rapidly and without conscious control. (p. 695)

refraction The bending of light due to a change in speed. (p. 700)

regeneration The ability of an organism to regrow body parts. (p. 386)

relative age The age of a rock compared to the ages of rock layers. (p. 169)

replication The process by which a cell makes a copy of the DNA in its nucleus. (p. 52)

reproduce The production of offspring that are similar to the parents. (p. 209)

reproduction The process by which living things produce new individuals of the same type. (pp. 209, 729)

reptile An exothermic vertebrate with lungs and scaly skin; lays eggs with tough, leathery shells. (pp. 187, 451)

resolution The ability to clearly distinguish the individual parts of an object. (p. 12)

respiration The process by which cells break down simple food molecules to release the energy they contain. (pp. 46, 250, 625)

responding variable The factor that changes as a result of changes to the manipulated variable in an experiment. (p. 763)

response An action or change in behavior that occurs as a result of a stimulus. (pp. 209, 685)

retina The layer of receptor cells at the back of the eye on which an image is focused; nerve impulses are sent from the retina to the brain. (p. 704)

rhizoid The thin, rootlike structure that anchors a moss and absorbs water and nutrients for the plant. (p. 316)

ribosome A tiny structure in the cytoplasm of a cell where proteins are made. (pp. 19, 247)

RNA Ribonucleic acid; a nucleic acid that plays an important role in the production of proteins. (p. 27)

rock The material that forms Earth's hard surface. (p. 162)

rock cycle A series of processes on the surface and inside Earth that slowly change rocks from one kind to another. (p. 162)

root cap A structure that covers the tip of a root, protecting the root from injury. (p. 339)

saliva The fluid released when the mouth waters that plays an important role in both mechanical and chemical digestion. (p. 578)

saturated fats Fats, such as butter, that are usually solid at room temperature. (p. 565)

scientific theory A well-tested concept that explains a wide range of observations. (p. 139)

scrotum An external pouch of skin in which the testes are located. (p. 730)

sedimentary rock A type of rock that forms when particles from other rocks or the remains of plants and animals are pressed and cemented together. (pp. 162, 462)

seed The plant structure that contains a young plant inside a protective covering. (p. 332)

selective breeding The process of selecting a few organisms with desired traits to serve as parents of the next generation. (p. 116)

selectively permeable A property of cell membranes that allows some substances to pass through, while others cannot. (p. 30)

semen A mixture of sperm cells and fluids. (p. 731)

semicircular canals Structures in the inner ear that are responsible for the sense of balance. (p. 707)

sensory neuron A neuron that picks up stimuli from the internal or external environment and converts each stimulus into a nerve impulse. (p. 686)

sepal A leaflike structure that encloses the bud of a flower. (p. 347)

sex-linked gene A gene that is carried on the X or Y chromosome. (p. 106)

sexual reproduction The reproductive process that involves two parents who combine their genetic material to produce a new organism, which differs from both parents. (pp. 250, 367)

skeletal muscle A muscle that is attached to the bones of the skeleton. (p. 541)

small intestine The part of the digestive system in which most chemical digestion takes place. (p. 584)

smooth muscle Involuntary muscle found inside many internal organs of the body. (p. 542)

social health A component of wellness that consists of how well a person gets along with others. (p. 523)

somatic nervous system The group of nerves that controls voluntary actions. (p. 694)

species A group of similar organisms that can mate with each other and produce fertile offspring. (pp. 137, 220, 367)

sperm A male sex cell. (p. 729)

sphygmomanometer An instrument that measures blood pressure. (p. 605)

spinal cord The thick column of nerve tissue that is enclosed by the vertebrae and that links the brain to most of the nerves in the peripheral nervous system. (p. 691)

spontaneous generation The mistaken idea that living things arise from nonliving sources. (p. 209)

spore A tiny cell that is able to grow into a new organism. (p. 275)

sporophyte The stage in the life cycle of a plant in which the plant produces spores for reproduction. (p. 307)

stamen The male reproductive parts of a flower. (p. 347)

stimulant A drug that speeds up body processes. (p. 712)

stimulus A change in an organism's surroundings that causes the organism to react. (pp. 208, 685)

stomach A J-shaped, muscular pouch located in the abdomen that expands to hold all of the food that is swallowed. (p. 580)

stomata The small openings on the undersides of most leaves through which oxygen and carbon dioxide can move. (pp. 42, 334)

stress The reaction of a person's body and mind to threatening, challenging, or disturbing events. (p. 519)

swim bladder An internal gas-filled organ that helps a bony fish stabilize its body at different water depths. (p. 442)

symbiosis A close relationship between two organisms in which at least one of the organisms benefits. (p. 274)

synapse The tiny space between the tip of an axon and the next structure (p. 688)

T cell A lymphocyte that identifies pathogens and distinguishes one pathogen from the other. (p. 658)

tar A dark, sticky substance produced when tobacco burns. (p. 634)

target cell A cell in the body that recognizes a hormone's chemical structure; a cell to which a hormone binds chemically. (p. 725)

taxonomic key A series of paired statements that describe the physical characteristics of different organisms. (p. 226)

taxonomy The scientific study of how living things are classified. (p. 219)

tendon Strong connective tissue that attaches a muscle to a bone. (p. 542)

testis Organ of the male reproductive system in which sperm and testosterone are produced. (p. 730)

testosterone A hormone produced by the testes that controls the development of physical characteristics in men. (p. 730)

thorax An insect's mid-section, to which its wings and legs are attached. (p. 413)

tissue A group of similar cells that perform a specific function in an organism. (pp. 302, 512)

tolerance A state in which a drug user, after repeatedly taking a drug, needs larger and larger doses of the drug to produce the same effect. (p. 711)

toxin A poison that is produced by bacterial pathogens and that damages cells. (pp. 260, 652)

trace fossils A type of fossil that provides evidence of the activities of ancient organisms. (p. 166)

trachea The windpipe; a passage through which air moves in the respiratory system. (p. 627)

trait A characteristic that an organism can pass on to its offspring through its genes. (p. 70)

transfer RNA RNA in the cytoplasm that carries an amino acid to the ribosome and adds it to the growing protein chain. (p. 93)

transpiration The process by which water is lost through a plant's leaves. (p. 336)

tropism The growth response of a plant toward or away from a stimulus. (p. 354)

tumor A mass of abnormal cells that develops when cancerous cells divide and grow uncontrollably. (pp. 61, 672)

umbilical cord A ropelike structure that forms in the uterus between the embryo and the placenta. (p. 736)

unconformity A place where an old, eroded rock surface is in contact with a newer rock layer. (p. 172)

unicellular A type of organism that is made up of a single cell. (p. 207)

unsaturated fats Fats, such as olive oil and canola oil, that are usually liquid at room temperature. (p. 565)

urea A chemical that comes from the breakdown of proteins and that is removed from the body by the kidneys. (p. 639)

ureter A narrow tube that carries urine from one of the kidneys to the urinary bladder. (p. 639)

urethra A small tube through which urine flows from the body. (p. 640)

urinary bladder A sacklike muscular organ that stores urine until it is eliminated from the body. (p. 640)

urine A watery fluid produced by the kidneys that contains urea and other waste materials. (pp. 453, 639)

uterus The hollow muscular organ of the female reproductive system in which a baby develops. (p. 732)

vaccination The process by which harmless antigens are deliberately introduced into a person's body to produce active immunity. (p. 665)

vaccine A substance used in a vaccination that consists of pathogens that have been weakened or killed but can still trigger the immune system into action. (pp. 263, 665)

vacuole A water-filled sac inside a cell that acts as a storage area. (pp. 20, 302)

vagina A muscular passageway through which a baby leaves the mother's body. (p. 733)

valve A flap of tissue in the heart or a vein that prevents blood from flowing backward. (p. 596)

variable Any factor that can change in an experiment. (pp. 209, 763)

variation Any difference between individuals of the same species. (p. 141)

vascular plant A plant that has vascular tissue. (p. 321)

vascular tissue The internal transporting tissue in some plants that is made up of tubelike structures. (p. 306)

vein A blood vessel that carries blood back to the heart. (p. 598)

ventricle Each of the two lower chambers of the heart that pumps blood out to the lungs and body. (pp. 446, 596)

vertebrae The bones that make up the backbone of an animal. (pp. 433, 533)

vertebrate An animal with a backbone. (pp. 186, 372)

villi Tiny finger-shaped structures that cover the inner surface of the small intestine and provide a large surface area through which digested food is absorbed. (p. 586)

virus A small, nonliving particle that invades and then reproduces inside a living cell. (p. 238)

visible light Electromagnetic radiation that can be seen with the unaided eye. (p. 699)

vitamins Molecules that act as helpers in a variety of chemical reactions within the body. (p. 567)

vocal cords Folds of connective tissue that stretch across the opening of the larynx and produce a person's voice. (p. 631)

voluntary muscle A muscle that is under conscious control. (p. 540)

water vascular system A system of fluid-filled tubes in an echinoderm's body. (p. 424)

wellness The state of being at the best possible level of health—in the body, the mind, and relationships with others. (p. 522)

white blood cell A blood cell that fights disease. (p. 609)

withdrawal A period of adjustment that occurs when a drug-dependent person stops taking the drug. (p. 712)

work Force exerted on an object that causes it to move. (p. 546)

xylem The vascular tissue through which water and nutrients move in some plants. (p. 331)

zygote A fertilized egg, produced by the joining of a sperm and an egg. (pp. 306, 729)

Acknowledgments

Illustration

Sally Bensusen: 401, 415
Warren Budd Associated Ltd.: 475
Patrice Rossi Calkin: 225, 242, 243, 272, 273, 370, 372, 387, 433, 452, 486, 487
Carmella Clifford: 555, 703, 707
Warren Cutler: 229, 447, 473
Bruce Day: 520
John Edwards and Associates: 475, 534–535 (Henry Hill), 687 (Dave Fischer)
Robert Fuller: 136–137
Function thru Form: 573
GeoSystems Global Corporation: 130–131, 145, 260, 753
Andrea Golden: 377, 392, 408
Biruta Hansen: 454
Floyd E. Hosmer: 686
Keith Kasnot: 16, 17, 18, 19, 53, 277, 579, 581, 640–641, 726, 727, 736
MapQuest.com: 1
Martucci Design: 56, 267, 297, 363, 421, 467, 529, 574, 620, 640, 653, 672, 699, 768, 769, 770
Matt Mayerchak: 36, 66, 126, 158, 234, 266, 296, 362, 394, 428, 528, 558, 590, 646, 680, 720, 766, 767
Fran Milner: 367, 409, 441, 449, 511, 543, 577, 586, 602–603, 608–609, 628–629, 731, 732
Morgan Cain & Associates: 10, 11, 23, 31, 33, 47, 54–55, 57, 58, 89, 92–93, 94–95, 150, 207, 210-211, 235, 240t, b, 241b, 288, 301, 312, 335, 444, 489, 512, 524, 552, 580, 596, 601, 607, 611, 632, 655, 659, 688, 694, 700tl, 728, 760, 761
Ortelius Design Inc.: 252, 253, 284, 548
Stephanie Pershing: 216-217
Matthew Pippin: 464
Precision Graphics: 700tc, tr, b, 701t
Pat Rossi: 537
Sandra Sevigny: 515, 533, 541, 595, 612, 691
Tim Spransy: 517
Walter Stuart: 286, 316, 322, 379, 403, 425, 460, 597, 627
Cynthia Turner: 307, 332, 344, 349
J/B Woolsey Associates: 37, 43, 62–63, 77, 81, 83, 88, 103, 105, 108, 119, 149, 152, 155, 208, 219, 223, 227, 241t, 279, 287, 314, 339, 347, 353, 357, 373, 374, 446, 476, 481, 578, 599, 625, 631, 695, 705, 715, 717, 734, 764
J/B Woolsey Associates (Mark Desman): 371, 390, 406, 432, 436, 456–457

Photography

Photo Research Sue McDermott, Sharon Donahue, Paula Wehde
Cover Image Brian Parker/Tom Stack and Associates

Unit 1

Nature of Science
Page xxiv, **1t,** Courtesy of Elroy Masters; **1b,** Pat O'Hara/DRK Photo; **2tl,** Vireo; **2bl,** Jeff Foott/Tom Stack & Assoc.; **2–3r,** M. Collier/DRK Photo; **3,** Gilbert Grant/Photo Researchers.

Chapter 1
Pages 4–5, Julie Habel/Westlight; **6t,** Richard Haynes; **6bl,** Joseph Nettis/Photo Researchers; **6br,** John Coletti/Stock Boston; **7, 8t,** The Granger Collection, NY; **8b,** Corbis-Bettmann; **9t,** H.R. Bramaz/Peter Arnold; **9bl,** Corbis-Bettmann; **9br,** Lawrence Migdale/Stock Boston; **10,** Anup Shah/Masterfile; **12,** CNRI/Science Photo Library/Photo Researchers; **13t,** Runk/Schoenberger/Grant Heilman Photography; **13b,** Doug Wilson/Westlight; **14t,** M. Abbey/Visuals Unlimited; **14b,** Runk/Schoenberger/Grant Heilman Photography; **15,** Dr. Dennis Kunkel/Phototake; **18,** Bill Longcore/Photo Researchers; **19,** K.G. Murtis/Visuals Unlimited; **20,** A.B. Dowsett/Photo Researchers; **21l,** Dr. David Scott/CNRI/Phototake; **21r,** Dr. Dennis Kunkel/Phototake; **22,** Runk/Schoenberger/Grant Heilman Photography; **23,** Russ Lappa; **24,** Okapia-Frankfurt/Photo Researchers; **24 inset,** Andrew Syred/Science Photo Library/Photo Researchers; **25,** Gary Bell/Masterfile; **26t,** Barry L. Runk/Grant Heilman Photography & Michael Mahovlich/Masterfile; **26l,** Lou Lainey; **26r,** Barry L. Runk/Grant Heilman Photography; **26 inset,** Michael Mahovlich/Masterfile; **27,** Hans Blohm/Masterfile; **28,** James Holmes/Farmer Giles Foods/Science Photo Library/ Photo Researchers; **30,** NASA; **32l,** Stanley Flegler/Visuals Unlimited; **32m, r,** David M. Phillips/Visuals Unlimited; **34,** M. Abbey/Visuals Unlimited; **35,** CNRI/Science Photo Library/Photo Researchers.

Chapter 2
Pages 38–39, Carr Clifton/Minden Pictures; **40t,** Russ Lappa; **40b,** Paul Barton/The Stock Market; **41r,** Cosmo Condina; **41 inset,** Biophoto Associates/Photo Researchers; **42t,** Russ Lappa; **42bl, br,** Dr. Jeremy Burgess/Science Photo Library/Photo Researchers; **44t,** Frans Lanting/Minden Pictures; **44b,** Tom J. Ulrich/Visuals Unlimited; **45,** William Johnson/Stock Boston; **46l,** Stephen Dalton/Photo Researchers; **46r,** Phil Dotson/Photo Researchers; **48,** Mark Newman/Visuals Unlimited; **49,** Terje Rakke/The Image Bank; **51t,** David Scharf/Peter Arnold; **51b,** Larry Lefever/Grant Heilman Photography; **52,** Art Wolfe/TSI; **53,** Biophoto Associates/Science Source/Photo Researchers; **54–55 all,** M. Abbey/Photo Researchers; **59,** Robert Knauft/Biology Media; **60t,** Richard Haynes; **60b,** Myrleen Ferguson/Photo Edit; **61,** National Cancer Institute/Science Photo Library/Photo Researchers; **64,** Joseph Sohm/Stock Boston; **65,** Frans Lanting/Minden Pictures.

Chapter 3
Pages 68–69, Ron Kimball; **70t,** Mike Rothwell/Tony Stone Images; **70b,** Corbis-Bettmann; **71,** Barry Runk/Grant Heilman Photography; **74 both,** Meinrad Faltner/The Stock Market; **75,** Inga Spence/The Picture Cube; **78-79,** Image Stop/Phototake; **82,** Hans Reinhard/Bruce Coleman; **85,** Richard Haynes; **86l,** David M. Phillips/Photo Researchers; **86r,** University "La Sapienza," Rome/Science Photo Library/Photo Researchers; **87l,** Jonathan D. Speer/Visuals Unlimited; **87r,** M. Abbey/Photo Researchers; **91,** AP/Wide World Photos; **96,** William E. Ferguson; **97t,** Jane Burton/Bruce Coleman; **97b,** Hans Reinhard/Bruce Coleman.

Chapter 4
Pages 100–101, Herb Snitzer/Stock Boston; **102,** Richard Haynes; **104,** Camille Tokerud/TSI; **105t,b,** Biophoto Associates/Science Source/Photo Researchers; **106,** Andrew McClenaghan/Science Photo Library/Photo Researchers; **108,** Superstock; **109t,** CNRI/Science Photo Library/Photo Researchers; **109b,** Lawrence Migdale/TSI; **110t,** Simon Fraser/RVI, Newcastle-upon-TYNE/Science Photo Library/Photo Researchers; **110b,** Stanley Flegler/Visuals Unlimited; **111,** Corbis-Bettmann; **112l,** CNRI/Science Photo Library/Photo Researchers; **112r,** Mugshots/The Stock Market; **113,** Will and Deni McIntyre/Photo Researchers Inc.; **114,** Richard Haynes; **116,** AP/Wide World Photos; **117,** Tim Barnwell/Stock Boston; **118,** Patricia J. Bruno/Positive Images; **119,** LeLand Bobbe/TSI; **120,** Gary Wagner/Stock Boston; **121,** AP/Wide World Photos; **122,** U.S. Department of Energy/Human Genome Management Information System, Oak Ridge National Laboratory; **123,** David Parker/Science Photo Library/Photo Researchers; **124,** Michael Newman/PhotoEdit; **125,** Lawrence Migdale/TSI.

Interdisciplinary Exploration
Page **128t,** Tim Fitzharris/Minden Pictures; **128b,** Bridgeman Art Library; **129,** Ron Kimball; **130tr,** Charles Philip/Westlight; 130b, Jack Daniels/TSI; **130tl, ml, mr,** Corel Corp.; **130ml,** C. Jeanne White/Photo Researchers; **131 all others,** Corel Corp.; **132t,** Peter Cade/TSI; **132b,** AP/ Wide World Photos; **132–133,** Nick Meers/Panoramic Images.

Unit 2

Chapter 5
Pages 134–135, Bill Varie/Westlight; **136t,** Portrait by George Richmond/Down House, Downe/The Bridgeman Art Library; **136b,** Corbis-Bettmann; **137t, b,** Tui De Roy/Minden Pictures; **137m,** Frans Lanting/Minden Pictures; **138l,** Zig Leszczynski/Animals Animals; **138r,** Tui De Roy/Minden Pictures; **139,** Dr. Jeremy Burgess/Science Photo Library/Photo Researchers; **140,** Mitsuaki Iwago/Minden Pictures; **141,** Jeff Gnass Photography/The Stock Market; **143,** Richard Haynes; **144l, 144r,** Breck P. Kent; **145l, 145r,** Pat & Tom Leeson/Photo Researchers; **146t,** John Cancalosi/Tom Stack & Associates; **146b,** Tom McHugh/Photo Researchers; **147t,** James L. Amos/Photo Researchers; **147b,** Sinclair Stammers/Science Photo Library/Photo Researchers; **155,** Robert Landau/Westlight; **159,** Richard Haynes; **161l,** Keith Gillett/Animals Animals; **161m,** George Whiteley/Photo Researchers; **161r,** David Spears Ltd./Science Photo Library/Photo Researchers; **162l,** Gary Milburn/Tom Stack & Associates; **162r,** Daryl Balfour/TSI; **165,** Tui De Roy/Minden Pictures.

Chapter 6
Pages 160–161, Phil Degginger; **162t,** John Cancalosi/Stock Boston; **162b,** Flowers & Newman/Photo Researchers; **165 both,** Runk/Schoenberger/Grant Heilman Photography; **166t,** Breck P. Kent; **166b,** Tom Bean; **167t,** Robert Landau/Westlight; **167b,** Howard Grey/TSI; **168,** Sinclair Stammers/Science Photo Library/Photo Researchers; **168,** Richard Haynes; **170,** Jeff Greenberg/Photo Researchers; **172l,** G.R. Roberts/Photo Researchers; **172r,** Tom Bean; **172b,** Breck P. Kent; **175,** Mitsuaki Iwago/Minden Pictures; **177,** James King-Holmes/Science Photo Library/Photo Researchers; **181t,** Fletcher & Baylis/Photo

Researchers; **181 inset,** John Cancalosi/Tom Stack & Associates; **183,** Richard Haynes; **184l,** Breck P. Kent; **184r,** Runk/Schoenberger/Grant Heilman Photography; **185r,** The Natural History Museum, London; **185l, 186,** John Sibbick; **187t,** ©The Field Museum, Neg. # CSGEO 75400c.; **187b,** Natural History Museum/London; **193,** 1989 Mark Hallett; **194l,** Jane Burton/Bruce Coleman; **194r,** David M. Dennis/Tom Stock & Associates; **195t,** D. Van Ravenswaay/Photo Researchers; **195b,** C.M. Dixon; **196,** John Reader/Science Photo Library/Photo Researchers; **197,** Tom Bean

Nature of Science
Page 200, University of Wyoming Public Relations; **202 both,** Courtesy of Kelli Trujillo; **203,** University of Wyoming Public Relations.

Unit 3

Chapter 7
Pages 204–205, Joe McDonald/DRK Photo; **206t,** Russ Lappa; **206b,** Beatty/Visuals Unlimited; **207,** John Pontier/Animals Animals; **209,** Michael Quinton/Minden Pictures; **210,** The Granger Collection, NY; **211,** The Granger Collection, NY; **212l,** James Dell/Science Source/Photo Researchers; **212r,** Zig Leszcynski/Animals Animals; **213,** Jim Brandenburg/Minden Pictures; **215,** Russ Lappa; **217,** Biological Photo Service; **218t,** Russ Lappa; **218b,** Inga Spence/The Picture Cube; **220,** Gerard Lacz/Animals Animals; **221t,** J. Serrao/Visuals Unlimited; **221bl,** Tom Brakefield/DRK Photo; **221br,** Ron Kimball **222–223,** Thomas Kitchin/Tom Stack & Associates; **224 all,** Tui de Roy/Minden Pictures; **226t,** Phil A. Dotson/Photo Researchers; **226b,** Richard Day/Animals Animals; **228,** Mike Ederegger/DRK Photo; **229tl,** Fernandez & Peck/Adventure Photo & Film; **229 all others,** Frans Lanting/Minden Pictures; **230,** Alan L. Detrick/Photo Researchers; **231t,** David M. Phillips/Photo Researchers; **231b,** Microfield Scientific Ltd/Science Photo Library/Photo Researchers; **232,** Ray Coleman/Photo Researchers; **233r,** Frans Lanting/Minden Pictures.

Chapter 8
Pages 236–237, Institut Pasteur/CNRI/Phototake; **238t,** Russ Lappa; **238bl,** Dr. Linda Stannard, UCT/Science Photo Library/Photo Researchers; **238bm,** Lee D. Simon/Science Source/Photo Researchers **238–239,** Dr. Brad Fute/Peter Arnold; **239m,** Tektoff-RM/CNRI/Science Photo Library/Photo Researchers; **239r,** CDC/Science Source/Photo Researchers; **243,** Lee D. Simon/Science Source/Photo Researchers; **244,** Henryk T. Kaiser/Photo Network Tustin; **245,** Custom Medical Stock; **246t,** Richard Haynes; **246b,** Science Photo Library/Photo Researchers; **247l,** Scott Camazine/Photo Researchers; **247m,** David M. Phillips/Visuals Unlimited; **247r,** Oliver Meckes/Photo Researchers; **248,** Dr. Tony Brain/Science Photo Library/Photo Researchers; **249,** Dr. K. S Kim/Peter Arnold; **250,** Dr. Dennis Kunkel/PhotoTake; **251,** Alfred Pasieka/Peter Arnold; **252t,** PhotoDisc; **252b,** Sally Ann Ullmann/FoodPix; **253t,** John Marshall/TSI; **253b,** FoodPix; **254t,** E. Webben/Visuals Unlimited; **254b,** Ben Osborne; **254 inset,** Michael Abbey/Photo Researchers; **255,** Hank Morgan; **257, 258,** Richard Haynes; **259t,** James Darell/TSI; **259b,** David M. Dennis/Tom Stack & Associates; **260,** Kevin Horan/TSI; **262,** American Lung Association of Wisconsin; **263,** B. Daemmrich/The Image Works; **264,** Johnathan Selig/Photo 20-20; **265t,** Biozentrum, University of Basel/Science Photo Library/Photo Researchers; **265b,** Alfred Pasieka/Peter Arnold.

Chapter 9
Pages 268–269, David M. Dennis/Tom Stack & Associates; **270t,** Science VU/Visuals Unlimited; **270b,** Jan Hinsch/Science Photo Library/Photo Researchers; **271l,** O.S.F./Animals Animals; **271tr,** A. Le Toquin/Photo Researchers; **271br,** Gregory G. Dimijian/Photo Researchers; **272,** Astrid & Hanns-Frieder Michler/Science Photo Library/Photo Researchers; **273,** Eric Grave/Science Source/Photo Researchers; **274l,** Jerome Paulin/Visuals Unlimited; **274r,** Michael P. Gadomski/Photo Researchers; **275t,** Oliver Meckes/Photo Researchers; **275b,** Dwight R. Kuhn; **276 both,** David M. Dennis/Tom Stack & Associates; **277l,** Sinclair Stammers Oxford Scientific Films; **277r,** Russ Lappa; **278t,** David M. Phillips/Visuals Unlimited; **278bl,** D. P. Wilson/Eric & Daid Hosking/Photo Researchers; **278br,** Andrew Syred/Science Photo Library/Photo Researchers; **280t,** Richard Haynes; **280b,** Doug Perrine/Hawaii Whale Research Foundation—NMFS permit#882/Innerspace Visions; **281,** Sanford Berry/Visuals Unlimited; **282,** Kenneth H. Thomas/Photo Researchers; **284,** Robert P. Falls; **285t,** Russ Lappa; **285b,** Michael Fogden/Animals Animals; **286,** Fred Unverhau/Animals Animals/Earth Scenes; **287,** Nobel Proctor/Science Source/Photo Researchers; **288,** David Scharf/Peter Arnold; **289tl,** E.R. Degginger/Photo Researchers; **289tr,** Rod Planck/Tom Stack & Associates; **289bl,** Michael Fogden/Animals Animals/Earth Scenes; **289br,** Andrew McClenaghan/Science Photo Library/Photo Researchers; **291,** Richard Haynes; **292,** David M. Dennis/Tom Stack & Associates; **293,** Rob Simpson/Visuals Unlimited; **294l,** Rod Planck/Tom Stack & Associates; **294r,** Frans Lanting/Minden

Pictures; **295l,** Gregory G. Dimijian/Photo Researchers; **295r,** Michael Fogden/Animals Animals/Earth Scenes.

Chapter 10
Pages 298-299, J. Lotter Gurling/Tom Stack & Associates; **300,** Joanne Lotter/Tom Stack & Associates; **301, 302,** Runk/Schoenberger/Grant Heilman Photography; **303,** Kjell B. Sandved/Photo Researchers; **304tl,** Richard J. Green/Photo Researchers; **304tr,** Brenda Tharp/Photo Researchers; **304m,** R. Van Nostrand/Photo Researchers; **304b,** Joe McDonald/Visuals Unlimited; **305tl,** Prenzel/Animals Animals/Earth Scenes; **305tr,** Frans Lanting/Minden Pictures; **305m,** Andrew J. Martinez/Photo Researchers; **305b,** Runk/Schoenberger/Grant Heilman Photography; **306,** Doug Wechsler/Animals Animals/Earth Scenes; **308,** Richard Haynes; **309,** Images International/Erwin C. Bud Nielsen/Visuals Unlimited; **310t,** Richard Haynes; **310b,** Runk/Schoenberger/Grant Heilman Photography; **311,** Carr Clifton/Minden Pictures; **312,** Runk/Schoenberger/Grant Heilman Photography; **313t,** Interfoto-Pressebild-Agentur; **313b,** Georg Gerster/Photo Researchers; **315t,** Russ Lappa; **315b,** Christi Carter/Grant Heilman Photography; **316,** Runk/Schoenberger/Grant Heilman Photography; **317t,** Silkeborg Museum; **317b,** Farrell Grehan/Photo Researchers; **318l,** Runk/Schoenberger/Grant Heilman Photography; **318r** William E. Ferguson; **319, 320t,** Richard Haynes; **322,** Rod Planck/Tom Stack & Associates; **323t,** Milton Rand/Tom Stack & Associates; **323b,** Joanne Lotter/Tom Stack & Associates; **324l,** Runk/Schoenberger/Grant Heilman Photography; **324r,** Frans Lanting/Minden Pictures; **325,** Rod Planck/Tom Stack & Associates.

Chapter 11
Pages 328-329, E.R. Degginger; **330t,** Russ Lappa; **330b,** E. R. Degginger/Animals Animals/Earth Scenes; **331l,** Thomas Kitchin/Tom Stack & Associates; **331m & r,** Carr Clifton/Tom Stack & Associates; **333tl,** D. Cavagnaro/Visuals Unlimited; **333tr,** Frans Lanting/Minden Pictures; **333bl,** E. R. Degginger; **333br,** William Harlow/Photo Researchers; **334 both,** Runk/Schoenberger/Grant Heilman Photography; **336,** Dani/Jeske/Animals Animals/Earth Scenes; **338t,** Runk/Schoenberger/Grant Heilman Photography; **338b both,** Robert Calentine/Visuals Unlimited; **340t,** Richard Haynes; **340b,** Bruce M. Herman/Photo Researchers; **341tl,** Ken Brate/Photo Researchers; **341tr,** Jim Strawser/Grant Heilman Photography; **341b,** Michael Fogden/Animals Animals/Earth Scenes; **342l,** Runk/Schoenberger/Grant Heilman Photography; **342r,** Breck P. Kent/Animals Animals/Earth Scenes; **343,** Breck P. Kent; **345,** C.J. Allen/Stock Boston; **346t,** Russ Lappa; **346b,** Jim Strawser/Grant Heilman Photography; **347,** E. R. Degginger; **348,** Private Collections/Art Resource; **351,** Alan Pitcairn/Grant Heilman Photography; **352,** Richard Haynes; **354,** William J. Weber/Visuals Unlimited; **355,** Porterfield-Chickering/Photo Researchers; **356tl,** E. R. Degginger; **356tr,** Mark E. Gibson/The Stock Market; **356b,** Larry Lefever/Grant Heilman Photography; **358,** Herve Donnezan/Photo Researchers; **359,** William James Warren/West Light; **360,** Arthur C. Smith III/Grant Heilman Photography; **361,** Arthur C. Smith III/Grant Heilman Photography.

Chapter 12
Pages 364–365, Hal Beral/Visuals Unlimited; **366t,** Richard Haynes; **366–367b,** Gary Bell/Masterfile; **368,** Robert Maier/Animals Animals; **369t,** Oliver Strewe/TSI; **369b,** Frans Lanting/Minden Pictures; **370,** David & Tess Young/Tom Stack & Associates; **373,** Corel Corp.; **374,** William C Jorgensen/Visuals Unlimited; **375l,** Daniel W. Gotshall/Visuals Unlimited; **375r,** Tim Davis/TSI; **376,** Ted Kerasote/Photo Researchers; **378t,** Russ Lappa; **381t,** Biophoto Associates/Photo Researchers; **381bl,** Stuart Westmorland/Natural Selection; **381br,** David B. Fleetham/Tom Stack & Associates; **383t,** Nancy Sefton/Photo Researchers; **383b,** Linda Pitkin/Masterfile; **384,** James Watt/Animals Animals; **385t,** Richard Haynes; **385bl,** Ed Robinson/Tom Stack & Associates; **385br,** Mary Beth Angelo/Photo Researchers; **386,** Kiell B. Sandved/Visuals Unlimited; **388t,** David M. Dennis/Tom Stack & Associates; **388b,** Sinclair Stammers/Science Photo Library/Photo Researchers; **389l, 389r,** Kjell B. Sandved/Visuals Unlimited; **393l,** Corel Corp.; **393r,** Linda Pitkin/Masterfile.

Chapter 13
Pages 396–397, Michael Fogden/DRK Photo; **398b,** Richard Nowitz; **398t,** Corel Corp.; **399l,** Douglas Faulkner/Photo Researchers; **399r,** Bruce Watkins/Animals Animals; **400,** Pete Atkinson/Masterfile; **402,** Kevin & Cat Sweeney/TSI; **404t,** Richard Haynes; **402–403,** Gary Retherford/Photo Researchers; **403r,** Richard Haynes; **404b,** Ron Broda/Masterfile; **405l,** John Gerlach/Tom Stack & Associates; **405r,** Donald Specker/Animals Animals; **406,** Robert A. Lubeck/Animals Animals; **407,** Andrew Syred/Science Photo Library/Photo Researchers; **410t,** Robert Calentine/Visuals Unlimited; **410b,** Tom McHugh/Photo Researchers; **410m,** Tim Flach/TSI; **411l,** Marty Cordano/DRK Photo; **411r,** Simon D. Pollard/Photo Researchers; **412t,** R Calentine/Visuals Unlimited; **412b,** Patti Murray/Animals Animals; **413,** CNRI/Science Photo Library/Photo Researchers; **414,** Belinda Wright/DRK Photo; **416l,** Valorie

Hodgson/Visuals Unlimited; **416r,** Art Wolfe/Tony Stone Images; **417,** John Trager/Visuals Unlimited; **418,** Robert A. Lubeck/Animals Animals; **419, 420,** Richard Haynes; **421t,** Paul Silverman/Fundamental Photographs; **421b,** Richard Magna/Fundamental Photographs; **422,** Russ Lappa; **423t,** Richard Haynes; **423b,** Kjell B. Sandred/Visuals Unlimited; **424,** Ed Robinson/Tom Stack & Associates; **426tl,** Brian Parker/Tom Stack & Associates; **426tr,** Tammy Peluso/Tom Stack & Associates; **426b,** Fred Whitehead/Animals Animals; **427t,** Bruce Watkins/Animals Animals; **427b,** Andrew Syred/Science Photo Library/Photo Researchers.

Chapter 14
Pages 430–431, Norbert Wu/DRK Photo; **432,** Russ Lappa; **433,** G.J. Bernard/Animals Animals; **434,** Michael Fodgen/DRK Photo; **435,** Corel Corp.; **437t,** Gerard Lacz/Animals Animals; **437b,** Flip Micklin/Minden Pictures; **439tl,** Larry Lipsky/DRK Photo; **439tr,** John D. Cummingham/Visuals Unlimited **439b,** Herve Berthoule Jacana/Photo Researchers; **440t,** Frank Burek/Animals Animals; **440b,** Jeff Rotman; **442l,** Norbert Wu; **442r,** Stuart Westmorland/ Photo Researchers; **443r,** Stuart Westmorland/TSI; **443l,** Norbert Wu/TSI; **445t,** Russ Lappa; **445b,** John M. Burnley/Photo Researchers; **446,** Michael Fogden/Photo Researchers; **448,** Richard Haynes; **450,** Justin W. Verforker/Visuals Unlimited; **451t,** Richard Haynes; **451b,** Joe McDonald/Tom Stack & Associates; **452,** Zig Leszczynski/Animals Animals; **453,** Brian Kenney/Natural Selection; **455l,** Joe McDonald/Tom Stack & Associates; **455r,** A.B. Sheldon/Animals Animals; **458t,** Dave B. Fleetham/Visuals Unlimited; **458m,** T.A. Wiewandt/DRK Photo; **458b,** M.C. Chamberlain/DRK Photo; 459, Gerald & Buff Corsi/ Tom Stack & Associates; **461t,** Richard Haynes; **461b,** Tom Bean/DRK Photo; **462t,** Ernst Mayr Library of the Museum of Comparative Zoology, Harvard University ©President and Fellows of Harvard; **462b,** By permission of the Houghton Library, Harvard University; **463t,** Louis Psihoyos Matrix; **463b,** James L. Amos/Photo Researchers; **465l,** Stuart Westmorland/TSI; **465r,** Joe McDonald/Tom Stack & Associates.

Chapter 15
Pages 468–469, Robert A. Tyrrell; **470,** Richard Haynes; **471,** Collection of The New York Historical Society; **472t,** Art Wolfe/TSI; **472m,** Jerome Wexler/Photo Researchers; **472b,** Darrell Gulin/DRK Photo; **474,** Richard Haynes; **477,** David Hosking/TSI; **478tl,** Dave Watts/Tom Stack & Associates; **478tm,** Stephen Krasemann/DRK Photo; **478tr,** S. Nielsen/DRK Photo; **478bl,** D. Allen/Animals Animals; **478br,** Joe McDonald/Visuals Unlimited; **479l,** Manfred Danegger/TSI; **479r,** Wayne Lankinen/DRK Photo; **480t,** Richard Haynes; **480b,** Stephen Dalton/Photo Researchers; **482,** David Tipling/TSI; **483t,** Richard Haynes; **483b,** Eric Valli/Minden Pictures; **484,** Daryl Balfour/ TSI; **485,** Art Wolfe/TSI; **486t,** Hilary Pooley/Animals Animals; **486–487b,** Michael Fogden/DRK Photo; **488,** Joe McDonald/Visuals Unlimited; **490,** Colin Milkins/Animals Animals; **491t,** Richard Haynes; **491bl,** Keren Su/TSI; **491br,** Penny Tweedie/TSI; **492l, 492r,** Tom McHugh/Photo Researchers; **493t,** Dave Watts/Tom Stack & Associates; **493b,** Jack Dermid; **494tl,** Michael Habicht/Animals Animals; **494tm,** Art Wolfe/TSI; **494tr,** Roger Aitkenhead/Animals Animals; **494ml,** Stephen Krasemann/TSI; **494mr,** Jeanne Drake/TSI; **494bl,** Renee Lynn/TSI; **495tl,** Corel Corp.; **495tr,** M.P. Kahl/DRK Photo; **495ml,** Stephen Krasemann/TSI; **495bl,** Chuck Davis/TSI; **495br,** Johnny Johnson/DRK Photo; **496,** Johnny Johnson; **497l,** Joe McDonald/Visuals Unlimited; **497r,** Penny Tweedie/TSI.

Interdisciplinary Exploration
Page 500, Cary Wolinsky/Stock Boston; **501t,** E.R. Degginger/Animals Animals; **501m, 501b,** Cary Wolinsky/Stock Boston; **501r,** Harry Rogers/Photo Researchers; **504,** Russ Lappa; **506t,** Xinhua/Gamma-Liaison International; **507t,** Russ Lappa; **507b,** Jean Marc Barey/Angence Vandystadt/Photo Researchers.

Unit 4

Chapter 16
Pages 508–509, Jean Francois Causse/TSI; **510t,** Richard Haynes; **510b,** Russ Lappa; **513tl,** Robert Becker/Custom Medical Stock; **513bl,** Fred Hossler/Visuals Unlimited; **513m,** Clive Brunckill/Allsport; **513tr,** Biophoto Associates/Science Source/Photo Researchers; **513br,** John D. Cunningham/Visuals Unlimited; **514,** Wayne Hoy/The Picture Cube; **516, 517,** Richard Haynes; **518,** Lori Adamski Peek/TSI; **519,** Paul J. Sutton/Duomo; **521,** Michael P. Manheim/ MidwestStock; **522–523,** Charles Gupton/TSI; **523tr,** Melanie Carr/Zephyr Pictures; **523br,** Bob Daemmrich/Stock Boston; **525,** Superstock; **526,** Betsy Fuchs/The Picture Cube; **527,** Charles Gupton/TSI.

Chapter 17
Pages 530–531, Globus, Holway & Lobel/The Stock Market; **532t,** Russ Lappa; **532b,** Cathy Cheney/Stock Boston; **533,** Richard Haynes; **534,** Andrew Syred/Science Photo Library/Photo Researchers; **536,** Salisbury District Hospital/Science Photo Library/Photo Researchers; **537,** William R. Sallaz/Duomo; **538,** The Granger Collection, NY; **539 both,** Superstock; **540t,** Richard Haynes;

540b, Superstock; **541tl,** Astrid & Hanns–Frieder Michler/Science Photo Library/Photo Researchers; **541bl,** Eric Grave/Photo Researchers; **541m,** Richard Haynes; **541r,** Ed Reschke/Peter Arnold; **542l,** Richard Haynes; **542r,** Jim Cummins/FPG International; **544,** Superstock; **545,** Richard Haynes; **546t,** Richard Haynes; **546b,** Bob Daemmrich/Stock Boston; **547l,** Russ Lappa; **547m,** Elliot Smith/International Stock; **547r,** Jerry Wachter/Photo Researchers; **549 all,** Richard Haynes; **550t,** Richard Haynes; **550b,** Jed Jacobson/Allsport; **551l,** David Young Wolff/TSI; **551r,** Lennart Nilsson/Behold Man; **553l,** Prof. P. Motta/Dept. of Anatomy/University "La Sapienza", Rome/Science Photo Library/Photo Researchers; **553r,** Russ Lappa; **554, 61,** Richard Haynes; **556,** Bob Daemmrich/Stock Boston; **557l,** Superstock; **557r,** Ed Reschke/Peter Arnold.

Chapter 18
Pages 560–561, Superstock; **562,** Bob Daemmrich/Stock Boston; **563l,** Richard Haynes; **563r, 564, 565, 566, 567 all, 568 all,** Russ Lappa; **569,** Joan Baron/The Stock Market; **570, 571t,** Richard Haynes; **571b,** David Young-Wolff/PhotoEdit; **572,** David Young Wolff/TSI; **575,** David Young-Wolff/PhotoEdit; **576,** The Granger Collection, NY; **577, 578,** Richard Haynes; **581,** CNRI/Science Photo Library/Photo Researchers; **583, 584t,** Richard Haynes; **584b,** Llewellyn/Uniphoto; **586,** Prof. P. Motta/Dept. of Anatomy/University "La Sapienza", Rome/Science Photo Library/Photo Researchers; **587,** CNRI/Science Photo Library/Photo Researchers; **588,** Donna Day/TSI; **589,** Joan Baron/The Stock Market.

Chapter 19
Pages 592–593, National Cancer Institute/Science Photo Library/Photo Researchers; **594, 595,** Richard Haynes; **596t,** Erich Lessing/Art Resource; **596b,** Science Photo Library/Photo Researchers; **598–599,** Pete Saloutos/The Stock Market; **600,** Scott Weersing/Allsport; **601,** Richard Haynes; **603,** Prof. P. Motta/Dept. of Anatomy/University "La Sapienza", Rome/Science Photo Library/Photo Researchers; **604,** Cabisco/Visuals Unlimited; **605,** Matt Meadows/Peter Arnold; **606,** Richard Haynes; **607,** Andrew Syred/Science Photo Library/Photo Researchers; **608,** Bill Longcore/Science Source/Photo Researchers; **609t,** Andrew Syred/Science Photo Library/Photo Researchers; **609b,** National Cancer Institute/Science Photo Library/Photo Researchers; **610,** Oliver Meckes/Photo Researchers; **612,** Richard Haynes; **614t,** Daemmrich/Stock Boston; **614b,** Thom Duncan/Adventure Photo; **615 both,** Custom Medical Stock; **616t,** AP/Wide World Photos; **616b,** The Granger Collection, NY; **617t,** Liaison International; **617b,** Brad Nelson/Custom Medical Stock; **618,** Nicole Katodo/TSI; **619,** Prof. P. Motta/Dept. of Anatomy/University "La Sapienza", Rome/Science Photo Library/Photo Researchers.

Chapter 20
Pages 622–623, Mark Gibson/The Stock Market; **624t,** Richard Haynes; **624b,** Dick Dickinson/Photo Network; **626l,** Richard Haynes; **626 inset,** Eddy Gray/Science Photo Library/Photo Researchers; **627,** Richard Haynes; **630,** Paul Harris/TSI; **632,** J. Sohm/The Image Works; **633,** Russ Lappa; **634,** Spencer Jones/FPG International; **635,** Ken Karp; **636,** Al Bello/TSI; **637l,** Clark Overton/Phototake; **637m,** SIV/Photo Researchers; **637r,** Martin Rotker/Phototake; **638,** Smoke Free Educational Services; **639, 642,** Richard Haynes; **644,** Ken Karp; **645,** Eddy Gray/Science Photo Library/Photo Researchers.

Chapter 21
Pages 648–649, Microworks/Phototake; **650t,** Richard Haynes; **650b,** The Granger Collection, NY; **651,** Pete Saloutos/The Stock Market; **652t,** CNRI/Science Photo Library/Photo Researchers; **652m,** Biozentrum/Science Photo Library/Photo Researchers; **652b,** Gucho/CNRI/Science Photo Library/Photo Researchers; **654t,** Mike Peres/Custom Medical Stock Photo; **654b,** Scott Camazine/Photo Researchers; **655,** Russ Lappa; **656,** Science Pictures Ltd./Science Photo Library/Photo Researchers; **657,** Lennart Nilsson/Boehringer Ingelheim International GmbH; **658,** Lori Adamski Peek/TSI; **660,** NIBSC/Science Photo Library/Photo Researchers; **661,** Jon Riley/TSI; **662, 663,** Richard Haynes; **664t,** Russ Lappa; **664b,** CNRI/Science Photo Library/Photo Researchers; **665,** Aaron Haupt/Photo Researchers; **666t,** Historical Picture Service/Custom Medical Stock; **666b,** The Granger Collection, NY; **667t,** Granger Collection, NY; **667b,** Giraudon/Art Resource; **669t,** Richard Haynes; **669b,** Richard Haynes; **670l,** Ron Kimball; **670r,** Andrew Syred/Science Photo Library/Photo Researchers; **671,** Therisa Stack/Tom Stack & Associates; **672,** Dept. of Clinical Radiology, Salisbury District Hospital/Science Photo Library/Photo Researchers; **673,** Yoav Levy/Phototake; **674,** Stevie Grand/Science Photo Library/Photo Researchers; **676t,** Richard Haynes; **676bl, 676–677,** The Granger Collection, NY; **678,** Phil Savoie/The Picture Cube; **679,** Biozentrum/Science Photo Library/Photo Researchers.

Chapter 22

Pages 682–683, 1998 Magic Eye Inc.; **684t,** Richard Haynes; **684b,** Lee Snider/The Image Works; **685,** Gordon R. Gainer/The Stock Market; **686,** Biophoto Associates/Photo Researchers; **689, 690t,** Richard Haynes; **690b,** Milton Feinberg/The Picture Cube; **691,** Richard Haynes; **693,** Art Resource; **694,** Tom Stewart/The Stock Market; **696,** William Sallaz/Duomo; **697,** Robert E. Daemmrich/TSI; **698,** Richard Megna/Fundamental Photographs; **699,** John Keiffer/Peter Arnold; **701b,** Richard Haynes; **702,** Superstock; **704t,** Prof. P. Motta/Dept. of Anatomy/U. "La Sapienza," Rome/Science Photo Library/Photo Researchers; **704b,** Lennart Nilsson; **706,** Renee Lynn/TSI; **708l,** Spencer Grant/The Picture Cube; **708r,** Lennart Nilsson; **709,** Mugshots/The Stock Market; **710t,** Russ Lappa; **710b,** Uniphoto; **711,** Tom Croke/Liaison International; **712,** David Young-Wolff/PhotoEdit; **716,** Index Stock; **718,** Bob Daemmrich/Stock Boston; **719,** Spencer Grant/The Picture Cube.

Chapter 23

Pages 722–723, Uniphoto; **724,** Keith Kent/Photo Researchers; **725l,** Chad Slattery/TSI; **725r,** Nancy Sheehan/The Picture Cube; **729,** Mitsuaki Iwago/Minden Pictures; **730 both,** Dr. Dennis Kunkel/Phototake; **733,** Prof. P.M. Motta & J. Van Blerkom/Science Photo Library/ Photo Researchers; **735tl,** Stephen R. Swinburne/Stock Boston; **735tm,** Stephen R. Swinburne/Stock Boston; **735b,** David Phillips/Science Photo Library/ Photo Researchers; **737,** Lennart Nilsson; **738,** Index Stock; **739l,** Roy Morsch/The Stock Market; **739r,** Frauke/Mauritius/H. Armstrong Roberts; **740l,** Penny Gentieu; **740r,** Elizabeth Hathol/The Stock Market; **741,** Don Semtzer/TSI; **742t,** Ken Karp; **742b,** Roy Morso/The Stock Market; **743l,** James D. Wilson/Liaison International; **743r,** Robert E. Daemmrich/TSI; **744,** Mark Burnett/Photo Researchers; **745,** Bruce Dale/National Geographic Society; **746,** David Young-Wolff/Photo Edit; **747,** David Young Wolff/TSI; **749t** David Phillips/Science Photo Library/ Photo Researchers; **749b,** Penny Gentieu.

Interdisciplinary Exploration

Page 752t, Duomo; **752b,** Scala/Art Resource; **753,** Louvre, Dpt. des Antiquités Grecques/Romaines, Paris, France. Photograph by Erich Lessing/Art Resource; **754,** Tony Duffy/Allsport USA; **755,** Pascal Rondeau/Allsport USA; **756–757,** Mark C. Burnett/Stock Boston/PNI;

Skills Handbook

Page 758, Mike Moreland/Photo Network; **759t,** Foodpix; **759m,** Richard Haynes; **759b,** Russ Lappa; **762,** Richard Haynes; **764,** Ron Kimball; **765,** Renee Lynn/Photo Researchers.

Appendix B

Page 774–775 all, Russ Lappa.